Anelastic Relaxation in Crystalline Solids

MATERIALS SCIENCE SERIES

EDITORS

ALLEN M. ALPER

GTE Sylvania Inc.
Precision Materials Group
Chemical & Metallurgical
Division
Towanda, Pennsylvania

JOHN L. MARGRAVE

Department of Chemistry
Rice University
Houston, Texas

A. S. NOWICK

Henry Krumb School
of Mines
Columbia University
New York, New York

Anelastic Relaxation in Crystalline Solids

A. S. NOWICK   and   B. S. BERRY

Henry Krumb School of Mines
Columbia University
New York, New York

Thomas J. Watson Research Center
IBM Corporation
Yorktown Heights, New York

 1972

ACADEMIC PRESS   New York and London

ACADEMIC PRESS, INC.
111 Fifth Avenue, New York, New York 10003

United Kingdom Edition published by
ACADEMIC PRESS, INC. (LONDON) LTD.
24/28 Oval Road, London NW1 7DD

LIBRARY OF CONGRESS CATALOG CARD NUMBER: 70-154378

PRINTED IN THE UNITED STATES OF AMERICA

To Joan and Maureen

Contents

Chapter 4 Continuous Spectra

Chapter 5 Internal Variables and the Thermodynamic Basis for Relaxation Spectra

Chapter 6 Anisotropic Elasticity and Anelasticity

Chapter 7 Point Defects and Atom Movements

Chapter 8 Theory of Point-Defect Relaxations

Chapter 9 The Snoek Relaxation

Chapter 10 The Zener Relaxation

Chapter 11 Other Point-Defect Relaxations

Chapter 12 Dislocations and Crystal Boundaries

Chapter 13 Dislocation Relaxations

Chapter 14 Further Dislocation Effects

Chapter 15 Boundary Relaxation Processes and Internal Friction at High Temperatures

Chapter 16   Relaxations Associated with Phase Transformations

Chapter 17   Thermoelastic Relaxation and the Interaction of Acoustic Waves with Lattice Vibrations

Chapter 18   Magnetoelastic Relaxations and Hysteresis Damping of Ferromagnetic Materials

Chapter 19   Electronic Relaxation and Related Phenomena

Preface

Anelasticity may be said to have originated as a distinct discipline in 1948 with the publication of Zener's pioneering monograph "Elasticity and Anelasticity of Metals." This book defined anelasticity and demonstrated the usefulness of separating it from the more general viscoelastic behavior treated in the earlier literature. In the years since Zener's book, an enormous growth in the literature of the subject has taken place, as is became apparent that the study of anelastic relaxation could contribute greatly to our understanding of almost the whole gamut of physical and chemical phenomena in crystalline solids. Accordingly, there has been a clear need both for a textbook and an up-to-date monograph on anelasticity in crystals. In writing the present book the authors have hoped, perhaps too ambitiously, to fulfill both requirements.

The first six chapters comprise the formal theory of the subject, the heart of which is covered in Chapters 3–5. It is this theory that provides the glue which holds together the diverse topics to be covered later. In this sense, anelasticity differs from the related topic of "internal friction," which does not possess such a unifying theoretical base. These first six chapters, together with selected readings from the later chapters, can constitute a text for self study, or for a graduate course such as one of the authors (A.S.N.) has given at Columbia University. These early chapters are by no means confined to crystals, and are therefore equally suitable as an introduction to anelasticity in the noncrystalline state, or, with simple changes in notation, to dielectric relaxation. To further aid the usefulness of the book as a text, we have designated with heavy asterisks those sections which may be omitted on a first reading. Also, a rather substantial number of problems are included in the early chapters.

The remainder of the book deals in some detail with the various physical phenomena in crystalline substances which can give rise to anelastic relaxation. In view of the fact that the book is intended for readers with diverse backgrounds, such as mechanical or metallurgical engineers, materials scientists, and solid-state physicists, we have felt it desirable to present the essential background material on each of the phenomena covered. In the case of the topics dealt with most extensively, namely point defects and dislocations, full chapters (7 and 12) of background material are presented; for other topics, a single section of background material seemed to be sufficient. For each of the physical phenomena, we have attempted to describe the current state of understanding of the anelastic effects in such a way that the reader can then go directly to the literature. With the enormous growth of the literature in the past decade, however, we regret that a complete or exhaustive literature survey could not be attempted, and that often work of some significance had to be omitted. Phenomena which involve ultrasonic attenuation or internal friction but which are not strictly describable as anelastic effects have generally been omitted, although (in Chapters 14 and 17–19) some borderline topics are discussed briefly because of their special importance. Finally, due to the limitations of the book as well as our own backgrounds, we have omitted consideration of organic crystalline compounds.

Acknowledgments

The authors owe a debt of gratitude to many colleagues and students who read individual chapters and contributed valuable criticisms and suggestions, particularly to D. N. Beshers, C. Elbaum, M. C. Franzblau, C. W. Garland, R. Gibala, D. F. Gibbons, W. R. Heller, G. M. Leak, W. P. Mason, D. I. Paul, D. S. Richter, J. T. A. Roberts, E. T. Stephenson, J. C. Swartz, T. J. Turner, and G. P. Williams. We are especially grateful for the support of much of the research leading to this book, as well as partial support of the writing itself, by the U. S. Atomic Energy Commission. We thank Miss Maureen Weaver for her skillful typing of a substantial fraction of the manuscript. Finally, we wish to express our deepest gratitude to our wives for their encouragement and understanding over the several years during which this book was being written.

Chapter 1 / Characterization of Anelastic Behavior

The first part of this book (Chapters 1–6) deals with the formal theory of anelasticity. We begin with the introduction of a set of postulates which serve to define the subject, and then proceed to develop the consequences of these postulates. The formal theory does not include the physical origins or atomistic mechanisms of anelasticity, but does embrace the interpretation of anelastic behavior as a manifestation of internal relaxation processes.

The function of the present chapter is to lay the groundwork for the formal theory, first, by introducing the postulates, and second, by deducing the characteristic response of an anelastic material to the imposition of certain simple histories of stress or strain. The *response functions* which emerge from this treatment are then taken as the basic manifestations of anelastic behavior. These objectives are, in fact, accomplished in Sections 1.1–1.3, so that the reader interested in the purely theoretical development of the subject may omit the remainder of the chapter.

In Sections 1.4–1.7 we turn to the various dynamical methods that are widely used in studying anelasticity. These methods are of such importance in practice that we have felt it necessary to present them here, even though the material constitutes a digression from the main development of the theory.

1.1 The Meaning of Anelasticity

In order to describe anelasticity in a formal way, it is convenient to consider first an *ideal elastic material*, for which Hooke's law defines the relation between stress σ and strain ε as

$$\sigma = M\varepsilon \tag{1.1-1}$$

or

$$\varepsilon = J\sigma \tag{1.1-2}$$

with

$$M = 1/J \tag{1.1-3}$$

1

The constant M is called the modulus of elasticity (or often just the *modulus*) while its reciprocal J is called the modulus of compliance (or simply the *compliance*).

For an arbitrary deformation, the stress and strain must be expressed as second-order tensors, and Hooke's law then becomes a set of linear equations expressing each component of the stress tensor in terms of all the components of the strain tensor (or vice versa). For present purposes, this generalization would merely add unnecessary complications, so we shall proceed from the statement of Hooke's law as given by Eqs. (1.1-1) and (1.1-2), leaving the more elaborate treatment to Chapter 6. We note however that the present approach implies a simple mode of deformation, such as pure shear, uniaxial deformation, or hydrostatic deformation. For such cases, the appropriate modulus M will be the shear modulus, Young's modulus, or the bulk modulus, respectively.

There are three conditions defining ideal elastic behavior which are implicit in Eqs. (1.1-1) and (1.1-2). These are: (1) that the strain response to each level of applied stress (or vice versa) has a *unique equilibrium value*; (2) that the equilibrium response is achieved *instantaneously*[†]; (3) that the response is linear (e.g., doubling the stress doubles the strain). It should be noted that a characteristic feature of elasticity, namely the *complete recoverability* of the response upon release of the applied stress or strain, is a corollary of condition (1).

In order to generalize upon ideal elastic behavior, the three conditions listed above may be lifted in various combinations. The possibilities are shown in Table 1-1 together with the name given to the discipline of study in each case. As already mentioned, if all three conditions apply, we have the case of ideal elasticity. If only the restriction of linearity is lifted, "nonlinear elasticity" is the obvious result. If both linearity and complete recoverability are dropped, the material becomes capable of exhibiting "instantaneous plasticity," which is often called "crystal plasticity" because this type of plasticity is best exemplified by the yielding of ductile crystals under high stress. In contrast to the first three entries in Table 1-1, the remaining two entries introduce *time dependence* into the response, by lifting the condition of instantaneity. If this is the only condition lifted, we produce the type of behavior known as anelasticity, the subject of this book. The more general behavior obtained by addition-

---

[†] Because of the finite velocity of sound, the response is actually instantaneous only in an infinitesimally small sample. The essential point is that Eqs. (1.1-1) and (1.1-2) do not contain time as a variable.

TABLE 1-1

DIFFERENT TYPES OF MECHANICAL BEHAVIOR,
CLASSIFIED ACCORDING TO THE CONDITIONS OBEYED BY THE STRESS–STRAIN RELATIONSHIP

	Unique equilibrium relationship (complete recoverability)	Instantaneous	Linear
Ideal elasticity	Yes	Yes	Yes
Nonlinear elasticity	Yes	Yes	No
Instantaneous plasticity	No	Yes	No
Anelasticity	Yes	No	Yes
Linear viscoelasticity	No	No	Yes

ally lifting the condition of complete recoverability is known as linear viscoelasticity, which thus includes anelasticity as a special case.

To summarize the definition of anelasticity, we may employ the following three postulates:

1. For every stress there is a unique equilibrium value of strain, and vice versa.
2. The equilibrium response is achieved only after the passage of sufficient time.[†]
3. The stress–strain relationship is linear.

The first and third postulates are, of course, merely a repetition of those for ideal elasticity. It should again be recalled that complete recoverability is a corollary of postulate (1), only now the recovery will, in general, be time dependent.

It should be noted that lifting the condition of instantaneity does not imply that *all* of the response of an anelastic material must develop in a time dependent manner, since to do so would produce the special (and unrealistic) case of a material without any component of elastic behavior. Rather, anelasticity implies that, in addition to an instantaneous (elastic) response, there also exists a time dependent nonelastic response.[‡] Another point of clarification is concerned with the meaning of the term "linear"

[†] There is no restriction on the time scale in these considerations, i.e., the achievement of equilibrium may require anything from microseconds (or less) to extremely long periods of time.

[‡] Thus, while the term "anelasticity" carries the connotation of being "without elasticity," this meaning applies in a literal sense only to a fraction (and often, a very small fraction) of the total response.

in postulate (3). In the present chapter linearity will be taken to mean that if the stress is doubled at each instant of time, the corresponding strain will also be doubled at every instant (and vice versa). On the other hand, this interpretation does not constitute the full meaning of linearity, as we shall see in Chapter 2. The full meaning of linearity is covered by the following statement: "If a given stress history $\sigma_1(t)$ produces the strain $\varepsilon_1(t)$, and if a stress $\sigma_2(t)$ gives rise to $\varepsilon_2(t)$, then the stress $\sigma_1(t) + \sigma_2(t)$ will give rise to the strain $\varepsilon_1(t) + \varepsilon_2(t)$."

The postulate of linearity is actually incorporated into the definition of anelasticity as a matter of practicality, since the theory becomes extremely difficult otherwise. Fortunately, except for some special circumstances, the observed behavior of materials at low stress levels usually meets the requirement of linearity. The basis for the other two postulates lies in thermodynamic and kinetic concepts which will be discussed briefly now and developed in detail in Chapter 5.

It will be recalled first that a thermodynamic substance is one which can assume a continuous succession of unique equilibrium states in response to a series of infinitesimal changes in an external variable. As a consequence, the first postulate of anelasticity, involving the unique equilibrium stress–strain relationship and the corollary of complete recoverability, is satisfied by all materials that qualify as thermodynamic solids. It should be noted that plastic and viscoelastic materials do not qualify as thermodynamic solids. The second postulate of anelasticity means that, in response to a change in the applied mechanical forces, time is required for the equilibration of an anelastic material. In general, the self-adjustment of a thermodynamic system with time toward a new equilibrium state in response to a change in an external variable is termed *relaxation*. Specifically, where the external variable is mechanical (a stress or a strain), the phenomenon is known as *anelastic relaxation* (or mechanical relaxation).[†] If stress is regarded as the independent variable,

---

[†] Similarly, dielectric or magnetic relaxation may occur under the influence of an electric or magnetic field, respectively. The formal theory of all these phenomena is similar and in large measure interconvertible by appropriate changes in terminology. For dielectric relaxation, electric field strength replaces stress, electric displacement replaces strain, and the dielectric constant replaces the elastic compliance. For magnetic relaxation, the corresponding variables are the magnetic field strength, intensity of magnetization, and magnetic susceptibility, respectively. The only differences in the formal theory of all of these phenomena arise from the tensor nature of stress and strain as compared with the vector nature of the corresponding variables in dielectric and magnetic relaxation. Dielectric relaxation has been the subject of a recent book by Daniel (1967).

Fig. 1-1. Illustration of the direct and indirect coupling between stress and strain in an anelastic solid, the indirect coupling taking place via an internal variable p.

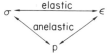

anelastic relaxation manifests itself as the time-dependent equilibration of the conjugate strain variable (or vice versa). It is important to recognize, however, that this external manifestation of relaxation merely parallels and reflects the adjustment of *internal variables* to new equilibrium values. For simplicity, consider the case where there is just one internal variable p, which is influenced by the stress and contributes to the strain. As shown in Fig. 1-1, the stress is now not only directly linked to strain through the purely elastic coupling, but is also linked indirectly through the internal variable p. For each value of applied stress, we may denote the equilibrium value of p by $\bar{p}$. Thus, as the internal variable relaxes toward equilibrium ($p \to \bar{p}$), ε concurrently changes toward a corresponding equilibrium value. In order to obtain anelastic behavior, the relaxation $p \to \bar{p}$ must proceed at a finite rate rather than instantaneously.[†] Such behavior will always occur when a change in p involves a transport process. For example, if p were a parameter characterizing the state of order in an alloy, a change in p would require atomic migration.

In summary, then, anelastic relaxation is inherently a thermodynamic phenomenon which arises from a coupling between stress and strain via certain internal variables which can change to new equilibrium values only through kinetic processes such as diffusion. The external manifestation of this internal relaxation behavior is the time dependent stress–strain behavior given in our previous formal definition of anelasticity. In returning to the development of the formal theory, we shall at first make use of the postulates only, and thereby eliminate any reference to internal variables. After we have gone as far as possible with this approach, internal variables and the thermodynamic basis for relaxation will be reintroduced in Chapter 5, to provide the basis on which specific molecular mechanisms of relaxation can later be discussed.

1.2 Quasi-Static Response Functions

An experiment in which either an applied stress or strain is held constant for any desired period of time is termed *quasi-static*. Under

---

[†] For, if the change $p \to \bar{p}$ did not take time, no operational distinction would exist from the case of pure elasticity.

such conditions, anelastic materials exhibit the phenomena of creep, the elastic aftereffect, and stress relaxation. These phenomena, and the response functions used to describe them, are discussed in turn below.

A. CREEP

In the creep experiment a stress σ_0 is applied abruptly to the sample at $t = 0$, and held constant while the strain ε is observed as a function of time. The experimental conditions may therefore be expressed by

$$\sigma = \begin{cases} 0, & t < 0 \\ \sigma_0, & t \geq 0 \end{cases}$$

From the requirement of linearity, it is clear that $\varepsilon(t)/\sigma_0$ is independent of σ_0. Accordingly, the response function called the *creep function* $J(t)$ and defined by

$$J(t) \equiv \varepsilon(t)/\sigma_0, \qquad t \geq 0 \tag{1.2-1}$$

characterizes the properties of the solid for the particular mode of deformation and temperature of the experiment. Equation (1.2-1) may be regarded as a generalization of (1.1-2) since for the ideal elastic case $J(t)$ becomes just the constant J. The initial value of $J(t)$ is called the *unrelaxed compliance* J_U since it is a measure of the deformation that occurs when no time is allowed for relaxation to take place. Thus,

$$J(0) \equiv J_U \tag{1.2-2}$$

The left-hand side of Fig. 1-2 contrasts the creep response of an ideal solid with that of the anelastic solid and the more general linear viscoelastic solid. The contrast between curves (b) and (c) is of special interest. In curve (c), following a transient period, the strain increases linearly with time, representing steady-state viscous creep. On the other hand, in (b) the strain approaches a definite final or equilibrium value after a sufficient amount of time. This behavior is in accordance with the second postulate of anelasticity. The equilibrium value of $J(t)$ attained in the anelastic case will be called the *relaxed compliance* J_R. Thus

$$J(\infty) \equiv J_R \tag{1.2-3}$$

Finally, the quantity δJ, called the *relaxation of the compliance* J, is defined as

$$\delta J \equiv J_R - J_U \tag{1.2-4}$$

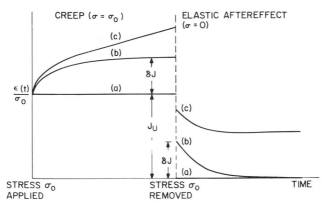

FIG. 1-2. Creep and elastic aftereffect for (a) ideal elastic solid, (b) anelastic solid, and (c) linear viscoelastic solid.

The creep behavior of a material which displays anelasticity, therefore, is such that under unit applied stress the strain increases from an instantaneous value J_U to a final equilibrium value J_R. The time-dependent creep process is also referred to in the literature as "strain relaxation" or "retarded elasticity."

B. ELASTIC AFTEREFFECT (OR CREEP RECOVERY)

If, after a creep experiment has been run for a given time t_1 (not necessarily long enough for attainment of equilibrium), the stress σ_0 is abruptly released, the instantaneous elastic spring-back is in general followed by a time dependent decay of strain. This effect is called the *elastic aftereffect* (in German, *elastische Nachwirkung*) or "creep recovery." In view of the requirement of linearity, the time dependent strain $\varepsilon(t)$ after release of the stress must again be proportional to σ_0. Thus, for the stress history

$$\sigma = \begin{cases} 0, & t < -t_1 \\ \sigma_0, & -t_1 \leq t < 0 \\ 0, & t \geq 0 \end{cases}$$

as illustrated in Fig. 1-3, we define an *aftereffect function* $N_{t_1}(t)$ as

$$N_{t_1}(t) \equiv \varepsilon(t)/\sigma_0, \qquad t \geq 0 \tag{1.2-5}$$

where the subscript t_1 is needed since, in general, the form of the function will depend on the length of time t_1 for which the stress was applied.

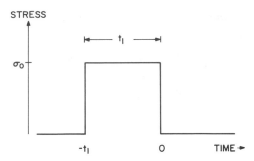

FIG. 1-3.   Loading cycle for an elastic aftereffect experiment.

The right-hand side of Fig. 1-2 shows the aftereffect functions for the three cases discussed previously. In the case of the ideal elastic solid there is an immediate return to zero strain and consequently no aftereffect, while for the case of anelasticity, curve (b), total recovery is completed only through the time-dependent aftereffect. By contrast, the linear viscoelastic solid shows only partial recovery; the contribution to the strain due to the steady-state viscous creep is not recoverable.

In view of our interest in relaxation processes and not in linear viscoelasticity in this book, we shall henceforth restrict our attention primarily to anelastic behavior.

C. STRESS RELAXATION

In a stress relaxation experiment a *constant strain* ε_0 is imposed on the specimen at $t = 0$ and maintained for $t \geq 0$ while the stress σ is observed as a function of time. Thus: $\varepsilon = 0$, $t < 0$; $\varepsilon = \varepsilon_0$, $t \geq 0$. By the linearity requirement $\sigma(t)$ will be proportional to ε_0. It is, therefore, convenient to define the *stress relaxation function* $M(t)$ as $\sigma(t)/\varepsilon_0$ (for $t \geq 0$). By analogy to the case of creep, we define the unrelaxed modulus M_U as the ratio $\sigma(0)$ to ε_0, so that

$$M(0) \equiv M_U \qquad (1.2\text{-}6)$$

From the definition of anelasticity, $M(t)$ must eventually approach a definite equilibrium value, defined as the *relaxed modulus* M_R, i.e.,

$$M(\infty) \equiv M_R \qquad (1.2\text{-}7)$$

The stress relaxation function for an anelastic material is illustrated in Fig. 1-4.

From the existence of a unique equilibrium relation between stress and strain, it follows that the relaxed modulus is the reciprocal of the relaxed compliance defined by Eq. (1.2-3), i.e.,

$$M_R = 1/J_R \tag{1.2-8}$$

The unrelaxed modulus and compliance are also reciprocals of each other

$$M_U = 1/J_U \tag{1.2-9}$$

This last result follows from the fact that on a short time scale, the material behaves as if it were ideally elastic and therefore Eqs. (1.1-1)–(1.1-3) apply with constants J_U and M_U. Since $J_R > J_U$, M_R must be less than M_U, as shown in Fig. 1-4.

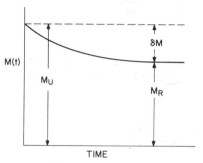

FIG. 1-4.   Stress relaxation of an anelastic solid.

It is also useful to define the quantity δM, called *the relaxation of the modulus M*, by

$$\delta M \equiv M_U - M_R \tag{1.2-10}$$

This quantity is also marked on Fig. 1-4. It should be noted that whereas M_U and M_R are, respectively, reciprocals of J_U and J_R, δM is not the reciprocal of δJ; in fact, $\delta M = \delta J/J_U J_R$.

D. NORMALIZED CREEP AND STRESS RELAXATION FUNCTIONS; RELAXATION STRENGTH

In parts A–C of this section we have introduced three quasi-static response functions, $J(t)$, $N_{t_1}(t)$, and $M(t)$. For some purposes it is desirable to introduce a *normalized creep function* $\psi(t)$ defined, for $t \geq 0$, by

$$J(t) = J_U + \delta J\, \psi(t) \tag{1.2-11}$$

It is clear (e.g., from comparison of this equation with Fig. 1-2) that $\psi(t)$ is defined so as to increase monotonically between the extreme values

$$\psi(0) = 0, \qquad \psi(\infty) = 1 \qquad\qquad (1.2\text{-}12)$$

It is also convenient to define a dimensionless quantity Δ, called the *relaxation strength*, by the equation

$$\Delta \equiv \delta J/J_\mathrm{U} = \delta M/M_\mathrm{R} \qquad\qquad (1.2\text{-}13)$$

The last equality follows from Eqs. (1.2-8)–(1.2-10). Equation (1.2-11) may also be written

$$J(t) = J_\mathrm{U}[1 + \Delta \cdot \psi(t)] \qquad\qquad (1.2\text{-}14)$$

In a similar way, we may define a *normalized stress relaxation function* $\varphi(t)$ by the equations

$$M(t) = M_\mathrm{R} + \delta M\, \varphi(t) = M_\mathrm{R}[1 + \Delta \cdot \varphi(t)] \qquad (1.2\text{-}15)$$

The function $\varphi(t)$ is a monotonically *decreasing* function between the extreme values

$$\varphi(0) = 1, \qquad \varphi(\infty) = 0 \qquad\qquad (1.2\text{-}16)$$

The following useful relations follow from the definitions of Δ, δJ, and δM:

$$J_\mathrm{R} = J_\mathrm{U}(1 + \Delta) \qquad\qquad (1.2\text{-}17)$$

$$M_\mathrm{U} = M_\mathrm{R}(1 + \Delta) \qquad\qquad (1.2\text{-}18)$$

1.3   The Primary Dynamic Response Functions

The quasi-static experiments described in Section 1.2 are used to obtain information on the behavior of materials over periods of several seconds and longer. For information about the behavior of a material at much shorter times, dynamic experiments are more appropriate. In these experiments a stress (or strain) which is periodic in time is imposed on the system, and the phase lag of the strain behind the stress is determined. The behavior of the system is most conveniently described with the aid of complex notation. Let the stress be written as

$$\sigma = \sigma_0 e^{i\omega t} \qquad\qquad (1.3\text{-}1)$$

where σ_0 is the stress amplitude and ω the circular frequency of vibration ($\omega = 2\pi f$, where f is the vibration frequency). The requirement of linearity of the stress–strain relation assures us that the strain is periodic with the same frequency, and therefore expressible in the form

$$\varepsilon = \varepsilon_0 e^{i(\omega t - \phi)} \tag{1.3-2}$$

where ε_0 is the strain amplitude and ϕ is the angle by which the strain lags behind the stress, often called the *loss angle*. Linearity also means that the ratio ε_0/σ_0 is independent of σ_0. Clearly, for ideal elasticity $\phi = 0$, and the ratio ε/σ gives the elastic compliance of the material J. For the anelastic case, however, ϕ is in general not zero, so that the ratio ε/σ is a complex quantity. Let us call this quantity the *complex compliance* $J^*(\omega)$, noting that in general it must be a function of ω. Thus,

$$J^*(\omega) \equiv \varepsilon/\sigma = |J|(\omega)e^{-i\phi(\omega)} \tag{1.3-3}$$

The quantity $|J|(\omega)$, which is the absolute value of J^*, is called the *absolute dynamic compliance*, and is given by

$$|J|(\omega) = \varepsilon_0/\sigma_0 \tag{1.3-4}$$

In terms of this description, two real dynamic response functions of a material have been defined, namely, $|J|(\omega)$ and $\phi(\omega)$. It is also convenient to introduce two other real response functions which are very closely related to $|J|(\omega)$ and $\phi(\omega)$. We first write Eq. (1.3-2) in the alternative form

$$\varepsilon = (\varepsilon_1 - i\varepsilon_2)e^{i\omega t} \tag{1.3-5}$$

where ε_1 is the amplitude of the component of ε in phase with the stress and ε_2 the amplitude of the component which is $90°$ out of phase. Dividing through by σ, we obtain

$$J^*(\omega) = J_1(\omega) - iJ_2(\omega) \tag{1.3-6}$$

where $J_1(\omega) \equiv \varepsilon_1/\sigma_0$ is the real part of $J^*(\omega)$ (sometimes called the "storage compliance") and $J_2(\omega) \equiv \varepsilon_2/\sigma_0$ is the imaginary part of $J^*(\omega)$ (sometimes called the "loss compliance"). The conventional vector diagram for the complex quantity J^* given in Fig. 1-5 shows the relationships between the various response functions discussed. From this diagram it is clear that the functions $|J|$ and ϕ are related to J_1 and J_2

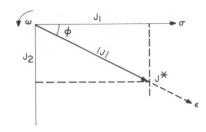

FIG. 1-5. Vector diagram in the complex plane showing the phase relationships between stress, strain, and the complex compliance. The entire diagram rotates about the origin with angular frequency ω.

by the simple equations

$$|J|^2 = J_1^2 + J_2^2 \tag{1.3-7}$$

$$\tan \phi = J_2/J_1 \tag{1.3-8}$$

In a similar way, we could have regarded the periodic strain as given, and the stress as leading the strain by angle ϕ. We then define the *complex modulus* $M^*(\omega)$ by

$$M^*(\omega) \equiv \sigma/\varepsilon = |M|(\omega)e^{i\phi(\omega)} \tag{1.3-9}$$

The absolute value $|M|(\omega)$ is called the *absolute dynamic modulus*. Comparison of (1.3-9) with (1.3-3) shows that the complex compliance is simply the reciprocal of the complex modulus and that $|M|(\omega)$ and $|J|(\omega)$ are also reciprocals. Thus,

$$M^*(\omega) = [J^*(\omega)]^{-1} \quad \text{and} \quad |M|(\omega) = [|J|(\omega)]^{-1} \tag{1.3-10}$$

It is also useful to write $M^*(\omega)$ in the alternate form

$$M^*(\omega) = M_1(\omega) + iM_2(\omega) \tag{1.3-11}$$

where $M_1(\omega)$ and $M_2(\omega)$ are, respectively, the real and imaginary parts of $M^*(\omega)$. A vector diagram similar to Fig. 1-5, or direct comparison of Eqs. (1.3-9) and (1.3-11), gives

$$|M|^2 = M_1^2 + M_2^2 \tag{1.3-12}$$

$$\tan \phi = M_2/M_1 \tag{1.3-13}$$

Comparing these results with Eqs. (1.3-7) and (1.3-8) shows that $M_2/M_1 = J_2/J_1$; also

$$J_1 = M_1/|M|^2 = [M_1(1 + \tan^2 \phi)]^{-1} \tag{1.3-14}$$

and

$$J_2 = M_2/|M|^2 \quad \text{or} \quad M_2 = J_2/|J|^2 \tag{1.3-15}$$

Thus, while the complex quantities $J^*(\omega)$ and $M^*(\omega)$ are reciprocals of one another, J_1 is not the reciprocal of M_1, nor is J_2 the reciprocal of M_2.

A very useful approximation results under the assumption that $\phi^2 \ll 1$. Since $\tan\phi = \phi(1 + \tfrac{1}{3}\phi^2 + \cdots)$ we find that under this assumption $\tan\phi \doteq \phi$. (The symbol $\doteq$ will be used here to signify equality to within terms of the order ϕ^2.) For $\phi = 0.2$, for example, the use of ϕ in place of $\tan\phi$ amounts to an error of about 1%. In view of the fact that $\phi = 0.2$ represents a much higher value of ϕ than is commonly encountered in the anelasticity of crystals, the above approximation can generally be used without significant error. To within this approximation $M_1 \doteq |M|$, $J_1 \doteq |J|$, and from (1.3-14),

$$M_1 \doteq J_1^{-1} \tag{1.3-14a}$$

i.e., the quantities M_1 and J_1 are reciprocals of each other to within terms of order ϕ^2.

At sufficiently low frequencies, the strain will be proportional to the stress, with the relaxed compliance as proportionality constant, so that

$$J^*(0) = 1/M^*(0) = J_{\mathrm{R}} \tag{1.3-16}$$

Conversely, at very high frequencies,

$$J^*(\infty) = 1/M^*(\infty) = J_{\mathrm{U}} \tag{1.3-17}$$

The analogy with Eqs. (1.2-2), (1.2-3), (1.2-6), and (1.2-7) should be noted. Equations (1.3-16) and (1.3-17) state that the complex compliance at the two extremes of frequency is real, and equal to the relaxed and unrelaxed compliance, respectively. It follows that

$$J_2(0) = J_2(\infty) = 0 \tag{1.3-18}$$

and similarly for $M_2(\omega)$.

The significance of the quantities J_1 and J_2 as "storage compliance" and "loss compliance," respectively, is illustrated by calculating the energy stored and the energy dissipated in a cycle of vibration. The energy per unit volume at any phase in the cycle is $\int \sigma \, d\varepsilon$, taken between the start of the cycle up to the point of interest. Thus, the energy ΔW dissipated in a full cycle, per unit of volume, is easily shown (see Problem 1-3) to be

$$\Delta W = \oint \sigma \, d\varepsilon = \pi J_2 \sigma_0^2 \tag{1.3-19}$$

On the other hand, the maximum stored energy W per unit volume is given by

$$W = \int_{\omega t=0}^{\pi/2} \sigma \, d\varepsilon = \tfrac{1}{2}J_1\sigma_0{}^2 \qquad (1.3\text{-}20)$$

The ratio of the energy dissipated to the maximum stored energy (when expressed as a percentage) is often called the "specific damping capacity." From Eqs. (1.3-19), (1.3-20), and (1.3-8), it is clear that this ratio is related to the loss angle ϕ by

$$\Delta W/W = 2\pi(J_2/J_1) = 2\pi \tan \phi \qquad (1.3\text{-}21)$$

In a similar way, taking $\varepsilon = \varepsilon_0 \cos \omega t$ and $\sigma = M^*\varepsilon$ with M^* given by Eq. (1.3-11) we can show that

$$\Delta W = \pi M_2\varepsilon_0{}^2 \qquad (1.3\text{-}22)$$

$$W = \tfrac{1}{2}M_1\varepsilon_0{}^2 \qquad (1.3\text{-}23)$$

and again arrive at the result $\Delta W/W = 2\pi \tan \phi$.

Because of the fact that ϕ (or $\tan \phi$) gives a measure of the fractional energy loss per cycle due to anelastic behavior, the quantity ϕ is commonly known as the *internal friction* of the material.

In summary, the above description of the dynamic behavior of anelastic solids leaves us with a choice of several pairs of dynamic response functions that may be used to designate the properties of the material. These are $|J|$ and ϕ, J_1 and J_2, $|M|$ and ϕ, or M_1 and M_2, each of which is a function of the frequency ω. Each of the four pairs of response functions may be converted to another pair by means of equations given above. Relationships between the members of each pair, e.g., between $J_1(\omega)$ and $J_2(\omega)$, have not appeared as a result of these considerations. To obtain such relations requires a further development of the theory involving the Boltzmann superposition principle, which will be discussed in Chapter 2.

1.4   Additional Dynamic Response Functions

The dynamic response functions considered in Section 1.3 can only be measured directly in an experiment carried out at frequencies well below any resonances of the mechanical system used. Such an experiment, which will be referred to as a "subresonant experiment," is very simple to carry out, in principle.[†] It is merely necessary to set a specimen into forced vibration at a frequency ω and to measure the amplitudes of stress and strain and their relative phases to obtain $\phi(\omega)$ and $|J|(\omega)$ [or $J_1(\omega)$ and $J_2(\omega)$]. These dynamic functions are theoretically the most useful ones, and in fact are all that are needed for the development of the formal theory of anelasticity in Chapters 2–6. In practice, however, the measurement of the phase angle $\phi(\omega)$ is difficult when it is very small, which is usually the case for crystalline materials. Accordingly, subresonant methods are not generally used. Instead, anelastic materials are usually tested at frequencies where the inertia of the system is appreciable. These methods are conveniently divided into two types: (a) methods employing resonant systems vibrating at a natural frequency, either in forced vibration or in free decay, and (b) wave propagation methods. These two types of methods will be discussed from an experimental point of view in Chapter 20. In the remainder of the present chapter our objective will be to study the theory of these methods in order to obtain the relationships between the response functions derived from them and the primary response functions of Section 1.3. Resonant systems will be dealt with in Section 1.5 and Appendices A and F, while wave propagation methods are discussed in Section 1.6.

1.5 Resonant Systems with Large External Inertia

In general, a resonant system must have two elements: the "elastic" element (which in fact may be anelastic), and the inertia. The situation is simplified considerably when a rigid inertia member which is large compared to the inertia of the specimen is added. Such a system has only one degree of freedom, since the motion of the system can be described completely in terms of a single coordinate. An example is a wire sample gripped at the top, and having a large weight hanging freely at the bottom; this system can be set either into longitudinal or into torsional oscillation. The latter case represents the well-known "torsion pendulum," in which the strain at any point can be expressed in terms

---

[†] A mechanical system shows resonance-type behavior if it contains inertial components as well as elastic ones, as, e.g., in the case of a mass on an ideal spring. Near resonance, the inertial and elastic forces are of comparable magnitude. However, at suitably low subresonant frequencies, the inertial force is negligible with respect to the elastic force. For an anelastic material, the subresonant response is therefore determined only by $J^*(\omega)$.

both be considered as constants. Equation (1.5-6) then becomes

$$x_0{}^2 \simeq \frac{(F_0/m)^2 \omega_r^{-2}}{4(\omega - \omega_r)^2 + \omega_r{}^2[\phi(\omega_r)]^2} \qquad (1.5\text{-}9)$$

This dependence on frequency is of the form

$$x_0{}^2 \propto [(\omega - \omega_r)^2 + \omega_r{}^2 \alpha^2]^{-1}$$

where α is a constant. This equation represents the well-known "Lorentzian" curve plotted in Fig. 1-7. It is easy to show that if ω_1 and ω_2 are the two values of frequency at which $x_0{}^2$ falls to half maximum value (or x_0 to $2^{-1/2}$ of its maximum), then

$$(\omega_2 - \omega_1)/\omega_r \equiv \mathcal{Q}^{-1} = \phi \qquad (1.5\text{-}10)$$

where this definition of $\mathcal{Q}$ corresponds to the one commonly used in the description of resonant electrical circuits. Equation (1.5-10) shows that the loss angle ϕ, which is a measure of the internal friction of the system, is obtainable directly from the width of the resonance peak at half-maximum in a plot of (amplitude)^2 versus frequency (or at $2^{-1/2}$ of maximum when amplitude is plotted versus frequency). In passing, it may be noted that the quantity $\mathcal{Q}$, defined above in terms of the sharpness of the resonance peak, is actually the magnification factor of the resonant system (see Problem 1-6).

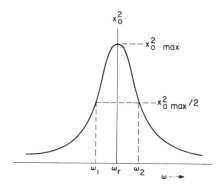

FIG. 1-7.   Lorentzian form for the resonance peak in forced vibration.

It should be remembered that Eq. (1.5-10) is valid only for $\phi \ll 1$, which means $(\omega_2 - \omega_1) \ll \omega_r$ (sharp resonance peak). If first we consider the effect of letting ϕ become larger but keeping ϕ and ω_r independent of ω, examination of Eq. (1.5-6) shows that the resonance peak becomes asymmetric. Nevertheless, it can be shown (see Problem 1-7) under these conditions that Eq. (1.5-10) is valid so long as $\phi^2 \ll 1$, i.e., up to $\phi = 0.1$ or 0.2. It is more difficult to compute the effect of letting ϕ and ω_r depend on ω. We shall see, however, in the further development of anelasticity theory, that generally ϕ and ω_r vary very little with frequency when the frequency changes by 10–20%. Under such circumstances, there is no objection to the use of the forced vibration technique, and of Eq. (1.5-10), so long as $\phi \lesssim 0.1$.

It has been shown that the quantity $\phi(\omega_r)$ is obtained in a resonance experiment directly from Q^{-1}, i.e., from the peak width expressed as a fraction of the resonant frequency. There is, however, a second important quantity obtained in the resonance experiment, namely the resonant frequency itself. Equation (1.5-7) relates ω_r to the known inertial mass and the dynamic force constant k_1 of the spring. Since $k^* \propto M^*$, the real part k_1 is proportional to the real part of the complex modulus $M_1(\omega)$ [or, from Eq. (1.3-14a), inversely proportional to $J_1(\omega)$]. We, therefore, have the general result

$$\omega_r^2 \propto M_1(\omega_r) \doteq J_1^{-1}(\omega_r) \tag{1.5-11}$$

The pertinent values of $M_1(\omega)$ and $J_1(\omega)$ are to be taken at the frequency ω_r, since the experiment is done at the resonant frequency. The proportionality constant in Eq. (1.5-11) is readily calculated. For example, for the case of the torsion pendulum (where M denotes the shear modulus) the proportionality constant is equal to $\pi a^4/2Il$. Here I is the moment of inertia of the cross-bar and a and l are the radius and length of the specimen, respectively. (See Problem 1-4.)

The forced-vibration experiment described therefore yields Q^{-1} and ω_r, which in turn give, respectively, the primary response functions $\phi(\omega_r)$ and $M_1(\omega_r)$, i.e., the values of the response functions $\phi(\omega)$ and $M_1(\omega)$ at a single frequency ω_r. By changing the inertia or the specimen dimensions, ω_r can be changed so that the response functions ϕ and M_1 can be obtained at different frequencies.

B. Free Vibrations of the System

In addition to the use of the resonance response in forced vibration, the oldest and still most popular method of obtaining the dynamic anelastic response involves the measurement of the decay or *damping* of free vibrations of a system, which after excitation is isolated from external forces. Figure 1-8 illustrates the vibration behavior during free decay. For this case, the equation of motion of the system is given by Eq. (1.5-4) except that F_a is now zero. If we employ Eq. (1.5-2) for F_s, the resulting equation of motion is[†]

$$m\ddot{x} + k_1(1 + i \tan \phi)x = 0 \qquad (1.5\text{-}12)$$

The solution which describes free vibration in the presence of internal friction is of the form

$$x = x_0 \exp(i\omega^* t), \qquad \omega^* = \omega_0[1 + (i\delta/2\pi)] \qquad (1.5\text{-}13)$$

or

$$x = x_0 \exp(-\delta \cdot f_0 t) \exp(i\omega_0 t) \equiv A(t) \exp(i\omega_0 t) \qquad (1.5\text{-}14)$$

where $f_0 = \omega_0/2\pi$ is the frequency, δ is a constant, and $A(t)$ is the amplitude or envelope function (see Fig. 1-8). This solution represents exponentially damped oscillations if δ is small. When this solution is substituted into Eq. (1.5-12), and the real and imaginary parts are separately equated, it is found that

$$\omega_0^2 = k_1/m[1 - (\delta^2/4\pi^2)] \doteq k_1/m \qquad (1.5\text{-}15)$$

while

$$\delta \doteq \pi\phi \qquad (1.5\text{-}16)$$

The dimensionless quantity δ represents the natural logarithm of the ratio of amplitudes (A_n) in two successive vibrations, i.e.,

$$\delta = \ln(A_n/A_{n+1}) \qquad (1.5\text{-}17)$$

and is called the *logarithmic decrement*. It is, clearly, a convenient measure of the damping, and in terms of (1.5-16) is directly related (by the factor

---

[†] The advantage of this approach over the usual one, which introduces a damping force proportional to the velocity, is that Eq. (1.5-12) may be expressed without knowledge of the differential or integral equation which relates stress and strain. On the other hand, it must be noted that this approach is not strictly correct. The basis on which Eq. (1.5-2) [or (1.3-9) combined with (1.3-11)] may be inserted into the differential equation for motion, Eq. (1.5-4), is that σ and ε are strictly harmonic in time. In the case of steady-state forced vibrations this assumption is valid; however, in the present case of free vibrations, it is clear from Eq. (1.5-14) that, due to the damping term, this assumption is not strictly true. In fact, Fourier analysis shows that Eq. (1.5-14) corresponds to a spectrum of frequencies, centered about f_0, and having a width that varies inversely as δ. The consequences of this point will be discussed later.

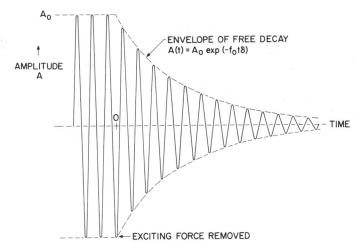

FIG. 1-8.   The free decay of natural vibrations of an anelastic solid.

π) to our earlier measure of internal friction, the loss angle ϕ. It is also seen by comparison of Eqs. (1.5-7) and (1.5-15) that, except for terms of order ϕ^2, the natural frequency in free decay ω_0 is equal to the resonant frequency in forced vibrations ω_r.

As already mentioned (see footnote p. 20) the use of the complex force constant in Eq. (1.5-12) is not strictly valid when the displacement is not simple harmonic. It is clear from (1.5-14) that, the higher the damping, the larger the deviation from the simple harmonic form of the solution, and the less valid Eq. (1.5-16) will be. To solve the damping problem exactly, one must utilize the specific differential equation relating stress and strain which is valid for the material in question. The relationship between δ and ϕ will then no longer be independent of the properties of the material, as in Eq. (1.5-16), but will now be determined by the specific form of this stress–strain equation. Zener (1947a) and, more recently, Parke (1966) have worked out this result for the special case of the "standard anelastic solid" dealt with in Chapter 3. For this case, the internal friction shows a peak, and Zener has evaluated the relationship between the peak value ϕ_m of the loss angle and the peak value of the logarithmic decrement, δ_m as follows:

$$\tan \phi_m \doteq \phi_m = (\delta_m/\pi)[1 - (\delta_m/2\pi) + \cdots] \qquad (1.5\text{-}18)$$

The important result is that the correction is of the *first order* in δ_m, so that the error in using Eq. (1.5-16) when $\phi_m \sim 0.1$ is about 5%, which is quite appreciable compared to cases where only terms in ϕ^2 are neglected. This result is significant, since it brings attention to the fact that the mere occurrence of a strictly exponential decay of vibrations [as given by (1.5-14)] does not guarantee the validity of Eq. (1.5-16).[†] Similarly, $\omega_0^2 \doteq k_1/m$ is still valid, but the second-order correction term in δ^2 depends on the specific model, and, in general, differs from that given in Eq. (1.5-15).

It is convenient to summarize the relationship between the various measures of internal friction discussed thus far. The following simple relationships [obtained by combining Eqs. (1.5-10) and (1.5-16) with Eq. (1.3-21)] are valid when $\phi \ll 1$:

$$\phi = \mathcal{Q}^{-1} = \delta/\pi = \Delta W/2\pi W, \qquad \phi \ll 1 \qquad (1.5\text{-}19)$$

C. CHARACTERISTIC ENERGIES OF THE SYSTEM

The vibrating system with one degree of freedom has been represented by the model of the mass on a spring (Fig. 1-6) which is characterized by the three parameters: m, k_1, and ϕ. In order to facilitate the generalization of the present results to systems with distributed inertia, in Appendix A, another approach to the present problem is very useful, viz., to characterize the system by appropriate energy parameters. These parameters are the maximum kinetic energy W_m^K, the maximum potential energy W_m^P, and the energy loss per cycle ΔW.[‡] These quantities may be shown (see Problem 1-8) to be given by

$$W_m^K = \tfrac{1}{2}m\omega^2 x_0^2, \quad W_m^P = \tfrac{1}{2}k_1 x_0^2, \quad \Delta W = \pi k_2 x_0^2 = \pi k_1 \phi x_0^2 \qquad (1.5\text{-}20)$$

The last two of these equations are analogous to Eqs. (1.3-23) and (1.3-22). It should be noted that each of these energies is proportional to the square of the maximum displacement x_0 with proportionality constants involving the three parameters m, k_1, and ϕ, respectively. The system is therefore characterized equally well by these three energies (for unit value of x_0^2) as by the original three parameters.

Another point worth noting is the direct way in which the natural or resonant frequency may be obtained by setting $W_m^K = W_m^P$. [Compare

---

[†] Actually, an exponential decay with time is a direct consequence of linearity. Departure from exponential decay indicates that the material is not behaving anelastically, in that the internal friction is a function of strain amplitude.

[‡] These quantities are now *total* energies rather than energies per unit volume.

this result with Eq. (1.5-7).] For a system with no damping, this equality is a consequence of the conservation of energy. The result is still valid in the presence of dissipative forces (provided $\Delta W \ll W_m^P$), since W_m^P is calculated as $\int_0^{x_0} k_1 x \, dx$, i.e., taking into account only the work that goes into stored energy and not that which is dissipated.

The resonant system with which we have dealt in detail in this section, namely one in which an external inertia is present which is large relative to the inertia of the specimen, is seldom encountered except for the torsion pendulum. More often, the distributed inertia of the specimen has to be taken into account. The importance of the example with which we have dealt here lies in the fact that all cases of distributed inertia, no matter how complex, can be shown to be mathematically equivalent to the problem involving one degree of freedom. This correspondence is demonstrated in Appendix A. As one consequence, it follows that, for a given frequency, the damping or internal friction exhibited by a homogeneous material is independent of the nature of the vibrating system employed for the measurements [see Eq. (A-5) in Appendix A].

1.6 Wave Propagation Methods

In the resonant method with distributed inertia (see Appendix A) a specimen is vibrated in one of its natural modes, so that a standing wave is set up in the sample. Such standing waves are produced by the interference of traveling waves moving in opposite directions as the result of successive reflections from the ends of the specimen. In contrast, wave propagation methods utilize a wave traveling down the specimen in only one direction at a time; interference effects are then absent. This can be accomplished by *continuous wave propagation* if the specimen is long enough and the damping high enough that absorption is complete before the wave reaches the free end. More commonly, for crystalline materials where the damping is generally low, a *pulse propagation method* is used. This method employs a pulse or wave packet whose length is small compared to the specimen length in the direction of propagation. The pulse is generated by an appropriate transducer bonded to one end of the sample. The velocity of such a pulse can be determined from the time for it to reach the other end, or from the time to return to the starting point after suffering a reflection at the free end, while the attenuation of the pulse may be determined from the decrease in amplitude after successive reflections. Figures 1-9 and 1-10 illustrate the method schematically. The purpose of this section is to relate the velocity and attenuation to the primary dynamic response functions of the specimen material that were discussed in Section 1.3.

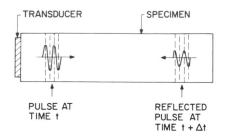

FIG. 1-9.   Schematic illustration of the ultrasonic pulse method.

The type of propagation which lends itself most easily to analysis is that of a plane (nonspreading) harmonic wave in an elastic medium. The propagation direction is taken along the x coordinate axis, while the particle displacement u may be in the x direction (longitudinal or dilatational wave) or normal to it (transverse, or shear wave). Such a

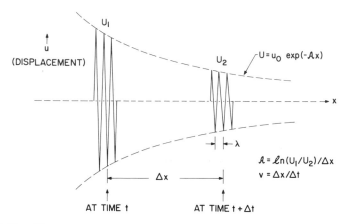

FIG. 1-10.   The attenuation of an ultrasonic pulse propagating through an anelastic medium.

case may be expressed by the well-known one dimensional wave equation, of the form (see, e.g., Kolsky, 1953)

$$\varrho\,\partial^2 u/\partial t^2 = M\,\partial^2 u/\partial x^2 \tag{1.6-1}$$

where ϱ is the density of the medium and M is the appropriate modulus.

For anelastic material, if the motion is strictly harmonic (circular frequency ω), M may be replaced by the complex modulus M^*. In this
case, we have

$$\varrho\ddot{u} = -\varrho\omega^2 u = M^*(\partial^2 u/\partial x^2) \tag{1.6-2}$$

Before proceeding further it is desirable to consider why Eq. (1.6-2)
is not strictly valid as a generalization of Eq. (1.6-1). There are two factors which give rise to deviations from the assumed condition of harmonic
motion, as follows: (a) The existence of damping, which means that the
amplitude of vibration decreases with time (see Fig. 1-10). In this respect,
the situation is no different from that of free decay of a resonant system
(see footnote p. 20), so that the validity of Eq. (1.6-2) is based on the
requirement that the damping be small, just as in the case of (1.5-12).
(b) The finite length of the wave packet in the pulse propagation method,
which means (by Fourier analysis) that the frequency is not sharply
defined even in the absence of attenuation. In fact, the result of Fourier
analysis of a periodic pulse of finite duration is that it may be represented
as a frequency distribution which becomes more sharply peaked as the
pulse is expanded to contain more and more waves. Thus, from the
viewpoint of defining the frequency, the longer the pulse, the better.
However, as already mentioned, for experimental reasons the pulse must
be short compared to the specimen length. A suitable compromise may
usually be obtained by taking pulses about ten waves long.

Returning to Eq. (1.6-2), we note that a solution of this equation may
be given in the form of a damped wave moving in the $+x$ direction:

$$u = u_0 \exp(-\mathscr{A}x) \exp\{i\omega[t - (x/v)]\} \tag{1.6-3}$$

Here v is the wave velocity, while $\mathscr{A}$ is called the *attenuation* and has
dimensions of reciprocal length. The significance of the attenuation is
best shown by considering the envelope

$$U(x) = u_0 \exp(-\mathscr{A}x)$$

of the high frequency wave. Comparing this envelope at two positions,
$x_2 > x_1$, one obtains

$$\mathscr{A} \, (\text{Np cm}^{-1}) = (x_2 - x_1)^{-1} \ln[U(x_1)/U(x_2)] \tag{1.6-4}$$

which expresses $\mathscr{A}$ in the units of nepers per centimeter. In addition,
$\mathscr{A}$ is also commonly expressed in two other units involving the ratio of

amplitudes in decibels:

$$\mathscr{A}\,(\text{dB cm}^{-1}) \equiv (x_2 - x_1)^{-1}20 \log_{10}[U(x_1)/U(x_2)] = 8.68\mathscr{A}\,(\text{Np cm}^{-1}) \tag{1.6-5}$$

$$\mathscr{A}\,(\text{dB }\mu\text{sec}^{-1}) = 8.68 \times 10^{-6}v\,(\text{cm sec}^{-1})\,\mathscr{A}\,(\text{Np cm}^{-1}) \tag{1.6-6}$$

Whenever the symbol $\mathscr{A}$ appears without specification of units, it will be understood to be in nepers per centimeter.

Equation (1.6-3) may be substituted into (1.6-2) to obtain the parameters v and $\mathscr{A}$. In view of the requirement of small damping ($\phi \ll 1$) for the validity of Eq. (1.6-2), it is certainly permissible to put $M^* \doteq M_1(1 + i\phi)$. Equating separately the real and imaginary parts, we obtain

$$v^2 \doteq M_1/\varrho \tag{1.6-7}$$

$$\mathscr{A} = \phi\omega/2v = \pi\phi/\lambda, \qquad \phi \ll 1 \tag{1.6-8}$$

where the wavelength λ is set equal to v/f. Thus the two observable parameters v and $\mathscr{A}$ which are measured in a wave propagation experiment are related, respectively, to the values of the two primary response functions $M_1(\omega)$ and $\phi(\omega)$ at the frequency of propagation ω.

The fact that M_1 is a function of ω means [from Eq. (1.6-7)] that v is also $v(\omega)$. This result implies the existence of *dispersion*. Since $M_1(\omega)$ is a monotonically increasing function of ω, a wave packet becomes elongated as it travels, with the lower-frequency components lagging in the tail. To minimize such distortion due to dispersion requires again that the pulse be long enough to keep the frequency distribution narrow.

It is worthwhile to review here the types of waves that may be generated in an isotropic medium, and the significance of the corresponding modulus M that appears in Eq. (1.6-1). (The case of anisotropic media will be considered in Chapter 6.) As already mentioned, the two simplest cases are those for which the particle displacement u is in the x direction or normal to it. These cases correspond, respectively, to longitudinal and shear waves. In the case of the *longitudinal wave* there are two relatively simple geometries: (a) wave propagation along a filament whose lateral dimensions are small compared to λ, where the displacement over the entire cross section is the same; and (b) propagation within a semi-infinite medium (i.e., lateral dimensions $\gg \lambda$). In case (a), it is clear that M is simply the value of Young's modulus E along the length of the filament. In case (b), however, the appropriate modulus is that for pure longitudinal extension without transverse (Poisson) contraction. For the case of a single crystal this is the elastic constant c_{11} (see Chapter 6). It is usual in a pulse propagation experiment to have conditions such that case (b) is valid, as discussed in Chapter 20. In the case of a *shear wave*, each volume element is always distorted without a change in volume, so that the appropriate modulus is in all cases the shear modulus G.

1.7 Summary of Results for Various Dynamic Experiments

The various dynamic methods outlined in this chapter may be classified in terms of the relation of the frequency employed to a resonant frequency ω_r of the complete mechanical system involved. Thus we have:

a. Subresonant experiments, for which $\omega \ll \omega_r$. Here the presence of inertia in the system does not matter and the angle between force and displacement is simply the quantity ϕ [see Eq. (1.5-8), setting $\omega \ll \omega_r$]. If ϕ is large, this method is the best one to use. Simultaneously one obtains $|M|(\omega)$ from the ratio σ_0/ε_0 [see Eq. (1.3-4) or (1.3-9)].

b. Resonant experiments, for which $\omega \sim \omega_r$. Here we may study free vibrations and measure the logarithmic decrement δ, or forced vibrations and measure $\mathcal{Q}^{-1}$. At the same time, the resonant frequency obeys the relation: $\omega_r{}^2 \propto M_1$.

c. Wave propagation experiments (which may be called "suprares-onant" since $\omega \gg \omega_r$). Here we obtain the attenuation $\mathcal{A}$ which measures the internal friction and the velocity v, which is proportional to M_1.

The relations between the quantities measured in these various experiments are simple only if ϕ is small compared to unity. [In most cases the relations may be used up to $\phi = 0.1$, although corrections up to 5% may be involved for this value of ϕ. See, e.g., Eq. (1.5-18).] These relations among the various measures of internal friction are summarized as

$$\phi = \delta/\pi = \mathcal{Q}^{-1} = \mathcal{A}\lambda/\pi, \qquad \phi \ll 1 \qquad (1.7\text{-}1)$$

Similarly, the various measures of dynamic modulus may be related by

$$\sigma_0/\varepsilon_0 = |M| \doteq M_1 \propto \omega_r{}^2 \propto v^2 \qquad (1.7\text{-}2)$$

It should be recalled that one difference between the dynamic response functions obtained from the subresonant type of experiment and the quantities measured in resonant or wave propagation experiments is that the former functions are characteristic only of the anelasticity of the system while some of the latter include the inertia of the system and sample dimensions. Since the quantities measured in each of the three types of experiments have been related to each other in the present chapter, it will not be necessary to deal with all of these quantities in subsequent chapters. Rather, because of the inherent simplicity of the primary dynamic response functions introduced in Section 1.3, these will be the functions in terms of which the formal theory of anelasticity will be further developed in Chapters 2–4.

PROBLEMS

1-1. Unit volume of anelastic material (originally in equilibrium under zero stress) is subject to a smoothly applied uniaxial stress σ, which produces initially an unrelaxed strain. The stress is then sustained for a long enough time to produce complete relaxation. Finally, the material is returned to its original state by unloading the sample slowly enough to maintain equilibrium. Draw the stress–strain loop for this loading cycle. Show that (i) the work done prior to relaxation is $\frac{1}{2}J_U\sigma^2$, (ii) the work done during relaxation is $(J_R - J_U)\sigma^2$, and (iii) the work regained during unloading is $\frac{1}{2}J_R\sigma^2$. Hence show that one-half of the work done during relaxation is stored in the sample, and one-half is dissipated as heat. Finally, show from energy considerations that J_R must be greater than J_U, i.e., that relaxation must always produce a strain of the same sign as the applied stress. Notice that this result justifies the following statement of Le Chatelier's principle, as applied to anelastic materials: If to a solid in equilibrium a force is applied, the solid will relax in a manner to make that force do work.

1-2. For $\Delta \ll 1$, show that one may expand $1/M(t)$ as given by Eq. (1.2-15) in powers of Δ [using Eq. (1.2-17)], to obtain

$$1/M(t) = J_U\{1 + \Delta[1 - \phi(t)] + \text{terms of order } \Delta^2 + \cdots\}$$

1-3. Prove Eqs. (1.3-19) and (1.3-20). (Note that in the evaluation of integrals of the type $\int \sigma \, d\varepsilon$, stress and strain must be expressed in real notation, e.g., $\sigma = \sigma_0 \cos \omega t$, since the complex notation is only valid for linear operations.)

1-4. Work out the form of the constants C_1 and C_2 in Eqs. (1.5-1) for the case of the torsion pendulum in terms of the moment of inertia

I of the inertia member, as well as the length l and the radius a of the specimen wire. Also, show that the proportionality constant in Eq. (1.5-11) is $\pi a^4/2Il$.

1-5. Verify Eqs. (1.5-6) and (1.5-8).

1-6. Show that the quantity $\mathcal{Q}$ defined by Eq. (1.5-10) is the magnification factor of the resonant system, in the sense that the amplitude excited at resonance is $\mathcal{Q}$ times the deflection that the same peak force would produce if applied statically.

1-7. Show from Eq. (1.5-6) that Eq. (1.5-10) is valid so long as ϕ and ω_r are constants and $\phi^2 \ll 1$ (i.e., that the correction terms to Eq. (1.5-10) are of the order ϕ^3).

1-8. Verify Eq. (1.5-20) for the model of Fig. 1-6.

General References

GROSS, B. (1953). "Mathematical Structure of the Theories of Viscoelasticity." Hermann, Paris.

MASON, W. P., ed. (1964). "Physical Acoustics," Vol. 1A. Academic Press, New York,

RAYLEIGH, LORD (1945). "Theory of Sound," Chaps. 4, 5. Reprinted by Dover, New York.

STAVERMAN, A. J., and Schwartzl, F. (1956). *In* "Die Physik der Hochpolymeren," H. A. Stuart, ed., Chap. 1. Springer Berlin.

Chapter 2 / Relations among the Response Functions: The Boltzmann Superposition Principle

In Chapter 1, Sections 1.2 and 1.3, we introduced a group of response functions each of which describes the behavior of an anelastic solid under specific experimental conditions. These are the creep function $J(t)$, the aftereffect function $N_{t_1}(t)$, the stress relaxation function $M(t)$, and the following pairs of dynamic functions (all functions of ω): $|J|$ and ϕ, J_1 and J_2, M and ϕ, and M_1 and M_2. Since equations for interconversion among the four pairs of dynamic functions are given in Chapter 1, it is not necessary to use all of these functions. Rather, we will find it convenient to consider here only the relations between $J(t)$ or $M(t)$ and the four dynamic functions[†] $J_1(\omega)$, $J_2(\omega)$, $M_1(\omega)$, and $M_2(\omega)$.

It might be expected intuitively that each response function constitutes a complete representation of the inherent anelastic properties of the solid.[‡] If this statement is true, it follows that any one of the various response functions can be used to specify completely the anelastic behavior of the solid, and further, that all other response functions are derivable from the selected one. The purpose of this chapter is to show the validity of this last statement and to derive the interrelationships among the various response functions.

[†] The utility of these functions is that they represent simply a strain (in the case of J_1 and J_2) or a stress (in the case of M_1 and M_2) in a specified experiment. The quantity ϕ is essentially a ratio of two strains or of two stresses, while $|J|$ is the square root of the sum of squares of two strains. The latter quantities do not permit one to take advantage of the simplicity inherent in the linear equations of anelasticity as easily as do the selected functions.

[‡] It should be realized, however, that some functions $[J(t), M(t), J_1(\omega), M_1(\omega)]$ contain both the elastic and anelastic properties of the material while others $[J_2(\omega), M_2(\omega)]$ do not. Thus, if the material is ideally elastic, the first group of functions goes into the elastic constant J or M, while the second group goes to zero. On the other hand, differencies such as $J_1(\omega) - J_U$ or $M(t) - M_R$ represent the anelastic response only, and may be then compared to functions of the second group.

2.1   Statement of the Boltzmann Superposition Principle

In this section, we introduce a concept which Boltzmann first presented in 1876, called the "superposition principle." According to this principle, *if a series of stresses are applied to a material at different times, each contributes to the deformation as if it alone were acting.* The total strain due to constant stresses σ_1 and σ_2 is then $\varepsilon_1(t) + \varepsilon_2(t)$, where ε_1 and ε_2 are, respectively, the strains which would be obtained if σ_1 or σ_2 were acting alone. Similarly, if $\sigma_1(t)$ is the stress necessary to produce a constant strain ε_1, and $\sigma_2(t)$ is necessary to produce ε_2, then a strain $\varepsilon_1 + \varepsilon_2$ is produced by $\sigma_1(t) + \sigma_2(t)$.

The superposition principle expresses the full meaning of linearity as contained in the definition of anelasticity given in Chapter 1. The reader is reminded that the meaning of linearity employed in Chapter 1 to define the response functions and their interrelations was of more restricted form. For example, it was recognized that a creep experiment performed under double the stress would produce double the strain at each instant of time. What was not considered, however, was the response to different stresses (or strains) imposed *at different times.* We will see in the present chapter that only the full consequences of linearity, as embodied in the Boltzmann principle, permit us to deduce all of the relationships between the response functions.

Consider that a stress σ_i is applied at time t_i'. Then from the definition of the creep function, $\varepsilon(t)$ is given for $t \geq t_i'$ by

$$\varepsilon(t) = \sigma_i J(t - t_i') \tag{2.1-1}$$

Now, suppose that a whole series of σ_i ($i = 1, 2, \ldots, m$) are applied, at successively increasing times $t_1', t_2', \ldots, t_m'$, respectively. From the superposition principle we can write immediately that the strain is given by [†]

$$\varepsilon(t) = \sum_{i=1}^{m} \sigma_i J(t - t_i') \tag{2.1-2}$$

This equation then relates $\varepsilon(t)$ to the previous stress history through the creep function.

Before going any further we can show the power of the superposition principle by deriving immediately an expression for the aftereffect func-

---

[†] In employing Eq. (2.1-2), we regard the creep function of a negative argument to be defined as equal to zero. In this way, no future stress can influence present behavior.

tion $N_{t_1}(t)$ in terms of the creep function. Clearly, the application of stress σ_0 at $t = -t_1$ and its release at $t = 0$, may alternatively be described as the application of stress σ_0 at $t = -t_1$ followed by application of a stress $-\sigma_0$ at $t = 0$. Equation (2.1-2) then gives, for $t > 0$,

$$\varepsilon(t) = \sigma_0[J(t + t_1) - J(t)]$$

The behavior of $\varepsilon(t)$ is depicted in Fig. 2-1. From the definition (1.2-5) of the aftereffect function,

$$N_{t_1}(t) = J(t + t_1) - J(t), \qquad t \geq 0 \qquad (2.1\text{-}3)$$

In particular, if $t_1 \to \infty$, $J(t + t_1) \to J_R$ and so

$$N_\infty(t) = J_R - J(t) \qquad (2.1\text{-}4)$$

Equation (2.1-4) shows that the aftereffect function $N_\infty(t)$ is very simply related to the creep function, namely that the relaxed compliance minus $N_\infty(t)$ is just $J(t)$. On the other hand, for $t_1 \neq \infty$, N_{t_1} is obtained by subtracting the value of the creep function at time $t + t_1$ from that at t. In view of Eqs. (2.1-3) and (2.1-4), it is no longer necessary to treat the aftereffect function as if it were distinct from the creep function; therefore, the function N_{t_1} will no longer be considered in the further development of the theory.

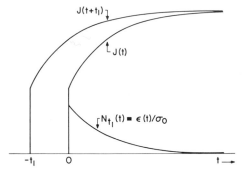

FIG. 2-1.   Illustration of the aftereffect function as given by Eq. (2.1-3).

Returning now to our development of the consequences of the superposition principle, we see that for a stress history in which σ is varied *continuously* instead of in discrete steps, Eq. (2.1-2) may be converted into the integral expression

$$\varepsilon(t) = \int_{-\infty}^{t} J(t - t') \frac{d\sigma(t')}{dt'} dt' \qquad (2.1\text{-}5)$$

In a similar way, if strain is the controlled (independent) variable and stress is observed as a function of time, it follows from the superposition principle, for the case of a series of strains ε_i imposed on the material at time t_i', that

$$\sigma(t) = \sum_{i=1}^{m} \varepsilon_i M(t - t_i') \qquad (2.1\text{-}6)$$

which expresses $\sigma(t)$ in terms of the stress relaxation function. For continuous variation of the imposed strain $\varepsilon(t')$, this function becomes

$$\sigma(t) = \int_{-\infty}^{t} M(t - t') \frac{d\varepsilon(t')}{dt'} \, dt' \qquad (2.1\text{-}7)$$

Equations (2.1-5) and (2.1-7) are linear integral equations which constitute a generalization of Hooke's law applicable to anelasticity (or, in fact, to linear viscoelasticity, since only the postulate of linearity has been utilized). These integral expressions bring out the fact that the sample acts as if it had a *memory* of its past history. Thus, Eq. (2.1-5) shows that the strain at time t is related to the entire previous stress history and to the function $J(t)$, which is characteristic of the material. This memory feature is a reflection of the fact noted in Chapter 1 that ε depends not only on the instantaneous value of σ, but also on internal variables whose instantaneous values reflect the previous history of the material.

If the stress history consists of both continuous and discontinuous changes in σ, we can use a combination of (2.1-2) and (2.1-5):

$$\varepsilon(t) = \sum_i \sigma_i J(t - t_i') + \int_{-\infty}^{t} J(t - t') \frac{d\sigma(t')}{dt'} \, dt' \qquad (2.1\text{-}8)$$

It is useful to obtain other forms of Eq. (2.1-8). First let $\xi = t - t'$ be the "elapsed time." Then, in terms of ξ as the integration variable

$$\varepsilon(t) = \sum_i \sigma_i J(t - t_i') - \int_{0}^{\infty} J(\xi) \frac{d\sigma(t - \xi)}{d\xi} \, d\xi \qquad (2.1\text{-}9)$$

Another useful form is obtained by separating $J(\xi)$ in (2.1-9) into the instantaneous response J_U and anelastic response $J(\xi) - J_U$

$$\varepsilon(t) = J_U \sigma(t) - \int_{0}^{\infty} [J(\xi) - J_U] \frac{d\sigma(t - \xi)}{d\xi} \, d\xi + \sum_i \sigma_i [J(t - t_i') - J_U]$$

$$(2.1\text{-}10)$$

Equation (2.1-10) follows from (2.1-9) so long as $\sigma(-\infty)$ is taken to be zero.

If we now integrate by parts, utilizing $J(0) = J_U$ and the condition $\sigma(-\infty) = 0$, we obtain

$$\varepsilon(t) = J_U \sigma(t) + \int_0^\infty \sigma(t - \xi)\, \frac{dJ(\xi)}{d\xi}\, d\xi \qquad (2.1\text{-}11)$$

Similarly, from Eqs. (2.1-6) and (2.1-7)

$$\sigma(t) = M_R \varepsilon(t) - \int_0^\infty [M(\xi) - M_R]\, \frac{d\varepsilon(t - \xi)}{d\xi}\, d\xi$$
$$+ \sum_i \varepsilon_i [M(t - t_i') - M_R] \qquad (2.1\text{-}12)$$

and

$$\sigma(t) = M_U \varepsilon(t) + \int_0^\infty \varepsilon(t - \xi)\, \frac{dM(\xi)}{d\xi}\, d\xi \qquad (2.1\text{-}13)$$

The summations over discrete steps of stress or strain, respectively, are deliberately omitted in Eqs. (2.1-11) and (2.1-13), since in these forms there is no singularity in the integrand even when σ or ε are permitted to undergo discontinuous changes.

2.2   Relations between the Creep and Stress Relaxation Functions

The existence of pairs of equations of the type (2.1-5) and (2.1-7) implies that there exists a relation between the $J(t)$ and $M(t)$ functions. One way of obtaining this relationship is by the methods of Laplace transforms (see Gross, 1947; Leaderman, 1958). Another approach is to start with (2.1-8) and to substitute $\varepsilon = 0$ for $t < 0$, $\varepsilon = \varepsilon_0$ for $t \geq 0$; therefore, σ must undergo the discrete step from 0 to $\varepsilon_0 M_U$ at $t' = 0$, while, by definition, $\sigma(t')/\varepsilon_0 = M(t')$ for $t' \geq 0$. Dividing through by ε_0, we obtain

$$1 = M_U J(t) + \int_0^t J(t - t')\, \frac{dM(t')}{dt'}\, dt' \qquad (2.2\text{-}1)$$

This equation implicitly relates the functions $J(t)$ and $M(t)$ but in such a manner that it is difficult to evaluate one of these functions when the other is known. The important result, however, is that, in principle at least, the stress relaxation function and creep function can be computed one from the other. A useful form for the numerical evaluation of $J(t)$

from $M(t)$, or vice versa, by an iterative method (Hopkins and Hamming, 1957) is

$$t = \int_0^t J(t')M(t - t')\, dt' \qquad (2.2\text{-}2)$$

This equation can be shown to be equivalent to Eq. (2.2-1) by differentiating both sides with respect to time.

Zener (1948, Chapter 5) has developed an important inequality starting from Eq. (2.2-1). He substitutes

$$J(t - t') = J(t) - [J(t) - J(t - t')]$$

into that equation and carries out the integration over the $J(t)$ term to obtain

$$J(t)M(t) = 1 + \int_0^t [J(t) - J(t - t')]\frac{dM(t')}{dt'}\, dt' \qquad (2.2\text{-}3)$$

It is clear that the integrand in (2.2-3) is always negative, since it is made up of a product of two factors, the first of which is always positive and the second always negative (as can be seen from Figs. 1-2 and 1-4). Thus the following inequality is obtained:

$$J(t)M(t) \leq 1 \qquad (2.2\text{-}4)$$

We know, of course, that the equality in Eq. (2.2-4) is valid both for $t = 0$ and $t = \infty$ [see Eqs. (1.2-8) and (1.2-9)]. Furthermore, Problem 2-2 shows that the equality holds approximately for the case of small relaxation strength, specifically, when $\Delta^2 \ll 1$. Finally, in Chapter 4 (Section 4.4) it will be shown that the equality also holds when J and M vary relatively slowly over a broad range of time, regardless of the magnitude of the relaxation strength. In the most general cases, however, Eq. (2.2-1) or (2.2-2) must be used to provide the implicit relation between the creep and stress relaxation functions.

2.3 Relations between Quasi-Static and Dynamic Properties

In order to relate the creep function to the dynamic response functions $J_1(\omega)$ or $J_2(\omega)$ we make use of Eq. (2.1-10) and substitute $\sigma(t) = \sigma_0 e^{i\omega t}$. Then

$$\varepsilon(i\omega t) = J_U \sigma_0 e^{i\omega t} + i\omega\sigma_0 \int_0^\infty [J(\xi) - J_U]e^{i\omega(t-\xi)}\, d\xi \qquad (2.3\text{-}1)$$

Recalling the definition of $J^*(\omega)$, we obtain

$$J^*(\omega) = \varepsilon(i\omega t)/\sigma_0 e^{i\omega t} = J_U + i\omega \int_0^\infty [J(\xi) - J_U]e^{-i\omega\xi}\, d\xi \qquad (2.3\text{-}2)$$

Finally, equating real and imaginary parts in Eq. (2.3-2) and recalling that $J^* = J_1 - iJ_2$, we find

$$J_1(\omega) - J_U = \omega \int_0^\infty [J(t) - J_U] \sin \omega t\, dt \qquad (2.3\text{-}3)$$

$$J_2(\omega) = -\omega \int_0^\infty [J(t) - J_U] \cos \omega t\, dt \qquad (2.3\text{-}4)$$

which express J_1 and J_2 in terms of the creep function.

Another useful form for expressing the relation of the dynamic functions to $J(t)$ is obtained starting from (2.1-11) and following a procedure similar to that just described to obtain the relations

$$J_1(\omega) - J_U = \int_0^\infty \frac{dJ(t)}{dt} \cos \omega t\, dt \qquad (2.3\text{-}5)$$

$$J_2(\omega) = \int_0^\infty \frac{dJ(t)}{dt} \sin \omega t\, dt \qquad (2.3\text{-}6)$$

These integrals may be transformed by the application of the Fourier inversion to obtain (see, e.g., Franklin, 1958)

$$dJ(t)/dt = (2/\pi) \int_0^\infty [J_1(\omega) - J_U] \cos \omega t\, d\omega \qquad (2.3\text{-}7)$$

$$dJ(t)/dt = (2/\pi) \int_0^\infty J_2(\omega) \sin \omega t\, d\omega \qquad (2.3\text{-}8)$$

which express the creep function in terms of the $J_1(\omega)$ and $J_2(\omega)$ functions, respectively. [In a similar way, Eqs. (2.3-3) and (2.3-4) could also have been inverted.]

Finally, in an analogous manner, starting from Eqs. (2.1-12) and (2.1-13) and substituting $\varepsilon = \varepsilon_0 e^{i\omega t}$ and $M^* = \sigma/\varepsilon$, we arrive at the expressions

$$M_1(\omega) - M_R = \omega \int_0^\infty [M(t) - M_R] \sin \omega t\, dt \qquad (2.3\text{-}9)$$

$$M_2(\omega) = \omega \int_0^\infty [M(t) - M_R] \cos \omega t\, dt \qquad (2.3\text{-}10)$$

and the alternative forms

$$M_1(\omega) = M_U + \int_0^\infty \frac{dM(t)}{dt} \cos \omega t \, dt \qquad (2.3\text{-}11)$$

$$M_2(\omega) = -\int_0^\infty \frac{dM(t)}{dt} \sin \omega t \, dt \qquad (2.3\text{-}12)$$

as well as expressions for $M(t)$ in terms of M_1 and M_2, obtained by using Fourier inversions of these expressions.

It is important to note that all relations between functions obtained in this section are explicit relations, in which one of the two functions appears on the left-hand side of the equation. These are much more useful relations than is the implicit one (2.2-1) between the functions $J(t)$ and $M(t)$.

2.4   Interrelation of the Dynamic Properties

In view of the fact that both $J_1(\omega)$ and $J_2(\omega)$ can be expressed in terms ao $J(t)$, it is possible to eliminate $J(t)$ to obtain a relation between J_1 nfd J_2. For example, inserting Eq. (2.3-8) into (2.3-5) we obtain

$$J_1(\omega) - J_U = (2/\pi) \int_0^\infty \cos \omega t \left[\int_0^\infty J_2(\alpha) \sin \alpha t \, d\alpha \right] dt \qquad (2.4\text{-}1)$$

while from Eqs. (2.3-7) and (2.3-6)

$$J_2(\omega) = (2/\pi) \int_0^\infty \sin \omega t \left[\int_0^\infty [J_1(\alpha) - J_U] \cos \alpha t \, d\alpha \right] dt \qquad (2.4\text{-}2)$$

Although Eqs. (2.4-1) and (2.4-2) establish in principle the interrelations between the functions J_1 and J_2, they are not useful for numerical computation because the integrals converge too slowly. These expressions can, however, be converted into the much more useful forms originally proposed by Kronig (1926) and by Kramers (1927), and now generally known as the Kronig–Kramers relations. These forms are

$$J_1(\omega) - J_U = \frac{2}{\pi} \int_0^\infty J_2(\alpha) \frac{\alpha \, d\alpha}{\alpha^2 - \omega^2} \qquad (2.4\text{-}3)$$

$$J_2(\omega) = \frac{2\omega}{\pi} \int_0^\infty [J_1(\alpha) - J_U] \frac{d\alpha}{\omega^2 - \alpha^2} \qquad (2.4\text{-}4)$$

A brief derivation of these relations is given in Appendix B. It should be noted that the integrals in Eqs. (2.4-3) and (2.4-4) are principal values.

An interesting result is obtained by setting $\omega = 0$ in Eq. (2.4-3). Since $J_1(0) = J_R$, we obtain

$$(2/\pi) \int_0^\infty J_2(\alpha) \, d(\ln \alpha) = J_R - J_U \equiv \delta J \qquad (2.4\text{-}5)$$

which states that the total area under the curve of $J_2(\omega)$ plotted against $\ln \omega$ is simply $\pi/2$ times the magnitude of the relaxation of J. Equation (2.4-4) with $\omega = 0$ and ∞ gives the additional result $J_2(0) = J_2(\infty) = 0$, which was already noted in Eq. (1.3-18).

The Kronig–Kramers relations between the functions $M_1(\omega)$ and $M_2(\omega)$ are derived in a similar way starting from (2.3-9) and (2.3-10) [or (2.3-11) and (2.3-12)] and their Fourier inversions. The results are

$$M_1(\omega) - M_R = \frac{2\omega^2}{\pi} \int_0^\infty \frac{M_2(\alpha)}{\alpha} \frac{d\alpha}{\omega^2 - \alpha^2} \qquad (2.4\text{-}6)$$

$$M_2(\omega) = \frac{2}{\pi} \int_0^\infty [M_1(\alpha) - M_R] \frac{\omega \, d\alpha}{\alpha^2 - \omega^2} \qquad (2.4\text{-}7)$$

The important qualitative consequence of the Kronig–Kramers relations is that dissipative behavior inevitably implies the existence of dispersion (i.e., a frequency dependence of J_1 or M_1), and vice versa.

2.5   Summary of Relations among Response Functions

The response functions that have been considered divide naturally into two groups. One group contains the creep function and the dynamic functions J_1 and J_2, which are the response functions corresponding to a specified stress (e.g., $\sigma = $ constant or $\sigma = \sigma_0 e^{i\omega t}$). For brevity, this group will be referred to as the *J-type response functions*. Similarly, the other group, consisting of response functions corresponding to a specified strain will be called the *M-type response functions*. Table 2-1 lists these two groups of functions in separate columns.

In general, the functions in one of the columns are directly related to each other, while those in different columns can only be related by more complex (implicit) equations. These relations are shown in the table by arrows labeled with the number of the equation(s) in the text that gives the relationship. The crossover points between the two columns are also

TABLE 2-1

RELATIONS AMONG RESPONSE FUNCTIONS

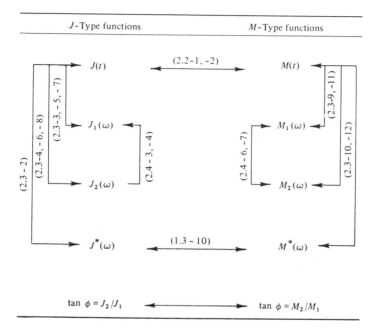

J-Type functions	M-Type functions

$\tan \phi = J_2/J_1$ ⟷ $\tan \phi = M_2/M_1$

given. One of these is the relation between the creep and stress relaxation functions, which is in fact a difficult relation to use. Another is the equality of M_2/M_1 and J_2/J_1. This is a simple enough relation in itself; however, if one wishes to express M_2 in terms of J_2 it requires substituting the appropriate Kronig–Kramers integrals for M_1 and for J_1. The resulting expression does not give M_2 in terms of J_2 directly but involves integrals of both of these functions. This same difficulty in crossing over between the M- and J-types of specifications of anelastic materials will persist in Chapters 3 and 4 where we introduce discrete and continuous spectra.

The problem of crossover between J-type and M-type functions is much simplified when ϕ and the relaxation strength $\varDelta$ are small. We have seen that, when $\phi^2 \ll 1$, $M_1(\omega)$ and $J_1(\omega)$ are simply reciprocals of one another [Eq. (1.3-14a)] while for $\varDelta^2 \ll 1$, $M(t)$ and $J(t)$ are reciprocals (Problem 2-2). Similar simplifications occur under other approximations, which will be discussed in Section 4.4.

The most important result of this chapter is that any one response function may be used to characterize the anelastic behavior of the material, since all other response functions may be derived from it with the aid of the Boltzmann principle. Although this is a major step forward, it does not meet all the requirements of a complete formal theory. Since a response function only describes the behavior of a material under given experimental conditions, the use of such a function to define the anelastic properties of a solid is not a completely satisfactory one. We may suspect that there is a more basic description of anelastic behavior in terms of which all of the response functions can be expressed. It will become apparent in the next two chapters that such a description is possible, and involves the concept of a relaxation spectrum.

PROBLEMS

2-1. Verify the equivalence of Eqs. (2.2-1) and (2.2-2).

2-2. Show that for $\Delta \ll 1$, the following relation exists between the normalized creep function $\psi(t)$ and the normalized stress relaxation function $\varphi(t)$:

$$\psi(t) \simeq 1 - \varphi(t)$$

Combine this result with Problem 1-2, to show that

$$1/M(t) = J(t) + O(\Delta^2)$$

where $O(\Delta^2)$ means terms of order Δ^2.

General References

GROSS, B. (1953). "Mathematical Structure of the Theories of Viscoelasticity." Hermann, Paris.

LEADERMAN, H. (1958). *In* "Rheology" (F. R. Eirich, ed.), Vol. 2, Chap. 1. Academic Press, New York.

MACDONALD, J. R., and BRACHMAN, M. K. (1956). *Rev. Mod. Phys.* **28**, 393.

Chapter 3 / Mechanical Models and Discrete Spectra

The response functions, whose interrelations were considered in the previous chapter, represent one approach for describing anelastic behavior. We proceed now to an alternative description in terms of a set of parameters which can be regarded as intrinsic attributes of the material. The starting point for this approach is a stress–strain relationship in the form of a linear differential equation involving stress, strain, and their time derivatives. The fact that the response of an anelastic solid can be described by such an equation can be inferred from the definition of anelasticity, which includes both the features of linearity and of time-dependent stress–strain behavior. Since each of the response functions is now recognized as a solution of the same differential equation for different imposed conditions of stress or strain, it is immediately obvious that the response functions must be interrelated, as has already been demonstrated in Chapter 2.

The visualization of the behavior of a material governed by any particular differential stress–strain equation is greatly aided by an inspection of an appropriate mechanical model. It will be found that the simplest differential stress–strain equation capable of representing anelasticity involves three independent parameters. Correspondingly, the equivalent model is constructed of three basic elements (two springs and a dashpot). The behavior corresponding to the three-parameter equation or model is of such basic importance that a material exhibiting this behavior is termed a *standard anelastic solid*. A major part of this chapter (Sections 3.3–3.5) is devoted to examining the detailed behavior of such a solid. The remainder of the chapter deals with the manner in which the standard anelastic solid may be generalized to describe more complex anelastic behavior.

3.1   Differential Stress–Strain Equations and the Construction of Models

Since the definition of anelasticity involves the requirement of linearity, it follows that all differential stress–strain equations of anelasticity must be of first degree. Further, any such equation must contain as many or as few independent constants as are needed to describe the anelastic behavior of a particular solid. The most general linear equation with constant coefficients has the form

$$a_0\sigma + a_1\dot{\sigma} + a_2\ddot{\sigma} + \cdots = b_0\varepsilon + b_1\dot{\varepsilon} + b_2\ddot{\varepsilon} + \cdots \qquad (3.1\text{-}1)$$

where dots are used to denote time derivatives, in the usual way.[†] For conciseness, an equation of this type will be referred to as a *differential stress–strain equation*. Since Eq. (3.1-1) contains both the features of linearity and time-dependence, it must provide the basis for a description of linear viscoelastic behavior (cf. Table 1-1). To represent only the more specialized case of anelasticity, where we have the additional requirement of a unique equilibrium relationship between stress and strain, further restrictions must be placed upon Eq. (3.1-1). The nature of these restrictions will emerge later in the chapter.

We proceed to examine cases of Eq. (3.1-1) in which all but a few of the coefficients a_i and b_i are zero. In doing this, it will be found that mechanical models provide a useful means for visualizing the anelastic behavior of materials, and that to every model there corresponds a unique differential stress–strain equation. In order to qualify as a model for a given anelastic material, a mechanical system must obey the same relations between force, displacement, and time as are valid between stress, strain, and time, respectively, in the anelastic body.

In the simplest case of Eq. (3.1-1), where only the coefficients a_0 and b_0 are not zero, we have the example of an ideal elastic body. Here the appropriate mechanical model is a Hookean spring. The force on the spring represents the stress, the displacement represents strain, and the spring constant k represents the appropriate modulus M (or k^{-1}, the

---

[†] It should be noted that Eq. (3.1-1) may be written in the more concise form $P\sigma = Q\varepsilon$ where P is the linear operator

$$\left(a_0 + a_1\frac{d}{dt} + a_2\frac{d^2}{dt^2} + \cdots\right)$$

and Q is the corresponding operator involving the b_i coefficients.

compliance J). Such a spring has the characteristics that energy is stored in it in a reversible way, and that it returns to zero displacement when the force on it is removed. One or more springs, therefore, constitute an essential part of mechanical models of anelastic behavior. A second element, needed to provide internal friction, is the *Newtonian dashpot*, represented by a piston moving in an ideally viscous liquid. Such a dashpot has the property that its velocity of motion is proportional to the applied force; therefore, work performed on it is entirely dissipated as heat. In terms of stress and strain, which will hereafter be used instead of force and displacement, we have $\sigma = \eta\dot{\varepsilon}$ where η is the viscosity of the dashpot. A dashpot alone represents a viscous (Newtonian) liquid; it is only useful for the description of solids when used in combination with springs.

In forming models, mechanical elements may be combined either in series or in parallel. In a series combination of two elements, 1 and 2, the stresses σ_1 and σ_2 are equal while the strains ε_1 and ε_2 are additive. The stress σ and the total strain ε are thus given by

$$\varepsilon = \varepsilon_1 + \varepsilon_2, \qquad \sigma = \sigma_1 = \sigma_2 \tag{3.1-2}$$

Similarly, for a parallel combination of the same elements

$$\varepsilon = \varepsilon_1 = \varepsilon_2, \qquad \sigma = \sigma_1 + \sigma_2 \tag{3.1-3}$$

Using these rules, it is easy to see that two springs in series or in parallel correspond to another spring, while two dashpots in series or in parallel correspond to another dahspot. Such combinations are, therefore, superfluous and will not be used. We are then led to the following as the two simplest models which combine more than one element: (1) a spring and dashpot in parallel, called the *Voigt* (or Kelvin) *model*; and (2) a spring and dashpot in series, called the *Maxwell model*.

3.2   The Voigt and Maxwell Models

The two models are illustrated in Fig. 3-1. In the *Voigt model* it is convenient to describe the spring by its compliance constant J, while for dimensional simplification it is most convenient to write the viscosity η of the dashpot as τ/J. In this way there are still only two independent parameters J and τ, but the constant τ has the dimensions of time. Inspection of Fig. 3-1 shows that the Voigt model exhibits the following

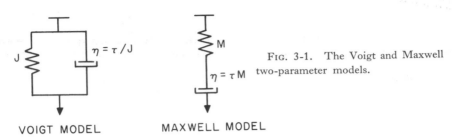

FIG. 3-1.   The Voigt and Maxwell two-parameter models.

VOIGT MODEL   MAXWELL MODEL

features: Since a dashpot will not yield instantaneously, there can be no deformation immediately upon application of stress. Therefore, if σ_0 is applied at $t = 0$, this stress must be sustained entirely by the dashpot at $t = 0$. As time passes, the dashpot will flow, i.e., creep will take place, until as $t \to \infty$ the stress becomes entirely sustained by the spring; the dashpot will then cease to flow since the stress upon it has vanished. Upon release of the stress, the dashpot again resists a sudden change. Accordingly, the spring remains extended, momentarily retaining the stress σ_0, while the dashpot must be subjected to stress $-\sigma_0$ in order that the total stress be zero [Eq. (3.1-3)]. As time passes, the dashpot creeps back to its initial position, at which time the stresses acting on the two elements σ_1 and σ_2 are both zero. Figure 3-2 illustrates the creep and aftereffect of the Voigt model.

The above description outlines qualitatively how creep and elastic aftereffect take place with this model. For obvious reasons the model is

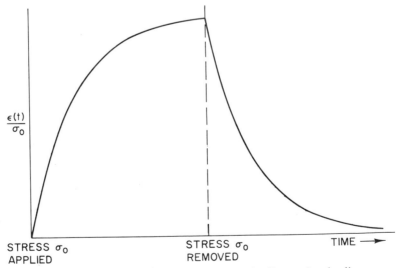

FIG. 3-2.   Behavior of the Voigt model on loading and unloading.

sometimes called a "retarded spring." To present a more quantitative description requires that we derive and then solve the differential stress–strain equation pertinent to the Voigt model. The result is easily obtained using $\varepsilon_1 = J\sigma_1$ for the spring, and $\dot{\varepsilon}_2 = J\sigma_2/\tau$ for the dashpot, together with the rules given by Eq. (3.1-3). In this way, we eliminate ε_1, ε_2, σ_1, and σ_2, to obtain

$$J\sigma = \varepsilon + \tau\dot{\varepsilon} \qquad (3.2\text{-}1)$$

This result is equivalent to Eq. (3.1-1) when all coefficients except a_0, b_0, and b_1 are set equal to zero, and the equation is divided through by b_0. In other words, Eq. (3.2-1) is one step higher in complexity than the case of ideal elasticity (for which τ would be zero).

Equation (3.2-1) is easily solved to obtain the creep function and the dynamic response functions $J_1(\omega)$ and $J_2(\omega)$. The reader may wish to carry out these solutions as an exercise (see Problem 3-1) at this point.[†] It is important to realize, however, that since this model allows for no instantaneous deformation, it does not represent a realistic model of a crystalline solid. Furthermore, since it is not possible to apply a sudden strain ε_0 at $t = 0$, the model will not display the property of stress relaxation. For these reasons, the Voigt model will not be pursued further here, although its usefulness as a unit of more complex models will soon become apparent.

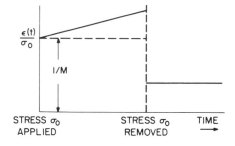

FIG. 3-3. Behavior of the Maxwell model on loading and unloading.

In the *Maxwell model*, it is most convenient to represent the spring by a modulus M and the viscosity of the dashpot by $\eta = M\tau$. Looking first at the qualitative features of the model, we note by examining Fig. 3-1 that upon sudden application of a stress there is an instantaneous strain suffered by the spring, followed by linear viscous creep due to the dashpot which gives rise to permanent set (see Fig. 3-3). On the other hand, if a

---

[†] These expressions may be obtained alternatively by letting $J_U \to \infty$ in the solutions for the standard anelastic solid (Sections 3.3 and 3.4).

constant strain ε_0 is applied at $t = 0$, there will be instantaneously a stress in the spring, since the dashpot will not yield. As time passes, the dashpot will continue to flow until the stress on it (and therefore on the spring) goes to zero. This will occur when the dashpot is extended to correspond to the strain ε_0. Thus, the Maxwell model is capable of stress relaxation, in fact of *complete* stress relaxation, to the point where σ goes to zero.

With the aid of Eq. (3.1-2) the generalized stress–strain equation appropriate to this model is readily derived, starting from $\sigma_1 = M\varepsilon_1$ and $\sigma_2 = M\tau\dot{\varepsilon}_2$, to be

$$\tau\dot{\sigma} + \sigma = \tau M\dot{\varepsilon} \qquad (3.2\text{-}2)$$

This equation is equivalent to (3.1-1) when all coefficients except a_0, a_1, and b_1 are zero, and the equation is divided through by a_0. Like Eq. (3.2-1) for the Voigt model, this result involves just one more term than the case of ideal elasticity which, in fact, is obtained in the limit of $\tau \to \infty$.

Expressions for the creep function and the stress relaxation function can easily be derived from Eq. (3.2-2). However, it is already clear that the Maxwell model does not describe an anelastic material, since it displays steady viscous creep, rather than the recoverable creep characteristic of anelasticity.

In this section we have reviewed the two possible models that can be described with just two parameters, and have shown that neither of them provides, even qualitatively, a suitable description of an anelastic crystalline material. We are forced to the conclusion that, for even the simplest description of anelasticity, we must consider at least a three-parameter model.

3.3 Three-Parameter Models; the Standard Anelastic Solid

From the foregoing it is clear that the Voigt model lacks the instantaneous elastic response characteristic of crystals. This missing feature can be obtained by attaching a spring in series with the Voigt model. Henceforth, the term *Voigt unit* will be used to refer to the combination of a spring and dashpot in parallel. The model of a spring in series with a Voigt unit is shown in Fig. 3-4. The qualitative features of this model are as follows. Upon application of stress at $t = 0$, the spring a deforms immediately while, due to the dashpot, the Voigt unit remains undeformed. As time elapses, the dashpot c yields until the stress upon the Voigt unit is transferred entirely to the spring b and the stress on the dashpot vanishes. At this point there will be no further change in the system with time. This creep behavior shows all of the characteristics of an anelastic material, in which the strain per unit stress goes from an instantaneous value J_U to a final value J_R. Clearly, from the model, the compliance of element a must be J_U while the combined compliance of elements a and b must be J_R. Therefore, if the compliance of element b is called δJ, we have J_R given by $J_U + \delta J$, in accordance with Eq. (1.2-4). Finally, paralleling the procedure followed in the case of the Voigt model, we set the viscosity η of the dashpot equal to a time constant divided by the compliance of the parallel spring. The reason for the designation of this time constant as τ_σ will soon become apparent.

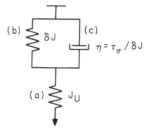

FIG. 3-4. The three-parameter model containing a Voigt unit.

This model also is capable of stress relaxation, since it is possible to hold a strain ε_0 starting at $t = 0$. Initially, only element a will be extended, but the dashpot will then start to flow until the stress σ_c upon it is zero. This flow will serve to reduce the stress from an initial value of ε_0/J_U to a final value of $\varepsilon_0/(J_U + \delta J)$.

Since the model of Fig. 3-4 is fairly simple, and yet has all of the characteristics of an anelastic material, its differential stress–strain equation and the solutions thereof are of great interest. Starting from the relations $\varepsilon_a = J_U \sigma_a$, $\varepsilon_b = \delta J\, \sigma_b$, and $\dot{\varepsilon}_c = \delta J\, \sigma_c/\tau_\sigma$, for elements a, b, and c, respectively, and working from the model and the rules given by (3.1-2) and (3.1-3) it is easy to show that

$$\varepsilon = \varepsilon_a + \varepsilon_b, \qquad \varepsilon_b = \varepsilon_c$$
$$\sigma = \sigma_a = J_U^{-1}\varepsilon_a = \sigma_b + \sigma_c = \delta J^{-1}(\varepsilon_b + \tau\dot{\varepsilon}_c) \tag{3.3-1}$$

From these equations, we eliminate ε_a, ε_b, ε_c, σ_a, σ_b, and σ_c, to obtain

$$J_R\sigma + \tau_\sigma J_U\dot{\sigma} = \varepsilon + \tau_\sigma\dot{\varepsilon} \tag{3.3-2}$$

where $J_U + \delta J$ has been set equal to J_R. Equation (3.3-2) is the differential stress–strain equation of our three-parameter model. It is equivalent to Eq. (3.1-1) when all coefficients except a_0, a_1, b_0, and b_1 are set equal

To put Eq. (3.3-2) into the form (3.3-4), where now y is to be replaced by σ, we divide through by J_R to obtain

$$\sigma + \tau_\varepsilon \dot{\sigma} = (\varepsilon/J_R) + (\tau_\varepsilon \dot{\varepsilon}/J_U) \qquad (3.3\text{-}8)$$

where we have set

$$\tau_\varepsilon \equiv \tau_\sigma(J_U/J_R) = \tau_\sigma(M_R/M_U) = \tau_\sigma/(1 + \Delta) \qquad (3.3\text{-}9)$$

Clearly, the new time constant τ_ε is less than τ_σ. Equation (3.3-8) can be solved immediately, subject to conditions (3.3-7) to yield

$$M(t) = \sigma(t)/\varepsilon_0 = M_R + (M_U - M_R)\exp(-t/\tau_\varepsilon) \qquad (3.3\text{-}10)$$

The quantity τ_ε, which determines the "time to $1/e$ of completion" of the stress relaxation process, is known as the *relaxation time at constant strain*. In accordance with Eq. (1.2-15), the normalized stress relaxation function $\varphi(t)$ is now the simple exponential decay function $\exp(-t/\tau_\varepsilon)$. Figure 3-6 shows a plot of this function against $\log t$ (together with a plot of the normalized M_1 function which will be discussed later).

Equation (3.3-10) expresses the stress relaxation function in terms of the three parameters M_U, M_R, and τ_ε, which are themselves readily expressed in terms of the three parameters of the mechanical model of Fig. 3-4, viz., J_U, δJ, and τ_σ.

The description of stress relaxation behavior with the model of Fig. 3-4 is not as direct as for creep behavior, owing to the fact that there is no single element in Fig. 3-4 which is identified with the relaxation of the modulus, $\delta M = M_U - M_R$. Accordingly, it is worthwhile to consider another three-parameter model which is ideally suited to the stress relaxation experiment. This model, shown in Fig. 3-7, consists of a *Maxwell unit* (defined as a spring and dashpot in series), which is placed in parallel with a spring. The parallel spring gets around the objection to the simple Maxwell model that the latter does not show creep recovery. It is easy to see how this model behaves in an experiment at constant strain ε_0. Initially, both springs are extended so that $\sigma = (M_R + \delta M)\varepsilon_0 = M_U \varepsilon_0$. As time passes, the dashpot flows until the stress on spring b is relaxed to zero. The stress is then all carried by spring a and is equal to $M_R \varepsilon_0$. It is clear from this description that the nomenclature used for the two spring constants of the model is consistent with that used previously, namely, that M_R is, indeed, the relaxed modulus and δM the relaxation of the modulus. It is next of interest to derive the differential stress–

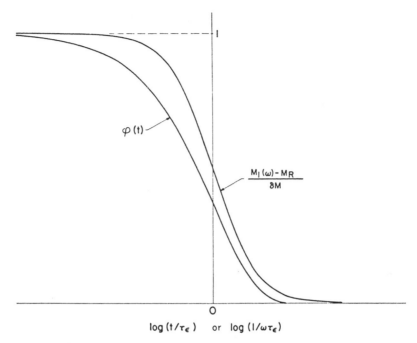

$$\log (t/\tau_\epsilon) \quad \text{or} \quad \log (1/\omega\tau_\epsilon)$$

Fig. 3-6. Stress relaxation and $M_1(\omega)$ functions for the standard anelastic solid.

strain equation for this model. From $\sigma_a = M_\mathrm{R}\varepsilon_a$, $\sigma_b = \delta M\,\varepsilon_b$, $\sigma = \tau_\varepsilon\,\delta M\,\dot\varepsilon_c$, combined with the rules given by (3.1-2) and (3.1-3) we obtain, in terms of the total strain ε and total stress σ the result

$$\sigma + \tau_\varepsilon\dot\sigma = M_\mathrm{R}\varepsilon + M_\mathrm{U}\tau_\varepsilon\dot\varepsilon \tag{3.3-11}$$

This equation is the same as Eq. (3.3-8), which has been regarded as the defining equation of the standard anelastic solid. The parameter τ_ε, which was initially introduced into the model of Fig. 3-7 as an arbitrary parameter, is now seen to be identical with τ_ε as given by Eq. (3.3-9).

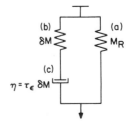

Fig. 3-7.　The three-parameter model containing a Maxwell unit.

Since the three-parameter model of Fig. 3-7 yields the same differential stress–strain equation as that of Fig. 3-4, it must be concluded that *the two models are equivalent*. Thus, either model can be used to represent the standard anelastic solid. The first, or *Voigt-type* model is most convenient in the analysis of the creep behavior while the second or *Maxwell-type* model most directly demonstrates the stress relaxation behavior of the material.

3.4   Dynamic Properties of the Standard Anelastic Solid

In order to obtain the dynamic response functions J_1 and J_2, corresponding to a given periodic stress, we substitute

$$\sigma = \sigma_0 e^{i\omega t}, \qquad \varepsilon = (\varepsilon_1 - i\varepsilon_2)e^{i\omega t}$$

into the differential Eq. (3.3-2), and recall the definitions $J_1 = \varepsilon_1/\sigma_0$, $J_2 = \varepsilon_2/\sigma_0$, from Chapter 1. Equating separately the real and the imaginary parts of the complex algebraic equation so obtained, we arrive at the following two equations:

$$J_R = J_1 + \omega\tau_\sigma J_2, \qquad \omega\tau_\sigma J_U = \omega\tau_\sigma J_1 - J_2 \qquad (3.4\text{-}1)$$

When these are solved for J_1 and J_2 the results are

$$J_1(\omega) = J_U + \frac{\delta J}{(1 + \omega^2\tau_\sigma^2)} \qquad (3.4\text{-}2)$$

$$J_2(\omega) = \delta J \, \frac{\omega\tau_\sigma}{(1 + \omega^2\tau_\sigma^2)} \qquad (3.4\text{-}3)$$

Equations (3.4-2) and (3.4-3) are often called the *Debye equations* since they were first derived by P. Debye for the case of dielectric relaxation phenomena. The quantity J_1 goes from J_U at high frequencies ($\omega\tau_\sigma \gg 1$) to J_R at low frequencies ($\omega\tau_\sigma \ll 1$). A plot of $J_1(\omega)$ versus $\log_{10} \omega\tau_\sigma$ is shown in Fig. 3-8, where it is compared to the function $J_2(\omega)$. The quantity J_2 plots as a peak function since it has small values at both high and low frequencies ($\omega\tau_\sigma \gg 1$ or $\omega\tau_\sigma \ll 1$), and goes through a maximum at $\omega\tau_\sigma = 1$. Any function of frequency which varies as $\omega\tau/(1 + \omega^2\tau^2)$ will be called a *Debye peak*.[†] It is easy to show that when such a function

---

[†] A convenient form for a Debye peak is obtained by substituting $x = \ln \omega\tau$ to get $\omega\tau/(1 + \omega^2\tau^2) = \frac{1}{2} \operatorname{sech} x$. This form will be particularly useful in Chapter 4.

is plotted against log $\omega\tau$, the curve is symmetrical about log $\omega\tau = 0$ (i.e., $\omega\tau = 1$), and the width of the peak at half maximum is given by

$$\Delta(\log_{10} \omega\tau) = 1.144 \quad \text{(Debye peak)} \tag{3.4-4}$$

In round numbers, Eq. (3.4-4) states that the width of a Debye peak at half-maximum is slightly greater than one decade in the quantity $\omega\tau$. This statement is well worth remembering.

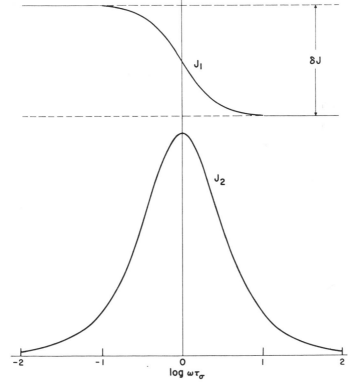

FIG. 3-8. Comparison of $J_1(\omega)$ and $J_2(\omega)$ as functions of $\log_{10} \omega\tau_\sigma$ for the standard anelastic solid.

Fig. 3-5 allows a comparison of the normalized function $[J_1(\omega) - J_U]/\delta J$ with the normalized creep function $\psi(t)$ when these two functions are plotted against $\log(1/\omega\tau_\sigma)$ and $\log(t/\tau_\sigma)$, respectively. The two curves are roughly similar when plotted this way, but it is noteworthy that the $\psi(t)$ curve lies above the normalized $J_1(\omega)$ curve. Also, the normalized J_1 function is antisymmetric about its midpoint (see Problem 3-7), while $\psi(t)$ is not.

Another feature of interest is the asymptotic form of Eq. (3.4-3) as well as that of (3.4-2). Thus, for $\omega\tau_\sigma \gg 1$,

$$J_2(\omega) \simeq \delta J/\omega\tau_\sigma$$
$$J_1(\omega) - J_{\mathrm{U}} \simeq \delta J/(\omega\tau_\sigma)^2 \qquad (\omega\tau_\sigma \gg 1) \qquad (3.4\text{-}5)$$

while at the other extreme, $\omega\tau_\sigma \ll 1$,

$$J_2(\omega) \simeq \delta J\,(\omega\tau_\sigma)$$
$$J_{\mathrm{R}} - J_1(\omega) \simeq \delta J\,(\omega\tau_\sigma)^2 \qquad (\omega\tau_\sigma \ll 1) \qquad (3.4\text{-}6)$$

These results show the comparative sharpness of the change in J_1 and in J_2 in the vicinity of $\omega\tau_\sigma = 1$, namely, that toward either low or high frequencies, J_1 approaches its asymptotic limits faster than J_2 approaches zero. This effective narrowness of the transition region of J_1 as compared to the J_2 peak is also clear from an examination of the plots of these quantities in Fig. 3-8.

Alternative dynamic response functions are the internal friction $\phi(\omega)$ and the absolute dynamic compliance $|J|(\omega)$. Expressions for these are obtainable from Eqs. (3.4-2) and (3.4-3) with the help of the relations $\tan\phi = J_2/J_1$ and $|J|(\omega) = [J_1^2 + J_2^2]^{1/2}$ derived in Chapter 1. We, therefore, obtain, for the standard anelastic solid,

$$\tan\phi = \frac{J_2}{J_1} = \delta J\,\frac{\omega\tau_\sigma}{J_{\mathrm{R}} + J_{\mathrm{U}}\omega^2\tau_\sigma^2} \qquad (3.4\text{-}7)$$

$$|J|(\omega) = [J_1^2 + J_2^2]^{1/2} = \left(\frac{J_{\mathrm{R}}^2 + J_{\mathrm{U}}^2\omega^2\tau_\sigma^2}{1 + \omega^2\tau_\sigma^2}\right)^{1/2} \qquad (3.4\text{-}8)$$

As already pointed out in Chapter 1, however, $|J|(\omega) \doteq J_1(\omega)$, so that $|J|(\omega)$ differs from the form given by Eq. (3.4-2) only by terms of order ϕ^2.

Turning now to the M-type dynamic response functions, M_1 and M may be obtained from Eq. (3.3-11) by substituting

$$\varepsilon = \varepsilon_0 e^{i\omega t}, \qquad \sigma = (\sigma_1 + i\sigma_2)e^{i\omega t}$$

and recalling the definitions $M_1 = \sigma_1/\varepsilon_0$, $M_2 = \sigma_2/\varepsilon_0$. The procedure is analogous to that used above to obtain J_1 and J_2, so that we will simply quote the results:

$$M_1(\omega) = M_U - \frac{\delta M}{1 + \omega^2 \tau_\varepsilon^2} = M_R + \delta M \frac{\omega^2 \tau_\varepsilon^2}{1 + \omega^2 \tau_\varepsilon^2} \qquad (3.4\text{-}9)$$

$$M_2(\omega) = \delta M \frac{\omega \tau_\varepsilon}{1 + \omega^2 \tau_\varepsilon^2} \qquad (3.4\text{-}10)$$

Thus, M_1 falls from M_U to M_R as the frequency decreases. The variation of M_1 with log $\omega \tau_\varepsilon$ is antisymmetric about the point $M_1 = (M_U + M_R)/2$, log $\omega \tau_\varepsilon = 0$. This function (in normalized form) is plotted versus $\log(1/\omega \tau_\varepsilon)$ in Fig. 3-6, where it is compared with the plot of $\varphi(t)$ versus $\log(t/\tau_\varepsilon)$. It is clear that the two curves are qualitatively similar, but that the normalized M_1 curve lies above the $\varphi(t)$ curve. The function $M_2(\omega)$, on the other hand, is a Debye peak, just like $J_2(\omega)$, except that the M_2 curve peaks at $\omega \tau_\varepsilon = 1$, while the J_2 curve had its peak at $\omega \tau_\sigma = 1$. Since [from Eq. (3.3-9)] τ_ε is less than τ_σ, a given standard anelastic solid will show the M_2 peak at a higher frequency than the J_2 peak.

The equation for the internal friction $\phi(\omega)$ may also be expressed as a Debye peak. In the case where $\delta J \ll J_U$ (or $\Delta \ll 1$), this conclusion is immediately evident since J_1 may be replaced by J_U in the expression $\phi \doteq J_2/J_1$ and then ϕ and J_2 differ only by a constant factor. Thus,

$$\phi \simeq \Delta \frac{\omega \tau}{1 + \omega^2 \tau^2}, \qquad \Delta \ll 1 \qquad (3.4\text{-}11)$$

(The subscript to τ may be omitted, since τ_σ and τ_ε become equal when $\Delta \ll 1$.) However, Zener (1948) has shown that $\phi(\omega)$ for the standard anelastic solid may be expressed as a Debye peak without any approximation concerning the relaxation strength. This is done by rearranging the exact expression (3.4-7), replacing τ_σ by $\bar{\tau}$, which is defined as the geometric mean of τ_σ and τ_ε,

$$\bar{\tau} \equiv (\tau_\sigma \tau_\varepsilon)^{1/2} = \tau_\sigma (J_U/J_R)^{1/2} = \tau_\sigma/(1 + \Delta)^{1/2} = \tau_\varepsilon (1 + \Delta)^{1/2} \qquad (3.4\text{-}12)$$

where Eq. (3.3-9) has been utilized. In this way one readily obtains the exact expression

$$\tan \phi = \frac{\delta J}{(J_U J_R)^{1/2}} \frac{\omega \bar{\tau}}{1 + \omega^2 \bar{\tau}^2} = \frac{\Delta}{(1 + \Delta)^{1/2}} \frac{\omega \bar{\tau}}{1 + \omega^2 \bar{\tau}^2} \qquad (3.4\text{-}13)$$

which is a Debye peak whose maximum occurs when $\omega \bar{\tau} = 1$. The relationship between the peak height and relaxation strength is particularly useful:

$$\tan \phi_{\max} = \Delta/2(1 + \Delta)^{1/2} \tag{3.4-14}$$

The relaxation strength Δ may therefore be obtained from the height of such a peak, while the mean relaxation time $\bar{\tau}$ is obtained from the frequency at which the peak occurs.

In a similar way, the quantity $\bar{\tau}$ may be substituted into expressions for the reciprocal functions $J_1^{-1}(\omega)$ and $M_1^{-1}(\omega)$ to obtain the simplified expressions given in Problem 3-10.

The results for the dynamic response function of the standard anelastic solid may be summarized as follows. There are three functions which vary with ω according to the formula for a Debye peak. These are:

1. $J_2(\omega)$, centered at $\omega = 1/\tau_\sigma$,
2. $M_2(\omega)$, centered at $\omega = 1/\tau_\varepsilon$,
3. $\tan \phi$, centered at $\omega = 1/\bar{\tau}$.

Also, the following functions obey a relaxation formula of the type

$$A \pm B/(1 + \omega^2\tau^2) \tag{3.4-15}$$

1. $J_1(\omega)$, with $\tau = \tau_\sigma$,
2. $J_1^{-1}(\omega)$, with $\tau = \bar{\tau}$,
3. $M_1(\omega)$, with $\tau = \tau_\varepsilon$,
4. $M_1^{-1}(\omega)$, with $\tau = \bar{\tau}$.

In all four cases, the plus sign appears when the response function has dimensions of compliance, in which case $A = J_U$ and $A + B = J_R$, while the minus sign appears when the function has dimensions of a modulus, in which case $A = M_U$ and $A - B = M_R$. We will designate a function of the type (3.4-15) as a *dynamic relaxation function*.

One property of the dynamic relaxation function of the standard anelastic solid which will be useful for later reference is its range of rapid variation when plotted against log $\omega\tau$. A convenient definition of this range may be taken from plots such as Fig. 3-5 for the normalized $J_1(\omega)$ function or Fig. 3-6 for the normalized $M_1(\omega)$ function, namely the increment in the variable log $\omega\tau$ over which the function $1/(1 + \omega^2\tau^2)$ falls from 0.75 to 0.25. This range is readily shown to be

$$\Delta(\log_{10} \omega\tau) = 0.477 \tag{3.4-16}$$

Comparison with Eq. (3.4-4) shows that this range is less than half of the width of the Debye peak, i.e., that the dynamic relaxation function shows its major variation in a narrower range than the Debye peak.[†] This fact is also clear from Fig. 3-8. It is also interesting to compare Eq. (3.4-16) with the equivalent range of variation of the normalized creep and stress relaxation functions as shown in Figs. 3-5 and 3-6. If Δ (log t/τ) is the increment of the variable log t/τ over which the function $\exp(-t/\tau)$ falls from 0.75 to 0.25, we readily find that

$$\Delta \ (\log_{10} t/\tau) = 0.683 \tag{3.4-17}$$

Thus the normalized quasi-static relaxation functions change more slowly than the normalized dynamic relaxation functions, as is also apparent from Figs. 3-5 and 3-6.

In this section we have derived the dynamic response functions of the standard anelastic solid by solving the appropriate differential stress–strain equation [either Eq. (3.3-2) or its equivalent form Eq. (3.3-11)]. It is important to emphasize, however, that all of these dynamic functions and the corresponding quasi-static functions are interrelated through the relations derived in Chapter 2, with the aid of the Boltzmann super-position principle. (See Problem 3-12.) The case of the standard anelastic solid illustrates another point made at the end of the last chapter, that although any one of the response functions could have been used to represent the anelastic properties of the solid, there is a greater value in expressing all of these functions directly in terms of certain inherent parameters that do not depend on a specific experiment. In the case of the standard anelastic solid there is the need for only three such in-dependent parameters, which may be chosen as either J_U, J_R, and τ_σ; or M_U, M_R, and τ_ε. In each case, one of the three parameters describes the *elastic* property of the material, so that only two parameters actually define its anelastic behavior. We shall soon see that the number of para-meters is readily increased to cover the behavior of more complex solids, for which the appropriate differential stress–strain equation contains a larger number of terms.

3.5   Dynamic Properties of the Standard Anelastic Solid as Functions of Temperature

The previous section shows that, for the standard anelastic solid, such dynamic properties as J_1, J_2, M_1, M_2, or tan ϕ, take on particularly

---

[†] The relative sharpness of the dynamic relaxation function has also been shown by consideration of the asymptotic forms, Eqs. (3.4-5) and (3.4-6). For still another measure, see Problem 3-11.

simple forms when plotted as a function of log $\omega\tau$, where τ is one of the appropriate relaxation times, τ_σ, τ_ε, $\bar{\tau}$. The implication, of course, has been that we vary the frequency ω keeping τ constant. Although a continuous variation in the frequency of vibration of a system is possible with a subresonant method, it is not possible when the more common resonance methods (as described in Section 1.5) are used. The equation of a Debye peak shows that, to trace out a peak reasonably completely, requires the ability to vary ω over about two decades. For a resonance method, this requirement usually means that several specimens, possibly vibrating in different modes, must be used to cover the range. (The range of frequency that can be covered simply by changing inertia members is usually insufficient to take a specimen through a Debye peak.) There is, however, another way of tracing out the peak, namely, by varying τ while keeping ω constant. This method is so important in practice, that we shall digress from the main theoretical development to deal with this topic in the present section.

The basis of the method under discussion is that in many cases the relaxation rate τ^{-1} is expressible by an Arrhenius equation

$$\tau^{-1} = \nu_0 e^{-Q/kT} \tag{3.5-1}$$

where T is the absolute temperature and ν_0, Q, and k are constants, viz., ν_0 is a frequency factor, Q is the activation energy, and k is Boltzmann's constant.[†] Such a form for τ^{-1} arises when the rate-limiting step of the relaxation process is that of movement over an energy barrier. While the condition of validity of Eq. (3.5-1), and the significance of the quantities Q and ν_0 will be discussed in Section 7.3, for the present purpose it suffices to recognize the existence of an Arrhenius relation. Often Eq. (3.5-1) is written as

$$\tau = \tau_0 e^{Q/kT} \tag{3.5-2}$$

in which $\tau_0 = \nu_0^{-1}$. The importance of such a relation is that, in cases where it applies, the quantity τ may be varied over a wide range simply by changing the temperature. (For example, see Problem 3-13.) Therefore, it becomes possible to treat the dynamic response functions as though they are functions of temperature simply by substituting Eq. (3.5-2) into expressions such as (3.4-2) or (3.4-3), while regarding ω as a constant.

[†] $k = 1.38 \times 10^{-16}$ erg $°K^{-1} = 8.64 \times 10^{-5}$ eV $°K^{-1}$. However, if Q is to be expressed in calories per mole, k becomes the gas constant, $R = 1.986$ cal mole^{-1} $°K^{-1}$.

From Eq. (3.5-2),

$$\ln \omega\tau = \ln \omega\tau_0 + (Q/k)(1/T) \tag{3.5-3}$$

so that there is a linear relation between $\ln \omega\tau$ and the reciprocal absolute temperature. It is clear then, that the plot of a given dynamic response function versus Q/kT differs from a plot of the same function versus $\ln \omega\tau$ only by a constant shift parallel to the abscissa. On the other hand, a plot versus $1/T$ involves an additional change in the scale of the abscissa by the factor Q/k.

For the case of a Debye peak, the condition that $\ln \omega\tau = 0$ at the peak gives

$$\ln \omega\tau_0 + (Q/k)(1/T_p) = 0 \tag{3.5-4}$$

where T_p is the temperature at the peak. If a series of peaks is obtained at a number of different frequencies, a straight line plot can be made of $\ln \omega$ versus $1/T_p$, whose slope is then Q/k.[†] This method, which is one of the most common ways of obtaining the activation energy, is illustrated with experimental data in Figs. 3-9 and 3-10.

Often it is desirable to obtain an approximate value for the activation energy knowing only the peak temperature at one frequency, or conversely, knowing Q, one may wish to determine at what temperature the peak will appear for a given frequency. These objectives can only be accomplished if the value of τ_0 is known. From the type of phenomenon occurring, one can often estimate τ_0 to within an order of magnitude, and then estimate Q from T_p or vice versa, using Eq. (3.5-4). In practice, such estimates are made so often that it is convenient to have a graph from which one can read the values directly. Figure 3-11 provides such plots, in which the product $f\tau_0$ is used as a parameter ($f = \omega/2\pi$ is the experimental frequency). Note that since $Q \propto T_p$ for a given value of $f\tau_0$, the same set of lines can be used in different ranges by simply multiplying both scales by the same factor. Thus, for example, doubling both scales extends the graph to temperatures of 600°K, and so on. The usefulness of such a plot was first pointed out by Wert and Marx (1953), who confined themselves to one frequency, $f = 1$ Hz and $\tau_0 \simeq 10^{-14}$ sec.

In cases in which data are given at only two frequencies ω_1 and ω_2, it is convenient to use the relation

$$\ln(\omega_2/\omega_1) = (Q/k)(T_{p_1}^{-1} - T_{p_2}^{-1}) \tag{3.5-5}$$

[†] More often $\log_{10} \omega$ is plotted versus $1/T_p$, in which case the slope obtained is $Q/2.303k$.

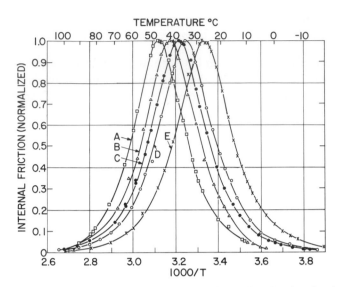

FIG. 3-9.   A series of internal friction peaks due to the Snoek relaxation in an Fe–C alloy, plotted as a function of $1/T$ for five different frequencies: A, 2.1; B, 1.17; C, 0 86; D, 0.63; E, 0.27 Hz. (From Wert and Zener, 1949.)

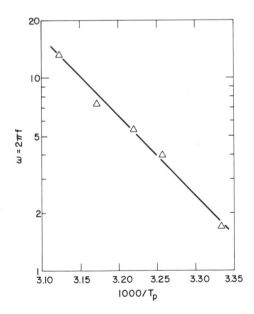

FIG. 3-10.   Semilogarithmic plot of ω versus $1/T_p$ from the data of Fig. 3-9. An activation energy $Q = 0.81$ eV is obtained from the slope of this graph.

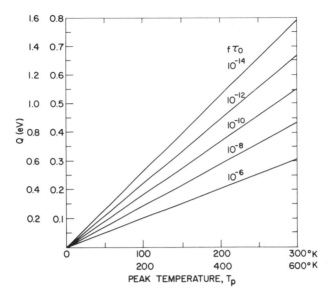

FIG. 3-11. Activation energy Q as a function of peak temperature T_p for various values of the parameter $f\tau_0$.

to calculate the activation energy from the shift, $(1/T_{p_1}) - (1/T_{p_2})$, in the peak position. A disadvantage of this simple procedure is that the location of the peak temperature is difficult to determine with high precision. It is therefore useful to note that Eq. (3.5-5) applies not only to the shift of the peak temperature itself, but also to the shift of every point on the peak. To prove this statement, we need only note that any normalized dynamic response function of a standard anelastic solid is a function only of the product $\omega\tau$. Equivalent values of the response function on curves taken at different frequencies, as shown for example in Fig. 3-12, must then correspond to the same value of $\omega\tau$. But if the

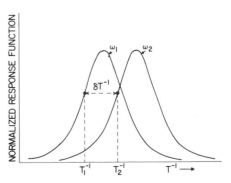

FIG. 3-12. Illustrating the constant shift in T^{-1} between normalized dynamic response functions obtained at two different frequencies ω_1 and ω_2.

same $\omega\tau$ value is to be obtained under conditions ω_1 and T_1 as at ω_2 and T_2, it follows from Eq. (3.5-3) that

$$\ln(\omega_2/\omega_1) = (Q/k)(T_1^{-1} - T_2^{-1}) \qquad (3.5\text{-}6)$$

of which Eq. (3.5-5) is a special case. This result states that plots of response functions versus T^{-1} for two different frequencies differ from each other only by a horizontal shift δT^{-1} along the $1/T$ axis, which is equal to $(k/Q)\ln(\omega_2/\omega_1)$. By applying Eq. (3.5-6) to the average shift over the whole peak, the activation energy can be determined with considerably higher precision than from just the peak location. It must be remembered, however, that since the relaxation strength $\varDelta$ is in general a function of temperature (though a slowly varying function), two Debye peaks at different frequencies must first be normalized before attempting to obtain the shift along the $1/T$ axis. The data shown in Fig. 3-9 have, in fact, been normalized in this way.

We can make further use of Eq. (3.5-3) to compute the width of a Debye peak in a plot versus $1/T$. From Eq. (3.4-4), which gives the width of the peak at half-maximum in a plot versus $\log_{10} \omega\tau$, and the change in scale of abscissa involved in going to the $1/T$ plot, we readily obtain

$$\varDelta(T^{-1}) = (1.144)(2.303k/Q) = 2.635k/Q \qquad (3.5\text{-}7)$$

The peak width is thus seen to be inversely proportional to the activation energy Q. Hence, the width may be used to measure Q, *provided it is known that the peak is truly a Debye peak*, i.e., that the material in question is a standard anelastic solid. It will be shown in Chapter 4 that for an anelastic material which is more complex than a standard anelastic solid, Eq. (3.5-5) still provides a valid means for obtaining Q, but Eq. (3.5-7) does not. In fact, for anything but a standard anelastic solid, the actual peak width will be greater than that given by Eq. (3.5-7). The percentage amount by which the left-hand side of Eq. (3.5-7) exceeds the right-hand side is often used as a measure of the extent to which the solid in question departs in its behavior from the standard anelastic solid.

Another severe test for the standard anelastic solid may be made with the aid of the asymptotic relations, such as those given for J_2 by Eqs. (3.4-5) and (3.4-6). These become, for the case in which T^{-1} is the independent variable,

$$\begin{aligned}
J_2/\delta J &\simeq (\omega\tau_0)^{-1}e^{-Q/kT}, & \omega\tau \gg 1 \\
J_2/\delta J &\simeq (\omega\tau_0)e^{Q/kT}, & \omega\tau \ll 1
\end{aligned} \qquad (3.5\text{-}8)$$

It should be noted that the condition $\omega\tau \gg 1$ applies at the low-temperature (high T^{-1}) side of the peak, while $\omega\tau \ll 1$ applies on the high-temperature side. The asymptotic forms given by Eq. (3.5-8) show that for the standard anelastic solid, a plot of $\ln J_2$ versus T^{-1} goes into two straight lines with equal and opposite slopes ($\pm Q/k$) at the extremes of temperature. It is sometimes found that even for a more complex anelastic solid there is apparent agreement with the asymptotic forms given by Eq. (3.5-8), except that the apparent activation energy calculated from the asymptotic slopes is smaller than the true value obtained from Eq. (3.5-5). In this case, the apparent Q values obtained from the asymptotic slopes and that obtained from the peak width [using Eq. (3.5-7)] may agree with each other, but both will be lower than the true value. This example shows why it is always important to determine Q independently, and correctly, by using more than one frequency.

In summary, it may be stated that the existence of an Arrhenius relation for the relaxation time makes possible the study of the dynamic response of a material as a function of temperature instead of frequency. Further, except for a scale factor, it would seem that the variation of each response function with $1/T$ should be the same as its variation with $\log \omega$. Unfortunately, this latter statement needs qualification because δJ is usually temperature dependent, thus requiring a small correction (see Problem 3-14). Other complications that arise in the study of the dynamic response as a function of temperature are discussed in Section 4.9, which includes cases more general than the standard anelastic solid.

3.6 Multiple Relaxations; Discrete Spectra

In Section 3.3, we have seen that the simplest mechanical models of an anelastic solid are three-parameter models, corresponding to a differential stress–strain equation that involves σ and ε and their first time derivatives only. For such a solid, it was shown that both the creep and the stress relaxation functions are exponentials, each involving a single relaxation time. Let us now examine the next order of complexity in a model which describes an anelastic solid. Starting from the Voigt-type model of Fig. 3-4, we can clearly meet the requirements for anelastic behavior by attaching a second Voigt unit in series with the first one. (An isolated spring or dashpot will not suffice, for reasons which were discussed when the previous model was developed.) In this way the five-parameter Voigt-type model, shown in Fig. 3-13 is obtained. The

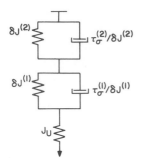

FIG. 3-13.   Five-parameter model containing two Voigt units.

appropriate five parameters are J_U, $\delta J^{(1)}$, $\tau_\sigma^{(1)}$, $\delta J^{(2)}$, and $\tau_\sigma^{(2)}$. The significance of the model is best seen by working out the differential stress–strain equation according to the rules of (3.1-2) and (3.1-3). Following the procedure of writing the appropriate stress–strain relation for each element and eliminating all variables but the total stress σ and the total strain ε we obtain (see Problem 3-15) with the aid of these rules

$$\ddot{\varepsilon} + \left(\frac{1}{\tau_\sigma^{(1)}} + \frac{1}{\tau_\sigma^{(2)}} \right) \dot{\varepsilon} + \frac{\varepsilon}{\tau_\sigma^{(1)} \tau_\sigma^{(2)}}$$

$$= J_U \ddot{\sigma} + \left[\frac{\delta J^{(1)}}{\tau_\sigma^{(1)}} + \frac{\delta J^{(2)}}{\tau_\sigma^{(2)}} + \left(\frac{1}{\tau_\sigma^{(1)}} + \frac{1}{\tau_\sigma^{(2)}} \right) J_U \right] \dot{\sigma}$$

$$+ \frac{\delta J^{(1)} + \delta J^{(2)} + J_U}{\tau_\sigma^{(1)} \tau_\sigma^{(2)}} \, \sigma \tag{3.6-1}$$

It should be noted that this result is equivalent to Eq. (3.1-1) when all coefficients except a_0, a_1, a_2, b_0, b_1, and b_2 are zero, and the equation is divided through by b_0. There are thus five independent parameters in the differential equation, as there are in the model. The step of adding a second Voigt unit has, therefore, changed the differential stress–strain equation from a first-order to a second-order equation in both σ and ε. Since the total strain is the sum of the strains in the lower spring, the first Voigt unit, and the second Voigt unit, the creep function is immediately obtainable from the model, without the need for solving the differential equation, as follows

$$J(t) = J_U + \delta J^{(1)}[1 - \exp(-t/\tau_\sigma^{(1)})] + \delta J^{(2)}[1 - \exp(-t/\tau_\sigma^{(2)})] \tag{3.6-2}$$

This solution can be checked by substituting it into the differential equation. It shows that the creep function is made up of the sum of two exponential growth expressions. Clearly, the relaxed compliance J_R is given by

$$J_R = J_U + \delta J^{(1)} + \delta J^{(2)} \qquad (3.6\text{-}3)$$

while $\tau_\sigma^{(1)}$ and $\tau_\sigma^{(2)}$ are the two relaxation times at constant stress.

In a similar way, it is possible to see that under alternating stress, $\sigma_0 e^{i\omega t}$, the contributions to the strain components ε_1 and ε_2 will be additive, so that

$$J_1(\omega) = J_U + \frac{\delta J^{(1)}}{1 + [\omega\tau_\sigma^{(1)}]^2} + \frac{\delta J^{(2)}}{1 + [\omega\tau_\sigma^{(2)}]^2} \qquad (3.6\text{-}4)$$

$$J_2(\omega) = \delta J^{(1)} \frac{\omega\tau_\sigma^{(1)}}{1 + [\omega\tau_\sigma^{(1)}]^2} + \delta J^{(2)} \frac{\omega\tau_\sigma^{(2)}}{1 + [\omega\tau_\sigma^{(2)}]^2} \qquad (3.6\text{-}5)$$

These relations follow by analogy to Eqs. (3.4-2) and (3.4-3).

On the other hand, it is not readily possible to obtain the M-type response functions from the model of Fig. 3-13. One could, of course, work with the differential equation (3.6-1), but in view of its complexity, it is more convenient to turn to a different mechanical model. The exis-

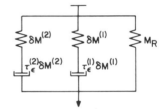

FIG. 3-14. Five-parameter model containing two Maxwell units.

tence of two equivalent models for the standard anelastic solid suggests that the same situation may obtain for the five element models. Accordingly, we are led to add another parallel Maxwell unit to the model of Fig. 3-7 to obtain the five-parameter Maxwell-type model given in Fig. 3-14. The derivation of the differential equation corresponding to this model is straightforward (see Problem 3-17) and gives

$$\ddot{\sigma} + \left(\frac{1}{\tau_\varepsilon^{(1)}} + \frac{1}{\tau_\varepsilon^{(2)}}\right)\dot{\sigma} + \frac{\sigma}{\tau_\varepsilon^{(1)}\tau_\varepsilon^{(2)}}$$

$$= M_U \ddot{\varepsilon} + \left[\frac{\delta M^{(1)}}{\tau_\varepsilon^{(2)}} + \frac{\delta M^{(2)}}{\tau_\varepsilon^{(1)}} + M_R\left(\frac{1}{\tau_\varepsilon^{(1)}} + \frac{1}{\tau_\varepsilon^{(2)}}\right)\right]\dot{\varepsilon}$$

$$+ \frac{M_R}{\tau_\varepsilon^{(1)}\tau_\varepsilon^{(2)}}\varepsilon \qquad (3.6\text{-}6)$$

where (from Fig. 3-14) the value of M_U is given by

$$M_U = M_R + \delta M^{(1)} + \delta M^{(2)} \qquad (3.6\text{-}7)$$

This equation involves the same six terms of the differential equation (3.1-1) as that derived from the Voigt-type model [Eq. (3.6-1)]. Further, it also contains five independent parameters. It must be concluded, therefore, that the two differential equations (and, therefore, the two mechanical models) are equivalent. The relations between the parameters of the Voigt-type model and the Maxwell-type model are obtainable by dividing Eq. (3.6-1) through by J_U, and then equating coefficients with Eq. (3.6-6). This gives three independent relations, which must then be combined with Eqs. (3.6-3) and (3.6-7) and the expressions, $M_U = J_U^{-1}$ and $M_R = J_R^{-1}$. It is clear that the relations between the parameters of the two models are not expressible in a simple form, although the conversion from one model to the other is unique.

The stress relaxation function may be obtained by solving Eq. (3.6-6) for $\varepsilon = $ constant. Alternatively, we may use the fact that the total stress must equal the sum of the stresses on the parallel spring, on the first Maxwell unit, and on the second Maxwell unit. In a manner analogous to that by which the creep function was obtained from the Voigt-type model, the stress relaxation function can be written down immediately as the sum of two exponential relaxations, with relaxation times $\tau_\varepsilon^{(1)}$ and $\tau_\varepsilon^{(2)}$:

$$M(t) = M_R + \delta M^{(1)} \exp(-t/\tau_\varepsilon^{(1)}) + \delta M^{(2)} \exp(-t/\tau_\varepsilon^{(2)}) \qquad (3.6\text{-}8)$$

Similarly, under alternating strain $\varepsilon_0 e^{i\omega t}$ we may deduce the dynamic functions $M_1(\omega)$ and $M_2(\omega)$

$$M_1(\omega) = M_R + \delta M^{(1)} \frac{[\omega \tau_\varepsilon^{(1)}]^2}{1 + [\omega \tau_\varepsilon^{(1)}]^2} + M^{(2)} \frac{[\omega \tau_\varepsilon^{(2)}]^2}{1 + [\omega \tau_\varepsilon^{(2)}]^2} \qquad (3.6\text{-}9)$$

$$M_2(\omega) = \delta M^{(1)} \frac{\omega \tau_\varepsilon^{(1)}}{1 + [\omega \tau_\varepsilon^{(1)}]^2} + \delta M^{(2)} \frac{\omega \tau_\varepsilon^{(2)}}{1 + [\omega \tau_\varepsilon^{(2)}]^2} \qquad (3.6\text{-}10)$$

It is concluded that for the five-parameter solid, the response functions $J(t)$, $M(t)$, $J_1(\omega)$, $J_2(\omega)$, $M_1(\omega)$, and $M_2(\omega)$ are all represented as sums containing two terms, each involving a single relaxation time, in place of the single term of the standard anelastic solid. In particular, J_2 and M_2 are now sums of two Debye peaks. On the other hand, the internal friction $\tan \phi$, which was represented as a single Debye peak in the case of the standard anelastic solid, is, in general, not expressible as a sum of two Debye peaks (see Problem 3-18).

The above treatment of the five-parameter solid shows that once again (as in the standard anelastic solid) it has been possible to use two equivalent models: the model made up of Voigt units, which is most directly suited to obtaining the J-type response functions, and that made up of Maxwell units, which is most useful for the M-type functions. This result is readily generalized to more complex models, as follows. First, it can be shown by mathematical induction (see Problem 3-19) that a model containing n Voigt units in series with each other and with a spring corresponds to a differential stress–strain equation which contains all terms up to order n in both the stress and the strain. Further, it may similarly be shown that a model containing n Maxwell units all in parallel with each other and with a spring is equivalent to a differential stress–strain equation of exactly the same form.[†] Thus, it can be concluded that the two different models are mechanically equivalent, and that, in principle, their parameters may be interrelated by equating like coefficients in the differential equation.

The reader may wonder why a mechanical model containing a *mass* as well as springs and dashpots was not introduced in the development of the more complex models. The reason is that the presence of a mass leads to resonance-type behavior rather than relaxation, except in the limiting case called "overdamped resonance." The simplest example of such resonance behavior, showing how a transition can occur between resonance and relaxation, is discussed in Appendix C.

Additional insights into the differential stress–strain equation may be obtained from the following theorem, the proof of which is left to the reader (see Problem 3-20). For a differential equation of the form (3.1-1) and of order n in both stress and strain, the ratio $a_0/b_0 = J_R$ and $a_n/b_n = J_U$. [That the theorem is true for $n = 1$ and 2 is readily verified from Eqs. (3.3-2) and (3.6-1), respectively.] The significance of this theorem is that, in order to have both elastic and anelastic behavior, the differential stress–strain equation must be of the same order in the stress and strain, and must start from terms of order zero. It therefore indicates that *any* anelastic material may be represented by such a differential equation and such models as we have considered. This question is considered from a different viewpoint in Sections 3.7 and 4.1.

[†] In addition to these, there are other equivalent models involving mixtures of Voigt and Maxwell units. Indeed, the number of equivalent models increases as the number of elements in the model increases. However, only the models which are entirely of the Voigt or of the Maxwell types are useful for present purposes.

The real advantage in the use of the models becomes especially apparent for the more complex cases ($n > 2$) in that certain response functions can be written down directly from a given model, without the need to know either the parameters of the other equivalent model or the coefficients of the differential stress–strain equation. Thus, the creep function for the five-parameter model ($n = 2$) of Eq. (3.6-2) is readily generalized for a model containing n Voigt units, as follows:

$$J(t) = J_\mathrm{U} + \sum_{i=1}^{n} \delta J^{(i)}(1 - \exp[-t/\tau_\sigma^{(i)}]) \tag{3.6-11}$$

where $\tau_\sigma^{(i)}$ and $\delta J^{(i)}$ are the relaxation time and the compliance constant, respectively, associated with the ith Voigt unit. Similarly, for the dynamic functions,

$$J_1(\omega) = J_\mathrm{U} + \sum_{i=1}^{n} \frac{\delta J^{(i)}}{1 + [\omega\tau_\sigma^{(i)}]^2} \tag{3.6-12}$$

$$J_2(\omega) = \sum_{i=1}^{n} \delta J^{(i)} \frac{\omega\tau_\sigma^{(i)}}{1 + [\omega\tau_\sigma^{(i)}]^2} \tag{3.6-13}$$

Such a solid may be described as showing a "discrete spectrum" of relaxation processes, or simply a "discrete relaxation spectrum." Each of the n "lines" of the spectrum is characterized by a relaxation time $\tau_\sigma^{(i)}$, and a magnitude $\delta J^{(i)}$. In this sense the standard anelastic solid is a one-line spectrum or the case of a "single relaxation time." Figure 3-15a shows a useful way of representing a spectrum of τ_σ values, where the time scale is logarithmic and the magnitude of each relaxation $\delta J^{(i)}$ is represented by the height of the corresponding line. It is important to note that the constant J_U, which represents the elasticity and not the anelasticity of the material, does not appear in the spectrum.

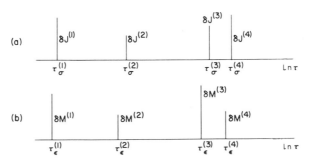

FIG. 3-15. Schematic illustration of (a) spectrum of relaxation times at constant stress, and (b) the corresponding spectrum of relaxation times at constant strain.

The equivalent Maxwell-type model containing n Maxwell units may also be used to describe a discrete relaxation spectrum, with each relaxation characterized by a value of relaxation time $\tau_\varepsilon^{(j)}$, and a magnitude $\delta M^{(j)}$. Clearly, the stress relaxation function is

$$M(t) = M_R + \sum_{j=1}^{n} \delta M^{(j)} \exp[-t/\tau_\varepsilon^{(j)}] \qquad (3.6\text{-}14)$$

while the dynamic functions are

$$M_1(\omega) = M_R + \sum_{j=1}^{n} \delta M^{(j)} \frac{[\omega\tau_\varepsilon^{(j)}]^2}{1 + [\omega\tau_\varepsilon^{(j)}]^2} \qquad (3.6\text{-}15)$$

$$M_2(\omega) = \sum_{j=1}^{n} \delta M^{(j)} \frac{\omega\tau_\varepsilon^{(j)}}{1 + [\omega\tau_\varepsilon^{(j)}]^2} \qquad (3.6\text{-}16)$$

The corresponding spectrum of relaxation times at constant strain is given in Fig. 3-15b. In the case of the Maxwell-type model, the parameter M_R represents the elasticity of the material, and does not appear in the relaxation spectrum.

In this formalism, the inherent characteristics of the material are defined in a dual manner, either by the set of parameters J_U, $\delta J^{(1)}$, $\delta J^{(2)}$, ..., $\delta J^{(n)}$, $\tau_\sigma^{(1)}$, ..., $\tau_\sigma^{(n)}$, or by the alternative set M_R, $\delta M^{(1)}$, ..., $\delta M^{(n)}$, $\tau_\varepsilon^{(1)}$, ..., $\tau_\varepsilon^{(n)}$. All response functions can be expressed in terms of either set of values, although the J-type functions are much more conveniently expressed in terms of the first set and the M-type functions in terms of the second. One way of expressing the stress relaxation function in terms of the first set of parameters is to obtain the relationship between the two sets of values by matching coefficients in the equivalent forms of the differential stress-strain equation. This method can become quite involved for $n > 2$. The second method is to express the creep function in terms of the first set of parameters, and then relate the stress relaxation function to the creep function via the methods of Chapter 2 [e.g., Eq. (2.2-1)].[†] In any case, either set of parameters given above constitutes a complete description of the anelasticity of the material from which all response functions may be obtained. The only difficulty is in converting from one set of parameters to the other, which is again the problem of crossover between the J-type and M-type functions, discussed in Chapter 2. (See Table 2-1.)

[†] Still another method, which involves obtaining the roots of a polynomial of order n, is presented by Gross (1953, Chap. VIII). This approach is derived starting from the relation between the two continuous spectra (see Section 4.2) and letting each continuous spectrum degenerate into a series of delta functions.

An important feature of discrete spectra is the "smearing out" that occurs in the response functions. For example, a spectrum consisting of a single relaxation time (i.e., the standard anelastic solid) corresponds to a peak in J_2 or M_2, at $\omega = \tau^{-1}$, whose width at half-maximum is more than one decade in the frequency [Eq. (3.4-4)]. The corresponding creep and stress relaxation curves, when plotted versus log t, show their major variation in a range of the order of one decade in t near $t = \tau$ [Eq.

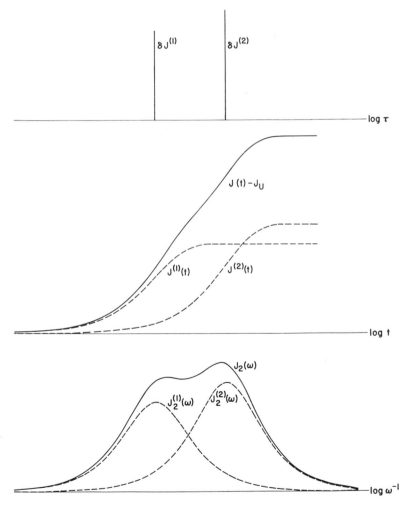

FIG. 3-16.   The response function $J(t)$ and $J_2(\omega)$ for a two line spectrum in which $\tau_1/\tau_2 = 1/10$ and $\delta J_1/\delta J_2 = 9/11$. The dashed curves show the response associated with each line separately.

(3.4-17)]. This is illustrated by the dashed curves of Fig. 3-16. It may, therefore, be deduced that for the case of a two-line spectrum (i.e., the five-parameter model) the response function will only be well resolved as two single relaxation functions if the pair of τ-values differ from each other by more than an order of magnitude. In such a case, the J_2 and M_2 functions show a double peak, while the functions $J(t)$ and $M(t)$ show a double inflection when plotted against log t [or $J_1(\omega)$ and $M_1(\omega)$ versus log ω]. Figure 3-16 shows the degree of resolution obtained in $J_2(\omega)$ and $J(t)$ for two τ_σ values which differ by a factor of ten. Problem 3-21 is also instructive on this point. If the effects are not resolved, response functions which plot as peaks are merely broadened, while those functions which plot as sigmoidal curves (e.g., J_1 or M_1 versus log ω; J or M versus log t) fall or rise more gradually than they do for a single relaxation. In either case, it is valuable to keep in mind the additivity of the effects due to the various relaxations, as shown in Eqs. (3.6-11)–(3.6-16), i.e., that each of the relaxations makes a contribution as if it alone were present. It may therefore be concluded that the ith relaxation will contribute appreciably to the dynamic functions only in the frequency range from $\omega = 0.1/\tau^{(i)}$ to $\omega = 10/\tau^{(i)}$, while it will contribute to the quasi-static functions primarily in the time interval between $t = 0.1\tau^{(i)}$ and $t = 10\tau^{(i)}$.

It is useful to note that the total relaxation of the compliance δJ is the sum of the individual relaxations $\delta J^{(i)}$, and similarly for δM in terms of $\delta M^{(j)}$. Thus:

$$\delta J \equiv J_R - J_U = \sum_{i=1}^{n} \delta J^{(i)} \tag{3.6-17}$$

$$\delta M \equiv M_U - M_R = \sum_{j=1}^{n} \delta M^{(j)} \tag{3.6-18}$$

On the other hand, if one chooses to work with the relaxation strengths, an ambiguity arises in attempting to define the individual relaxation strengths $\Delta^{(i)}$ of a set of well-separated relaxations (see Problem 3-22).

3.7   Obtaining the Spectrum from a Response Function

We turn now to the question of how the relaxation spectrum can be obtained from an experimentally measured response function. In approaching this problem, we should keep in mind the "smearing out" characteristic of a response function mentioned in the last section, i.e., that a single sharp relaxation manifests itself in response functions which show their principal variations over a range of time or frequency of about one decade. When the lines of the spectrum are well separated (i.e., τ values at least one decade apart), we may expect to be able to resolve uniquely the contributions to a given response function from each spectral component. For the analysis of a quasi-static function into a sum of exponentials, numerical methods may be used.[†] In addition, a "subtraction of tails" method has been used by Keefer and Wert (1963a) for graphically obtaining discrete spectra from quasi-static data. This method is useful if the spectrum consists of discrete lines separated by about half-decade intervals. The procedure first assumes that in such cases, the long time tail of an aftereffect curve[‡] is dominated by the spectral line δJ_n, τ_n, which has the longest relaxation time. A semilogarithmic plot is made of the aftereffect strain versus linear time, and the slope and intercept of the straight line portion in the long time region are used to obtain the relevant values of δJ_n, τ_n, respectively. This contribution is then subtracted from the experimental data, and a second plot made to determine the next pair of values. The procedure is repeated until the

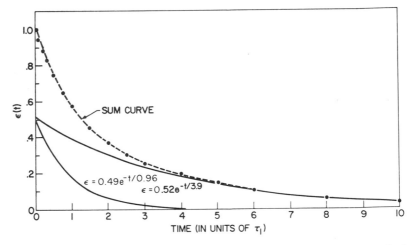

FIG. 3-17. A "subtraction of tails" analysis applied to a set of points calculated from the relationship $\varepsilon(t) = 0.5\, e^{-t/1.0} + 0.5\, e^{-t/4.0}$. The results of the analysis are shown by the two solid curves. The broken curve is the sum of the two solid curves for comparison with the original points. (After Wert, 1966.)

[†] The problem of fitting an experimental curve to a sum of exponentials is discussed by Lanczos (1956, Chap. IV).

[‡] A similar procedure could of course be applied to creep or stress-relaxation measurements.

response is fully accounted for. Figure 3-17 shows an example of this graphical procedure applied to the sum of two exponentials of equal strength, where the relaxation times differ by a factor of four. In this rather favorable case, the errors incurred in the graphical separation of the components are less than 5%. Attempts to improve the accuracy and reliability of the method by computer analysis of the data have been described by Wert (1966) and Gibala and Wert (1966a).

As the lines of the spectrum move closer together, and particularly if the number of lines is large, the "smearing out" effect makes it difficult to obtain a unique spectrum from a given response function. For example, if a broad creep curve were given, we could use a Voigt-type model with a closely spaced set of τ_σ values over a total range which is the same as that of the time t over which appreciable creep occurs. These τ values may be spaced arbitrarily; the only requirement is that they be close enough to avoid irregularities (e.g., multiple inflection points) in the calculated response functions. Having arbitrarily selected the set of $\tau_\sigma^{(i)}$ values, one may fit the given creep curve by calculating $\delta J^{(i)}$'s such that the computed creep curve fits the experimental curve at a series of selected points. For a model consisting of n Voigt units plus a spring, there are $n + 1$ points at which the calculated curve may be fitted to the experimental curve. Thus, any desired accuracy of fitting can be obtained, although the computational problem becomes difficult when n is large. The chief disadvantage of this approach is that the spectrum obtained is not unique, since the set of τ values is an arbitrary choice. In such a case, it makes more sense to go to the limit of arbitrarily closely spaced τ values and thereby to obtain a *continuous* relaxation spectrum, as discussed in Chapter 4.

In summary, description of an anelastic material in terms of a discrete spectrum is useful only when both the τ values and the magnitudes ($\delta J^{(i)}$ or $\delta M^{(j)}$) can be obtained in a unique manner from the response functions.

PROBLEMS

3-1.   Derive the differential stress–strain equation (3.2-1) for the Voigt model and solve this equation to obtain the response functions $J(t)$, $J_1(\omega)$, and $J_2(\omega)$.

3-2.   Derive the differential stress–strain equation (3.2-2) for the Maxwell model and solve this equation to obtain the response functions $J(t)$, $M(t)$, $M_1(\omega)$, and $M_2(\omega)$.

3-3. Derive Eqs. (3.3-1) and (3.3-2) for the three parameter Voigt-type model (Fig. 3-4).

3-4. Derive the differential stress–strain equation (3.3-11) for the three parameter Maxwell-type model (Fig. 3-7).

3-5. Carry through the steps in the derivation of the Debye equations (3.4-2) and (3.4-3).

3-6. Show that the Debye peak $\omega\tau/(1 + \omega^2\tau^2)$, when plotted versus $\log_{10} \omega\tau$, is a symmetrical peak about $\log_{10} \omega\tau = 0$ whose (full) width at half-maximum is given by Eq. (3.4-4).

3-7. Show, from Eq. (3.4-2), that the function $J_1(\omega) - (J_U + \frac{1}{2}\,\delta J)$ is antisymmetric about $\log_{10} \omega\tau_\sigma = 0$.

3-8. Construct an Argand diagram or complex plane locus in which the imaginary part J_2 of J^* is plotted versus the real part J_1, each part corresponding to a given frequency. From the Debye equations show that the plot is a semicircle of radius $\delta J/2$, its center being on the abscissa at a distance $(J_U + J_R)/2$ from the origin and intersecting the abscissa at $J_1 = J_U$ and $J_1 = J_R$, respectively. (This plot, in the literature of dielectric relaxation, is often termed the "Cole–Cole" plot.)

3-9. Derive Eqs. (3.4-7) and (3.4-8) and show that (3.4-7) can be converted into the form (3.4-13).

3-10. Show, for the standard anelastic solid, that the functions $J_1^{-1}(\omega)$ and $M_1^{-1}(\omega)$ are given in terms of the mean relaxation time $\bar{\tau}$, of Eq. (3.4-12), by

$$J_1^{-1}(\omega) = M_U - \delta M/(1 + \omega^2\bar{\tau}^2)$$

$$M_1^{-1}(\omega) = J_U + \delta J/(1 + \omega^2\bar{\tau}^2)$$

Note, by comparison with Eq. (3.4-2), that $M_1^{-1} \geq J_1$ everywhere, although the difference is only of order ϕ^2. [This is a special case of Eq. (1.3-14).]

3-11. A dynamic relaxation function of the type (3.4-15) expressed as a function of the variable $\log \omega\tau$ can be converted into a peak function by differentiation. Show that the peak thereby obtained is symmetric about $\log \omega\tau = 0$, and has a width at half-maximum of

$$\Delta(\log_{10} \omega\tau) = 0.765$$

Note that this is substantially narrower than the Debye peak to which Eq. (3.4-4) applies.

3-12. Using the response function of the standard anelastic solid, verify the following relations derived from the Boltzmann superposition principle: Eqs. (2.2-1), (2.3-3)–(2.3-12), (2.4-1), and (2.4-2). To obtain this result for the Kronig–Kramers relations (2.4-3) and (2.4-4), use the principal values [see Eq. (B-3), Appendix B].

3-13. Assume the relaxation time for a particular process is 10^2 sec at 100°C. Using Eq. (3.5-2), calculate the temperatures at which τ is 1 sec and 10^4 sec, assuming in turn that Q is 0.5, 1.0, and 2.0 eV.

3-14. Consider the plot of a Debye peak versus $1/T$ when δJ itself varies with temperature as $1/T$. Show that the peak will become slightly asymmetric (broadened on the low temperature side and narrowed on the high temperature side), but that, to first order, the peak width at half-maximum is still given by Eq. (3.5-7).

3-15. Obtain the differential stress–strain equation (3.6-1) from the five-parameter Voigt-type model (Fig. 3-11).

3-16. Starting with the differential equation (3.6-1), verify Eqs. (3.6-4) and (3.6-5) for the dynamic response functions.

3-17. Obtain the differential stress–strain equation (3.6-6) from the five-parameter Maxwell-type model (Fig. 3-12), and verify Eqs. (3.6-9) and (3.6-10).

3-18. Obtain a general expression for the internal friction $\tan \phi$ in the case of the five-parameter solid. Show that this is expressible as the sum of two Debye peaks only if either (a) $\delta J^{(1)}$ and $\delta J^{(2)}$ are both $\ll J_U$, or (b) if $\tau_\sigma^{(1)}$ and $\tau_\sigma^{(2)}$ differ from each other by several orders of magnitude.

3-19. (a) Given that for a Voigt-type model containing n Voigt units plus a spring, the corresponding differential equation is of nth order in both σ and ε with all coefficients greater than 0, prove that for $n + 1$ Voigt elements, the equation is of $(n + 1)$st order in σ and ε with all coefficients greater than 0. This result, together with Eq. (3.3-2) or (3.6-1), constitutes a proof by induction that the model containing n units is equivalent to the differential equation of order n. [Hint: Write the differential stress–strain equation (3.1-1) in the form $P\varepsilon = Q\sigma$ where P and Q are operators as defined in the footnote on p. 42.] (b) Following the same procedure, prove the same result for the Maxwell-type model containing n units. (c) Show that the characteristic roots of the operators P and Q defined in part (a) are $-1/\tau_\sigma^{(i)}$ and $-1/\tau_\varepsilon^{(j)}$, respectively.

3-20. In a differential stress–strain equation of form (3.1-1) and of nth order, show, from the definition of anelasticity, that $a_0/b_0 = J_R$. Also show that $a_n/b_n = J_U$. (Hint: Use a dynamic approach letting $\omega \to \infty$.)

3-21. Consider the sum of two Debye peaks of equal heights and relaxation times τ_1 and τ_2 ($\tau_2 > \tau_1$). Show that if $\tau_2/\tau_1 < 3 + 2\sqrt{2}$ the resultant curve has a single maximum, while if $\tau_2/\tau_1 > 3 + 2\sqrt{2}$ the curve has two maxima with a minimum in between. Show also that at the transitional value $\tau_2/\tau_1 = 3 + 2\sqrt{2}$ the ratio of the peak width at half maximum to that of a single Debye peak is $\ln[2 + \sqrt{3} + (6 + 4\sqrt{3})^{1/2}]/\ln(2 + \sqrt{3}) = 1.51$.

3-22. Consider a relaxation spectrum consisting of two or more widely separated relaxations whose individual relaxation strengths are not small. Suppose that an observer works in a range of frequency or temperature such that he is only aware of the ith relaxation. Show from Eq. (1.2-13), that this observer will, in general, define the relaxation strength $\Delta^{(i)}$ differently from one who is aware of the entire relaxation spectrum. Further, if this observer's definition is accepted for each partial strength $\Delta^{(i)}$, then the additivity relation $\Delta = \sum_i \Delta^{(i)}$ will not be valid. Note that such problems do not arise if results are expressed in terms of $\delta J^{(i)}$ or $\delta M^{(j)}$ [see Eqs. (3.6-17) and (3.6-18)].

General References

ALFREY, T. (1948). "Mechanical Behavior of High Polymers," Part. B and Appendix II. Wiley (Interscience), New York.

LEADERMAN, H. (1958). In "Rheology" (F. R. Eirich, ed.), Vol. II. Academic Press, New York.

STAVERMAN, A. J., and SCHWARTZL, F. (1956). In "Die Physik der Hochpolymeren" (H. A. Stuart, ed.), Vol. IV, Chap. 1. Springer-Verlag, Berlin.

Chapter 4 / Continuous Spectra

In Chapter 3, we introduced the concept of relaxation spectra, beginning from the case of a single spectral line (the "standard anelastic solid"), then the two-line spectrum (the five-parameter models) and finally generalizing to an n-line spectrum. In the present chapter, we go to the limit in considering the case of a continuous distribution of relaxation times. Because of the importance of continuous spectra, much of the chapter is concerned with the practical problem of obtaining a spectrum from a given response function. Finally, the fact that the relaxation times for most processes obey the Arrhenius equation is shown to have a profound effect on the way relaxation spectra are interpreted and data are analyzed.

4.1 Continuous Relaxation Spectra at Constant Stress and Constant Strain

In the previous chapter, it was shown that a given J-type response function can be duplicated to any desired accuracy by choosing a sufficiently large discrete set of relaxation times $\tau_\sigma^{(i)}$ ($i = 1, \ldots, n$), which are reasonably closely spaced and whose magnitudes $\delta J^{(i)}$ are then treated as adjustable parameters. This procedure amounts to finding a Voigt-type model with n Voigt units whose response behavior simulates that of the actual material. In a similar way, an M-type response function can be duplicated by the selection of a discrete set of relaxation times $\tau_\varepsilon^{(j)}$ ($j = 1, \ldots, n$), with magnitudes $\delta M^{(j)}$, corresponding to an appropriate Maxwell-type model. Except in the case of well-separated spectral lines, however, the choice of the τ values to fit a response function is subjective, so that the spectrum cannot be regarded as a unique characterization of the material. It is then preferable to allow τ to exhibit all values, so that the spectrum may be expressed as a function of the continuous variable[†] τ. The transition from a discrete to a continuous spectrum is best accomplished by the identification

$$\delta J^{(i)} \rightarrow X(\ln \tau)\, d(\ln \tau) \qquad (4.1\text{-}1)$$

Note that we have chosen $\ln \tau$ rather than τ as the appropriate variable.[‡] Thus, $X(\ln \tau)\, d(\ln \tau)$ is the contribution to the total δJ for values of $\ln \tau$ which fall between $\ln \tau$ and $\ln \tau + d(\ln \tau)$. The function $X(\ln \tau)$ is called the *relaxation spectrum at constant stress*,[§] and has dimensions of compliance. In a similar way

$$\delta M^{(i)} \rightarrow Y(\ln \tau)\, d(\ln \tau) \qquad (4.1\text{-}2)$$

defines the *relaxation spectrum at constant strain* $Y(\ln \tau)$, which has dimensions of a modulus. All of the expressions for the various J-type functions which were given in Section 3.6 for the case of discrete spectra may, with the help of Eq. (4.1-1), be translated into corresponding expressions involving the continuous spectra. Thus, Eq. (3.6-11) for the creep function becomes

$$J(t) = J_U + \int_{-\infty}^{\infty} X(\ln \tau)(1 - e^{-t/\tau})\, d(\ln \tau) \qquad (4.1\text{-}3)$$

while Eqs. (3.6-12) and (3.6-13) become

$$J_1(\omega) = J_U + \int_{-\infty}^{\infty} \frac{X(\ln \tau)}{1 + \omega^2 \tau^2}\, d(\ln \tau) \qquad (4.1\text{-}4)$$

$$J_2(\omega) = \int_{-\infty}^{\infty} X(\ln \tau)\, \frac{\omega \tau}{1 + \omega^2 \tau^2}\, d(\ln \tau) \qquad (4.1\text{-}5)$$

It should be remembered that, as a generalization of (3.6-17),

$$\int_{-\infty}^{\infty} X(\ln \tau)\, d(\ln \tau) = \delta J \qquad (4.1\text{-}6)$$

[†] When τ is a continuous variable, the subscript σ or ε will be dropped. When associated with the J-type functions, the variable τ will be understood to represent the relaxation time at constant stress. Similarly, when the M-type functions are used, τ refers to conditions of constant strain.

[‡] The use of logarithmic scales for time and frequency variables turns out to be particularly convenient, as has already been seen in Figs. 3-5, 3-6, and 3-8. Strictly, the logarithmic function is, of course, only meaningful for a dimensionless variable, but we may always convert to a ratio, e.g., τ/τ_1 where τ_1 is some reference value.

[§] Many of the treatises on viscoelasticity call $X(\ln \tau)$ the "retardation spectrum" and $Y(\ln \tau)$ the "relaxation spectrum."

The quantity δJ thus continues to serve as a measure of the magnitude of the complete relaxation spectrum for constant stress. To include the case of a spectrum which is continuous in one τ region and discrete in others, we may have both a discrete set $\delta J^{(i)}$, $\tau_\sigma^{(i)}$ and the continuous function $X(\ln \tau)$, or in a more formal way, we may include some Dirac δ functions in $X(\ln \tau)$. In a similar way, the M-type response functions are expressible in terms of the relaxation spectrum $Y(\ln \tau)$

$$M(t) = M_R + \int_{-\infty}^{\infty} Y(\ln \tau) e^{-t/\tau} \, d(\ln \tau) \tag{4.1-7}$$

$$M_1(\omega) = M_R + \int_{-\infty}^{\infty} Y(\ln \tau) \frac{\omega^2 \tau^2}{1 + \omega^2 \tau^2} \, d(\ln \tau) \tag{4.1-8}$$

$$M_2(\omega) = \int_{-\infty}^{\infty} Y(\ln \tau) \frac{\omega \tau}{1 + \omega^2 \tau^2} \, d(\ln \tau) \tag{4.1-9}$$

with

$$\int_{-\infty}^{\infty} Y(\ln \tau) \, d(\ln \tau) = \delta M \tag{4.1-10}$$

It is convenient to introduce also the *normalized spectra* or *distribution functions*, defined by

$$\Psi(\ln \tau) = (1/\delta J) X(\ln \tau) \tag{4.1-11}$$

$$\Phi(\ln \tau) = (1/\delta M) Y(\ln \tau) \tag{4.1-12}$$

so that, from Eqs. (4.1-6) and (4.1-10),

$$\int_{-\infty}^{\infty} \Psi(\ln \tau) \, d(\ln \tau) = 1 \tag{4.1-13}$$

$$\int_{-\infty}^{\infty} \Phi(\ln \tau) \, d(\ln \tau) = 1 \tag{4.1-14}$$

Recalling the definitions of the normalized creep function $\psi(t)$ given by Eq. (1.2-11) and the normalized stress relaxation function $\varphi(t)$ given by (1.2-15), we note that these functions may be expressed in terms of the corresponding normalized spectra,

$$1 - \psi(t) = \int_{-\infty}^{\infty} \Psi(\ln \tau) e^{-t/\tau} \, d(\ln \tau) \tag{4.1-15}$$

$$\varphi(t) = \int_{-\infty}^{\infty} \Phi(\ln \tau) e^{-t/\tau} \, d(\ln \tau) \tag{4.1-16}$$

It is important to note that Eqs. (4.1-15) and (4.1-16) are essentially[†] Laplace integrals. Such integrals can be used to describe *any* continuous, monotonically decreasing, integrable function of t which goes to zero as $t \to \infty$. We may therefore conclude that the description of creep and stress relaxation in terms of a spectrum of relaxation times has general validity.

The description of anelastic behavior in terms of discrete or continuous relaxation spectra offers another means for verifying the interrelations between response functions which were derived in Chapter 2 using the Boltzmann superposition principle (see Problem 4-1).

Equations (4.1-4), (4.1-5), (4.1-8), and (4.1-9) deal with the simplest dynamic response functions from which the others, e.g., $|M|(\omega)$, $|J|(\omega)$, $\phi(\omega)$, may be obtained using the relations given in Chapter 1. These other functions are not expressible as a single integral over the appropriate spectrum, as are J_1, J_2, M_1, and M_2. Thus the internal friction, given by $\tan \phi = J_2/J_1 = M_2/M_1$ involves, in general, integrals in both numerator and denominator. In the special case in which the relaxation strength $\Delta \ll 1$, however, we may set $J_1 \simeq J_U$ and $M_1 \simeq M_R$ or

$$\tan \phi \simeq J_2/J_U \simeq M_2/M_R, \qquad \Delta \ll 1 \qquad (4.1\text{-}17)$$

Under these conditions, it is clear from inserting Eqs. (4.1-11) and (4.1-12) into (4.1-5) and (4.1-9), and remembering $\delta J/J = \delta M/M = \Delta$, that $\Psi(\ln \tau) \simeq \Phi(\ln \tau)$, so that there is only one spectrum involved.[‡] (The situation is, of course, analogous to the case of the standard anelastic solid where, for $\Delta \ll 1$, $\tau_\varepsilon \simeq \tau_\sigma$.) For many actual anelastic relaxation processes the condition $\Delta \ll 1$ is not valid. Accordingly, we must maintain the description in terms of two spectra, $X(\ln \tau)$ and $Y(\ln \tau)$ (or Ψ and Φ). Just as in the discrete case, these two spectra are not independent, however, since either one suffices to define completely the properties of the solid.

[†] To convert Eqs. (4.1-15) and (4.1-16) to standard Laplace integrals of the form $\int_0^\infty f(s)e^{-ts}\, ds$ requires substitution of $s = \tau^{-1}$ and changing the integration variable to ds. The mathematical significance of the distribution function Ψ is then that

$$\tau \Psi(\ln \tau)\,|_{\tau=1/s}$$

is the inverse Laplace transform of the normalized function $1 - \psi(t)$. See, e.g., Franklin (1949).

[‡] The equality of the distribution functions for small Δ could also have been obtained from Eqs. (4.1-15) and (4.1-16) as a consequence of the equality of $\varphi(t)$ and $1 - \psi(t)$ (see Problem 2-2).

4.2   Relations between the Two Relaxation Spectra

For the case of a single relaxation (standard anelastic solid) the relationship between the relaxation time at constant stress τ_σ and relaxation time at constant strain τ_ε is quite a simple one [Eq. (3.3-9)]. For a multiple discrete spectrum, the relations between the set of values $\tau_\sigma^{(i)}$ and the set $\tau_\varepsilon^{(j)}$ are quite complex (see Section 3.6), and not expressible in a form which is easily solved. It is appropriate now to consider the relationship between the continuous spectra $X(\ln \tau)$ and $Y(\ln \tau)$. As already mentioned in the last section, unless $\varDelta \ll 1$, these two functions are not proportional to one another. Several authors have worked out various approximate relationships between the two spectra; however, Gross (1947) has succeeded in obtaining exact relationships which are sufficiently amenable to numerical computational methods as to make the use of approximation methods unnecessary. The relationships are

$$Y(\ln \tau) = \frac{X(\ln \tau)}{\left[J_{\mathrm{U}} + \int_{-\infty}^{\infty} X(\ln u)[1 - (u/\tau)]^{-1} \, d(\ln u) \right]^2 + \pi^2 X^2(\ln \tau)}$$

$$(4.2\text{-}1)$$

$$X(\ln \tau) = \frac{Y(\ln \tau)}{\left[M_{\mathrm{R}} - \int_{-\infty}^{\infty} Y(\ln u)(u/\tau)[1 - (u/\tau)]^{-1} \, d(\ln u) \right]^2 + \pi^2 Y^2(\ln \tau)}$$

$$(4.2\text{-}2)$$

In these equations the integrals are principal values, i.e., taken so as to avoid singular points of the integrand (see, e.g., Appendix B).

Equations (4.2-1) and (4.2-2) show that, apart from values of τ at which singularities occur, both spectra are zero or finite in the same ranges of the variable τ. It is interesting that these equations may be used to calculate the relationship between discrete relaxation spectra as a special case, by allowing the continuous distribution functions to degenerate into a series of Dirac δ functions (Gross, 1953, Chap. 8).

The importance of Eqs. (4.2-1) and (4.2-2) is that they provide a useful bridge between the M-type response functions, which are all calculable from $Y(\ln \tau)$, and the J-type response functions which are expressed in terms of $X(\ln \tau)$.

4.3   Direct Methods for the Calculation of Spectra

The equations of the last two sections express all of the necessary relationships between response functions and spectra, so that in principle, the matter of obtaining spectra from response functions, or vice versa, is solved. Nevertheless, in practice there may be some formidable problems involved in inverting integrals of the types given in Section 4.1, particularly, when it is realized that the response functions are generally obtained (from experiment) in graphical form. The present section will, therefore, be concerned with both exact and approximate methods for calculating spectra from response functions. Other, "indirect," methods will be discussed in Section 4.5.

A. EXACT METHODS

For the case of the quasi-static response functions, i.e., creep or stress relaxation, the problem of obtaining the appropriate spectrum is one of inverting the Laplace integral. The use of standard methods of inversion of this integral has been discussed by Gross (1947), but the formulas which he obtains to not lend themselves to easy computation. One can, of course, carry out the inversion exactly if the experimental data for the normalized functions $1 - \psi(t)$ or $\varphi(t)$ can be fitted to a sufficiently high degree of accuracy by one member of a standard Laplace pair. Under these conditions, the other member of the pair gives the corresponding distribution function directly. This approach has been suggested and employed by Macey (1948), but its application is rather limited.

In the case of the dynamic response functions, a method for the exact inversion of the various integrals has been given by Fuoss and Kirkwood (1941). This method has been widely used in studies of dielectric relaxation, although, surprisingly enough, it is practically never mentioned in the literature on anelasticity of crystals. The Fuoss–Kirkwood method utilizes the analytic continuation of the appropriate dynamic response function onto the whole of the complex plane, and can therefore only be applied when the functions $J_2(x)$ and $J_1(x)$ are integrable analytic functions of the variable $x = \ln \omega$. The results may be expressed as

$$X(\ln \tau) = (1/\pi)[J_2(x + \tfrac{1}{2}i\pi) + J_2(x - \tfrac{1}{2}i\pi)]_{x=-\ln\tau} \qquad (4.3\text{-}1)$$

$$X(\ln \tau) = (i/\pi)[J_1(x + \tfrac{1}{2}i\pi) - J_1(x - \tfrac{1}{2}i\pi)]_{x=-\ln\tau} \qquad (4.3\text{-}2)$$

In a similar way, $Y(\ln \tau)$ may be derived from either $M_1(x)$ or $M_2(x)$

$$Y(\ln \tau) = (1/\pi)[M_2(x + \tfrac{1}{2}i\pi) + M_2(x - \tfrac{1}{2}i\pi)]_{x=-\ln\tau} \qquad (4.3\text{-}3)$$

$$Y(\ln \tau) = (-i/\pi)[M_1(x + \tfrac{1}{2}i\pi) - M_1(x - \tfrac{1}{2}i\pi)]_{x=-\ln\tau} \qquad (4.3\text{-}4)$$

These results show how we can obtain the spectra, when starting from the response functions in analytic form, by means of only the operations of complex algebra, i.e., substituting $x \pm (i\pi/2)$ for x and separating the resultant functions into real and imaginary parts. It should be noted that the fact that $J_2(x)$ is real when x is real guarantees that the expression for $X(\ln \tau)$ given by Eq. (4.3-1) will be real, since the imaginary parts of $J_2(x + \frac{1}{2}i\pi)$ and of $J_2(x - \frac{1}{2}i\pi)$ must be the negative of each other. A similar argument applies to the other equations, (4.3-2)–(4.3-4).

An important example of the application of this method has been given by Fuoss and Kirkwood in their original paper. These authors found empirically that for many dielectric relaxation processes they could fit the data for the out-of-phase component of the dielectric constant (the analog of J_2) to an expression of the form

$$J_2(x) = J_2(x_0) \operatorname{sech} \alpha(x - x_0), \qquad 0 < \alpha \le 1 \qquad (4.3\text{-}5)$$

Here $x_0 = -\ln \tau_m$ where τ_m^{-1} is the value of the frequency ω at the peak. This equation is a simple generalization of the standard anelastic solid, which obeys this same equation with $\alpha = 1$ [see footnote, p. 52]. It is clear from Eq. (4.3-5) that the peak width at half-maximum is larger than that for the standard anelastic solid by the factor α^{-1} (see Problem 4-2). In terms of Eq. (4.3-1), it is quite simple to derive the exact expression for the distribution function which produces the $J_2(x)$ function given by (4.3-5). It is left to the reader to carry out the algebra to show that the appropriate spectrum is

$$X(\ln \tau) = \frac{2J_2(x_0)}{\pi} \left. \frac{\cos(\alpha\pi/2) \cosh \alpha s}{\cos^2(\alpha\pi/2) + \sinh^2 \alpha s} \right|_{s = \ln \tau/\tau_m} \qquad (4.3\text{-}6)$$

and finally, by integrating this function and using (4.1-6), it follows that

$$J_2(x_0) = (\alpha/2) \, \delta J \qquad (4.3\text{-}7)$$

Of course, if $M_2(x)$ obeys Eq. (4.3-5), then $Y(\ln \tau)$ is given by this same expression. The corresponding distribution function $\Psi(\ln \tau) = X(\ln \tau)/\delta J$ (or $\Phi = Y/\delta M$), obtained from combining Eqs. (4.3-6) and (4.3-7), will be called the *Fuoss–Kirkwood distribution*. In crystalline materials many examples are known where Eq. (4.3-5) is applicable.

To summarize the discussion of exact methods, it may be concluded that the determination of spectra from static response functions is difficult, since it involves the inversion of a Laplace integral. On the other hand, the calculation of spectra from dynamic functions is relatively straightforward, in terms of complex algebra, provided that the appropriate response function is expressible in analytic form. Since response functions are usually available graphically in the form of plots of original data, it does not follow that finding an analytic function to fit the data is always easy. Therefore, in spite of the availability of exact methods for obtaining spectra from response functions, wide use has been made of approximation methods suited to the analysis of data in graphical form.

B. APPROXIMATION METHODS

The simplest (and crudest) approximation method, originally due to Alfrey and Doty (1945), can be very useful in giving a semiquantitative picture of the relationship of the various response functions to each other and to the spectra. We will, therefore, develop these relationships in some detail.

Consider first the creep, expressed as a function of the variable $y = \ln t$. Equation (4.1-3) then becomes

$$J(y) - J_U = \int_{-\infty}^{\infty} X(z)[1 - \exp(-e^{y-z})] \, dz \qquad (4.3\text{-}8)$$

where $z = \ln \tau$. The function $1 - \exp(-e^{y-z})$ is a "steplike" function of z, which falls rather rapidly from a value of unity for $z \ll y$ to a value of zero for $z \gg y$. A plot of this function has been given in Fig. 3-5, (except that the sign of the abscissa must now be reversed, since the function ψ is plotted there against y instead of z). It is clear that if $X(z)$ *varies slowly with* z in the range near $z = y$, we may let the steplike function become an abrupt step at $y = z$, without substantially changing the value of the integral. Thus,

$$J(y) - J_U \approx \int_{-\infty}^{y} X(z) \, dz \qquad (4.3\text{-}9)$$

or

$$dJ(y)/dy \approx X(y) \qquad (4.3\text{-}10)$$

In other words, to this first order of approximation, $X(\ln \tau)$ is obtained from the slope of the creep curve, as $dJ/d(\ln t)|_{t=\tau}$. Equation (4.3-10) is often referred to as "Alfrey's rule."

While this approximate expression gives a reasonably good picture of the spectrum when the spectrum extends over several decades and varies gradually, it fails to do so if the spectrum is discrete or contains sharp peaks. It is important to note that, whereas in the exact relationship

[Eq. (4.3-8)] the creep rate depends on the whole range of the function $X(\ln \tau)$, in Eq. (4.3-10) it depends only on the value of $X(\ln \tau)$ at $\tau = t$. The latter result can therefore only be valid to a rough approximation.

The application of this approximation under the worst conditions, i.e., for the standard anelastic solid where the spectrum certainly does not meet the requirement of being a slowly varying function, is illustrated in Fig. 4-1. Comparison of the function dJ/dy with $X(y)$ for a single line spectrum (located at $\tau = \tau_1$) shows that Eq. (4.3-10) is not obeyed. Nevertheless, even in this extreme case, the function dJ/dy serves as a rough approximation to $X(y)$, in the sense that it is a peak function over a relatively small range of y, with the peak located at $t = \tau_1$.

The case of stress relaxation is completely analogous to that of creep and gives, to the same order of approximation as Eq. (4.3-10),

$$Y(y) \approx -dM(y)/dy \qquad (4.3\text{-}11).$$

The negative sign is due to the fact that $M(y)$ is a decreasing function of y.

Turning now to the dynamic properties, we may follow a similar procedure for $J_1(y)$ where[†] $y = \ln \omega^{-1}$. Equation (4.1-4) may be written

$$J_1(y) - J_U = \int_{-\infty}^{\infty} \frac{X(z)\,dz}{1 + e^{2(z-y)}} \qquad (4.3\text{-}12)$$

The function $[1 + e^{2(z-y)}]^{-1}$, with $z = $ constant, is just the normalized J_1 function of the standard anelastic solid (Fig. 3-5). It is again a steplike function which goes from unity for $z \ll y$ to zero for $z \gg y$. Thus, when $X(z)$ is a slowly varying function of z, we may again use the approximation of a sharp step at $z = y$, to obtain

$$J_1(y) - J_U \approx \int_{-\infty}^{y} X(z)\,dz \qquad (4.3\text{-}13)$$

and

$$dJ_1(y)/dy \approx X(y) \qquad (4.3\text{-}14)$$

[This approximation is slightly better than for the case of the creep function, since the steplike function for the dynamic case is sharper than for the quasi-static case, and is also symmetric about $y = z$. See Eqs. (3.4-16) and (3.4-17) and Fig. 3-5.] Finally, for J_2 we may write, in the

---

[†] The variable y is again chosen as the logarithm of a time variable, here ω^{-1}. In this way various response functions as well as the spectra can all be plotted against the same abscissa.

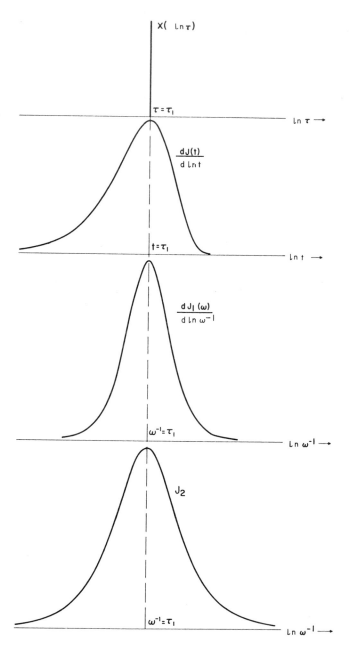

FIG. 4-1.   Comparison of the four peak functions for the case of the standard anelastic solid.

present notation

$$J_2(y) = \tfrac{1}{2} \int_{-\infty}^{\infty} X(z)\, \mathrm{sech}(z - y)\, dz \qquad (4.3\text{-}15)$$

The function $\mathrm{sech}(z - y)$, when $z = $ constant, is the Debye peak centered at $z = y$. If $X(z)$ is slowly varying over the major range of this peak, it may be replaced approximately by $X(y)$ and taken out of the integral. When the integration is then carried out we obtain

$$J_2(y) \approx \tfrac{1}{2}\pi X(y) \qquad (4.3\text{-}16)$$

which is equivalent to the statement that $X(\ln \tau) \approx (2/\pi)J_2(\ln \omega)\,|_{\omega=1/\tau}$.

A test of Eqs. (4.3-14) and (4.3-16) for the worst case (i.e., for the standard anelastic solid) is again given in Fig. 4-1. It may be noted that, just as for the function dJ/dy, the peaks dJ_1/dy and $J_2(y)$ occur at $\omega^{-1}=\tau_1$. Actually, Fig. 4-1 serves to demonstrate the "smearing out" effect discussed in Section 3.6.

Analogously to Eqs. (4.3-14) and (4.3-16), we may obtain the approximate results for the relationship between the M-type functions and the $Y(\ln \tau)$ spectrum:

$$Y(\ln \tau) \approx \frac{dM_1(\ln \omega)}{d(\ln \omega)}\bigg|_{\omega=1/\tau} \approx \frac{2}{\pi}\, M_2(\ln \omega)\bigg|_{\omega=1/\tau} \qquad (4.3\text{-}17)$$

Summarizing the result of the first approximation, we may state that, for broad spectra, the spectrum $X(y)$ is proportional to $J_2(y)$ and to the peak functions obtained by differentiating the sigmoidal functions $J(y)$ and $J_1(y)$; similarly for the M-type functions in relation to $Y(y)$. Thus

$$X(y) \approx (2/\pi)J_2(y) \approx dJ_1(y)/dy \approx dJ(y)/dy \qquad (4.3\text{-}18)$$

and

$$Y(y) \approx (2/\pi)M_2(y) \approx -dM_1(y)/dy \approx -dM(y)/dy \qquad (4.3\text{-}19)$$

An important point is that all of these approximate equalities apply at the same value of y, where y is the natural logarithm of a time variable (either τ, t, or ω^{-1}). Clearly, no approximation of this type can be accurate; the exact integral expression (4.1-5), for example, shows that $J_2(y)$ depends on the values of $X(z)$ over its entire range, not just at $z = y$. Nevertheless, this approximation is useful for obtaining a general picture of the spectrum, and is a useful first approximation for the interconversion among the various response functions (see Section 4.4).

Various authors have tried to improve on the above approximation method to obtain the spectra more accurately from the experimental response functions. We will mention such improvements only briefly since they have had only limited usefulness in dealing with the anelasticity of crystalline materials, and also in view of the availability of the exact relationships (4.3-1)–(4.3-4) for the case of the dynamic functions.

Schwartzl and Staverman (1952, 1953) developed higher approximations for the spectra in terms of the response functions, involving higher differential coefficients. The results obtained, up to the second order of approximation, are given in Table 4-1. In this table the "order of ap-

TABLE 4-1

SCHWARTZL'S APPROXIMATIONS IN ORDER OF INCREASING ACCURACY

Order of Approximation	Approximate formula
A. Expressions for $X(\ln \tau)$	
0	$(2/\pi)J_2(\omega)\,\big|_{\omega=1/\tau}$
1	$[d/d(\ln t)]J(t)\,\big|_{t=\tau}$
1	$-[d/d(\ln \omega)]J_1(\omega)\,\big|_{\omega=1/\tau}$
2	$[d/d(\ln t) - d^2/d(\ln t)^2]J(t)\,\big|_{t=2\tau}$
2	$(2/\pi)[1 - d^2/d(\ln \omega)^2]J_2(\omega)\,\big|_{\omega=1/\tau}$
B. Expressions for $Y(\ln \tau)$	
0	$(2/\pi)M_2(\omega)\,\big|_{\omega=1/\tau}$
1	$-[d/d(\ln t)]M(t)\,\big|_{t=\tau}$
1	$[d/d(\ln \omega)]M_1(\omega)\,\big|_{\omega=1/\tau}$
2	$[-d/d(\ln t) + d^2/d(\ln t)^2]M(t)\,\big|_{t=2\tau}$
2	$(2/\pi)[1 - d^2/d(\ln \omega)^2]M_2(\omega)\,\big|_{\omega=1/\tau}$

proximation" is the order of the highest derivative of the response function in the approximate expression for X or Y. Schwartzl and Staverman describe a test for the quality of any given approximation in terms of its ability to resolve a spectrum of two lines. The results of this test are incorporated into the table by making a listing whereby the further down the relation in the table, the better the quality of the approximation. Thus, among the relations given in Eq. (4.3-18) the one involving the J_1 function is the best. (The fact that the derivative of the J_1 function gives the sharpest peak is apparent from Fig. 4-1 for the case of the standard anelastic solid.) From a practical point of view, second and higher derivatives of an experimental response curve are very sensitive to experimental errors, so that one cannot go too far with this approach.

Other workers have obtained higher-order approximations for the spectra which are somewhat different from those in Table 4-1 (see Ferry, 1958, and Andrews, 1952).

Finally, it should be mentioned that as a consistency check, any spectrum derived from a given response function should be used to calculate the response function from which it was derived, to verify that agreement is obtained to within the experimental error of the data.

4.4 Approximate Relations among Response Functions

With approximate expressions available for the spectra in terms of the response functions, it is easy enough to eliminate the spectra and retain approximate relations between the response functions themselves. Such relations have also been obtained by starting from the exact relations between the response functions given in Chapter 2 (see e.g., Zener, 1948). On the other hand, the approximations are obtained most simply by using the spectra as intermediaries, in the manner of Section 4.3B. Accordingly, we now digress to state these results explicitly. The desired results, which are already contained in Eqs. (4.3-18) and (4.3-19), may be expressed as[†]

$$\frac{dJ(t)}{d(\ln t)}\bigg|_{t=1/\omega} \approx -\frac{dJ_1(\omega)}{d(\ln \omega)} \approx \frac{2}{\pi}J_2(\omega) \qquad (4.4\text{-}1)$$

By combining the first approximate equality in Eq. (4.4-1) with the conditions $J(0) = J_1(\infty) = J_U$ and $J(\infty) = J_1(0) = J_R$, we obtain

$$J(t)\,|_{t=1/\omega} \approx J_1(\omega) \qquad (4.4\text{-}2)$$

The degree to which Eq. (4.4-2) is valid is shown for the worst case of a standard anelastic solid in Fig. 3-5. The agreement, even in this case, is not too bad. On the other hand, the test of Eqs. (4.4-1) is obtained for this same case by comparing the three peaks in Fig. 4-1. Finally, for the

[†] Since experimental plots are usually against $\log_{10} \omega$ as abscissas, it is important to remember in these formulas that $d(\ln t)$ may be replaced by $2.303\, d(\log_{10} t)$, and the same for $d(\ln \omega)$.

internal friction $\tan \phi$ we have

$$\tan \phi(\omega) = \frac{J_2}{J_1} \approx -\frac{\pi}{2} \frac{d[\ln J_1(\omega)]}{d(\ln \omega)} \approx \frac{\pi}{2} \frac{d[\ln J(t)]}{d(\ln t)}\bigg|_{t=1/\omega} \qquad (4.4\text{-}3)$$

Similarly,

$$-\frac{dM(t)}{d(\ln t)}\bigg|_{t=1/\omega} \approx \frac{dM_1(\omega)}{d(\ln \omega)} \approx \frac{2}{\pi} M_2(\omega) \qquad (4.4\text{-}4)$$

gives the approximate relation between $M(t)$, $M_1(\omega)$, and $M_2(\omega)$. From the first approximate equality in Eq. (4.4-4) we obtain, by analogy to Eq. (4.4-2),

$$M(t)\,|_{t=1/\omega} \approx M_1(\omega) \qquad (4.4\text{-}5)$$

and for the internal friction

$$\tan \phi(\omega) = \frac{M_2}{M_1} \approx \frac{\pi}{2} \frac{d[\ln M_1(\omega)]}{d(\ln \omega)} \approx -\frac{\pi}{2} \frac{d[\ln M(t)]}{d(\ln t)}\bigg|_{t=1/\omega} \qquad (4.4\text{-}6)$$

The following important approximate relation is derived by combining the two expressions for $\tan \phi(\omega)$ given by Eqs. (4.4-3) and (4.4-6), remembering that $J_U = M_U^{-1}$ and $J_R = M_R^{-1}$:

$$J(t)M(t) \approx 1 \qquad (4.4\text{-}7)$$

It is interesting to compare this result with the more general result (2.2-4). In an analogous way one can derive the result $M_1(\omega)J_1(\omega) \approx 1$. This latter result has already been shown to be valid to within terms in ϕ^2 [see Eq. (1.3-14a)]. The condition that $\phi^2 \ll 1$ for all ω is obeyed in two important cases: (1) when the relaxation spectrum is slowly varying, as in the present approximation (see Problem 4-5); and (2) when the relaxation strength is small ($\Delta^2 \ll 1$), even for a single relaxation [see Eq. (3.4-14)]. From the results of Eq. (4.4-7), and of Problem 2-2, it is clear that $J(t)M(t) \approx 1$ in these same two cases. In view of the complexity of the exact relationship between $J(t)$ and $M(t)$ [see Eq. (2.2-1) or (2.2-2)], Eq. (4.4-7) can be quite useful as a bridge between the J-type and M-type functions when the spectral distribution is reasonably broad (see, e.g., Problem 4-6).

Experimentally, Eqs. (4.4-5)–(4.4-7) have been tested by Kê (1947a)

---

† Actually Kê tested the relations derived by Zener (by using a somewhat different approximation method) which differ from Eqs. (4.4-5) and (4.4-6) by having $t = (\pi/4)\omega^{-1}$ instead of $t = \omega^{-1}$. This difference is too slight to be significant experimentally.

and found to be valid to within experimental error for the grain-boundary relaxation effect in aluminum, as shown in Fig. 4-2. These data correspond to a relaxation spectrum covering about three decades in τ. In another application of these results, Eq. (4.4-3) has also been used by Kê and Zener (1950) and by Nowick (1951a) to convert creep to internal friction, in a range where the latter measurements could not be carried out conveniently.

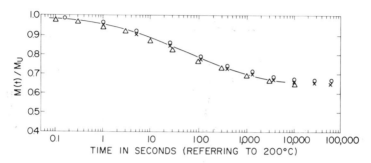

FIG. 4-2. Comparison of $M(t)$ for the grain boundary relaxation in Al as observed directly (solid curve) and as calculated from Eqs. (4.4-5), (4.4-6), and (4.4-7) using dynamic modulus ($\bigcirc$), internal friction ($\times$) and creep data ($\triangle$). (After Kê, 1947a.)

More precise relations between response functions than those quoted in this section may be obtained by using next higher approximations (or order two) from Table 4-1, again eliminating the spectra. As already stated, the difficulty in using such relations is that they require derivatives higher than the first, which are difficult to obtain with precision from experimental curves.

4.5 Indirect or Empirical Methods for the Determination of Spectra

In Section 4.3, we attacked the problem of obtaining the relaxation spectrum starting from a given response function. We now approach this problem in a different way, which is much less direct but often quite useful. The procedure is as follows: (1) A guess is made at a reasonable mathematical form for a spectral distribution function which contains an arbitrary parameter (the "distribution parameter"). (2) The corresponding response functions are derived. (3) An attempt is made to fit the derived functions to the experimental data by adjusting the arbitrary parameter as well as the value of δJ or δM. If the method is successful, i.e., if data for a particular response function matches the theoretical expression within experimental error, we can then use the assumed distribution function with the empirical value of the distribution parameter to compute the other response functions. The chief advantage of the method is that, when applicable, it permits the use of one distribution parameter to characterize the material. Also, it does not require that an analytic expression be found to represent the experimental data, a process which is not always easy to carry out. Instead, the indirect method furishes a mathematical form for the response function which may be tried out against the data.

A large number of distribution functions that have been used may be found in the literature; a rather complete listing of such functions has been given by Gross (1953, Chap. XIII). In the present section just two such functions will be examined. Both represent symmetrical distributions in the variable $z = \ln(\tau/\tau_m)$ centered at the value $z = 0$, which corresponds to $\tau = \tau_m$, (i.e., τ_m is defined as the logarithmic mean relaxation time). Consequently, both are associated with symmetrical $J_2(\ln \omega)$ peaks.

A. The Box Distribution

As the name implies, the box distribution function is constant within a given range of z and zero outside. This is the most artificial of the distributions to be considered, but it is nevertheless useful because the response functions obtained from it can be expressed in terms of well-tabulated functions. It was first introduced by Becker and Döring (1939, p. 254) in discussing magnetic relaxation processes in ferromagnetic materials and later used by a number of workers in the field of viscoelasticity of polymers (see Tobolsky, 1960). This distribution function may be applied either to the relaxation spectrum at constant stress or at constant strain (but, in general, not to both). For purposes of illustration, we will use this distribution for the normalized spectrum $\Psi(\ln \tau)$. The definition of the box distribution is then

$$\Psi(z) \equiv X(z)/\delta J = \begin{cases} 0, & \text{for} \quad z > \gamma \\ (2\gamma)^{-1}, & \text{for} \quad -\gamma < z < \gamma \\ 0, & \text{for} \quad z < -\gamma \end{cases} \quad (4.5\text{-}1)$$

where

$$z = \ln(\tau/\tau_m) \quad (4.5\text{-}2)$$

The parameter γ then has the significance of the half-width of the box

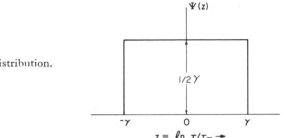

FIG. 4-3.   The box distribution.

distribution, as shown in Fig. 4-3. The value $1/2\gamma$ for $\Psi(z)$ is that required by the normalization condition (4.1-13). Substituting Eq. (4.5-1) into Eq. (4.1-4) and introducing

$$x = \ln \omega\tau_m \qquad (4.5\text{-}3)$$

so that $\omega\tau = \exp(x + z)$ gives, after integration, the following expression for the normalized J_1 function:

$$\frac{J_1(x) - J_U}{\delta J} = 1 - \frac{1}{4\gamma} \ln\left[\frac{1 + e^{2(x+\gamma)}}{1 + e^{2(x-\gamma)}}\right] = F_1(x, \gamma) \qquad (4.5\text{-}4)$$

The J_2 function obtained from Eq. (4.1-5) combined with Eqs. (4.5-1)-(4.5-3) is given by

$$J_2(x)/\delta J = (1/2\gamma)[\tan^{-1} e^{(x+\gamma)} - \tan^{-1} e^{(x-\gamma)}] = F_2(x, \gamma) \qquad (4.5\text{-}5)$$

The functions $F_1(x, \gamma)$ and $F_2(x, \gamma)$ defined by these equations are readily calculated numerically. For practical purposes it is more convenient to calculate these functions for the variable x' defined by

$$x' = \log_{10} \omega\tau_m = x/2.303 \qquad (4.5\text{-}6)$$

since experimental data are usually plotted versus $\log_{10} \omega$. As γ increases, the function $F_1(x)$ falls more and more gradually, but always has the value $\frac{1}{2}$ when $x = 0$, as may be verified directly from Eq. (4.5-4). In the case of the J_2 (or F_2) function, the peak always occurs at $x = 0$ (i.e., $\omega\tau_m = 1$), but its height decreases as γ increases. Correspondingly, the peaks become broader. For the limit $\gamma \to 0$, it is readily shown that the F_2 function approaches the form sech x, characteristic of the standard anelastic solid.

To calculate the creep function for a box distribution, we introduce the variable

$$y \equiv \ln(t/\tau_m) \tag{4.5-7}$$

and substitute Eqs. (4.5-1), (4.5-2), and (4.5-7) into Eq. (4.1-3), so that $t/\tau = e^{y-z}$. The normalized creep function is

$$1 - \psi(y) = (-1/2\gamma) \int_{e^{y+\gamma}}^{e^{y-\gamma}} u^{-1} e^{-u} \, du = F_3(y, \gamma)$$

$$= (1/2\gamma)[Ei(-e^{y+\gamma}) - Ei(-e^{y-\gamma})] \tag{4.5-8}$$

where

$$-Ei(-p) = \int_p^\infty u^{-1} e^{-u} \, du, \qquad 0 < u < \infty \tag{4.5-9}$$

is the well-known and fully tabulated[†] exponential integral function. For graphical use, it is convenient to use the variable

$$y' = \log_{10} t/\tau_m = y/2.303 \tag{4.5-10}$$

Again, it may readily be shown that as $\gamma \to 0$, the function F_3 degenerates into that characteristic of a single relaxation time, viz., $\exp(-e^y)$.

Equations (4.5-4), (4.5-5), and (4.5-8) give the J-type response functions when the distribution function $\Psi(z)$ for the relaxation time at constant stress is the box distribution, Eq. (4.5-1). In an analogous way, if the distribution function $\Phi(z)$ for the relaxation time at constant strain is given by Eq. (4.5-1), we obtain for the M-type response functions

$$[M_U - M_1(x)]/\delta M = F_1(x, \gamma)$$
$$M_2(x)/\delta M = F_2(x, \gamma) \tag{4.5-11}$$
$$\varphi(y) = F_3(y, \gamma)$$

where the functions F_1, F_2, and F_3 are exactly those defined by Eqs. (4.5-4), (4.5-5), and (4.5-8), respectively.

B. THE GAUSSIAN (LOGNORMAL) DISTRIBUTION

The chief advantage in the use of the box distribution is that it yields expressions for the response functions in terms of tabulated functions. Its disadvantage, however, lies in its artificiality, namely, that no physical

---

[†] See "Tables of Sine, Cosine and Exponential Integrals," WPA Tables, New York, 1940.

system can be expected to display a sharp cutoff in the participating relaxation times. Accordingly, it is desirable to find a more realistic distribution function. The choice of a Gaussian distribution in $\ln \tau$ was made by Wiechert as early as 1893, in an attempt to interpret elastic aftereffect functions which were much different from a simple exponential. It was also used later by Wagner (1913) to interpret dielectric relaxation phenomena. This distribution (also called the "lognormal distribution") may be defined by

$$\left.\begin{array}{l} \Psi(z) \\ \text{or} \\ \Phi(z) \end{array}\right\} = \beta^{-1}\pi^{-1/2}\exp[-(z/\beta)^2] \qquad (4.5\text{-}12)$$

The factor in front of the exponential is the normalizing factor, while the parameter β is a measure of the width of the distribution since, for $z = \beta$, $\Psi(z) = \Psi(0)/e$. The quantity 2β is then the width of the distribution at relative height $1/e$, as illustrated in Fig. 4-4. The parameter β

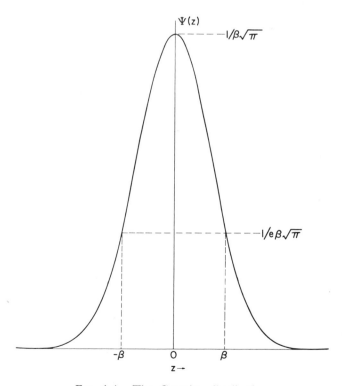

Fig. 4-4. The Gaussian distribution.

is therefore equivalent to the parameter γ of the box distribution (see Fig. 4-3). If the distribution of relaxation times at constant stress (the Ψ function) is given by Eq. (4.5-12) we obtain for the J-type dynamic response functions (putting $w = z/\beta$)

$$[J_1(x) - J_U]/\delta J = \pi^{-1/2} \int_{-\infty}^{\infty} e^{-w^2}[1 + e^{2(x+\beta w)}]^{-1} \, dw \equiv f_1(x, \beta) \quad (4.5\text{-}13)$$

$$J_2(x)/\delta J = (2\pi^{1/2})^{-1} \int_{-\infty}^{\infty} e^{-w^2} \operatorname{sech}(x + \beta w) \, dw \equiv f_2(x, \beta) \quad (4.5\text{-}14)$$

and for the normalized creep function

$$1 - \psi(y) = \pi^{1/2} \int_{-\infty}^{\infty} e^{-w^2} \exp[-e^{(y-\beta w)}] \, dw \equiv g(y, \beta) \quad (4.5\text{-}15)$$

where the variables x and y are again those defined by Eqs. (4.5-3) and

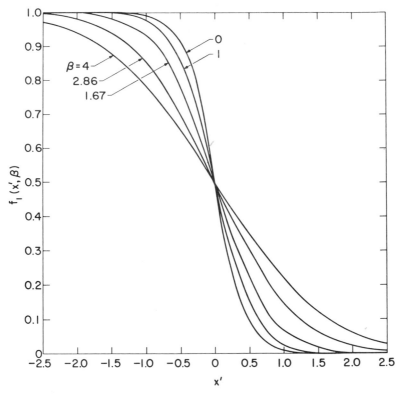

FIG. 4-5.   The function $f_1(x', \beta)$ for various values of the distribution parameter β. (After Yager, 1936.)

(4.5-7), respectively. In a similar way, if the distribution function $\Phi(z)$ obeys Eq. (4.5-12), we obtain a set of equations similar to Eq. (4.5-11) with $F_1(x, \gamma)$, $F_2(x, \gamma)$, and $F_3(y, \gamma)$ replaced by $f_1(x, \beta)$, $f_2(x, \beta)$, and $g(y, \beta)$, respectively.

Until recently, the chief disadvantage of the lognormal distribution had been that the response functions obtained from it were not expressible in terms of tabulated functions. This disadvantage has been largely eliminated by the numerical calculation of the functions f_1, f_2, and g. Wiechert (1893) carried out some computations of g in his early paper, while Yager (1936) computed f_1 and f_2 as a function of x' for a limited set of β values. Figure 4-5, taken from Yager, shows the variation of f_1 with x' ($= x/2.303$) for various values of β. Nowick and Berry (1961a) have computed the functions $f_2(x', \beta)$ and $g(y', \beta)$ at close intervals of the variables x' and y' ($= y/2.303$) and with values of β ranging in small steps between 0 and 7. Tables of these functions are given in Appendix G. In addition, Fig. 4-6 shows normalized plots of $f_2(x', \beta)$ versus x' for various values of β. The case of $\beta = 0$ corresponds to the

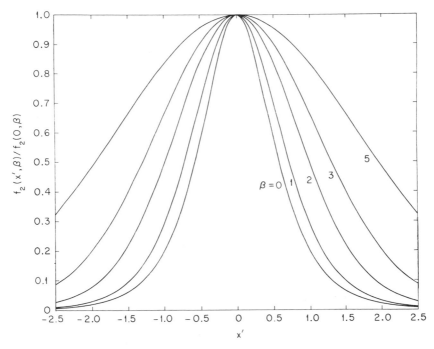

FIG. 4-6.   Normalized plots of $f_2(x', \beta)$ for various values of the distribution parameter β.

standard anelastic solid, i.e., the peak for this value is a Debye peak with width at half maximum $\Delta x'$ given by Eq. (3.4-4), or

$$\Delta x'(0) = 1.144 \qquad\qquad (4.5\text{-}16)$$

With increasing β, the peak width increases, while the peak height $f_2(0, \beta)$ decreases. Figure 4-7 shows the variation with β of the relative peak width $r_2(\beta)$ defined by

$$r_2(\beta) \equiv \Delta x'(\beta)/\Delta x'(0) \qquad\qquad (4.5\text{-}17)$$

and twice the peak height $2f_2(0, \beta)$. Table 4-2 lists numerical values for these two quantities as a function of β up to $\beta = 5$. For higher values, asymptotic forms of these functions given by Nowick and Berry (1961a) are useful.

Because of the wide applicability of the lognormal distribution we shall discuss how to obtain the three appropriate parameters starting from experimental data for the various response functions. We begin

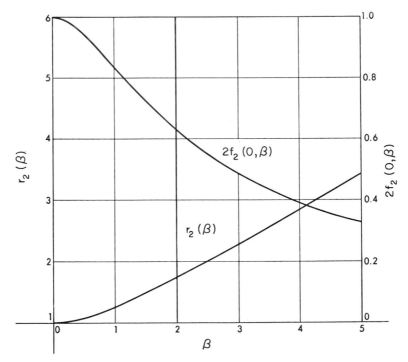

FIG. 4-7.   Dependence of the relative peak height $2f_2(0, \beta)$ and the relative peak width $r_2(\beta)$, on the distribution parameter β.

by considering the J_2 peak. From the experimental peak width and the $r_2(\beta)$ function, given in Fig. 4-7 or Table 4-2, a value of β can be determined. This value of β then gives a value for $f_2(0, \beta)$ which may be compared with the measured peak height $J_2(0) = \delta J f_2(0, \beta)$ to give the value of δJ. The third parameter τ_m is obtained from the condition that $\omega \tau_m = 1$ at the peak. Thus, it is possible to obtain the three parameters τ_m, β, and δJ from the peak location, width, and height, respectively. It is then necessary to test the lognormal distribution by comparing the *entire*

TABLE 4-2

RESULTS OF NUMERICAL COMPUTATIONS FOR THE
DEPENDENCE OF RELATIVE PEAK HEIGHT $2f_2(0, \beta)$ AND
RELATIVE PEAK WIDTH $r_2(\beta)$ ON THE DISTRIBUTION
PARAMETER β

β	$2f_2(0, \beta)$	$r_2(\beta)$
0.00	1.00000	1.00000
0.10	0.99752	1.00327
0.20	0.99024	1.01296
0.30	0.97866	1.02866
0.40	0.96346	1.04981
0.50	0.94540	1.07576
0.60	0.92520	1.10585
0.70	0.90350	1.13946
0.80	0.88088	1.17605
0.90	0.85774	1.21515
1.50	0.83448	1.25637
1.20	0.77722	1.36670
1.50	0.72316	1.48480
1.75	0.67332	1.60849
2.00	0.62798	1.73640
2.25	0.58698	1.86763
2.50	0.54998	2.00159
2.75	0.51664	2.13783
3.00	0.48654	2.27602
3.25	0.45934	2.41590
3.50	0.43466	2.55727
3.75	0.41224	2.69996
4.00	0.39182	2.84382
4.25	0.37314	2.98873
4.50	0.35604	3.13459
4.75	0.34032	3.28130
5.00	0.32584	3.42879

experimental curve with a calculated curve, i.e., with an interpolation of the functions given in Appendix G. In a similar way, values of the same three parameters can be obtained from measurements of the J_1 function. In particular, β can be obtained from the range which variable x' covers when J_1 goes from 0.25 to 0.75 of its total change δJ (see Nowick and Berry, 1961a, Fig. 4).

Finally, we turn to the problem of obtaining the relaxation parameters from quasi-static measurements, for which the function $g(y', \beta)$ has been calculated. Figure 4-8 shows this function for some representative β values. It is convenient to define a quantity $\Delta y'$ which measures the range of rapid decrease of the creep function, and which is defined as the difference in the variable y' $(= \log_{10} t/\tau_m)$ between the point at which $\psi = 0.75$ (or $g = 0.25$) and that at which $\psi = 0.25$ (or $g = 0.75$). For the case of the standard anelastic solid $(\beta = 0)$ $\Delta y' = 0.683$ [see Eq. (3.4-17)]. The dependence of $\Delta y'$ on β is shown in Fig. 4-9. This plot may be used to obtain β from the experimental value $\Delta y'$. The quantity δJ is obtained from the total creep $J(\infty) - J_U$. The problem of obtaining the mean relaxation time τ_m is not as simple here as it is for the dynamic

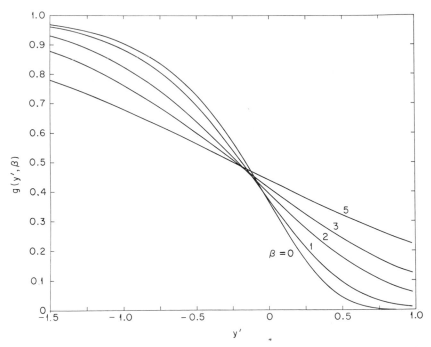

FIG. 4-8.   Plots of the function $g(y', \beta)$ versus y' for various values of the distribution parameter β.

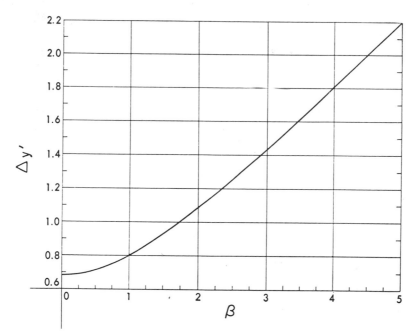

FIG. 4-9.   Dependence of $\Delta y'$ on β for the g function.

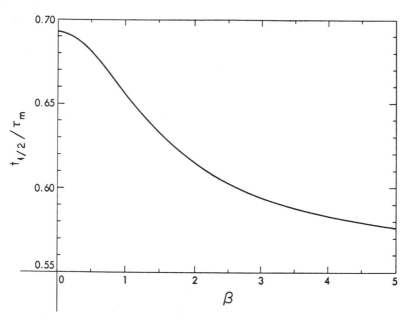

FIG. 4-10.   Dependence of $t_{1/2}/\tau_{\mathrm{m}}$ on the distribution parameter β.

functions, since $\psi(y)$ is not symmetric about $y = 0$. To obtain τ_m, it is convenient to work with the quantity $t_{1/2}$, defined as the time for ψ to reach the value $\frac{1}{2}$. For the standard anelastic solid, where $\psi = 1 - \exp(-t/\tau)$, it is clear that $t_{1/2} = \tau(\ln 2)$, or $\tau = 1.44t_{1/2}$. More generally, the variation of $t_{1/2}/\tau_m$ with β is given in Fig. 4-10. This plot may be used to determine τ_m once β is known from the observed value of $\Delta y'$ (Fig. 4-9). The variation of $t_{1/2}/\tau_m$ with β is by no means negligible, and must be considered where precise values of τ_m are desired (as, e.g., in obtaining an accurate value for the activation energy governing the quantity τ_m). Again, the final step is to check the data against a complete calculated curve, as obtained from Appendix G for the selected value of β.

4.6 Remarks on the Use of Direct and Indirect Methods

The direct and indirect methods for calculation of the spectra differ with regard to their starting points. The direct method starts from a response function, presumably in the form of a graph. If the spectrum is broad, i.e., if the response function does not change appreciably over a decade in the independent variable (t or ω), then the spectrum may be calculated directly by the approximation methods of Section 4.3B. If the spectrum is not very broad, it is necessary to find some analytic form for the response function. If such a function can be found, one can then obtain the spectrum by one of the methods discussed in Section 4.3A. On the other hand, the indirect or empirical method starts from the spectrum and then derives the response functions, as in Eqs. (4.5-4), (4.5-5), (4.5-8), and (4.5-13)–(4.5-15). Once the appropriate response functions corresponding to a given distribution function are calculated, however, (as, e.g., in Fig. 4-5, 4-6, or 4-8), the results may be used in a direct fashion. For this purpose, the response functions derived from the box or lognormal distributions are especially well worth trying for two reasons. First, if such a distribution for a given parameter should fit the data, the distribution function is immediately known. Second, these distribution functions are conveniently describable in terms of a single parameter (γ or β, respectively). This offers the advantage that, no matter how broad the spectrum, the complete description of the behavior of the system requires only one parameter in addition to those which are required to describe the standard anelastic solid. For these reasons, the use of simple empirical distribution functions has achieved widespread popularity. (Of course, this scheme implicitly requires that the particular type of response function, with *some* value of the distribution parameter, must fit the data within experimental error over the entire curve.)

On the other hand, it must be realized that just because a given distribution function accounts for the observed behavior of the specimen, it does not follow that this function uniquely characterizes the material. To illustrate this point, we consider the example of a J_2 peak which is symmetric in ln ω and whose width at half maximum is 1.56 times that of the standard anelastic solid. Let us see what happens when this peak is fitted to three different (symmetric) distribution functions considered in this chapter, namely, the Fuoss–Kirkwood [Eqs. (4.3-5) and (4.3-6)], the lognormal, and the box distributions. In each case there are three parameters to be fitted: δJ, τ_m, and the distribution parameter (α, β, or γ, respectively). The distribution parameter in each case is first obtained by matching the theoretical curves to the peak width. Next, we could take the area under the curve to obtain δJ. This is not too practical an approach, however, since in experimental situations the tails of the peak may not go to zero due to the onset of relaxation phenomena other than the one of interest. Instead, it is more convenient to fit the theoretical curves to the peak value of the function J_2. Finally, the location in frequency of this peak gives the third parameter τ_m, independently of which distribution is selected. The three distribution functions, so fitted to give the same height and width of the J_2 peak, are shown in Fig. 4-11. Note that these three distributions are very different, the Fuoss–Kirkwood being the most sharply peaked and the box distribution the broadest of the three. On the other hand, the corresponding response functions $J_2(\ln \omega)$, which are plotted in Fig. 4-12, are very nearly the same unless one chooses to go well into the tails of the peaks. It is therefore concluded that the response function $J_2(\ln \omega)$, in this range of relatively narrow distributions, is insensitive to the choice of the distribution function. The value of δJ obtained by fitting to the peak height, described above, is somewhat dependent on the choice of the distribution (see Problem 4-8). In the absence of further information to distinguish among distributions, the present authors have favored use of the lognormal distribution, first, because it is realistic in many physical situations and second, because it is compatible with a distribution in activation energies (see Section 4.7).

For much broader distributions, it is already clear from Eq. (4.3-16) that the J_2 peak becomes essentially the same as the distribution function. Under these circumstances, widely different distributions must show striking differences in $J_2(\ln \omega)$. The best procedures in such cases of broad distributions is to use the approximation methods of Section 4.3B.

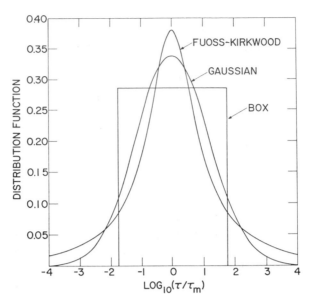

FIG. 4-11.   Comparison of three distribution functions which produce J_2 peaks of the same width (1.56 times that of the standard anelastic solid).

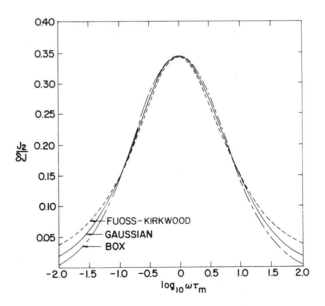

FIG. 4-12.   Comparison of the shape of the J_2 peaks corresponding to the three distribution functions of Fig. 4-11.

4.7   Restrictions on the Form of Distribution Functions for Thermally Activated Processes

Until now, we have dealt with a distribution in relaxation times as the fundamental function which determines anelastic behavior. At this point we recall the Arrhenius equation (3.5-2) for the relaxation time τ, which applies when the relaxation is controlled by a thermally activated process. The quantity $\ln \tau$ may then be written

$$\ln \tau = \ln \tau_0 + (Q/kT) \qquad (4.7\text{-}1)$$

This equation serves to relate τ to the more fundamental parameters τ_0 and Q. In fact, it is apparent from Eq. (4.7-1) that, for such thermally activated processes, the occurrence of a distribution in the relaxation times may reflect the existence of a distribution in τ_0, in Q, or in both of these quantities. The remainder of this chapter will deal with the consequences of this statement, first in its effect on the distribution functions and then on the corresponding response functions.

Consider the case of a distribution in activation energies. If the corresponding distribution of relaxation times has the same functional form (allowing for changes in the values of parameters) at different temperatures, it will be said to be *compatible* with the existence of a distribution of activation energies. The requirement of compatibility puts severe restrictions on the form of the distribution function, and in fact most of the commonly used distribution functions do not meet this criterion. We now show that a sufficient condition for compatibility of $\Psi(\ln \tau)$ with a distribution of activation energies is for the function Ψ to depend on $\ln \tau$ through the composite variable $b^{-1} \ln(\tau/\tau_m)$, where b is a temperature dependent distribution parameter which appears only in the above composite variable and in the normalization constant,[†] and τ_m is some particular value from the spectrum (e.g., the most probable relaxation time). Thus, for a distribution in Q only, each value of $\ln \tau$ obeys Eq. (4.7-1) with the same τ_0 but a different value of Q. In particular τ_m then obeys the equation

$$\ln \tau_m = \ln \tau_0 + (Q_m/kT) \qquad (4.7\text{-}2)$$

[†] Actually Ψ must take the form $\Psi(z) = b^{-1} F(b^{-1} z)$ [where z is given by Eq. (4.5-2)] to maintain the normalization condition.

The composite variable $b^{-1}\ln(\tau/\tau_m)$ is then given by

$$b^{-1}\ln(\tau/\tau_m) = (1/bkT)(Q - Q_m) \qquad (4.7\text{-}3)$$

The distribution function Ψ, which may be written

$$\Psi[(1/bkT)(Q - Q_m)] \qquad (4.7\text{-}4)$$

then has the same functional form for all temperatures, provided that bT is a constant, or $b \propto 1/T$. This result is then in accord with our definition of compatibility.

   The reader can easily verify that this compatibility condition is obeyed for the box and lognormal distributions, noting that in the case of the box distribution the parameter b becomes γ while in the lognormal case it becomes β (see Problem 4-9). On the other hand, the condition is not obeyed for many of the well-known distribution functions (Macdonald, 1962a). For example, it is easy to see that the Fuoss–Kirkwood distribution, Eq. (4.3-6), is not compatible with a distribution of activation energies. Accordingly, if that distribution function were to apply at one temperature, it cannot be valid at other temperatures. Clearly, such a distribution function is of limited use for treating relaxations which are controlled by thermally activated processes. The usefulness of the lognormal distribution stems in part from its compatibility. However, the lognormal distribution is symmetrical in $\ln \tau$, and some experimental data call for a distribution function which is asymmetrical and at the same time compatible with a distribution in activation energies. Macdonald (1962a) has suggested such a function in the form of a power law in τ. For further details, the reader is referred to Macdonald's papers (1962a, 1963).

4.8   Temperature Dependence of the Gaussian Distribution Parameter

   It was shown in the previous section that for a distribution in $\ln \tau$ which originates in a distribution of activation energies and which depends on the composite variable $b^{-1}\ln(\tau/\tau_m)$, the distribution parameter b varies as T^{-1}. In the specific case of a lognormal distribution, b becomes the Gaussian distribution parameter β, and

$$\beta = \beta_Q/kT \qquad (4.8\text{-}1)$$

It is readily shown (see Problem 4-10) that the distribution of Q values in this case is Gaussian, and that the β_Q in Eq. (4.8-1) is simply the distribution parameter for the activation energies.

A strikingly different result is found when the distribution in $\ln \tau$ arises, not from a distribution in Q, but entirely from a distribution in $\ln \tau_0$. Under these circumstances, it can be shown quite generally (see Problem 4-11) that the distribution function Ψ is independent of temperature. Thus, in particular, if $\ln \tau_0$ is distributed according to a Gaussian distribution with parameter β_0, the distribution of $\ln \tau$ will also be Gaussian with parameter

$$\beta = \beta_0 \tag{4.8-2}$$

In this case, therefore, the distribution parameter β is independent of the temperature. It is thus possible to distinguish a distribution of activation energies from a distribution of frequency factors (i.e., of τ_0) by the temperature dependence of the distribution parameter.

The intermediate case where a distribution exists for *both* Q and $\ln \tau_0$ is more complex, since further information is needed concerning the interrelation between Q and $\ln \tau_0$. We will here confine ourselves only to the lognormal distribution, since this is the one which has been most widely applied to such cases.[†] Nowick and Berry (1961a) have considered the case in which $\ln \tau_0$ and Q do not vary independently but both depend linearly on a single internal variable (e.g., local composition or local order). It can then be shown (see Problem 4-12) that if the internal variable is distributed in a Gaussian manner, both the variables Q and $\ln \tau_0$ will have a Gaussian distribution, the former with parameter β_Q and the latter with parameter β_0. Further, the variable $\ln \tau$ also obeys a Gaussian distribution with variable β given by

$$\beta = |\,\beta_0 \pm (\beta_Q/kT)\,| \tag{4.8-3}$$

Clearly this result yields Eqs. (4.8-1) and (4.8-2) for the special cases considered earlier. The plus sign occurs in Eq. (4.8-3) if the quantities $\ln \tau_0$ and Q both increase and decrease together with a change in the internal variable, while the minus sign occurs when $\ln \tau_0$ and Q vary oppositely from each other.

The above assumption of the interdependence of τ_0 and Q via an internal variable is, of course, not the only reasonable one to consider.

[†] Macdonald (1962b) has dealt with the problem under more general considerations.

In the other extreme, we may assume that $\ln \tau_0$ and Q are distributed independently of each other, each in a Gaussian manner. In this case, β is related to β_0 and β_Q by

$$\beta^2 = \beta_0{}^2 + (\beta_Q/kT)^2 \qquad (4.8\text{-}4)$$

This result is obtained from the theory of multivariate distributions.[†] Experimentally, it is rather difficult to distinguish between Eqs. (4.8-3) and (4.8-4) for the range of data usually available. It has been argued, however (Nowick and Berry, 1961a), that the interdependence of $\ln \tau_0$ and Q via an internal variable is often a more realistic assumption than that of complete independence. Figure 4-13 shows an illustration of some

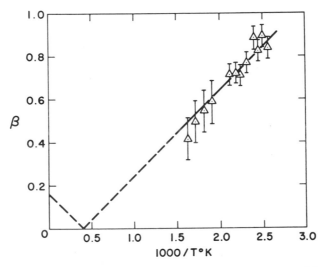

FIG. 4-13.   Temperature dependence of the distribution parameter β for the Zener relaxation in the alloy Ag–24 at % Zn. (From Berry and Orehotsky, 1968a.)

careful measurements of the variation of β with temperature for the case of the Zener relaxation (Chapter 10). Within experimental error, these measurements fit Eq. (4.8-3) with the negative sign on the right-hand side. The point at which the line intersects the abscissa corresponds to a temperature at which the distributions in $\ln \tau_0$ and in Q so compensate each other that all τ values are the same, i.e., the material behaves as a standard anelastic solid. The possibility of this exceptional situation was first pointed out by Macdonald (1962b).

[†] See, e.g., Condon and Odishaw (1958, Part I, Chap. 12, pp. 1–149).

4.9   Dynamic Properties as Functions of Temperature

In Section 3.5 we showed how the dynamic response of a standard anelastic solid could be studied as a function of $1/T$ instead of as a function of $\ln \omega\tau$. This approach was based on the validity of the Arrhenius equation for τ^{-1}, which results in the linear relation between $\ln \omega\tau$ and $1/T$ given by Eq. (3.5-3). Because of this linear relation, it followed that the dynamic response functions versus $1/T$ (at constant frequency) were similar to those versus $\ln \omega$ (at constant T), except for a scale factor of Q/k. The great convenience in studying dynamic response functions by varying temperature instead of frequency makes it now desirable to consider the more general situation of a continuous spectrum. First, however, it should be noted that there are several factors which present complications in the precise analysis of the dynamical data to obtain such basic parameters as the relaxation magnitude δJ, the most probable relaxation time τ_m, and the distribution parameter. These complications arise from the following facts: (a) $\tan \phi$ rather than J_2 is usually the experimentally measured quantity; (b) δJ is itself a function of T; (c) dynamical experiments by the resonant method are carried out at constant inertia (rather than at constant frequency) so that, due to the temperature dependence of J_1, ω is a slowly varying function of temperature; (d) the appropriate distribution parameter is generally a function of temperature. The first three of these complications occur for the standard anelastic solid as well as for the case where a spectrum of relaxation times is operative. These complications will not be dealt with here, but the corrections which must be made for these various factors have been considered in detail by Nowick and Berry (1961b) for cases of relatively narrow distributions. It was found that factors (a), (b), and (d) have the effect of requiring a small correction to the location of the J_2 peak but, to first order, no correction to the width. On the other hand, factor (c) has just the reverse effect.

With this aside, we proceed to the important question of how to obtain the appropriate activation energy from dynamical data measured as a function of temperature. The discussion will not be limited to any special distribution function, such as the lognormal. It will be limited, however, to the two simple cases where (a) the distribution is only in the quantity $\ln \tau_0$, and (b) where the distribution is only in the activation energy Q.

Case of a τ_0 Distribution Only

We will deal here with a distribution in $\ln \tau$ that is due only to the existence of a distribution in frequency factors, i.e., in $\ln \tau_0$, and where the activation energy Q is the same for all contributing relaxation processes. In the notation used in Section 4.5, we put $z = \ln(\tau/\tau_m)$ and $x = \ln \omega \tau_m$, where τ_m is some specific value in the distribution, e.g., the most probable value. The specific case of the J_2 function will be selected here, although it will be clear that the same general conclusions can be drawn for the other dynamic functions (see Problem 4-13). Substituting the above definitions of z and x into Eq. (4.1-5) and using (4.1-11), we obtain

$$J_2(x)/\delta J = \tfrac{1}{2} \int_{-\infty}^{\infty} \Psi(z) \operatorname{sech}(z + x) \, dz \qquad (4.9\text{-}1)$$

As yet, the fact that the distribution is in $\ln \tau_0$ and that Q is a constant, has not been employed. This assumption means that $\tau/\tau_m = \tau_0/\tau_{0m}$, where τ_{0m} is the value of τ_0 which corresponds to τ_m. It therefore follows that z is equal to $\ln(\tau_0/\tau_{0m})$. Consequently, $\Psi(z)$ is also the distribution function for $\ln(\tau_0/\tau_{0m})$ which, by definition, is temperature independent. Thus, in the integrand of Eq. (4.9-1), temperature and frequency appear only in the variable x, i.e., as the product $\omega e^{Q/kT}$. It is concluded that when the function J_2 is plotted versus $\ln \omega$ (after normalizing, to take into account the temperature dependence of δJ), the curves for two different temperatures T_1 and T_2 are displaced from each other along the abscissa by a constant amount $\delta \ln \omega = (Q/k)(T_1^{-1} - T_2^{-1})$. A more important conclusion, on the other hand, is that $J_2/\delta J$ can be plotted versus $1/T$ at constant frequency to obtain a curve of similar form to the plot versus $\ln \omega$, except for the scale factor Q/k. Further, the curves versus $1/T$ for two different frequencies are displaced from each other by a constant increment in the abscissa, $\delta(1/T)$, given by the relation $\ln(\omega_2/\omega_1) = (Q/k) \, \delta(1/T)$ which is the same as Eq. (3.5-6) for the standard anelastic solid. From this shift in the curves with frequency the value of Q may be obtained, just as for the standard anelastic solid (cf. Fig. 3-12).

In summary, the above discussion shows that a normalized dynamic function, plotted versus $1/T$, is uniformly displaced in $1/T$ over the entire curve when the frequency is changed. It is now clear that this result is characteristic of a unique activation energy, regardless of whether a single relaxation time or a distribution of relaxation times is involved. In fact, if the data cover a wide enough range of temperature, the degree to which the shift with frequency $\delta(1/T)$ is the same over the entire curve may be used as a measure of the validity of the assumption that the distribution is in τ_0 only.

Case of a Q Distribution Only

When the distribution is in the activation energy, we no longer find as simple a result as in the last section. The fundamental distribution, which is assumed to be independent of T, is the distribution in Q about a convenient value Q_m, e.g., the most probable value. Let $G(Q - Q_m)$ represent this distribution function, in the sense that $G(Q - Q_m) \, dQ$ is the probability for Q values in the range from Q to $Q + dQ$. This reflects itself in the distribution $\Psi(z)$, so that $\Psi(z) \, dz = G(Q - Q_m) \, dQ$.[†] Noting from the Arrhenius relation that $z = (Q - Q_m)/kT$, we may write

$$\Psi(z) = kTG(kT z) \qquad (4.9\text{-}2)$$

This equation shows that the width of the distribution in z is proportional to $1/T$, as we have already seen in (4.8-1). Inserting Eq. (4.9-2) into (4.9-1), we see that $J_2/\delta J$ is no longer a function of T through the variable x alone, but that T now also appears explicitly. In order to obtain a simple result we shall restrict ourselves to the case of a broad distribution, i.e., sufficiently broad that the approximations of Section 4.3B apply [in particular Eq. (4.3-16) for the J_2 function]. Then,

$$J_2(x) \approx \tfrac{1}{2}\pi \, \delta J \, \Psi(-x) = \tfrac{1}{2}\pi \, \delta J \, kTG[kT \ln(\omega\tau_0)^{-1} - Q_m] \qquad (4.9\text{-}3)$$

where z has been set equal to $-x$ ($x = \ln \omega\tau_m$) in accordance with the approximation employed. Equation (4.9-3) defines the dependence of J_2 on both T and ω. Equivalent values of the G function are obtained for T_1 and ω_1 as for T_2 and ω_2, if the values for the argument of this function are the same, or when

$$kT_1 \ln(\omega_1\tau_0)^{-1} - Q_m = kT_2 \ln(\omega_2\tau_0)^{-1} - Q_m = Q - Q_m \qquad (4.9\text{-}4)$$

where Q is the specific value of activation energy for which $\omega_1\tau(T_1)$

[†] The activation energy Q can reasonably run over the range 0 to ∞. This range corresponds to $\ln \tau$ going from $\ln \tau_0$ to ∞ rather than the usual range of $-\infty$ to $+\infty$. Actually, this discrepancy poses no serious problems, since for ordinary values of Q_m the probability function $G(Q - Q_m)$ falls off to extremely small values as $Q \to 0$, so that the lower limit of integration is immaterial.

$= \omega_2\tau(T_2) = 1$. By eliminating Q_m and τ_0 from Eq. (4.9-4) we obtain

$$\ln(\omega_2/\omega_1) = (Q/k)(T_1^{-1} - T_2^{-1}) \qquad (4.9\text{-}5)$$

which is the same condition as Eq. (3.5-6), except that Q is now variable, not constant. Equation (4.9-5), taken together with (4.9-3), then states that the shift $\delta(1/T)$ between plots of $J_2/T \, \delta J$ for two different frequencies, gives the value of Q for that part of the spectrum (i.e., for the value of τ which equals ω^{-1}).[†] The fact that Q is not a constant means that there will be a variation in $\delta(1/T)$ at different positions along the curve. For the case of a broad distribution, the above analysis thus shows that it is possible to map out directly the activation energy spectrum from measurements of J_2, just as it was possible to map out the spectrum $X(\ln \tau)$ directly using Eq. (4.3-16). [See also a somewhat different approach by Kimmel and Uhlmann (1969).]

In a similar way, the analysis given here can be extended to the other dynamic functions $J_1 - J_U$, M_2, and $M_1 - M_R$. However, extension of this analysis to narrow distributions and to the case where distributions exist in both Q and $\ln \tau_0$ has apparently not been carried out. For this reason, the treatment in Section 4.8 is particularly useful in those cases where the lognormal distribution applies, since it is then possible to determine from the data both the distribution in Q and in $\ln \tau_0$, which constitutes all of the relevant information about the anelasticity of the material.

PROBLEMS

4-1. In view of the results of Problem 3-12, which verify the relations derived from the Boltzmann superposition principle for the standard anelastic solid, show that these same relations apply as well to a discrete or a continuous spectrum of relaxation times. This problem then constitutes a separate proof of the validity of the relations obtained in Chapter 2.

4-2. In Eq. (4.3-5) show that the peak width at half-maximum is larger than that of the standard anelastic solid by the factor α^{-1}. Starting with Eq. (4.3-5) derive the Fuoss–Kirkwood distribution function (4.3-6). Integrate this function to obtain (4.3-7).

[†] It is noteworthy that if $\delta J \propto 1/T$, as is often the case (e.g., see Chapter 8), the product $T \, \delta J$ is a constant and the above remarks apply directly to plots of the J_2 function itself.

4-3. Calculate the form of the function $dJ/d(\ln t)$ in Fig. 4-1, and verify that the peak is located at $t = \tau_1$.

4-4. As a consistency check on Eq. (4.3-18), integrate over y from $-\infty$ to $+\infty$ and show that each term becomes equal to δJ.

4-5. Show that if the distribution function $\Psi(z)$ is slowly varying (i.e., breadth of at least several decades) and $\Delta \lesssim 1$ (i.e., δJ is not $\gg J_U$), then $\phi^2 \ll 1$ for all ω. Hint: Start from Eqs. (4.3-13) and (4.3-16).

4-6. Show that under the condition of a slowly varying spectrum where Eq. (4.4-7) relates the creep and relaxation functions, the two distribution functions Ψ and Φ are, in general, not the same. Work out the relation between these two distribution functions for this case.

4-7. Carry out the steps in the derivation of Eqs. (4.5-4), (4.5-5), and (4.5-8) for the box distribution. Show that in all cases letting $\gamma \to 0$ gives the response function for the standard anelastic solid. Also, show that the value of $F_1(0, \gamma) = \frac{1}{2}$ for all γ.

4-8. Consider the comparison of the three distribution functions carried out in Figs. 4-11 and 4-12 where each distribution is adjusted to match the height and width of a J_2 peak which is 1.56 times broader than a standard anelastic solid. Show that the values of δJ obtained by such fitting are different for the three distributions, specifically, that the value of δJ for the Fuoss–Kirkwood case is 7.6% higher than for the lognormal, which in turn is 2% higher than that for the box.

4-9. Show that the box and lognormal distributions are compatible with a distribution of activation energies, while the Fuoss–Kirkwood distribution is not.

4-10. For the case of the lognormal distribution, where the Arrhenius equation is obeyed and only Q is distributed, show that $\beta = \beta_Q/kT$ where β_Q is the Gaussian distribution parameter of the activation energies.

4-11. Show, from the Arrhenius equation (4.7-1), that for the case of a distribution only in $\ln \tau_0$ (with constant Q), the distribution function is independent of temperature. Then, in the particular case where $\ln \tau_0$ is distributed according to a Gaussian with distribution parameter β_0, show that $\ln \tau$ is also Gaussian with $\beta = \beta_0$.

4-12. Consider the case in which $\ln \tau_0$ and Q are both linearly related to an internal variable p which is distributed about a most probable value p_m according to a Gaussian distribution. Show that both $\ln \tau_0$ and Q then obey a Gaussian distribution, and that Eq. (4.8-3) is obeyed. Verify the conditions under which the plus and minus signs apply.

4-13. Repeat the argument which follows Eq. (4.9-1) for the normalized dynamic functions $(J_1 - J_U)/\delta J$, $M_2/\delta M$, and $(M_1 - M_R)/\delta M$, to show that all obey the equation $\ln(\omega_2/\omega_1) = (Q/k)\,\delta(1/T)$ when the distribution is in τ_0 only.

4-14. Show that for a distribution in $\ln \tau_0$ only, the normalized creep functions at two different temperatures, when plotted versus $\ln t$ are shifted with respect to each other by a horizontal shift along the $\ln t$ axis. The resulting ability to combine creep data at various temperatures into one master curve has been called "time–temperature superposition," and is particularly widely used in the polymer literature.

General References

FERRY, J. D. (1961). "Viscoelastic Properties of Polymers," Chaps. 3 and 4. Wiley, New York.

GROSS, B. (1953). "Mathematical Structure of the Theories of Viscoelasticity," Hermann, Paris.

LEADERMAN, H. (1958). *In* "Rheology" (F. R. Eirich, ed.), Vol. 2, Chap. 1. Academic Press, New York.

McCRUM, N. G., READ, B. E., and WILLIAMS, G. (1967). "Anelastic and Dielectric Effects in Polymeric Solids," Chap. 4. Wiley, New York.

NOWICK, A. S., and BERRY, B. S. (1961). *IBM J. Res. Develop.* **5**, 297, 312.

STAVERMAN, A. J., and SCHWARTZL, F. (1956). *In* "Die Physik der Hochpolymeren" (H. A. Stuart, ed.), Vol. 4, Chap. 1. Springer, Berlin.

TOBOLSKY, A. V. (1960). "Properties and Structure of Polymers," Chap. III. Wiley, New York.

Chapter 5 / Internal Variables and the Thermodynamic Basis for Relaxation Spectra

The theory of the last three chapters is based on the generalization of Hooke's law to include time dependent behavior. This approach gives no insight into the internal changes which give rise to anelasticity. On the other hand, in Chapter 1 it was briefly mentioned that the origin of anelastic behavior lies in the existence of internal variables whose equilibrium values depend on the state of stress or strain in the sample. In the present chapter, we shall show that the existence of a relaxation spectrum follows as a direct consequence of the existence of a set of internal variables which obey rather simple equations. The relation between the relaxation parameters of the mechanical models ($\delta J^{(i)}$, $\tau_\sigma^{(i)}$ or $\delta M^{(j)}$, $\tau_\varepsilon^{(j)}$) and the parameters which appear in the equations for the internal variables then provide the link between these two descriptions of an anelastic solid. This connection between the mechanical models and the internal variables has been brought out by Staverman and Schwartzl (1952, 1956) who lean heavily on the work of Meixner (1949, 1954) which deals with the application of the thermodynamics of irreversible processes to relaxation phenomena.

5.1 Case of a Single Internal Variable

In this section we start by considering the simplest case, i.e., a solid whose state is completely defined by the temperature, the state of stress (or of strain), and the value of just one internal variable ξ which couples to the mechanical quantities. Such an internal variable may be, e.g., a short-range or a long-range order parameter, or a parameter describing the electron distribution in the solid. Without loss of generality, we may define $\xi = 0$ as the equilibrium value of ξ when the sample is in a state of zero stress.

Since we are seeking a linear theory, both the stress σ and internal variable ξ must appear to the first degree in the subsequent equations.

All functional relationships between variables should therefore constitute Taylor (or Maclaurin) expansions taken only to the linear approximation. Thus treating σ and ξ as independent variables,[†] we write the strain ε as

$$\varepsilon(\sigma, \xi) = J_U\sigma + \varkappa\xi \qquad (5.1\text{-}1)$$

In this way, ε is defined as zero for $\sigma = 0$, $\xi = 0$. Aside from the fact that only linear terms are kept, the assumption of (5.1-1) is that ε is dependent on ξ. The last term in Eq. (5.1-1) is the *anelastic strain*, $\varepsilon^{\mathrm{an}} = \varkappa\xi$, i.e., the coefficient $\varkappa$ measures the coupling between the internal variable ξ and the mechanical strain ε. It should be noted that the value of $\varkappa$ depends on the nature of ε (e.g., ε may be a shear strain or a uniaxial strain in a particular crystallographic direction). For the second assumption it is required that there be a definite equilibrium value of ξ (designated by $\bar{\xi}$) for each value of σ. Since $\bar{\xi} = 0$ for $\sigma = 0$, the required linear relation becomes the simple proportionality

$$\bar{\xi} = \mu\sigma \qquad (5.1\text{-}2)$$

The proportionality constant μ depends on the type of stress applied, and is also a function of the temperature. For the final assumption we require that, with a change in stress, ξ approaches its equilibrium value over a period of time. Again, only the linear approximation is desired; therefore, we obtain a first-order kinetic equation stating that $d\xi/dt$ is proportional to the negative of the deviation of ξ from its equilibrium value,

$$d\xi/dt = -(1/\tau)(\xi - \bar{\xi}) \qquad (5.1\text{-}3)$$

where the proportionality constant is called $1/\tau$ because it has dimensions of reciprocal time.

The above three equations are sufficient to define a standard anelastic solid. The relaxation of the compliance δJ is obtained by substituting Eq. (5.1-2) into the anelastic part of Eq. (5.1-1). Thus

$$\delta J = \bar{\varepsilon}^{\mathrm{an}}/\sigma = \varkappa\bar{\xi}/\sigma = \varkappa\mu \qquad (5.1\text{-}4)$$

The differential stress–strain relation is obtained from Eqs. (5.1-1)–(5.1-3) by eliminating ξ, $\dot{\xi}$, and $\bar{\xi}$ (see Problem 5-1). The result obtained

---

[†] The third independent variable is the temperature T, which for the present may be regarded as constant.

is the same as Eq. (3.3-2) for the standard anelastic solid with $\delta J = \varkappa \mu$ and τ_σ given by the quantity τ which appears in Eq. (5.1-3).

As an alternative proof that the above assumptions define a standard anelastic solid, we may employ the creep function, i.e., with the condition of constant σ applied at $t = 0$. The solution of Eq. (5.1-3) under this condition gives

$$\xi = \bar{\xi}[1 - \exp(-t/\tau)] \qquad (5.1\text{-}5)$$

Thus, from Eqs. (5.1-1) and (5.1-2),

$$\varepsilon^{\mathrm{an}}/\sigma \equiv J(t) - J_{\mathrm{U}} = \varkappa\mu[1 - \exp(-t/\tau)] \qquad (5.1\text{-}6)$$

This result may be compared to the creep function [Eq. (3.3-6)] obtained from the three-parameter Voigt-type model (Fig. 3-4), where the parameters of the Voigt unit are now $\delta J = \varkappa \mu$ and $\tau_\sigma = \tau$. In view of the relations between response functions obtained from the Boltzmann superposition principle (Chapter 2), it is only necessary to check this one response function to verify that complete correspondence exists with the model. The equivalence of the present case (involving a single internal variable) to the three-element Voigt-type model is, therefore, demonstrated without explicit reference to the differential stress–strain equation.

It should be noted that we could just as well have started with the strain, rather than stress, as the independent variable and have written equations analogous to (5.1-1), (5.1-2), and (5.1-3) ($\bar{\xi}$ is then $\propto \varepsilon$) (see Problem 5-2). In that case, we could readily have derived a relaxation function $M(t)$ which is the same as that of the three-element Maxwell-type model. The quantity τ which appears in Eq. (5.1-3) is then identified with the parameter τ_ε obtained from that model. (Note that now $\tau^{-1} \equiv -\partial\dot{\xi}/\partial\xi\,|_\varepsilon.$)

In summary, a material describable by a single internal variable has been shown to be completely equivalent to the standard anelastic solid. Since the assumptions involved in Eqs. (5.1-1)–(5.1-3) are reasonable ones for a simple material at low stress levels, one may anticipate that the standard anelastic solid represents a physically important situation.

5.2   Case of a Set of Coupled Internal Variables

Now we consider the more general problem in which the internal state of the material is describable in terms of a finite number n of internal variables ξ_p ($p = 1, \ldots, n$) which couple to the mechanical variables, and attempt to generalize Eqs. (5.1-1)–(5.1-3). Again, without loss of generality, it is possible to define $\bar{\xi}_p = 0$ at $\sigma = 0$, for all values of p. Thus

$$\varepsilon = J_U \sigma + \sum_{p=1}^{n} \varkappa_p \xi_p \tag{5.2-1}$$

represents the obvious extension of (5.1-1) to the case of many variables in the linear approximation. Similarly, each ξ_p has an equilibrium value given by

$$\bar{\xi}_p = \mu_p \sigma \tag{5.2-2}$$

analogous to Eq. (5.1-2). The generalization of Eq. (5.1-3) is more complex, however. Thus when all the ξ_p's are not in equilibrium, each internal variable will, in general, approach equilibrium at a rate which depends on the deviation of *all* of the variables from their equilibrium values. This behavior constitutes *coupling* of the internal variables.[†] Thus, to maintain the linear approximation in its full generality, we must write

$$\dot{\xi}_p = - \sum_{q=1}^{n} \omega_{pq}(\xi_q - \bar{\xi}_q), \qquad p = 1, 2, \ldots, n \tag{5.2-3}$$

in terms of a set of coefficients ω_{pq}. Equations (5.2-3) constitute a coupled set of n linear first-order differential equations in n unknowns. Meixner (1949, 1954) has shown that it is always possible to find a linear transformation to a new set of variables

$$\xi_r' = \sum_{p} B_{rp} \xi_p \tag{5.2-4}$$

such that Eqs. (5.2-3) become

$$\dot{\xi}_r' = -\tau_r^{-1}(\xi_r' - \bar{\xi}_r'), \qquad r = 1, 2, \ldots, n \tag{5.2-5}$$

i.e., the variables ξ_r' are decoupled. Further, it can be shown that all of the quantities τ_r are real and positive.

   In order not to lose the thread of the argument, we defer to Section 5.3 a discussion of the basis for the existence of such a transformation and the method of obtaining the coefficients B_{rp}. For now, we shall accept the fact that such a new set of variables can be found. The quanti-

---

[†] It is by no means required that all internal variables be coupled. The case of uncoupled variables is included in this formalism whenever $\omega_{pq} = 0$ for $p \neq q$.

ties ξ_r' are actually just as good a set of internal variables for describing the system as the original ξ_p's, since we had made no special assumptions about ξ_p. Further, the new variables still obey Eqs. (5.2-1) and (5.2-2) but with different coefficients, e.g.,

$$\varepsilon = J_U\sigma + \sum_r \varkappa_r'\xi_r' \qquad (5.2\text{-}1a)$$

$$\dot{\xi}_r' = \mu_r'\sigma \qquad (5.2\text{-}2a)$$

where the new coefficients $\varkappa_r'$ and μ_r' are expressible in terms of the old coefficients $\varkappa_p$ and μ_p (see Problem 5-3). The important difference lies in the third equation, i.e., in the absence of a summation over all the variables on the right-hand side of Eq. (5.2-5).

There is an important analogy between Eqs. (5.2-3) and the coupled set of equations in a mechanical vibration problem, such as the vibration equations for a polyatomic molecule. The vibration problem involves linear equations of *second* order, i.e., $\ddot{\xi}$ appears, but in that problem too, the coupled equations are decoupled by choosing an appropriate linear transformation to a new set of coordinates. This new set of coordinates in the vibration problem are the well-known "normal coordinates." For this reason, Meixner and others refer to the coordinates ξ_r' in the relaxation problem as the "normal internal variables."

The solution to Eqs. (5.2-5) under creep conditions (constant stress) can be written immediately as

$$\xi_r' = \bar{\xi}_r'[1 - \exp(-t/\tau_r)] \qquad (5.2\text{-}6)$$

This is the same solution as that which was obtained for the case of a single internal variable [Eq. (5.1-5)]. Accordingly, we see that each of the normal internal variables ξ_r' undergoes relaxation independently of the others. Each solution of the type (5.2-6) is also referred to as a *relaxational normal mode*, again by analogy to the mechanical vibration problem.

Substituting Eqs. (5.2-6) and (5.2-2a) into (5.2-1a) we obtain

$$\varepsilon^{an}/\sigma \equiv J(t) - J_U = \sum_{r=1}^{n} \varkappa_r'\mu_r'[1 - \exp(-t/\tau_r)] \qquad (5.2\text{-}7)$$

This creep behavior corresponds to that of a Voigt-type model with n Voigt units, the rth having parameters $\delta J^{(r)} = \varkappa_r'\mu_r'$, and $\tau_\sigma^{(r)} = \tau_r$. Note, however, that in the case of degeneracy, i.e., when two or more of the quantities τ_r are equal, the terms in Eq. (5.2-7) with the same τ_r are best lumped together. In this case, the appropriate mechanical model has fewer than n Voigt units. (This point is discussed further in Section 5.3 and Problem 5-6.) In any case, the total magnitude of relaxation is

$$\delta J = \sum_r \varkappa_r' \mu_r' = \sum_p \varkappa_p \mu_p \qquad (5.2\text{-}8)$$

where the latter equality can be obtained directly from Eqs. (5.2-1), (5.2-2), (5.2-1a), and (5.2-2a).

It could next be shown that the dynamical behavior for the case of a set of internal variables is that describable by the same Voigt-type model. Actually, this is unnecessary, since we have already shown through the formal theory (Chapter 3) that a solid whose creep function is a discrete sum of exponentials will display a $J_2(\omega)$ function in the form of a sum of Debye functions with the same set of τ values. Similar statements apply to the $J_1(\omega)$ function. It is concluded therefore, that in the absence of degeneracy, the changes in internal variables which give rise to anelastic behavior can be described in terms of n pairs of constants $\{\tau_r; \varkappa_r' \mu_r'\}$ where $r = 1, \ldots, n$. These constants give the relaxation times and magnitudes of a set of n lines and, as such, describe a spectrum of relaxation times at constant stress. (Clearly, for large enough n it may approach, and in fact be better described as, a continuous spectrum.) The important result is that each spectral line, which in Chapter 3 was related to one Voigt unit in the mechanical model, is here related to one of the normal internal variables (or to a set of such variables having the same relaxation time).

In the same manner as in the case of a single internal variable, we could have started with strain as the independent variable and developed the spectrum for the relaxation time at constant strain (Problem 5-4). In view of the fact that the formal theory is capable of interrelating the two spectra, there is no purpose to following this alternative approach in detail. It is clear, however, that the parameters of each Maxwell unit in the mechanical model relate to one or more normal internal variables which have a particular relaxation time.

5.3 Thermodynamic Considerations

The reader should recall that the key point to the reasoning of the last section was the statement that a set of normal coordinates [Eq. (5.2-4)] can be found in terms of which the rate equations are decoupled, as in Eqs. (5.2-5). In this section we will indicate the basis for this statement which originates in classical thermodynamics and the thermodynamics of irreversible processes. The thermodynamic approach has additional advantages, in providing interrelations between some of the parameters which appear in the expressions of the previous section. In this theory, thermodynamic functions such as the free energy or internal energy are not only functions of the external state variables (with stress–strain terms replacing the usual pressure–volume terms) but are also functions of the internal variables ξ_p. The underlying idea behind such a description is that a pseudoequilibrium can be established within the solid (i.e., among its vibrational degrees of freedom) even though insufficient time is allowed for the internal variables to attain their equilibrium values. To completely describe such a state, it is therefore necessary to include the internal variables. [For complete equilibrium the internal variables lose their independence and become functions of the other variables of the system, as e.g., in Eq. (5.2-2).] We may write a characteristic thermodynamic free energy function which depends on the internal variables as well as the other independent variables chosen to describe the system. Thus, if stress, temperature, and the ξ_p's are taken as independent variables, we may define the Gibbs function per unit volume,[†]

$$g = u - Ts - \varepsilon\sigma \qquad (5.3\text{-}1)$$

where u and s are, respectively, the internal energy and entropy per unit volume. If we apply the first and second laws of thermodynamics in the form

$$du = T\,ds + \sigma\,d\varepsilon - \sum A_p\,d\xi_p \qquad (5.3\text{-}2)$$

where the quantities A_p are the conjugate variables to ξ_p known as the *affinities*, and combine Eqs. (5.3-1) and (5.3-2), we obtain the differential form for g

$$dg = -s\,dT - \varepsilon\,d\sigma - \sum A_p\,d\xi_p \qquad (5.3\text{-}3)$$

from which

$$A_p = -(\partial g/\partial \xi_p)_{\sigma,\,T,\,\xi_{q\neq p}} \qquad (5.3\text{-}4)$$

For complete equilibrium at constant stress and temperature, $dg = 0$; therefore

$$A_p = 0, \quad \text{all} \quad p$$

[†] "Per unit volume" means as determined prior to deformation. The Gibbs function defined here has a stress–strain term, in place of the usual pressure–volume term which applies when pressure is the only form of external stress.

The affinity A_p can then be regarded as a driving force toward equilibrium when the ξ_p's are not at their equilibrium values. From Eq. (5.3-3) we also see that

$$s = -(\partial g/\partial T)_{\sigma,\xi} \tag{5.3-5}$$

and

$$\varepsilon = -(\partial g/\partial \sigma)_{T,\xi} \tag{5.3-6}$$

Each of these quantities may be expressed as a linear function of the independent variables T, σ, ξ_p, when these variables undergo only small changes. By taking, as a reference state, the temperature T_0, stress $\sigma = 0$, and $\xi_p = 0$ (defined as the equilibrium values of ξ_p at $\sigma = 0$ and $T = T_0$) we obtain, for small changes

$$\Delta s = (c_\sigma/T_0)\,\Delta T + \alpha\sigma + \sum_p \chi_p \xi_p \tag{5.3-7}$$

$$\varepsilon = \alpha\,\Delta T + J_U\sigma + \sum_p \varkappa_p \xi_p \tag{5.3-8}$$

$$A_p = \chi_p\,\Delta T + \varkappa_p\sigma - \sum_p \beta_{pq}\xi_q \tag{5.3-9}$$

where $\Delta T = T - T_0$. In these equations we have made use of such thermodynamic reciprocity relations as $\partial\varepsilon/\partial\xi_p = \partial A_p/\partial\sigma \equiv \varkappa_p$, which are valid because dg is a perfect differential [Eq. (5.3-3)].[†] The quantity $\alpha = (\partial\varepsilon/\partial T)_{\sigma,\xi}$ is a thermal expansion coefficient, while c_σ, the specific heat per unit volume at constant σ, is the same as the usual specific heat at constant pressure. It should be noted that Eq. (5.3-8) is the same as Eq. (5.2-1), except that it allows for strain due to thermal expansion.

Equations (5.3-7)–(5.3-9), taken together with Eqs. (5.3-4)–(5.3-6) imply that the Gibbs function g may be expanded as a Taylor series to quadratic terms in the variables σ, ξ_p, and ΔT, as

$$g(\sigma,\,\xi_p,\,T) = g(0,\,0,\,T) - \tfrac{1}{2}J_U\sigma^2 - \sigma\sum_p \varkappa_p\xi_p$$
$$-\alpha\sigma\,\Delta T - \Delta T\sum_p \chi_p\xi_p + \tfrac{1}{2}\sum_{p,q} \beta_{pq}\xi_p\xi_q \tag{5.3-10}$$

where $g(0,\,0,\,T) = g(0,\,0,\,T_0) - \tfrac{1}{2}(c_\sigma/T)(\Delta T)^2$ gives the dependence of g on temperature when σ and all ξ_p are zero. Thus Eqs. (5.3-7)–(5.3-9) are readily obtained by taking the various partial derivatives of this g function.

[†] These relations are generalizations of the well-known "Maxwell relations" of classical thermodynamics.

To obtain the equilibrium values, $\bar{\xi}_p$ of the internal variables, we must set $A_p = 0$ [see text below Eq. (5.3-4)]. Equation (5.3-9) then gives

$$\sum_q \beta_{pq}\bar{\xi}_q = \chi_p \, \Delta T + \varkappa_p \sigma \qquad (5.3\text{-}11)$$

This result may be combined with Eq. (5.3-9) to give

$$A_p = - \sum_q \beta_{pq}(\xi_q - \bar{\xi}_q) \qquad (5.3\text{-}12)$$

showing that A_p is linearly dependent on the deviation of all ξ_q from their equilibrium values. The term χ_p in Eq. (5.3-11) allows for the fact that $\bar{\xi}_p$ may be a function of temperature as well as stress, a possibility not considered in Eq. (5.2-2).

Another consequence of the fact that dg is a perfect differential is that $\partial A_p/\partial \xi_q = \partial A_q/\partial \xi_p$, i.e., $\beta_{pq} = \beta_{qp}$. The coefficients β_{pq} may therefore be formed into a symmetric matrix $\boldsymbol{\beta}$. They may also be used to generate the quadratic form $\frac{1}{2}\sum_{p,q} \beta_{pq}\xi_p\xi_q$. It is easily seen from Eq. (5.3-10) that this quadratic form represents the g function for zero stress and constant temperature T_0. Since g is a minimum at equilibrium (where all ξ_p are zero), this quadratic form is *positive definite* (i.e., it has no negative values, and is zero only when all of the ξ's are zero). Thus the matrix of coefficients β_{pq} is both symmetric and positive definite.

As already mentioned, one may consider the affinities A_p as the driving forces toward a state of complete equilibrium. It is therefore reasonable to expect that for small A_p values (i.e., small departures from equilibrium), the rate of approach to equilibrium $\dot{\xi}_p$ depends linearly upon all the affinities, or

$$\dot{\xi}_p = \sum_q L_{pq}A_q \qquad (5.3\text{-}13)$$

defining a matrix of coefficients L_{pq}. A fundamental principle of irreversible thermodynamics is given by the "Onsager relations" according to which

$$L_{pq} = L_{qp} \qquad (5.3\text{-}14)$$

Further, the matrix L_{pq} is also positive definite (since the rate of entropy production multiplied by the temperature is a positive definite quadratic form in the products A_pA_q with the L_{pq} as coefficients).[†]

[†] For example, see the general references given at the end of this chapter. The inverse of the matrix **L** also yields a quadratic form in the products $\dot{\xi}_p\dot{\xi}_q$ representing the rate of entropy production times temperature.

When Eqs. (5.3-12) and (5.3-13) are combined so as to eliminate the affinities, the earlier form (5.2-3) is obtained with

$$\omega_{pq} = \sum_l L_{pl}\beta_{lq} \tag{5.3-15}$$

In matrix notation this is simply the statement that the matrix $\boldsymbol{\omega}$ is the product of matrices $\mathbf{L}$ and $\boldsymbol{\beta}$. In general $\boldsymbol{\omega}$ is not a symmetric matrix even though $\mathbf{L}$ and $\boldsymbol{\beta}$ are. Because of the symmetric and positive definite properties of $\mathbf{L}$ and $\boldsymbol{\beta}$, it follows from a fundamental theorem of algebra that a linear transformation Eq. (5.2-4) can be found which will simultaneously diagonalize each of the three matrices $\mathbf{L}, \boldsymbol{\beta}$, and $\boldsymbol{\omega}$ (i.e., eliminate off-diagonal terms, for which $p \neq q$) leaving only real, positive numbers along the diagonal. [†] In the present problem the allowed values of the reciprocal relaxation times τ^{-1} are solutions of the determinantal or "secular equation"

$$\det(\omega_{pq} - \tau^{-1}\,\delta_{pq}) = 0 \tag{5.3-16}$$

where ω_{pq} is given by Eq. (5.3-15) and δ_{pq} is the Kronecker delta. (See problem 5-5.) Equation (5.3-16) is a polynomial of degree n; therefore, there are n solutions for τ^{-1}, corresponding to the n relaxational normal modes, Eq. (5.2-6). Once the set of relaxation times τ_r are determined, the coefficients B_{rp} required to take the original set of coordinates ξ_p into the normal internal variables ξ_r' can be determined by standard methods (see references in the previous footnote). Actually, for the purposes of this chapter it is more important to know that such a set of normal internal variables and the corresponding relaxation times τ_r *can* be found than are the details of how to obtain them.

In the new coordinate system ξ_r' we obtain Eqs. (5.3-7)–(5.3-12) with new parameters $\varkappa_r', \chi_r', \beta_{rs}' = \beta_r'\,\delta_{rs}$, and $L_{rs}' = L_r'\,\delta_{rs}$, since the transformation diagonalizes $\boldsymbol{\beta}$ and $\mathbf{L}'$. Accordingly, Eq. (5.3-11) is readily solved as follows:

$$\bar{\xi}_r' = \beta_r'^{-1}(\chi_r'\,\varDelta T + \varkappa_r'\sigma) \tag{5.3-17}$$

Note that the quantity μ_r' of Eq. (5.2-2a) is, in terms of the present thermodynamic approach, equal to $\varkappa_r'/\beta_r'$. Finally, comparison with

---

[†] See, e.g., Hohn (1958, Chapter 9). The situation is similar to the well-known problem of a vibrating mechanical system where it is desired to diagonalize simultaneously the matrices of coefficients giving the kinetic and the potential energies. (See Wilson *et al.*, 1955, Chapter IV and Appendix VIII.)

Eq. (5.2-8), or substituting Eq. (5.3-17) into (5.3-8), gives

$$\delta J = \sum_r \varkappa_r'^2/\beta_r' \equiv \sum_r \delta J^{(r)} \qquad (5.3\text{-}18)$$

Equation (5.3-18) has defined $\varkappa_r'^2/\beta_r' \equiv \delta J^{(r)}$ as the *partial relaxation magnitude* for the rth normal mode. Note that since β_r' is always positive, $\delta J^{(r)}$ is positive. The corresponding relaxation rates, obtained from Eq. (5.3-15) in the diagonalized form as

$$\tau_r^{-1} = L_r' \beta_r' \qquad (5.3\text{-}19)$$

are also always positive. The relaxation spectrum can then be described by the set of n pairs of quantities $\{\tau_r; \delta J^{(r)}\}$ giving the relaxation time and partial magnitude of each of the n normal modes. In the case of degeneracy, however, it is necessary to lump together the partial magnitudes of all normal modes which possess the same relaxation time, to avoid ambiguity (see Problem 5-6).

*5.4 Relaxation Spectra under Different Conditions[†]

In the previous section, the thermodynamics was developed in terms of a Gibbs function with temperature and stress as the independent variables of the system. The spectrum thus obtained relates to the conditions of constant T and σ, i.e., τ_r means $\tau_{\sigma,T}^{(r)}$, while $\delta J^{(r)}$ means $\delta J_T^{(r)}$. On the other hand, experiments are often carried out adiabatically and/or at constant strain. The relations between spectra for constant stress and for constant strain have been obtained from the formal theory of relaxation phenomena (Chapters 3 and 4), but to distinguish adiabatic from isothermal conditions requires a thermodynamic approach.

In thermodynamics there is a characteristic function which is appropriate to each set of independent variables. Thus, the enthalpy per unit volume defined by $h = g + Ts$, obeys the differential expression

$$dh = T\,ds - \varepsilon\,d\sigma - \sum_p A_p\,d\xi_p \qquad (5.4\text{-}1)$$

which may be obtained from Eq. (5.3-2) and the above definition of h. This function is most convenient for considering relaxation when s, σ, and ξ_p are the independent variables in the problem, and therefore for

---

[†] This section may be omitted on a first reading. All such sections throughout this book will be starred.

obtaining the spectrum $\{\tau_{\sigma,s}^{(r)};\ \delta J_s^{(r)}\}$ for adiabatic (constant s) and constant stress conditions. Similarly the Helmholtz free energy per unit volume, $f = g + \sigma\varepsilon$, which obeys the relation

$$df = -s\,dT + \sigma\,d\varepsilon - \sum_p A_p\,d\xi_p \qquad (5.4\text{-}2)$$

it most suited to describing the spectrum $\{\tau_{\varepsilon,T}^{(r)};\ \delta M_T^{(r)}\}$ for constant strain and temperature. Finally, the internal energy per unit volume, u, which obeys

$$du = T\,ds + \sigma\,d\varepsilon - \sum_p A_p\,d\xi_p \qquad (5.4\text{-}3)$$

is most suitable for the adiabatic spectrum at constant strain $\{\tau_{\varepsilon,s}^{(r)};\ \delta M_s^{(r)}\}$. In each of these cases, by following an approach completely analogous to that in Section 5.3, the appropriate spectrum can be derived. Since each of these four spectra completely defines the thermodynamic system, they are necessarily interrelated. In the case of an arbitrary spectrum, however, the relations can be quite complex (recall, e.g., the relation between spectra at constant stress and at constant strain, Section 4.2). For present purposes, therefore, we shall illustrate the relations only for the case of a single internal variable, i.e., for the standard anelastic solid, where these interrelationships are comparatively simple.

To obtain these results, we return to Eqs. (5.3-7)–(5.3-9), dropping the subscripts p and q. We must now add subscripts to denote which variables are held constant. Thus J_U becomes $J_{U;T} = (\partial\varepsilon/\partial\sigma)_{\xi,T}$, the isothermal unrelaxed compliance, while the isothermal relaxed compliance is $J_{R;T} = (\partial\varepsilon/\partial\sigma)_{A,T}$. (Constant A, or specifically $A = 0$, indicates that $\xi = \bar{\xi}$.) The difference $J_{R;T} - J_{U;T}$ is denoted by δJ_T. Similarly one can define the adiabatic quantities $J_{U;s}$, $J_{R;s}$, and δJ_s. Since

$$(\partial\varepsilon/\partial\sigma)_{\xi,s} = (\partial\varepsilon/\partial\sigma)_{\xi,T} + (\partial\varepsilon/\partial T)_{\xi,\sigma}(\partial T/\partial\sigma)_{\xi,s} \qquad (5.4\text{-}4)$$

and by setting $\Delta s = 0$ in (5.3-7), we obtain

$$(\partial T/\partial\sigma)_{\xi,s} = -\alpha T_0/c_\sigma \qquad (5.4\text{-}5)$$

it follows that

$$J_{U;s} = J_{U;T} - \alpha^2 T_0/c_\sigma \qquad (5.4\text{-}6)$$

This is simply the well-known relation between the adiabatic and isothermal elastic constants. One may also write Eq. (5.4-4) with A constant throughout instead of ξ. From Eqs. (5.3-8) and (5.3-11),

$$(\partial\varepsilon/\partial T)_{A,\sigma} = \alpha + \varkappa\chi/\beta \qquad (5.4\text{-}7)$$

while from Eqs. (5.3-7) and (5.3-11),

$$(\partial T/\partial\sigma)_{A,s} = -(\alpha\beta + \varkappa\chi)/(\chi^2 + c_\sigma\beta T^{-1}) \qquad (5.4\text{-}8)$$

Accordingly,

$$\delta J_s = \delta J_T - \left[\frac{T}{\beta}\frac{(\alpha\beta + \varkappa\chi)^2}{(T\chi^2 + \beta c_\sigma)} - \frac{T\alpha^2}{c_\sigma}\right] \qquad (5.4\text{-}9)$$

It is noteworthy that the bracketed quantity in Eq. (5.4-9) vanishes if $\chi = 0$, i.e., from (5.3-11) if the value of $\bar{\xi}$ for $\sigma = 0$ is independent of T.

We wish next to obtain the relation between the isothermal and adiabatic relaxation times at constant stress, i.e., $\tau_{\sigma,T}$ and $\tau_{\sigma,s}$. For this we turn to Eq. (5.3-19) and note [from (5.3-13)] that $L = d\dot{\xi}/dA$ is independent of whether the conditions are isothermal or adiabatic. The quantity β in (5.3-9), on the other hand, here becomes

$$\beta_{\sigma,T} = -(\partial A/\partial\xi)_{\sigma,T} \qquad (5.4\text{-}10)$$

The corresponding quantity $\beta_{\sigma,s}$ is obtained from

$$\left(\frac{\partial A}{\partial\xi}\right)_{\sigma,s} = \left(\frac{\partial A}{\partial\xi}\right)_{\sigma,T} + \left(\frac{\partial A}{\partial T}\right)_{\sigma,\xi}\left(\frac{\partial T}{\partial\xi}\right)_{\sigma,s} \qquad (5.4\text{-}11)$$

Finally, noting that $(\partial A/\partial T)_{\sigma,\xi} = \chi$ and [from (5.3-7)] that $(\partial T/\partial\xi)_{\sigma,s} = -\chi T/c_\sigma$, we obtain the desired relation

$$\tau_{\sigma,s}^{-1} = \tau_{\sigma,T}^{-1}[1 + (T\chi^2/c_\sigma\beta)] \qquad (5.4\text{-}12)$$

Again, as in Eq. (5.4-9), the difference between the adiabatic and isothermal case vanishes if $\chi = 0$. Equation (5.4-12) can also be expressed in a different form by defining a "relaxed specific heat" at constant stress (per unit volume)

$$c_{R,\sigma} \equiv T(\partial s/\partial T)_{\sigma,A} = c_\sigma + T\chi(\partial\bar{\xi}/\partial T)_\sigma$$
$$= c_\sigma + T\chi^2/\beta \qquad (5.4\text{-}13)$$

It, therefore, follows from Eq. (5.4-12) that

$$\tau_{\sigma,s}^{-1} = \tau_{\sigma,T}^{-1}(c_{R,\sigma}/c_\sigma) \qquad (5.4\text{-}14)$$

In an analogous way, the relationship between relaxation parameters for constant strain and temperature to those for constant stress and temperature may be obtained. The results are

$$\delta M_T = M_{U;T} - M_{R;T} = \delta J_T/(J_{R;T}J_{U;T}) \qquad (5.4\text{-}15)$$

$$\tau_{\varepsilon,T}^{-1} = \tau_{\sigma,T}^{-1}(J_{R;T}/J_{U;T}) \qquad (5.4\text{-}16)$$

which are the same relations as those obtained from the formal theory (Section 3.3). The proof of these equations from the present thermo-dynamic viewpoint is left as an exercise for the reader (see Problem 5-7).

Finally, the case of adiabatic relaxation at constant strain must be considered. In this case, the magnitude δM_s is related to δJ_s, $J_{R;s}$ and $J_{U;s}$ in a manner analogous to Eq. (5.4-15), where $J_{U;s}$ and δJ_s are given by Eqs. (5.4-6) and (5.4-9), respectively. The relaxation time is

$$\tau_{\varepsilon,s}^{-1} = -L(\partial A/\partial \xi)_{\varepsilon,s} = \tau_{\sigma,T}^{-1}(c_{R,\sigma}/c_\sigma)(J_{R;s}/J_{U;s}) \qquad (5.4\text{-}17)$$

As already indicated, in the case of more than one internal variable, the thermodynamic parameters are similarly interrelated; however, in general, each normal mode relaxation time under a new set of experimental conditions is related to *all* of the original relaxation times. Therefore, the generalization of equations such as (5.4-12), (5.4-16), and (5.4-17) to the case of several variables leads to more complex expressions (see, e.g., Problem 5-8).

PROBLEMS

5-1. Eliminate the variable ξ from Eqs. (5.1-1)–(5.1-3) to obtain the differential stress–strain equation for the standard anelastic solid.

5-2. Write the analogous equations to (5.1-1)–(5.1-3) in terms of strain, rather than stress, as the independent variable and obtain the corresponding differential stress–strain equation. Compare the parameters with those of the standard anelastic solid.

5-3. Using the transformation (5.2-4) obtain expressions for the coefficients $\varkappa_r'$ and μ_r' of Eqs. (5.2-1a) and (5.2-2a) in terms of the original coefficients $\varkappa_p$ and μ_p. Also, prove Eq. (5.2-8). Finally, obtain the relation between the coefficients ω_{pq} of Eq. (5.2-3) and the relaxation rates τ_r^{-1} of Eq. (5.2-5).

5-4. Develop the spectrum for the relaxation time *at constant strain* starting from a coupled set of internal variables, in a manner analogous to Eqs. (5.2-1)–(5.2-8).

5-5. Verify the condition (5.3-16) as follows. Look for a "relaxational normal mode" in which each ξ_p takes the form $\xi_p - \bar{\xi}_p = C_p \times \exp(-t/\tau)$. Substitute into Eq. (5.2-3) to obtain a set of linear, homogeneous, algebraic equations in the coefficients C_p. Then note that the condition (5.3-16) is precisely that for a nontrivial solution.

5-6. Consider the case of degeneracy, i.e., when two or more normal internal variables possess the same relaxation time at constant stress τ_r. Show that an ambiguity will occur in the definition of the partial relaxation magnitudes (due to the possibility of forming new normal internal variables as linear combinations of the original degenerate ones), and that this ambiguity can be avoided by lumping together a set of degenerate modes into a single spectral line of partial magnitude $\delta J^{(i)} = \sum_{r=1}^{m} \varkappa_r'^2/\beta_r'$, where m is the degeneracy. For the corresponding relaxation time, we have $\tau_\sigma^{(i)} = \tau_r$.

5-7. Verify Eqs. (5.4-15) and (5.4-16) using the thermodynamic approach of Section 5.4. Similarly, verify Eq. (5.4-17).

5-8. Show that, in general, the set of normal internal variables for adiabatic conditions is not the same as those for isothermal conditions. [Hint: Show that $(\partial A_r'/\partial \xi_t')_{\sigma,s} \neq 0$ when $r \neq t$ even though $(\partial A_r'/\partial \xi_t')_{\sigma,T} = 0$.] Similarly, show that the normal internal variables for constant stress conditions are generally not suitable normal coordinates for constant strain.

General References

BAUER, H. J. (1965). *In* "Physical Acoustics" (W. P. Mason, ed.), Vol. 2A. Academic Press, New York.

DE GROOT, S. R., and MAZUR. P. (1962). "Non-Equilibrium Thermodynamics." Wiley, New York.

DENBIGH, K. G. (1951). "The Thermodynamics of the Steady State," Methuen, London.

MEIXNER, J. (1954). *Z. Naturforsch.* **9a**, 654.

Chapter 6 / Anisotropic Elasticity and Anelasticity

To this point, our discussion of both elastic and anelastic behavior has treated stress and strain as though they were scalar quantities. This approach allowed us to concentrate our attention on the time-dependent response which differentiates anelasticity from elasticity. In the present chapter, we are ready to recognize that stress and strain are only fully described as symmetric second rank tensors, involving six components. Just as in Chapter 1, where anelasticity was first approached via the scalar form of Hooke's law ($\sigma = M\varepsilon$ or $\varepsilon = J\sigma$), we shall approach anisotropic anelasticity by way of anisotropic elasticity. In the most general case of anisotropic anelasticity, as many as 21 elastic constants may be dependent on time (or frequency). However, we shall see that for crystals of the higher symmetries, the problem is not really as formidable as might be imagined. We shall, in fact, see that the material presented in Chapters 1–5 is directly applicable to the case of crystals deformed in appropriately simple ways, and is readily extended to more general cases.

It might also be remarked that, even for isotropic materials, the behavior of a specimen under an arbitrary mode of deformation is best related to certain characteristic response functions obtained from the more general formulation of Hooke's law.

6.1 Stress, Strain, and Hooke's Law

In view of the availability of several excellent reviews of the subject of crystal elasticity (see the general references at the end of the chapter), we will outline here only the equations needed for the treatment of anelasticity in subsequent sections. We will work with the conventional definitions of the stress and strain components as follows. The components of stress at a point are defined in terms of the forces which act on the faces of a unit cube, one corner of which is at the origin O and the edges of which are parallel to the coordinate axes, i.e., to Ox_1, Ox_2, and Ox_3, respectively, as shown in Fig. 6-1. For convenience of reference the faces

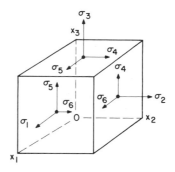

FIG. 6-1. A unit cube, showing the six components of stress.

perpendicular to Ox_1, Ox_2, and Ox_3, are designated as faces 1, 2, and 3, respectively. The force transmitted across each face (i.e., exerted by the material outside the cube on the material inside) may be resolved into components parallel to the three axes, so that there are nine components in all. However, by virtue of the requirement of static equilibrium, certain of these components are equal. The result is that there are six independent components. The *tensile* components σ_1, σ_2, and σ_3, are defined as the forces per unit area normal to faces 1, 2, and 3, respectively. The shear stress σ_4 is the force acting on face 2 which is directed parallel to Ox_3 (or that on face 3 directed parallel to Ox_2). It may, therefore, be referred to as the 2–3 shear stress component. Similarly σ_5 is the 3–1 shear stress, and σ_6 the 1–2 shear stress. Each of these is shown in Fig. 6-1.

The components of strain are defined as follows. At any point in the medium let $\mathbf{u}(x_1, x_2, x_3)$ be the vector displacement of the point from its position in a reference (unstrained) state. Let u_i ($i = 1, 2, 3$) be the ith component of this displacement. Then

$$\varepsilon_i = \partial u_i / \partial x_i, \qquad i = 1, 2, \text{ or } 3 \tag{6.1-1}$$

defines the three components of tensile strain, while

$$\varepsilon_4 = \frac{\partial u_2}{\partial x_3} + \frac{\partial u_3}{\partial x_2}, \quad \varepsilon_5 = \frac{\partial u_3}{\partial x_1} + \frac{\partial u_1}{\partial x_3}, \quad \varepsilon_6 = \frac{\partial u_1}{\partial x_2} + \frac{\partial u_2}{\partial x_1} \tag{6.1-2}$$

are the shear strain components. Both the stress and strain components may be defined in terms of a two-index tensor notation [†] which is helpful

[†] The components of stress and strain as defined here are often called the "engineering" stresses and strains. These quantities may be converted into the two-index tensor components σ_{ij} and ε_{ij} as

$$\sigma_i \rightarrow \sigma_{ii}, \qquad \varepsilon_i \rightarrow \varepsilon_{ii}, \qquad i = 1, 2, 3$$
$$\sigma_4 \rightarrow \sigma_{23}, \qquad \sigma_5 \rightarrow \sigma_{31}, \qquad \sigma_6 \rightarrow \sigma_{12}$$
$$\varepsilon_4 \rightarrow 2\varepsilon_{23}, \qquad \varepsilon_5 \rightarrow 2\varepsilon_{31}, \qquad \varepsilon_6 \rightarrow 2\varepsilon_{12}$$

for the determination of how the components change under a transformation of the coordinate axes. Such notation will be needed, e.g., in Chapter 8. For present purposes, however, the commonly used single index ($i = 1$–6) notation is sufficient. In terms of this notation, we obtain as the generalization of Hooke's law, the statement that the six stress components are *linearly related* to the six strain components. Thus

$$\sigma_i = \sum_{j=1}^{6} c_{ij}\varepsilon_j \qquad\qquad (6.1\text{-}3)$$

The 36 c_{ij}, which form a 6×6 matrix, are called the "moduli of elasticity" or "elastic stiffness constants." Conversely, the strain components may be expressed as linear functions of the stress components, or

$$\varepsilon_i = \sum_{j=1}^{6} s_{ij}\sigma_j \qquad\qquad (6.1\text{-}4)$$

The 36 quantities s_{ij} are known as the "moduli of compliance" or "elastic compliance constants." Clearly, s_{ij} may be expressed in terms of the constants c_{kl} by the straightforward use of determinants. In these forms, Hooke's law has the same general features as did the simpler relation of Chapter 1, viz., the deformation is instantaneous, linear, and recoverable.

The constants s_{ij}, for which $i = j$ (i.e., the diagonal elements of the s_{ij} matrix), have the simplest interpretation. From Eq. (6.1-4) it is clear, for example, that $s_{11} = \varepsilon_1/\sigma_1$ when $\sigma_2 = \sigma_3 = \cdots = 0$. The quantity s_{11} is, therefore, equal to $1/E_1$, the reciprocal of Young's modulus in the Ox_1 direction. Similarly, $s_{22} = E_2^{-1}$, and $s_{33} = E_3^{-1}$. The quantities s_{44}, s_{55}, and s_{66} are reciprocal shear moduli, since each represents the ratio of a shear strain to the corresponding shear stress when all other stress components are zero. The off-diagonal components s_{ij} ($i \neq j$) have a simple interpretation in terms of Poisson ratios when i and j are both ≤ 3. Thus, for example, $s_{21} = \varepsilon_2/\sigma_1$ when $\sigma_2 = \sigma_3 \cdots = 0$, is related to the Poisson contraction in direction Ox_2 when a tensile stress is applied parallel to Ox_1. If the Poisson ratio for this effect is denoted by χ_{21}, then $s_{21} = -\chi_{21}/E_1$. The compliance constants s_{ij} ($i \leq 3, j \geq 4$) are more difficult to interpret. These constants, which represent the ratio of a tensile strain to a shear stress, are zero for isotropic materials and also for crystalline materials in which the coordinate axes coincide with directions of high symmetry. On the other hand, they are not zero for arbitrarily oriented or low symmetry crystals. Finally, the constants s_{ij} ($i, j \geq 4$) represent shear strain produced by a unit shear stress in a perpendicular plane. These constants also have nonzero values only for low-symmetry crystals or arbitrary orientations.

The stiffness constants c_{ij} have analogous interpretations. For example $c_{11} = \sigma_1/\varepsilon_1$ is the ratio of a tensile stress to the corresponding tensile strain *when all other strains are zero*. Since this means that Poisson contractions must be prohibited, it is clear that $c_{11} \neq E_1$, i.e., $c_{11} \neq 1/s_{11}$. The c_{ij} constants do appear quite naturally, however, in the interpretation of the velocity in ultrasonic pulse experiments, as will be discussed later.

A significant simplification of the c_{ij} matrices results from the fact that the increment of elastic energy per unit volume dW of a deformed body which may be written (Nye, 1957)

$$dW = \sum_{i=1}^{6} \sigma_i \, d\varepsilon_i \qquad (6.1\text{-}5)$$

is a perfect differential. Thus $\partial W/\partial \varepsilon_i = \sigma_i$, and $\partial W/\partial \varepsilon_j = \sigma_j$, and on taking cross derivatives, we obtain

$$\partial \sigma_i/\partial \varepsilon_j = \partial \sigma_j/\partial \varepsilon_i \qquad (6.1\text{-}6)$$

or

$$c_{ij} = c_{ji} \qquad (6.1\text{-}7)$$

Equation (6.1-7) means that off-diagonal elements of the c_{ij} matrix are equal in pairs, so that the matrix is symmetric. The 36 stiffness constants are thereby reduced to 21. Similar relations hold for the moduli of compliance s_{ij}.

The bulk modulus K of a material (or its reciprocal, the compressibility) may readily be expressed in terms of the s_{ij} or c_{ij} coefficients. Since $K = -P/(\Delta V/V)$, where $\Delta V/V$ is the dilation ($= \varepsilon_1 + \varepsilon_2 + \varepsilon_3$) and P the hydrostatic pressure ($P = -\sigma_1 = -\sigma_2 = -\sigma_3$), we obtain from Eq. (6.1-4) the result (Problem 6-2):

$$K^{-1} = s_{11} + s_{22} + s_{33} + 2(s_{12} + s_{23} + s_{31}) \qquad (6.1\text{-}8)$$

It is sometimes necessary to distinguish between moduli measured adiabatically (at constant entropy) or isothermally (at constant temperature). In fact, quasi-static measurements usually yield the isothermal constants, while high-frequency dynamic measurements yield the adiabatic constants. The difference between the adiabatic and isothermal compliance constants is obtained by an obvious generalization of Eqs. (5.4-4)–(5.4-6):

$$[s_{ij}]_s = [s_{ij}]_T - \alpha_i \alpha_j T/c_\sigma \qquad (6.1\text{-}9)$$

where the subscript s on the left-hand side denotes constant entropy, and $\alpha_i \equiv (\partial \varepsilon_i / \partial T)_\sigma$. This difference is usually small, of the order of 1%, but for some types of anelasticity this difference becomes important (see e.g., Section 16.1 and Chapter 17).

6.2 The Characteristic Elastic Constants

It is important to realize that the entire matrix of coefficients (s_{ij}) or (c_{ij}) changes as the orientation of the coordinate axes for stress and strain are changed with respect to the axes of crystal symmetry. In particular, the matrices take their simplest forms when the coordinate axes for stress and strain are in a standard orientation with respect to the crystal axes.[†] The number of independent constants for each crystal class and the form of the (s_{ij}) and (c_{ij}) matrices when the coordinate axes are in this standard orientation with respect to the crystal axes are given in books on elasticity and crystal physics (see the general references at the end of the chapter). The elastic constants for a crystal in its standard orientation are called the *characteristic constants* of the material. Henceforth, we shall use the capital symbols C_{ij} and S_{ij} to denote these characteristic constants. For illustration, we will give some examples of the form of the matrices for the higher symmetry crystals. Thus, for the tetragonal case,[‡] with Ox_3 taken parallel to the tetragonal axis, the matrix (S_{ij}) takes the form

$$\begin{pmatrix} S_{11} & S_{12} & S_{13} & 0 & 0 & 0 \\ & S_{11} & S_{13} & 0 & 0 & 0 \\ & & S_{33} & 0 & 0 & 0 \\ & & & S_{44} & 0 & 0 \\ & & & & S_{44} & 0 \\ & & & & & S_{66} \end{pmatrix}_{\text{tetragonal}} \qquad (6.2\text{-}1)$$

[†] The manner of choosing a mutually perpendicular set of coordinate axes suited to each crystal system is given by Nye (1957, pp. 282–283).

[‡] Throughout this chapter the term "tetragonal crystals" will refer to the higher symmetry tetragonal crystals, belonging to the crystal classes D_{4h}, D_{2d}, C_{4v}, and D_4. These have six independent elastic constants. The lower tetragonal symmetry classes, C_{4h}, C_4, and S_4, which have seven independent constants will not be dealt with explicitly. Similarly, for the trigonal crystals, we refer only to the higher symmetry classes D_{3h}, C_{3v}, and D_3 which have six independent elastic constants.

while the (C_{ij}) matrix has an identical form. Only half the matrix need be shown because of its symmetric form, i.e., Eq. (6.1-7). The matrix for hexagonal crystals (with Ox_3 parallel to the hexagonal axis) is similar to (6.2-1) except that here $S_{66} = 2(S_{11} - S_{12})$ and $C_{66} = \frac{1}{2}(C_{11} - C_{12})$, so that there are only five independent elastic constants. The trigonal case is similar to the hexagonal but with an additional independent constant $S_{14} = -S_{15} = \frac{1}{2}S_{56}$ or $C_{14} = -C_{15} = C_{56}$.

In a similar way the matrix for the cubic case takes the standard form when the three coordinate axes coincide with the three cube axes,

$$
\begin{pmatrix}
S_{11} & S_{12} & S_{12} & 0 & 0 & 0 \\
 & S_{11} & S_{12} & 0 & 0 & 0 \\
 & & S_{11} & 0 & 0 & 0 \\
 & & & S_{44} & 0 & 0 \\
 & & & & S_{44} & 0 \\
 & & & & & S_{44}
\end{pmatrix}_{\text{cubic}}
\tag{6.2-2}
$$

The (C_{ij}) matrix has the same form. Thus there are only three independent constants for the cubic case. As already mentioned, for a crystal which is arbitrarily oriented with respect to the standard axes, all components of the matrix are, in general, nonzero. The components s_{ij} of the matrix for arbitrary orientation may be expressed in terms of the characteristic constants and the direction cosines between the coordinate axes and the standard axes. Equations of this type are given in numerous references (see, e.g., Hearmon, 1946).[†]

For present purposes it is of interest to quote the results for certain special cases. First, we express Young's modulus E in an arbitrary direction for the three crystal systems of highest symmetry noting that $E^{-1} = s_{11}$. Thus, for the tetragonal case,

$$
E^{-1} = (\gamma_1^4 + \gamma_2^4)S_{11} + \gamma_3^4 S_{33} + \gamma_1^2\gamma_2^2(2S_{12} + S_{66})
$$
$$
+ \gamma_3^2(1 - \gamma_3^2)(2S_{13} + S_{44})
\tag{6.2-3}
$$

where γ_1, γ_2, and γ_3 are the direction cosines between the direction of deformation and the three crystal axes. Similarly, for the hexagonal case

---

[†] The derivation of such relations requires the use of tensor notation, according to which the stiffness and compliance constants are represented as components of a tensor of fourth rank, with the corresponding use of a four-index notation.

E^{-1} is given by

$$E^{-1} = (1 - \gamma_3^2)^2 S_{11} + \gamma_3^4 S_{33} + \gamma_3^2(1 - \gamma_3^2)(2S_{13} + S_{44}) \quad (6.2\text{-}4)$$

For the cubic case,

$$E^{-1} = S_{11} - 2(S_{11} - S_{12} - \tfrac{1}{2}S_{44})\Gamma \quad (6.2\text{-}5)$$

where

$$\Gamma = \gamma_1^2\gamma_2^2 + \gamma_2^2\gamma_3^2 + \gamma_3^2\gamma_1^2 \quad (6.2\text{-}6)$$

The quantity Γ varies from zero for deformation in a $\langle 100 \rangle$ direction to a maximum value of $\tfrac{1}{3}$ for a $\langle 111 \rangle$ direction. Note the similar relation for c_{11} in an arbitrary direction in a cubic crystal (Problem 6-7). Another quantity of interest is the torsional modulus G of a crystal in the form of a rod of circular cross section. If γ_1, γ_2, and γ_3 are the direction cosines between the axis of the rod and the three standard crystal axes, the torsional modulus for the three crystal systems of interest is given by

$$\begin{aligned}
G^{-1} = {}& \tfrac{1}{2}(S_{44} + S_{66})(\gamma_1^4 + \gamma_2^4) + S_{44}\gamma_3^4 \\
& + [4(S_{11} - S_{12}) + (S_{44} - S_{66})]\gamma_1^2\gamma_2^2 \\
& + [2(S_{11} + S_{33} - 2S_{13}) + \tfrac{1}{2}(S_{66} - S_{44})]\gamma_3^2(1 - \gamma_3^2)
\end{aligned}$$
$$\text{(tetragonal)} \quad (6.2\text{-}7)$$

$$\begin{aligned}
G^{-1} = {}& S_{44} + (S_{11} - S_{12} - \tfrac{1}{2}S_{44})(1 - \gamma_3^2) \\
& + 2(S_{11} + S_{33} - 2S_{13} - S_{44})\gamma_3^2(1 - \gamma_3^2)
\end{aligned}$$
$$\text{(hexagonal)} \quad (6.2\text{-}8)$$

$$G^{-1} = S_{44} + 4(S_{11} - S_{12} - \tfrac{1}{2}S_{44})\Gamma \quad \text{(cubic)} \quad (6.2\text{-}9)$$

It is interesting to note that, for the hexagonal case, both E and G depend only on the direction cosine γ_3 of the angle between the specimen axes and the hexagonal axis. This result means that the elastic properties of a hexagonal crystal are invariant with respect to rotation about the hexagonal axis.

Before closing this section it is useful to consider also the case of *isotropic elasticity*. Although this book is concerned primarily with crystals, it is often necessary to deal with a random polycrystalline aggregate which behaves macroscopically as an isotropic medium. An isotropic material may be considered as the special case of a cubic crystal in which E and G are independent of orientation (i.e., of Γ). From Eqs. (6.2-5) and (6.2-9), this condition is met when

$$S_{44} = 2(S_{11} - S_{12}) \qquad (6.2\text{-}10)$$

or

$$C_{44} = \tfrac{1}{2}(C_{11} - C_{12}) \qquad (6.2\text{-}11)$$

Because of Eq. (6.2-10) or (6.2-11) there are now only two independent elastic constants, which may be taken as the shear modulus $G = 1/S_{44}$ and the bulk modulus $K = [3(S_{11} + 2S_{12})]^{-1}$ obtained by combining Eq. (6.1-8) with (6.2-2). In terms of these relations, Young's modulus E may be expressed by the well-known equation:

$$\frac{3}{E} = \frac{1}{G} + \frac{1}{3K} \qquad (6.2\text{-}12)$$

It is useful to express the mean isotropic constants of a polycrystal in terms of the crystal constants, for the cubic case. We first note that, since there is no change of shape of a cubic crystal under hydrostatic pressure, the mean bulk modulus K for the polycrystal should be equal to the value of K measured for a single crystal. This anticipated result turns out to be valid experimentally (Hearmon, 1956). For the mean shear modulus, the theory can become rather involved. Two extreme assumptions produce simple answers, however. The first approach is that of Voigt, who took the stiffness of the polycrystalline aggregate to be the space average of the stiffness of the single crystal. This procedure amounts to the assumption that the strain is uniform from grain to grain, and therefore that the stress is not. From this assumption it can be shown that

$$G = \tfrac{3}{5}C_{44} + \tfrac{2}{5}[\tfrac{1}{2}(C_{11} - C_{12})] \qquad (6.2\text{-}13)$$

The alternative approach is that of Reuss, who assumed that the *stress* is uniform throughout the polycrystalline aggregate. This assumption leads to the result (see Problem 6-8)

$$G^{-1} = \tfrac{3}{5}S_{44} + \tfrac{2}{5}[2(S_{11} - S_{12})] \qquad (6.2\text{-}14)$$

The actual experimental results appear to fall between these two extreme cases (see Hearmon, 1956). Though we shall not discuss them here, it is worth noting that other attempts have been made to derive more precise expressions, including the cases of noncubic crystals [see references in Hearmon (1956), Meister and Peselnick (1966)].

6.3　Use of Symmetrized Stresses and Strains

Still further simplifications of Hooke's law for crystals can be effected if, instead of the usual components of stress and strain, we choose six independent linear combinations of the usual components which possess certain fundamental symmetry properties associated with the crystal in question. These linear combinations which are known as *symmetry coordinates* of stress or strain, or as *symmetrized stresses and strains*, are obtained by means of group theory (Nowick and Heller, 1965). We will not attempt to derive these symmetrized linear combinations here, but have listed them for cubic, hexagonal, tetragonal and trigonal crystals in Tables 6-1 and 6-2. The reader will note that, taking both tables

TABLE 6-1

SYMMETRIZED STRESSES, STRAINS, AND COMPLIANCES OF TYPE I

Crystal system	Symmetry designation	Stress	Compliance	Strain
Cubic	A	$\sigma_1 + \sigma_2 + \sigma_3 \longrightarrow$	$S_{11} + 2S_{12} \longrightarrow$	$\varepsilon_1 + \varepsilon_2 + \varepsilon_3$
Hexagonal, tetragonal, or trigonal	A	$\dfrac{1}{\sqrt{2}}(\sigma_1 + \sigma_2) \longrightarrow$	$S_{11} + S_{12}$	$\dfrac{1}{\sqrt{2}}(\varepsilon_1 + \varepsilon_2)$
			$\sqrt{2}\,S_{13}$	
		$\sigma_3 \longrightarrow$	$S_{33} \longrightarrow$	ε_3

together, there are a total of six symmetrized stresses, and six corresponding strains,[†] listed for each crystal system. These symmetrized stresses and strains are separated according to the different ways in which they transform under the symmetry operations of the crystal. These ways of transforming are indicated by an appropriate symmetry

[†] Corresponding stresses and strains have similar indices. The fact that in some cases (e.g., the hexagonal and trigonal cases of Table 6-2) the strains do not always have the same numerical coefficients as the stresses to which they correspond is due to the unsymmetrical way that the "engineering" shear strains are defined in Eq. (6.1-2).

TABLE 6-2

SYMMETRIZED STRESSES, STRAINS, AND COMPLIANCES OF TYPE II

Crystal system	Symmetry designation	Stress	Compliance	Strain
Cubic	E	$2\sigma_1 - \sigma_2 - \sigma_3 \longrightarrow$	$S_{11} - S_{12} \longrightarrow$	$2\varepsilon_1 - \varepsilon_2 - \varepsilon_3$
		$\sigma_2 - \sigma_3 \longrightarrow$	$S_{11} - S_{12} \longrightarrow$	$\varepsilon_2 - \varepsilon_3$
	T (or F)	$\sigma_4 \longrightarrow$	$S_{44} \longrightarrow$	ε_4
		$\sigma_5 \longrightarrow$	$S_{44} \longrightarrow$	ε_5
		$\sigma_6 \longrightarrow$	$S_{44} \longrightarrow$	ε_6
Hexagonal	E_1	$\sigma_4 \longrightarrow$	$S_{44} \longrightarrow$	ε_4
		$\sigma_5 \longrightarrow$	$S_{44} \longrightarrow$	ε_5
	E_2	$\sigma_1 - \sigma_2 \longrightarrow$	$S_{11} - S_{12} \longrightarrow$	$\varepsilon_1 - \varepsilon_2$
		$\sigma_6 \longrightarrow$	$S_{11} - S_{12} \longrightarrow$	$\varepsilon_6/2$
Tetragonal (higher symmetry classes)	B_1 B_2	$\sigma_1 - \sigma_2 \longrightarrow$ $\sigma_6 \longrightarrow$	$S_{11} - S_{12} \longrightarrow$ $S_{66} \longrightarrow$	$\varepsilon_1 - \varepsilon_2$ ε_6
	E	$\sigma_4 \longrightarrow$	$S_{44} \longrightarrow$	ε_4
		$\sigma_5 \longrightarrow$	$S_{44} \longrightarrow$	ε_5
Trigonal (higher symmetry classes)	E	$\sigma_4 \longrightarrow$	$S_{44} \longrightarrow$	ε_4

$$\sqrt{2}\, S_{14}$$

$$\frac{1}{\sqrt{2}}(\sigma_1 - \sigma_2) \longrightarrow S_{11} - S_{12} \longrightarrow \frac{1}{\sqrt{2}}(\varepsilon_1 - \varepsilon_2)$$

- -

$$\sigma_5 \longrightarrow S_{44} \longrightarrow \varepsilon_5$$

$$\sqrt{2}\, S_{14}$$

$$\frac{1}{\sqrt{2}}\sigma_6 \longrightarrow S_{11} - S_{12} \longrightarrow \frac{1}{\sqrt{2}}\varepsilon_6$$

designation [†] (the letter A, B, E, or T) given in the tables. Since a symmetry operation produces a linear transformation of coordinates, it will, in general, take one component of stress (or strain) into a linear combination of all six components. The symmetrized quantities, however, show much simpler transformation behavior, as we shall now see.

For the study of anelasticity, it is advantageous to single out one of the symmetry designations from all the others. This is the one designated by the letter A which is often referred to as "totally symmetric." The linear combinations of stress (or strain) components listed under this heading are unchanged by carrying out any of the symmetry operations of the crystal. (For example, in the tetragonal crystal, rotation through $\pi/2$ about the tetragonal axis x_3 takes $x_1 \to x_2$ and $x_2 \to -x_1$. Thus, $\sigma_1 \to \sigma_2$ and $\sigma_2 \to \sigma_1$, but the linear combination $\sigma_1 + \sigma_2$ remains unchanged. Similarly, every symmetry operation of the crystal leaves $\sigma_1 + \sigma_2$ invariant.) Those symmetrized stresses and strains which meet this requirement of invariance will henceforth be classified as type I; these are the ones listed in Table 6-1. The remaining symmetrized components will be called type II. The special feature of a strain of type I is that a crystal subjected to such a strain is not lowered in symmetry by the deformation. On the other hand a crystal under a type II strain *is* lowered in symmetry. Thus, for example, a hexagonal crystal subjected to a tensile strain ε_3 along the hexagonal axis is still hexagonal, although its c/a ratio is changed. Similarly, in the cubic case, only a hydrostatic stress or strain is of type I. The type II stresses and strains on the other hand, represent pure shears. [‡] These are listed in Table 6-2, for the crystal systems of greatest interest.

Among the symmetry designations listed in Table 6-2 are those denoted by the letter B (e.g., B_1 or B_2). The corresponding symmetrized stresses or strains are not invariant under the symmetry operations of the crystal, as are those of type I, but they transform simply into plus or minus themselves. Symmetry designations involving the letter E, on the other hand, are doubly degenerate. This means that the symmetrized quantities occur in pairs, and that under a symmetry operation one of the quantities is, in general, taken into a linear combination of *both* members of the pair. Finally, the letter T (which occurs only for cubic crystals) refers to a triply degenerate symmetry designation.

[†] In group theory, these are the symbols of the corresponding *irreducible representations* of the point group (crystal class) to which the crystal belongs.

[‡] The converse is not true, however, since for lower symmetry crystals some shear strains are of type I. In particular, for triclinic crystals *all* strains are of type I.

In reducing the original set of stresses (or strains) to symmetry co-ordinates, it may be found that more than one symmetrized stress for a symmetry designation A or B, or more than one pair of stresses for designation E, may occur. In such a case we say that the particular symmetry designation is "repeated." In Table 6-1 this situation is found only under the designation A for hexagonal, tetragonal, and trigonal crystals, while in Table 6-2 it occurs under the doubly degenerate designation E for trigonal crystals. For lower symmetry crystals, it occurs more frequently. The significance of such repeated symmetry designations will soon be discussed.

Tables 6-1 and 6-2 also list, in the column following the stress, the *symmetrized compliance*.[†] This is the quantity which, when multiplied by a symmetrized stress, gives the corresponding symmetrized strain. As already stated, the importance of the symmetrized stresses and strains is the simplification which occurs in Hooke's law when they are used. The group theoretical theorems which serves as the basis for this simplification may be stated in simple terms as follows: (1) A symmetrized stress and a symmetrized strain which belong to different symmetry designations cannot be coupled to each other, i.e., the compliance constant relating such a stress and strain must be zero. (2) For a degenerate (E or T) designation, where symmetrized stresses and strains occur in matching sets (of two or three), the corresponding stresses and strains of a given set are related by the *same* compliance constant, while those which do not correspond are not coupled to each other.

A particular consequence of the first theorem is that a type I stress cannot give rise to a type II strain. For example, in a cubic crystal, hydrostatic pressure gives rise only to a volume change, but not to shear distortion of the crystal. To illustrate the second theorem, note that in cubic crystals under symmetry designation T, the stress σ_4 is not coupled to the strains ε_5 and ε_6. On the other hand, $\varepsilon_4/\sigma_4 = \varepsilon_5/\sigma_5 = \varepsilon_6/\sigma_6 = S_{44}$.

Whenever a symmetrized stress is decoupled from all symmetrized strains except the one which corresponds to it, Hooke's law reverts to the simple form $\varepsilon = J\sigma$. The appropriate compliance J is given in Tables 6-1 and 6-2 in terms of the coefficients S_{ij} for each such case. Each such compliance in the tables may be verified with the aid of Eq. (6.1-4) by

---

[†] A simple count based on Tables 6-1 and 6-2 shows that there are three symmetrized compliances for the cubic case, five for the hexagonal, and six for tetragonal and trigonal cases, which is the same as the numer of independent S_{ij} coefficients.

setting the other five symmetrized stresses equal to zero.[†] For example, for hydrostatic deformation in the cubic case, setting $\sigma_4 = \sigma_5 = \sigma_6 = 2\sigma_1 - \sigma_2 - \sigma_3 = \sigma_2 - \sigma_3 = 0$ (which implies $\sigma_1 = \sigma_2 = \sigma_3$), we readily obtain

$$\varepsilon_1 + \varepsilon_2 + \varepsilon_3 = (S_{11} + 2S_{12})(\sigma_1 + \sigma_2 + \sigma_3) \qquad (6.3\text{-}1)$$

as the relation between the symmetrized stress and strain of type I. Since the hydrostatic pressure P is given by $P = -\frac{1}{3}(\sigma_1 + \sigma_2 + \sigma_3)$ and the volume change by $\Delta V/V = \varepsilon_1 + \varepsilon_2 + \varepsilon_3$, it is clear that $3(S_{11} + 2S_{12})$ represents the bulk compressibility of the crystal. For other examples, see Problem 6-6.

Only when a given symmetry designation is repeated do we have coupling between different stresses and strains. As already mentioned, one example of this kind for the crystals considered here is in Table 6-1 for hexagonal, tetragonal, and trigonal crystals, where there are two symmetrized stresses (and two strains) of type I. Since these belong to the same symmetry designation, they are not decoupled, but the off-diagonal components in the matrix of coefficients are still symmetric. Accordingly there are three elastic compliance constants, as indicated by the arrows in the table. For this case, the appropriate Hooke's law relations among the two stresses and strains of type I is

$$[(\varepsilon_1 + \varepsilon_2)/\sqrt{2}] = (S_{11} + S_{12})[(\sigma_1 + \sigma_2)/\sqrt{2}] + \sqrt{2}S_{13}\sigma_3$$
$$\varepsilon_3 = \sqrt{2}S_{13}[(\sigma_1 + \sigma_2)/\sqrt{2}] + S_{33}\sigma_3 \qquad (6.3\text{-}2)$$

Thus, the complete matrix of symmetrized compliances for the tetragonal case takes the form

$$
\begin{pmatrix}
S_{11} + S_{12} & \sqrt{2}S_{12} & 0 & 0 & 0 & 0 \\
\sqrt{2}S_{12} & S_{33} & 0 & 0 & 0 & 0 \\
 & & S_{11} - S_{12} & 0 & 0 & 0 \\
 & & & S_{66} & 0 & 0 \\
 & & & & S_{44} & 0 \\
 & & & & & S_{44}
\end{pmatrix}
$$

which, though not completely diagonalized, is one step closer to diagonalization than (6.2-1). The second example of a repeating symmetry

[†] In general, the six symmetrized stresses are orthogonal, i.e., any five of them may be set equal to zero and the remaining one may then be applied by itself.

designation, occurs under designation E for trigonal crystals in Table 6-2. The situation here is analogous to the case just discussed, except that the E designation is doubly degenerate, so that now there are two sets of equations of the type of Eq. (6.3-2), each involving the same three compliances. The arrows in Table 6-2 illustrate the relationships involved. As we pass to crystals of lower symmetries, the occurrence of repeated symmetry designations becomes more and more frequent. Finally, for the triclinic case, all six stress and strain components are of type I, and we return to a set of completely coupled equations of the type (6.1-4). The reason for the absence of any simplification is that the triclinic crystal shows no symmetry[†]; therefore, there can be no simplification of Hooke's law as a consequence of symmetry considerations.

To summarize, the use of symmetrized stresses and strains takes us a long way toward decoupling of the general stress–strain (Hooke's law) relation, especially for the higher-symmetry crystals. Thus, for the cubic case, all six symmetrized stresses and strains are decoupled into relations of the form $\varepsilon = J\sigma$, while for hexagonal and tetragonal crystals four of the six stresses and strains are decoupled in this way.

Still another advantage to the use of the symmetrized quantities appears with respect to the difference between the adiabatic and isothermal moduli [see Eq. (6.1-9)]. Since thermal expansion cannot change the crystal symmetry, the quantity α_i can only contribute to a strain of type I. Thus, *the difference between adiabatic and isothermal compliance constants of type II is always zero.* For the cubic case, the only symmetrized compliance constant which shows such a difference is the compressibility $3(S_{11} + 2S_{12})$. In this case, since the linear thermal expansion coefficient α is the same in all directions, we have

$$3[S_{11} + 2S_{12}]_s = 3[S_{11} + 2S_{12}]_T - 9\alpha^2 T/c_\sigma \qquad (6.3\text{-}3)$$

It is clear that in the above presentation we could just as well have inverted the procedure and written the symmetrized stresses in terms of the symmetrized strains via the C_{ij} coefficients with the same subscripts as the corresponding compliances which appear in the two tables. This leads to particularly simple relations whenever stress–strain decoupling occurs and the appropriate modulus is the reciprocal of the corresponding

---

[†] A center of inversion is allowed in a triclinic case, but since the stress tensor already possesses such a symmetry on its own, this one symmetry operation produces no simplification.

compliance constant. Thus, for the cubic case[†]

$$C_{11} + 2C_{12} = (S_{11} + 2S_{12})^{-1}$$
$$C_{11} - C_{12} = (S_{11} - S_{12})^{-1} \qquad (6.3\text{-}4)$$
$$C_{44} = S_{44}$$

while for the hexagonal and tetragonal cases

$$C_{11} - C_{12} = (S_{11} - S_{12})^{-1}, \qquad \text{and} \qquad C_{44} = 1/S_{44} \qquad (6.3\text{-}5)$$

In addition, for tetragonal crystals

$$C_{66} = 1/S_{66} \qquad (6.3\text{-}6)$$

Only when there are coupled equations, such as Eqs. (6.3-2), does the inversion give a more complex relation between the C_{ij} and S_{ij} coefficients.

6.4   The "Practical" Moduli

In the previous section, we have shown that the simplest elastic behavior is obtained when the applied stresses are of the symmetrized types given in Tables 6-1 and 6-2. In the later parts of this chapter we shall see that the use of such symmetrized stresses results in simpler anelastic behavior as well. From a practical viewpoint, however, it is difficult to apply these theoretically simple stress systems to an actual sample. For example, it is difficult to excite a cubic crystal to oscillations in which the stress system consists only of the stress σ_4, or only of $\sigma_1 = -\sigma_2$. For static or resonant-type dynamic methods, the "practical" elastic constants are the Young's modulus (E) and torsional modulus (G) while for wave propagation methods, the practical moduli are those obtained from the longitudinal and transverse sound velocities. For a crystal oriented in an arbitrary direction, such practical moduli involve all or several of the symmetrized compliances. This is already clear from rela-

---

[†] Many authors use the following shorthand notation for the symmetrized elastic constants of cubic crystals:

$$S \equiv S_{44}, \qquad S' \equiv 2(S_{11} - S_{12}), \qquad S'' \equiv S_{11} + 2S_{12}$$
$$C \equiv C_{44}, \qquad C' \equiv \tfrac{1}{2}(C_{11} - C_{12}), \qquad C'' \equiv C_{11} + 2C_{12}$$

so that $C = 1/S$, $C' = 1/S'$, and $C'' = 1/S''$. This notation will, in fact, be used in Chapters 9 and 10.

tions already given, such as Eqs. (6.2-3)–(6.2-9). On the other hand, with a proper choice of crystal orientation, the practical moduli take on greatly simplified forms. It is therefore important to know the relationships between the practical moduli and the symmetrized compliances or stiffness constants. Of special importance for anelasticity are those experiments for which the practical modulus is related to only one symmetrized constant, or to no more than one symmetrized constant of type I and one of type II. Relations which meet this requirement are listed below for the four crystal systems of highest symmetry. In these equations v_l and v_t are the longitudinal and transverse sound velocities, respectively, and ϱ is the density. Finally, the subscript $\langle hkl \rangle$ refers to the orientation of the specimen axis for the E and G moduli, and to the direction of wave propagation for the velocity measurements.[†] For transverse waves, a superscript is also used to give the direction of polarization, when this direction needs to be specified.

Cubic Crystals

$$E_{\langle 100 \rangle}^{-1} = S_{11} = \tfrac{1}{3}[(S_{11} + 2S_{12}) + 2(S_{11} - S_{12})] \tag{6.4-1}$$

$$E_{\langle 111 \rangle}^{-1} = \tfrac{1}{3}[(S_{11} + 2S_{12}) + S_{44}] \tag{6.4-2}$$

$$G_{\langle 100 \rangle}^{-1} = S_{44} \tag{6.4-3}$$

$$(v_l^2 \varrho)_{\langle 100 \rangle} = C_{11} = \tfrac{1}{3}[(C_{11} + 2C_{12}) + 2(C_{11} - C_{12})] \tag{6.4-4}$$

$$(v_t^2 \varrho)_{\langle 100 \rangle} = (v_t^2 \varrho)_{[110]}^{[001]} = C_{44} \tag{6.4-5}$$

$$(v_t^2 \varrho)_{[110]}^{[1\bar{1}0]} = \tfrac{1}{2}(C_{11} - C_{12}) \tag{6.4-6}$$

$$(v_l^2 \varrho)_{\langle 111 \rangle} = \tfrac{1}{3}[(C_{11} + 2C_{12}) + 4C_{44}] \tag{6.4-7}$$

Hexagonal Crystals

$$E_{[001]}^{-1} = S_{33} \tag{6.4-8}$$

$$E_{[hk0]}^{-1} = S_{11} = \tfrac{1}{2}[(S_{11} + S_{12}) + (S_{11} - S_{12})] \tag{6.4-9}$$

$$G_{[001]}^{-1} = S_{44} \tag{6.4-10}$$

$$(v_l^2 \varrho)_{[001]} = C_{33} \tag{6.4-11}$$

$$(v_t^2 \varrho)_{[001]} = C_{44} \tag{6.4-12}$$

[†] Following customary notation, the angle brackets $\langle \ \rangle$ are used to designate a type of direction (e.g., $\langle 100 \rangle$ for any cube axis in a cubic crystal), while brackets [ ] are used when a *specific* direction in the crystal is intended.

$$(v_l{}^2\varrho)_{[hk0]} = C_{11} = \tfrac{1}{2}[(C_{11} + C_{12}) + (C_{11} - C_{12})] \tag{6.4-13}$$

$$(v_t{}^2\varrho)_{[hk0]}^{[\bar{k}\bar{h}0]} = \tfrac{1}{2}(C_{11} - C_{12}) \tag{6.4-14}$$

$$(v_t{}^2\varrho)_{[hk0]}^{[001]} = C_{44} \tag{6.4-15}$$

Tetragonal Crystals

$$E_{[001]}^{-1} = S_{33} \tag{6.4-16}$$

$$E_{\langle 100\rangle}^{-1} = S_{11} = \tfrac{1}{2}[(S_{11} + S_{12}) + (S_{11} - S_{12})] \tag{6.4-17}$$

$$E_{\langle 110\rangle}^{-1} = \tfrac{1}{2}[(S_{11} + S_{12}) + \tfrac{1}{2}S_{66}] \tag{6.4-18}$$

$$G_{[001]}^{-1} = S_{44} \tag{6.4-19}$$

$$(v_l{}^2\varrho)_{[001]} = C_{33} \tag{6.4-20}$$

$$(v_t{}^2\varrho)_{[001]} = C_{44} \tag{6.4-21}$$

$$(v_l{}^2\varrho)_{\langle 100\rangle} = C_{11} = \tfrac{1}{2}[(C_{11} + C_{12}) + (C_{11} - C_{12})] \tag{6.4-22}$$

$$(v_t{}^2\varrho)_{[100]}^{[010]} = C_{66} \tag{6.4-23}$$

$$(v_t{}^2\varrho)_{[100]}^{[001]} = (v_t{}^2\varrho)_{[110]}^{[001]} = C_{44} \tag{6.4-24}$$

$$(v_l{}^2\varrho)_{\langle 110\rangle} = \tfrac{1}{2}(C_{11} + C_{12}) + C_{66} \tag{6.4-25}$$

$$(v_t{}^2\varrho)_{[110]}^{[1\bar{1}0]} = \tfrac{1}{2}(C_{11} - C_{12}) \tag{6.4-26}$$

Trigonal Crystals

Same as (6.4-8)–(6.4-12). Also

$$(v_l{}^2\varrho)_{[100]} = C_{11} = \tfrac{1}{2}[(C_{11} + C_{12}) + (C_{11} - C_{12})] \tag{6.4-27}$$

There will be circumstances, of course, where crystals in the special orientations required to measure these simplest practical moduli will not be available. It may then be necessary to work from more general equations involving, in general, all of the symmetrized constants. For static or resonant dynamic methods Eqs. (6.2-3)–(6.2-9) are applicable. Nowick and Heller (1965) give a more complete listing, including crystals of lower symmetry. An important additional complication which may arise when crystals of arbitrary orientation are used, however, is related to the phenomenon of "torsion-flexure" coupling. This complication is discussed in Appendix D. For wave propagation methods, there is an analogous complication for crystals of arbitrary orientation, namely, that in such situations a transducer does not generate a pure wave (i.e., a longitudinal wave or a transverse wave of a defined polarization). This point is discussed in further detail in Appendix E. These two appendices are, in part, intended to impress the reader with the benefits to be derived by using the practical moduli listed above wherever possible. It should be noted, however, that not all the symmetrized constants are represented in Eqs. (6.4-1)–(6.4-27). Specifically, for hexagonal, tetragonal, and trigonal crystals, the compliance S_{13} cannot be obtained by means of the measurements listed. For anelasticity, however, we shall see that the measurement of S_{13} is not very important, since the other compliances of type I give essentially the information required. Similar remarks apply to the compliance S_{14} in trigonal crystals.

6.5   Transition from Elasticity to Anelasticity

In order to generalize the equations of elasticity of a crystal, as given by (6.1-3) and (6.1-4), to allow for time-dependent effects, one may employ any of the approaches used in Chapters 1–4. Thus, it is possible to introduce time derivatives for each of the stress and strain components, in the manner of Eq. (3.1-1), as a first method. A second method would be to generalize the Boltzmann relation (2.1-5), and the other integral equations which follow from it, to take into account the existence of six components of stress and of strain. In view of the relative conceptual simplicity of the formulation of anelasticity in terms of relaxation spectra, however, as well as its interpretation in terms of internal variables (see Chapter 5), we have chosen to base our formulation of anisotropic anelasticity on this approach. The results of other formulations can, of course, be derived from the one which will be used here.

In passing from the equations of anisotropic elasticity to those of anelasticity, each of the quantities s_{ij} (as well as the c_{ij}) must become a function of time for quasi-static experiments and must become complex and frequency dependent, $s^*(\omega)$, for dynamic experiments. Thus, each compliance constant s will now vary between the extreme values s_U and s_R, where s_U is the value of $s(t)$ for $t \to 0$ or the value of $s^*(\omega)$ for $\omega \to \infty$, while similarly, $s_R = s(t = \infty) = s^*(\omega = 0)$. The characteristic constants S_{ij} and C_{ij} thus go into *characteristic response functions*. It is useful to note that all of the relations of anisotropic elasticity which appeared in Sections 6.2 and 6.3 must be valid both in the limit of zero relaxation ($t \to 0$, $\omega \to \infty$) and in the limit of complete relaxation ($t \to \infty$, $\omega \to 0$).

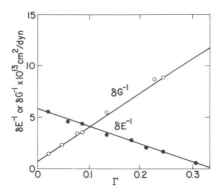

FIG. 6-2. Orientation dependence of the relaxations of the reciprocal Young's modulus and torsional modulus for the alloy Ag–26 at. % Zn at 350°C. (After Seraphim and Nowick, 1961).

Stated differently, an anelastic crystal reverts to an elastic crystal both when unrelaxed and when completely relaxed. Thus, following our earlier notation, the equations of the previous sections apply to an anelastic crystal either with a subscript U or with subscript R throughout. Furthermore, if $\delta s \equiv s_R - s_U$, the magnitude of the relaxation of any elastic compliance may be obtained from the equations of elasticity by taking differences between relaxed and unrelaxed quantities, i.e., by introducing the symbol δ before each compliance. For cubic crystals, for example, Eqs. (6.2-5) and (6.2-9) become

$$\delta E^{-1} \equiv \delta J_E = \delta S_{11} - 2[\delta(S_{11} - S_{12}) - \tfrac{1}{2}\delta S_{44}]\Gamma \qquad (6.5\text{-}1)$$

$$\delta G^{-1} \equiv \delta J_G = \delta S_{44} + 4[\delta(S_{11} - S_{12}) - \tfrac{1}{2}\delta S_{44}]\Gamma \qquad (6.5\text{-}2)$$

Equations (6.5-1) and (6.5-2) show that, for cubic crystals, the magnitude of relaxation δJ_E is linear in Γ, while δJ_G is also linear in Γ but has a slope opposite in sign and double in magnitude. Since these relations follow from the formal theory, and involve no assumptions beyond a knowledge of the crystal symmetry, they must apply in all cases. Accordingly, the extent to which these relations are obeyed may be used as a check on the internal consistency of a set of experiments. An example of an experimental test of Eqs. (6.5-1) and (6.5-2) is given in Fig. 6-2 for the case of the Zener relaxation effect in an Ag–Zn alloy; the equations are found to be valid to within experimental error.

The equivalent equations for the relaxation strengths are not so simple. Since $\Delta = \delta J / J_U$, we obtain expressions for the relaxation strengths by dividing Eqs. (6.5-1) and (6.5-2), respectively, by (6.2-5) and (6.2-9).

---

† Note that where there is the possibility of ambiguity, it is desirable to add a subscript to the relaxation strength (e.g., Δ_M) to denote the appropriate modulus M which is involved.

Clearly, the resulting expressions are not, in general, linear functions of the orientation factor Γ. An example is shown in Fig. 6-3 which plots relaxation strength data for the same samples that were used for Fig. 6-2.

The anelastic anisotropy for a cubic crystal is conveniently taken as the ratio $2\delta(S_{11} - S_{12})/\delta S_{44}$. In general, this ratio will be different from the elastic anisotropy ratio $2(S_{11} - S_{12})/S_{44}$. For example, a crystal which is nearly isotropic elastically can show a high degree of anelastic anisotropy (Berry, 1961).

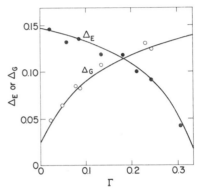

FIG. 6-3. Orientation dependence of the relaxation strengths for the same alloy as in Fig. 6-2.

Equations (6.5-1) and (6.5-2) give the magnitudes of the relaxations for the case of cubic crystals. Similar considerations may be applied to other crystal systems. In particular, any equation expressing a particular elastic or compliance constant in terms of the characteristic constants may be converted into a difference equation involving the relaxed and unrelaxed constants. It should be noted however that in the terminology of Appendix D, the equations of elasticity always involve the "free" elastic constants, and not those measured under conditions where the deformation is "pure," or of a more involved character. In general, for crystal orientations in which torsion-flexure coupling occurs, the difference equation must include correction terms, such as those given in Appendix D. Such corrections have, in fact, been made in obtaining the results plotted in Figs. 6-2 and 6-3.

Turning now from the question of the relaxation magnitude to the complete relaxation spectrum (i.e., the time or frequency dependence of the various moduli), we can readily see the benefit in using the symmetrized stresses and strains. Let us denote these symmetrized quantities by ε' and σ'. Consider first the case in which such a symmetrized pair, say ε_γ' and σ_γ', are decoupled from all other stresses and strains, or

$$\varepsilon_\gamma' = S_\gamma' \sigma_\gamma' \qquad (6.5\text{-}3)$$

where γ denotes the symmetry designation and S_{γ}' is the appropriate symmetrized compliance. The fact that such decoupling occurs frequently for crystals of higher symmetry is clear from Tables 6-1 and 6-2. In each such case the elastic stress–strain relation is of the form $\varepsilon = J\sigma$, and so the transition to anelasticity is made exactly as in Chapters 1–4. Specifically, to each such symmetrized modulus there corresponds a relaxation spectrum at constant stress, $X_{\gamma}(\ln \tau)$, and a relaxation spectrum at constant strain $Y_{\gamma}(\ln \tau)$ which are interrelated via Eqs. (4.2-1) and (4.2-2). Further, each such pair of spectra is independent of the spectra of any other symmetrized modulus belonging to a different symmetry designation.

When complete decoupling does not occur, the situation is more complex. Then, in general, there will be as many relaxation spectra at constant stress as there are independent symmetrized compliances. To examine this case in detail, it is helpful to invoke the thermodynamic viewpoint and the introduction of internal coordinates, as given in Chapter 5. In using this approach in the following section, we shall again benefit greatly from considerations of symmetry.

*6.6 Thermodynamic Considerations

This section is a generalization of Section 5.3, taking into account the existence of all six components of stress and of strain. We confine our treatment to a discussion centering about the Gibbs function, so that temperature, the various stress components σ_i and the internal variables ξ_p are taken as the independent variables. (Other thermodynamic potentials, such as the Helmholtz free energy, may be treated in an analogous manner; see Section 5.4.) The expression for the Gibbs function g per unit volume is a quadratic form in the independent variables σ_i, $\varDelta T$, and ξ_p. By analogy to Eq. (5.3-10), it takes the form

$$g(\sigma_i, \xi_p, T) = g(0, 0, T) - \tfrac{1}{2} \sum_{i,j} S_{ij}\sigma_i\sigma_j - \varDelta T \sum_i \alpha_i\sigma_i - \sum_{i,p} \varkappa_{ip}\sigma_i\xi_p$$

$$-\varDelta T \sum_p \chi_p\xi_p + \tfrac{1}{2} \sum_{p,q} \beta_{pq}\xi_p\xi_q \qquad (6.6-1)$$

where $g(0, 0, T)$ is the value of g when all σ_i and ξ_p are zero, but at a general temperature T. The coefficients S_{ij} are unrelaxed compliances, but the subscript U has been dropped. The differential expression for the Gibbs function is

$$dg = - \sum_i \varepsilon_i \, d\sigma_i - s \, dT - \sum_p A_p \, d\xi_p \qquad (6.6\text{-}2)$$

where the functions A_p are the affinities. Comparison of Eqs. (6.6-1) and (6.6-2) yields

$$\varepsilon_i = -\partial g/\partial \sigma_i = \sum_j S_{ij}\sigma_j + \alpha_i \, \varDelta T + \sum_p \varkappa_{ip}\xi_p \qquad (6.6\text{-}3)$$

$$A_p = -\partial g/\partial \xi_p = \sum_i \varkappa_{ip}\sigma_i - \sum_q \beta_{pq}\xi_q + \chi_p \, \varDelta T \qquad (6.6\text{-}4)$$

At equilibrium $A_p = 0$ for all p, so that

$$\sum_q \beta_{pq}\bar{\xi}_q = \sum_i \varkappa_{ip}\sigma_i + \chi_p \, \varDelta T \qquad (6.6\text{-}5)$$

is an equation for the equilibrium values of the internal variables $\bar{\xi}_p$. Substituting Eq. (6.6-5) into (6.6-4) we obtain

$$A_p = - \sum_q \beta_{pq}(\xi_q - \bar{\xi}_q) \qquad (6.6\text{-}6)$$

which is the same as Eq. (5.3-12). For small departures from equilibrium, it is again assumed that the rate of change of ξ_p is linearly related to all the affinities A_p, or

$$\dot{\xi}_p = - \sum_l L_{pl}A_l \qquad (6.6\text{-}7)$$

so that

$$\dot{\xi}_p = - \sum_q \omega_{pq}(\xi_q - \bar{\xi}_q) \qquad (6.6\text{-}8)$$

where ω_{pq} is again defined as in Eq. (5.3-15).

As discussed in Chapter 5, the problem could have been simplified if, instead of the original ξ_p coordinates we had used appropriate linear combinations in the form of the *normal internal variables* ξ_r'. That such coordinates can always be found was discussed in the last chapter. A further property of such normal coordinates is that they are also symmetry coordinates, i.e., each transforms under the symmetry operations of the crystal according to one of the simple ways denoted by the various symmetry designations of Tables 6-1 and 6-2 (Wilson *et al.*, 1955, Chap. 5). It is, therefore, desirable to symmetrize fully the above equations by using the symmetry coordinates of stress and strain (which we now denote by σ_k' and ε_l') as well as the appropriate symmetrized compliances (denoted here by S'_{kl}), some of which were given in Tables 6-1 and 6-2. Equations (6.6-1)–(6.6-8) may all be rewritten with primes on the variables ε, σ, ξ, and A, as well as on the coefficients, S, β, L, and ω. It should be regarded that each primed quantity also carries a label γ, referring to the symmetry designation to which it belongs, but this label will be dropped to simplify the notation.

The benefits derived by rewriting the equations in terms of symmetrized quantities and normal internal variables are as follows: (a) Equation (6.6-8) is simplified to the extent that there is no longer a summation over q, by virtue of the fact that the coordinates ξ' are the normal internal variables. We may then write this equation as

$$\dot{\xi}_r' = -\tau_r^{-1}(\xi_r' - \bar{\xi}_r') \tag{6.6-9}$$

for which the solution under creep conditions is

$$\xi_r' = \bar{\xi}_r'[1 - \exp(-t/\tau_r)] \tag{6.6-10}$$

(b) The matrix of coefficients β_{pq} in Eq. (6.6-1) is diagonalized so that

$$\beta'_{rs} = \delta_{rs}\beta_r' \tag{6.6-11}$$

where δ_{rs} is the Kronecker delta. (c) All equations involve coupling only among quantities belonging to the same symmetry designations. Thus Eq. (6.6-3) becomes

$$\varepsilon_k' = \sum_l S'_{kl}\sigma_l' + \alpha_k' \, \varDelta T + \sum_n \varkappa'_{kr}\xi_r' \tag{6.6-12}$$

where each of the primed quantities belongs to the same symmetry designation γ. Although Eq. (6.6-12) does not look simpler than (6.6-3), it must be remembered that the indices k and l usually run only over a comparatively small number of values, namely, over the number of times the symmetry designation is repeated (e.g., at most twice for the crystals in Tables 6-1 and 6-2). Substituting Eq. (6.6-10) into (6.6-12) shows that *the same set of relaxation times is associated with all moduli S'_{kl} which belong to a given symmetry designation.* For the special case (already discussed in Section 6.5) in which there is only one modulus S_{γ}' associated with the symmetry designation γ, the spectrum of lines whose relaxation times are $\tau_r^{(\gamma)}$ can only be obtained by studying the relaxation of that particular modulus. When, however, there is more than one modulus belonging to γ, the set of lines (i.e., the relaxation times) can be obtained by studying any one of the moduli S'_{kl} belonging to γ, but the magnitudes of the individual relaxations will be different for each S'_{kl}.

In order to calculate the isothermal relaxation magnitude, we utilize Eq. (6.6-12) to get

$$\delta S'_{kl} = \bar{\varepsilon}'^{\mathrm{an}}_k / \sigma_l' = \left(\sum_r \varkappa'_{kr} \bar{\xi}'_r \right) \Big/ \sigma_l' \qquad (6.6\text{-}13)$$

and utilizing Eq. (6.6-5) with the symmetrized (primed) quantities [noting Eq. (6.6-11)]

$$\bar{\xi}_n' = \beta_r'^{-1} \sum_r \varkappa'_{lr} \sigma_l' + \chi_r' \, \Delta T \qquad (6.6\text{-}14)$$

If, now, only the stress σ_l' is not zero, Eqs. (6.6-13) and (6.6-14) give

$$\delta S'_{kl} = \sum_r \beta_r'^{-1} \varkappa'_{kr} \varkappa'_{lr} \qquad (6.6\text{-}15)$$

for the magnitude of relaxation of the compliance S'_{kl}. This result may be compared with Eq. (5.3-18) for the case of simple stress and strain. In the absence of degeneracy, the magnitude of relaxation contributed by the spectral line r, and denoted as the partial relaxation magnitude $\delta S'^{(r)}_{kl}$, is then given by

$$\delta S'^{(r)}_{kl} = \varkappa'_{kr} \varkappa'_{lr} / \beta_r' \qquad (6.6\text{-}16)$$

so that, in general, $\delta S'^{(r)}_{kl}$ for different indices k and l are different. From Eq. (6.6-16) it is clear, however, that the partial relaxation magnitude for a compliance S'_{kl} for which $k \neq l$, is not an independent quantity, but is related to $\delta S'^{(r)}_{kk}$ and $\delta S'^{(r)}_{ll}$ by the relation

$$\delta S'^{(r)}_{kl} = [\delta S'^{(r)}_{kk} \, \delta S'^{(r)}_{ll}]^{1/2} \qquad (6.6\text{-}17)$$

Thus, for example, for the type I compliances of the hexagonal or tetragonal crystals (Table 6-1), the partial magnitude δS_{13} is not an independent quantity but can be derived completely from a knowledge of the partial magnitudes of the compliances S_{33} and $S_{11} + S_{12}$. (Here $S'_{11} = S_{33}$, $S'_{22} = S_{11} + S_{12}$ and $S'_{12} = S_{13}$). A similar remark may be applied to the compliance S_{14} for the case of trigonal crystals (see Table 6-2).

To summarize, for a discrete spectrum of well-resolved lines, each compliance of the type S'_{kk} possesses an independent spectrum (although the set of relaxation times for all S'_{kk} belonging to the same symmetry designation γ is the same). On the other hand, the modulus S'_{kl} ($k \neq l$)

has a relaxation spectrum which can be obtained from those of S'_{kk} and S'_{ll} by means of Eq. (6.6-17).

Unfortunately, the situation is more complex for the case of a continuous spectrum. In the latter case there is no longer a simple relation between spectra $X_{kl}(\ln \tau)$ and the spectra $X_{kk}(\ln \tau)$ and $X_{ll}(\ln \tau)$. To see how the breakdown of Eq. (6.6-17) comes about, one may simply consider two spectral lines which are close enough together so that they nearly coincide. It is easy to see that, although for each of the two lines Eq. (6.6-17) must apply, for the two taken together the relation breaks down. We must, therefore, conclude that for the case of a continuous spectrum, the number of independent spectra is the same as the number of independent compliances.

The entire argument of this section has been based on the thermodynamic g function, and the resulting spectra have been those of isothermal relaxation times at constant stress. As already mentioned, other thermodynamic functions could have been used, so that the same considerations apply to the alternative spectra in terms of which an anelastic material can be described.

PROBLEMS

6-1. Explain clearly why the elastic constant C_{11} is not the reciprocal of the compliance S_{11}.

6-2. Derive Eq. (6.1-8), using Eq. (6.1-4).

6-3. Show that, for the cubic, tetragonal, and hexagonal crystal systems, the compliance $S_{11} - S_{12}$ represents the proportionality constant between a pure shear stress and a corresponding shear strain.

6-4. Using Eq. (6.2-5), show that Young's modulus is isotropic in the (111) plane of a cubic crystal, and obtain the value for this modulus in terms of the characteristic compliances.

6-5. Verify Eq. (6.2-12) for an isotropic substance.

6-6. Using the matrices of coefficients (6.2-1) and (6.2-2) with the appropriate form for the hexagonal case given below (6.2-1), verify all of the symmetrized compliances of Table 6-2. In particular, show that there is complete decoupling among different symmetrized stresses and strains. Also verify the three compliance constants for the stresses and strains of type I in the hexagonal and tetragonal systems, as given in Table 6-1.

6-7. Show that the expression for the quantity c_{11} in an arbitrary direction in a cubic crystal is given analogously to Eq. (6.2-5) by $c_{11} = C_{11} - 2(C_{11} - C_{12} - 2C_{44})\Gamma$. [Hint: Use the fact that tensor components of stress and strain transform in the same way under a rotation of the axes, as well as the relations between the tensor components and the engineering stresses and strains (see footnote on page 131).] Use a similar argument to obtain the expressions analogous to Eqs. (6.2-3) and (6.2-4).

6-8. The orientation factor Γ for a cubic crystal is given by Eq. (6.2-6). Show that, in terms of the usual spherical coordinates θ and ϕ (θ = polar angle, ϕ = azimuthal angle), Γ becomes $\Gamma = \sin^2 \theta$ $(\cos^2 \theta + \sin^2 \theta \cos^2 \phi \sin^2 \phi)$. If now $J(\theta, \phi)$, the compliance for the direction determined by these two angles, has the form $J = a + b\Gamma$, where a and b are independent of orientation, show that for a random polycrystalline aggregate, the condition of uniform stress implies that the average orientation factor is $\bar{\Gamma} = \frac{1}{5}$. Discuss the meaning of this result. From Eqs. (6.2-5) and (6.2-9), identify the constants a and b for the cases $J = E^{-1}$ and $J = G^{-1}$. Compare with Eq. (6.2-14).

General References

FEDOROV, F. I. (1968). "Theory of Elastic Waves in Crystals." Plenum Press, New York.

HEARMON, R. F. S. (1946). *Rev. Mod. Phys.* **18**, 409.

HEARMON, R. F. S. (1956). *Advan. Phys.* **5**, 323.

HEARMON, R. F. S. (1961). "Applied Anisotropic Elasticity." Oxford Univ. Press, London and New York.

HUNTINGTON, H. B. (1958). *Solid State Phys.* **7**,

MEIXNER, J. (1954). *Z. Naturforsch.* **9a**, 654.

NEIGHBOURS, J. R., and SCHACHER, G. E. (1967). *J. Appl. Phys.* **38**, 5366.

NOWICK, A. S., and HELLER, W. R. (1965). *Advan. Phys.* **14**, 101.

NYE, J. F. (1957). "Physical Properties of Crystals." Oxford Univ. Press, London and New York.

Chapter 7 / Point Defects and Atom Movements

At this point we are ready to turn to the physical origin of anelastic relaxation processes, and, wherever possible, to discuss them in terms of atomic models. We shall first consider (in Chapters 8–11) those relaxation processes that originate from the class of crystal imperfections known as point defects. The present chapter is intended only to provide a brief account of the background material needed for this purpose. The reader who wishes to cover the field more thoroughly should also consult the list of general references given at the end of the chapter.

7.1 Types of Point Defects in Crystals

The simplest types of point defects are those produced in a crystal by the operations of removing an atom to an external surface, by substituting one atom of a different species, or by bringing an extra atom (either of the same or a different species) into a position which is not a normal lattice site. These operations produce defects which are called, respectively, a vacancy, a substitutional atom, and an interstitial atom. These defects may be regarded as the *elementary* point defects, in contrast to the *composite defects* or *defect complexes* which can be created by combining two or more elementary defects. Figure 7-1 provides a schematic representation of some of the possible defects. Defect *a* is the elementary vacancy, *b* the substitutional atom, *c* and *d* show two different types of *self-interstitials* (i.e., an interstitial atom of the same species as the host crystal), and *e* represents a foreign interstitial atom. The self-interstitial defect is often simply called an "interstitial." Among the simpler composite defects, *f* is the vacancy pair or divacancy, *g* the vacancy–substitutional pair, and *h* is a pair of adjacent substitutional atoms.

In crystalline solids composed of two or more atomic species, the important types of point defect are affected considerably by such factors as the existence of sublattices for different kinds of atoms, and possible requirements of stoichiometry or electrical charge balance. Due to these

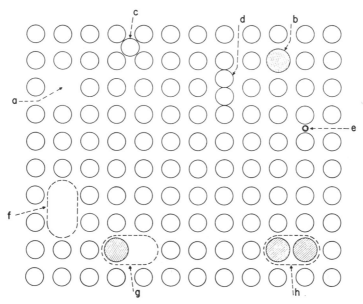

FIG. 7-1.   Schematic illustration of some point defects in monatomic crystal: *a*, vacancy; *b*, substitutional impurity; *c* and *d*, self-interstitials; *e*, interstitial impurity; *f*, divacancy; *g*, vacancy–substitutional impurity pair; *h*, substitutional impurity pair.

differences, monoatomic and compound crystals will be treated separately later in this section.

From the viewpoint of anelasticity, point defects possess several general characteristics of special importance. First, they are in general mobile, i.e., capable of migrating in the crystal. Second, a defect distorts the lattice, so that its introduction into the crystal is accompanied by a change in the dimensions of the crystal. A great deal more will be said about these characteristics later on. Other major attributes of a point defect are the thermodynamic parameters which serve to define the equilibrium concentration of the defect species in the crystal under given conditions. The most important of these is the *energy of formation* of the defect (strictly, the *enthalpy of formation* Δh_{d}). In some cases, this quantity can be measured experimentally. Frequently, however, information on the magnitude of Δh_{d} is available only from theoretical calculations, which may be performed by a number of techniques, most often by means of assumed pairwise atomic interaction potentials. A second important quantity is the *vibrational entropy* Δs_{d} of the defect, which is the change in entropy of the lattice when one defect is inserted in a specific location (i.e., excluding the configurational entropy). The theory of the vibrational entropy will be discussed further in Section 7.4B, but it is sufficient to state for now that Δs_d is positive for a relatively open defect, e.g., a vacancy, while it tends to be negative for a defect which crowds the surrounding atoms. We now turn to the more detailed consideration of monatomic crystals and compounds.

A. Monatomic Crystals

Of crystals in this category, most is known about defects in the face-centered cubic (fcc) metals. Detailed calculations have been made of defect formation energies in the noble metals, principally copper. Such calculations are not very reliable, but are nevertheless indicative of approximate magnitudes. For copper, the best calculations give a value for the enthalpy of formation of a vacancy Δh_v of about 1.0 eV, while for the interstitial a value $\Delta h_i \sim 4$ eV is obtained. Several possible configurations have been postulated for the interstitial in the fcc lattice, of which two have been widely discussed. The first (see Fig. 7-2a) is in the

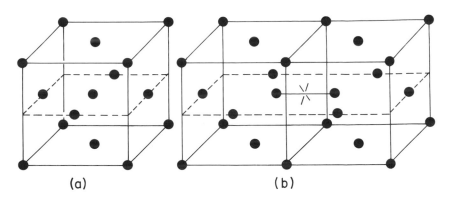

(a)   (b)

FIG. 7-2. (a) Body-centered, and (b) the $\langle 100 \rangle$ split interstitial in the fcc lattice.

center of the largest void, which occurs at positions typified by the center of the cube. In the second case, the extra atom plus one lattice atom together form a "split" or "dumbbell" configuration, as shown in Fig. 7-2b. The energy difference between these two configurations is small, but several calculations indicate that, for copper at least, the dumbbell configuration is the more stable one. Rough estimates of the entropies of formation Δs_v of the vacancy, and of Δs_i of the interstitial defects have been made. For the vacancy in the noble metals $\Delta s_v/k \sim 1$, while for the interstitial, even the sign of Δs_i is somewhat in doubt.

Composite defects have also been considered for the noble metals. An important defect is the divacancy (here denoted by vv), which is made up of a pair of vacancies in a nearest neighbor configuration. By considering the reduction in the number of broken bonds as well as the reduction in lattice strain energy, it is clear that the formation of a divacancy from a pair of single vacancies should reduce the enthalpy of the crystal. The *association or binding enthalpy* Δh_b is defined by

$$\Delta h_b = 2\,\Delta h_v - \Delta h_{vv} \qquad (7.1\text{-}1)$$

Calculations for Δh_b in the noble metals give a range of values varying from about 0.1 to 0.3 eV. Vacancies and certain substitutional impurities may also bind together to form complexes. Other composite defects include pairs of interstitial impurities, interstitial–substitutional impurity pairs, and higher complexes of vacancies and/or impurities.

Whereas the same types of defects must also occur in the body-centered cubic (bcc) metals and in elemental semiconductors of the diamond structure, there is not as much known about defects in these materials as in the fcc metals. It appears that Δh_v is relatively high in the diamond cubic structure, being about 2 eV in germanium and still higher in silicon (Bennemann, 1965).

B. STOICHIOMETRIC COMPOUNDS

This class of materials includes ionic crystals as well as highly ordered intermetallic compounds, both of which have separate sublattices for the A and B atoms. For simplicity we shall concentrate on compounds of the AB type. In order to maintain the chemical composition (or in the ionic crystals, electrical neutrality), vacancies may not form on one sublattice alone, but it is possible to have an equal number of vacancies on the two sublattices. A (dissociated) pair of vacancies on opposite sublattices is known as a *Schottky defect*. Similarly, a pair of interstitial defects is also a possibility (sometimes called an "anti-Schottky defect"). Another defect which maintains the exact chemical composition is the *Frenkel defect*, consisting of a vacancy on the A sublattice plus an A interstitial, or the same for the B sublattice. Figure 7-3 illustrates the Schottky and Frenkel defects. In addition to these defects, crystals that are not ionic allow *antistructure disorder*, such as an A atom on the B sublattice plus a B atom on the A sublattice.

An important defect complex is the AB divacancy (i.e., an associated Schottky pair), also shown in Fig. 7-3. In an ionic crystal of the type

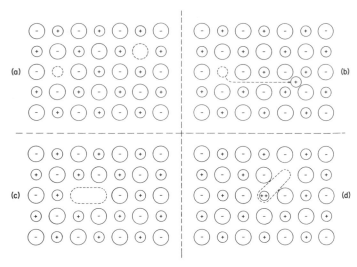

FIG. 7-3.   Illustration of point defects in an ionic crystal. *a*, Schottky defect; *b*, Frenkel defect; *c*, associated Schottky pair; *d*, divalent impurity–vacancy complex.

A^+B^-, the A vacancy is a center of negative charge (i.e., absence of a positive charge) and the B vacancy a center of positive charge. Thus the two members of a Schottky pair should have a Coulomb attraction to each other when at a large distance, and a relatively high association energy. Another interesting possibility occurs when impurities are added which differ in valence from the corresponding host-crystal atoms. Thus, for example, if a small concentration of a compound CB_2 is dissolved in an ionic AB lattice, electrical charge compensation must occur in order to maintain the charge neutrality of the crystal as a whole. Such compensation can take place by the introduction of one vacancy on the A sublattice for every molecule of CB_2. This is precisely what happens when $CaCl_2$ is dissolved in NaCl, for example. The Ca^{2+} ion and the vacancy then attract one another with a Coulomb force to form bound impurity–vacancy complexes (see Fig. 7-3d). In general, to compensate for an impurity with an excess charge requires a vacancy on the same sublattice or an interstitial on the opposite sublattice; the situation is reversed for an impurity which is deficient in charge.

Just as copper has become the prototype of the monatomic close-packed crystal, so NaCl (or KCl) is the most completely studied stoichiometric crystal. The theoretical calculation of the energy of formation of defects in ionic crystals is somewhat easier than for metals, since a large part of the energy arises from electrostatic forces. For the NaCl crystal, the enthalpy of formation of the Schottky defect Δh_S is found to lie in the range 1.9–2.1 eV depending on the choice of the repulsive potential. For the Frenkel defect Δh_F on the Na^+ sublattice, a value of about 3.5 eV is obtained. On the other hand, in the silver halides, which have also been widely studied, there is good evidence that $\Delta h_F < \Delta h_S$. This is a consequence of the small radius of the Ag^+ ion as well as the large van der Waals energy in the silver halides.

The energy of simple complexes in the alkali halides has also been calculated. The calculated value for the binding energy of the two vacancies of the Schottky defect is about 0.72 eV, while the binding of a divalent Ca^{2+} ion to a cation vacancy is 0.4 eV.

C. NONSTOICHIOMETRIC COMPOUNDS

Many compounds which are not strongly ionic show a strong tendency to deviate from exact stoichiometric proportions, and, in fact, may be difficult to prepare in a stoichiometric condition. Nonstoichiometry inevitably involves the presence of defects, since the number of lattice sites for A atoms and for B atoms in a crystal are always in a simple integral ratio. In a compound AB, for example, nonstoichiometry may arise when the element (A or B) present in excess enters interstitial positions, or when lattice vacancies are present on the opposite kind of site.

Some notable examples of compounds that tend to be nonstoichiometric are the II–VI compounds such as ZnO and CdS, and some transition metal oxides such as FeO and TiO. The latter compounds show nonstoichiometry to an extreme, involving such composition ranges as $TiO_{0.6}$ to $TiO_{1.35}$ and $Fe_{0.85}O$ to $Fe_{0.96}O$. A common way to control the degree of nonstoichiometry, and therefore the concentration of point defects, is to bring the crystal into equilibrium with a controlled external atmosphere (e.g., O_2 gas, in the case of oxides).

7.2 Defects in Equilibrium

Defects can be produced in a crystal in various ways. For example, a wide variety of defects (even those which have a high enthalpy of formation) may be created by irradiation with high energy particles or by cold working (see Section 7.6). Of more general interest, however, are defects which are present in equilibrium at a given temperature, since these defects usually play a major role in controlling atom movements. To be specific, let us consider the vacancy. It is well known that the equilibrium concentration of vacancies in a monatomic crystal at any temperature T is given by the Boltzmann-type expression

$$\bar{C}_v = \exp(-\Delta g_v/kT) = [\exp(\Delta s_v/k)][\exp(-\Delta h_v/kT)] \qquad (7.2\text{-}1)$$

where $\bar{C}_v$ is the equilibrium mole fraction of vacancies, and Δg_v is the free energy of formation of a vacancy (exclusive of the configurational entropy) which is given by

$$\Delta g_v = \Delta h_v - T \Delta s_v \qquad (7.2\text{-}2)$$

Equation (7.2-1) is derived by minimizing the total Gibbs free energy of a crystal containing vacancies, and is strictly valid only when $\bar{C}_v \ll 1$.

For interstitial defects, an equation similar to (7.2-1) applies, except that there will be an additional factor β_i, equal to the ratio of the number of interstitial sites to the number of substitutional sites. Thus $\bar{C}_i = \beta_i \times \exp(-\Delta g_i/kT)$, where $\bar{C}_i$ and Δg_i are the concentration and free energy of formation of interstitials. From expressions of this type, it is clear that only defects of relatively low enthalpy of formation can be present to any extent in equilibrium. Thus, from the numbers quoted in the previous section, it is clear that for the noble metals, such as copper, $\bar{C}_v \gg \bar{C}_i$ at all temperatures (see also Problem 7-1).

The net excess of vacancies over interstitials (or vice versa) in a crystal may be measured directly by comparing the macroscopic thermal expansion with precision x-ray lattice parameter measurements as a function of temperature. For a cubic crystal, the net fraction of excess vacant lattice sites at any temperature T is given by

$$\frac{\Delta N(T)}{N} = 3\left[\frac{\Delta l(T)}{l_0} - \frac{\Delta a(T)}{a_0}\right] \qquad (7.2\text{-}3)$$

where Δl is the change of length of a sample between temperature T and a reference temperature T_0 (where the length is l_0), and similarly for the lattice parameter values Δa and a_0. The temperature T_0 must be chosen sufficiently low that the defect concentration at T_0 is negligible. If only single vacancies are present in appreciable amounts, $\Delta N/N = \bar{C}_v$, and the measurements can then be analyzed in accordance with Eq. (7.2-1) to yield Δh_v and Δs_v. Table 7-1 lists some of the values of Δh_v which have been determined in this way for a number of pure metals, as well as the corresponding concentration $\bar{C}_v(T_m)$ of vacancies at the melting point.

TABLE 7-1

VALUES FOR ENTHALPY OF FORMATION OF A VACANCY Δh_v AND FOR THE ACTIVATION
ENERGY FOR SELF-DIFFUSION Q IN VARIOUS SIMPLE METALS

Metal	$\bar{C}_v(T_m)$	Δh_v (eV)	Q (eV)	$\Delta h_v/Q$	$\Delta h^* = Q - \Delta h_v$
Ag	1.7×10^{-4}	1.09	1.91	0.57	0.82
Al	9.0	0.75	1.40	0.54	0.65
Au	7.2	0.94	1.81	0.52	0.87
Pb	1.7	0.49	1.05	0.47	0.56
Na	7.0	0.42	0.45	0.93	0.03

For stoichiometric compounds, the auxiliary condition that the concentrations of the two types of vacancies must be equal gives, for Schottky
defects, the relation

$$\bar{C}_S^2 = \exp(-\Delta g_S/kT) \tag{7.2-4}$$

where the subscript S refers to the Schottky defect. Thus $\bar{C}_S$ is proportional to an exponential involving $\frac{1}{2}\Delta g_S$. A similar result applies in the
case of Frenkel defects.

Defect complexes may be regarded as produced by a "reaction"
between two defects. Thus, for example, the combining of two vacancies
to form a divacancy in a monatomic crystal may be represented by the
reversible association reaction $2v \rightleftharpoons vv$. From elementary statistical mechanics, it follows that

$$C_{vv}/C_v^2 = (z/2)\exp(\Delta g_b/kT) \tag{7.2-5}$$

where C_{vv} and C_v are the concentrations (mole fractions) of divacancies
and single vacancies, respectively, z is the coordination number, and
Δg_b is the free energy of binding of the two vacancies, given by

$$\Delta g_b = 2\,\Delta g_v - \Delta g_{vv} \tag{7.2-6}$$

Here Δg_{vv} is the free energy of formation of the divacancy. Equation
(7.2-5) is a form of the law of mass action for the vacancy association
reaction.

In an analogous way, the reaction between a vacancy v and a solute
atom s (where the solute is present in a low concentration) to form a

vacancy–solute pair may be expressed as v + s ⇌ vs. The corresponding mass action equation is

$$C_{vs}/C_vC_s = z \exp(\Delta g_b/kT) \qquad (7.2\text{-}7)$$

where Δg_b is now the free energy of binding of the vs pair.

7.3   Kinetics of Atom or Defect Migration

The jump of an atom or defect from one site to another in a crystal lattice is a simple example of a rate process, and may be treated by the theory which has been applied widely to chemical kinetics. Zener was apparently the first to recognize that the problem of atom movements is much simpler than most chemical reactions. He showed that a formula for the rate of jump may be profitably derived from classical statistical mechanics, starting from first principles [e.g., see Lidiard (1957) or a

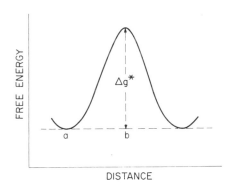

FIG. 7-4.   Schematic diagram of free energy barrier which must be surmounted when an atom migrates through one lattice distance. Position *b* represents the activated state or "saddle point."

more general treatment by Vineyard (1957)]. The result, which describes the rate at which an atom or defect surmounts a barrier of the type shown in Fig. 7-4, may be expressed in the form

$$w = w_0 \exp(-\Delta g^*/kT) = w_0[\exp(\Delta s^*/k)][\exp(-\Delta h^*/kT)] \qquad (7.3\text{-}1)$$

where w is the probability of a jump per second, w_0 is an appropriate average lattice vibration frequency, and Δg^* is the *free energy of activation* given by

$$\Delta g^* = \Delta h^* - T\,\Delta s^* \qquad (7.3\text{-}2)$$

in terms of an enthalpy of activation Δh^* and a vibrational entropy of activation Δs^*. The quantity Δg^* may be interpreted as a true thermodynamic free energy, since it represents the work done to take the atom in question from its minimum position a to the activated state or "saddle point" b while allowing it to vibrate freely in the plane perpendicular to Fig. 7-4. (At the same time, the motions of all other atoms of the crystal are unconstrained.)

Equation (7.3-1) may be compared with the empirical Arrhenius rate equation written in the form

$$w = W_0 e^{-Q/kT} \tag{7.3-3}$$

where W_0 and Q are constants. If Δh^* and Δs^* are independent of temperature, this comparison clearly shows that

$$W_0 = w_0 \exp(\Delta s^*/k) \tag{7.3-4}$$

while $Q = \Delta h^*$. The case in which Δh^* is a function of temperature will be dealt with in Section 7.4A.

The process of thermal activation is not the only way by which a particle can pass over a potential barrier. It is also possible for the particle in question to make a transition from one potential minimum to another, even at the absolute zero of temperature, by *quantum-mechanical tunneling*. This possibility occurs because the wave functions which describe the system with the particle localized in one or another valley are not orthogonal and, therefore, are not true eigenfunctions. Quantum-mechanical tunneling will be most likely to manifest itself for the case of electrons or light atoms, small barrier heights, and low temperatures.

7.4 General Remarks Applicable to Both Formation and Activation of Defects

There is an important similarity between the equation for the equilibrium concentration of defects, as given, for example, by Eq. (7.2-1), and that for the rate of migration as given by Eq. (7.3-1); namely, in both cases the equation takes the form

$$\ln y = \ln K + (\Delta s/k) - (\Delta h/kT) \tag{7.4-1}$$

where y refers either to $\bar{C}_d$ or to w, and K takes on the value unity[†] or

---

[†] As pointed out in Section 7.2, in some cases of defect formation the factor K is a small integer rather than just unity. Furthermore, often C_d is not measured directly but rather a quantity proportional to it, such as a resistivity change $\Delta\varrho_d$. In such a case, the proportionality constant involved may be lumped into K.

w_0, respectively. In both cases, Δs is an appropriate vibrational entropy and Δh an enthalpy. Because of this similarity, certain features in the handling and interpretation of this equation can be given in a single discussion applicable to both situations.

A. GRAPHICAL DETERMINATION OF Δh AND Δs

The form of Eq. (7.4-1) suggests a plot of $\ln y$ versus $1/T$ as a means of obtaining the parameters Δh and Δs. This statement is, of course, based on the assumption that Δh and Δs are constants, independent of T. Under such conditions, the negative slope of the plot is $\Delta h/k$. Further, the intercept at $1/T = 0$ gives $\ln K + (\Delta s/k)$. If K is known, a value for Δs is then obtained. For the case of activated processes, a reasonable value for w_0 ($= K$) is usually estimated from the Debye frequency, i.e., by setting $w_0 = k\Theta/h$ where Θ is the Debye temperature and h is Planck's constant. For a typical Debye temperature of $300°K$, $w_0 = 6 \times 10^{12}$ sec^{-1}.

It turns out that there is no theoretical basis for expecting Δh and Δs to be strictly independent of T; a slow dependence of these quantities on temperature due, e.g., to thermal expansion of the lattice, is in fact very reasonable. To analyze this more general case, it helps to remember that both for formation of defects and for activation the quantities Δh and Δs are true thermodynamic quantities representing the differences between two specific states of the crystal. It is therefore possible to apply the combined first and second laws of thermodynamics in the form $d(\Delta h) = T\, d(\Delta s) + \Delta v\, dP$, relating Δh, Δs, and the appropriate formation or activation volume Δv. If constant pressure is maintained, so that $dP = 0$, the changes in Δh and in Δs (e.g., with temperature) are inter-related according to

$$d(\Delta h) = T\, d(\Delta s) \tag{7.4-2}$$

The negative slope of the $\ln y$ versus $1/T$ plot, when Δh and Δs are functions of T is, therefore,

$$-\frac{d(\ln y)}{d(1/T)} = \frac{\Delta h(T)}{k} - \frac{1}{k}\frac{d(\Delta s(T))}{d(1/T)} + \frac{1}{kT}\frac{d(\Delta h(T))}{d(1/T)} \tag{7.4-3}$$

In obtaining Eq. (7.4-3) it has been assumed that the temperature dependence of K is negligible. From Eq. (7.4-2), the last two terms of Eq. (7.4-3) must just cancel each other. It is therefore concluded that the negative slope of the plot of $\ln y$ versus $1/T$ is $\Delta h/k$ regardless of whether or not Δh depends on T. The significance of this result is that if $\Delta h = \Delta h(T)$, there will be *curvature* in the plot of $\ln y$ versus $1/T$, and further that the slope of the plot in a limited region gives the value of $\Delta h(T)$ corresponding to the average temperature of that region.

B. THEORIES OF Δs

The vibrational entropy of formation of a defect Δs_d, or the vibrational entropy of activation Δs^*, is the change in entropy of the crystal associated with the formation of the defect or the activation of a defect, respectively, at a specific location. The existence of either quantity Δs stems from the change in the vibration frequencies of the lattice associated with the formation (or the activation) of the defect. Thus, if the crystal of N atoms initially possesses a set of $3N$ frequencies, v_i $(i = 1, 2, \ldots, 3N)$ for its normal modes of vibration, and after formation (or activation) of the defect these frequencies become v_i', then the quantity Δs is given by (Huntington *et al.*, 1955)

$$\Delta s/k = \sum_{i=1}^{3N} \ln(v_i/v_i') \tag{7.4-4}$$

Clearly, in a large crystal, only a small number of the $3N$ frequencies will be appreciably changed by the defect. Equation (7.4-4) shows the result mentioned earlier, that if most or all of the frequency changes constitute reductions (i.e., $v_i' \leq v_i$), then $\Delta s < 0$; conversely, if $v_i' \geq v_i$, $\Delta s < 0$.

In calculating Δs, it is convenient to separate the effects of local vibration frequencies from the longer-range effects. These second effects arise (at least in part) from the long-range strain field about a point defect, which is primarily a shear stress (entirely so for the case of a defect in an infinite, isotropic, elastic medium). Zener (1951) assumes that the part of the free energy, $\Delta g_2 = \Delta h_2 - T \Delta s_2$, due to the strain field represents the work done to produce the strain, and that it is therefore proportional to G, the average shear modulus. From this assumption it is readily shown (see Problem 7-2) that

$$\Delta s_2 = -\left[\frac{\partial(\Delta g_2)}{\partial T}\right]_P \simeq -\Delta h_2 \left(\frac{1}{G_0} \frac{dG}{dT}\right) \tag{7.4-5}$$

where G_0 is the value of the shear modulus at $T = 0$, and Δh_2 is the value of Δg_2 at $T = 0$. Since dG/dT is usually negative, the contribution Δs_2 due to the long-range stress field is positive. For simple activated processes, it appears possible to attribute Δs^* entirely to this strain effect, i.e., to compute Δs^* from Eq. (7.4-4) with reasonable accuracy (Wert and Zener, 1949).

C. FORMATION AND ACTIVATION VOLUMES

The quantity Δh in Eq. (7.4-1) is an enthalpy and may, therefore, be written as

$$\Delta h = \Delta u + P\, \Delta v \tag{7.4-6}$$

in which P is the pressure, while Δu and Δv are the internal energy change and volume change, respectively, associated with either the formation or the activation of the defect. At zero pressure, there is no distinction between Δh and Δu. On the other hand, high-pressure experiments offer the opportunity to obtain Δv separately. Thus, combining Eqs. (7.4-1) and (7.4-6), we obtain

$$\ln y = \text{constant} - (\Delta v/kT)P \tag{7.4-7}$$

where the constant is independent of pressure. From the slope of a plot of $\ln y$ versus P, the formation or activation volume Δv may be obtained.

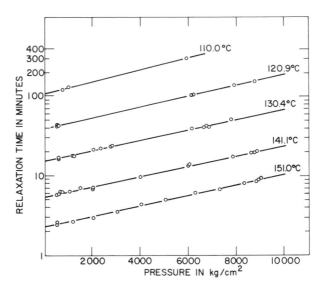

FIG. 7-5. Variation of relaxation time with pressure for the Zener relaxation in Ag–27.7 at. % Zn. (After Tichelaar and Lazarus, 1959.) From the slope of the lines, an activation volume of 5.36 cm³/gm atom is obtained, which corresponds to 54% of the atomic volume.

An example of such a plot for the kinetics of the Zener relaxation is shown in Fig. 7-5.

It is readily anticipated that Δv for formation of a vacancy should be positive (and in magnitude, somewhat less than an atomic volume), while Δv for an interstitial should be negative. The activation volume Δv^* of a defect should also generally be positive, though smaller in magnitude.

7.5 Diffusion

A. FORMAL THEORY

The simplest definition of the diffusion coefficient or diffusivity D is that given by *Fick's first law*, which relates the flux of matter J (e.g., the number of atoms per square centimeter per second) to the concentration gradient:

$$J = -D(\partial N/\partial x) \qquad (7.5\text{-}1)$$

where N is the number of diffusing atoms per unit volume, and D is in units of cm^2 sec^{-1}. (This equation is expressed in the one-dimensional form for simplicity; it is readily extended to three dimensions.) Equation (7.5-1) can be converted into a differential equation in $N(x, t)$, when the principle of conservation of matter is applied to an infinitesimally small region, to obtain Fick's second law:

$$\partial N/\partial t = D(\partial^2 N/\partial x^2) \qquad (7.5\text{-}2)$$

This differential equation may be solved for various boundary conditions, as discussed in standard treatises on diffusion. A most important problem is one in which a fixed total amount of solute (usually a radioactive tracer) is applied as a thin film to the surface of a long specimen rod, and then allowed to diffuse inward over a time t at temperature T. The solution for the concentration of the diffusing species $N(x, t)$ as a function of depth x and diffusion time t is

$$N(x, t) \propto (Dt)^{-1/2} \exp(-x^2/4Dt) \qquad (7.5\text{-}3)$$

where the proportionality constant depends on the total quantity of material initially deposited. Equation (7.5-3) shows that a plot of log N versus x^2 gives a straight line whose negative slope is $1/4Dt$. Such a plot provides a convenient method for obtaining D experimentally.

B. ATOMISTIC INTERPRETATION OF D

The diffusivity D is readily expressed in terms of the mean jump rate Γ, of the migrating atom. From the theory of random walk, assuming that successive jumps occur in a completely random manner, the equation

$$D = \tfrac{1}{6}\Gamma d^2 \qquad\qquad (7.5\text{-}4)$$

is obtained, where d is the distance that an atom moves in one atomic jump. In the case of cubic crystals, it is more useful to express D in terms of the lattice parameter a, and in terms of the jump rate w between *specific* sites ($w = \Gamma/z$ where z is the number of equivalent directions in which the jump can occur):

$$D = \alpha a^2 w \qquad\qquad (7.5\text{-}5)$$

involving a numerical constant α. For substitutional diffusion in the fcc lattice $d = a/\sqrt{2}$ and $z = 12$, and in the bcc lattice $d = a\sqrt{3}/2$ and $z = 8$, so that in both cases $\alpha = 1$, while in the diamond cubic structure $d = a\sqrt{3}/4$ and $z = 4$, giving $\alpha = 1/8$. On the other hand, for the diffusion of interstitial solutes among octahedral sites in the bcc lattice, $d = a/2$ and $z = 4$ and therefore $\alpha = 1/6$. This latter case is of particular interest in relation to the Snoek relaxation (see Chapter 9).

C. DIFFUSION BY THE VACANCY MECHANISM

In the early literature, it was believed that substitutional diffusion occurred through a direct interchange of nearest-neighbor atoms. Later the possibility of diffusion through the agency of defects developed. In recent years several convincing reasons have been found for believing that diffusion, particularly in the close-packed metals, occurs by means of a vacancy mechanism. One of these reasons is that the calculated enthalpy of activation for the direct interchange process, and even for "ring" diffusion (Zener, 1950) is too large to account for the observed activation energy. The experimental reasons include: (1) the observation of marker movements (the "Kirkendall effect") in substitutional diffusion, showing that solute and solvent atoms do not move at the same rates; and (2) the observation via anelasticity (see Section 10.5) of enhanced atomic movements after quenching, showing that a defect which can be quenched in from high temperatures is involved. The direct measurement of vacancy concentrations and formation energies discussed in Section

7.2 has further added confidence to the idea that single vacancies are responsible for diffusion.

Equations (7.5-4) and (7.5-5) were derived under general considerations, irrespective of the detailed mechanism, and would therefore appear to be valid for the vacancy mechanism. These equations, however, were based on the assumption that successive jumps are completely random, i.e., uncorrelated. In the case of a vacancy mechanism, however, an atom that has just jumped still has the vacancy next to it; therefore, it has a higher than random probability of making the reverse jump which annuls the effect of the original jump. To correct for this effect requires the introduction of a factor f, called the "correlation factor," in Eqs. (7.5-4) and (7.5-5). For self-diffusion (i.e., tracer diffusion), this is simply a numerical factor less than unity. For example, for the fcc and hcp lattice $f = 0.781$ while for the bcc case $f = 0.727$. On the other hand, for diffusion in alloys, the correlation factor involves the individual jump frequencies of the solute and solvent, as well as the rate of dissociation of an impurity–vacancy pair. Thus f can be strongly temperature dependent in such a situation. For example, for impurity diffusion by a vacancy mechanism in fcc crystals, and under the simplifying assumption that correlation effects extend only to nearest-neighbor distances, the following expression is obtained:

$$f = [w_1 + (7/2)w_3]/[w_1 + w_2 + (7/2)w_3] \tag{7.5-6}$$

Here w_1 and w_2 are the rates of solvent–vacancy and impurity–vacancy exchanges, respectively (both jumps retaining an impurity–vacancy pair), while w_3 is the rate of dissociation of a vacancy from an impurity atom.

The second complication that must be considered when a vacancy mechanism is operating is that the jump frequency w is no longer given by a simple expression of the type (7.3-1). Rather, w is now the product of the probability that a vacancy is in a specific site next to the atom under consideration (which equals $\bar{C}_v$, the equilibrium concentration of vacancies) and the jump frequency of a vacancy. Thus

$$w = \bar{C}_v w_v = \bar{C}_v[w_0 \exp(-\Delta g^*/kT)] \tag{7.5-7}$$

and in view of (7.2-1) and (7.3-1), we again find the Arrhenius form $w = A \exp(-Q/kT)$, except that now

$$Q = \Delta h_v + \Delta h^* \tag{7.5-8}$$

$$W_0 = w_0 \exp(\Delta s_v + \Delta s^*)/k \tag{7.5-9}$$

Combining these results with (7.5-5) and introducing the correlation factor f gives (for cubic crystals) the well-known form for D

$$D = D_0 e^{-Q/kT} \qquad (7.5\text{-}10)$$

with Q given by Eq. (7.5-8) and

$$D_0 = \alpha f a^2 w_0 \exp(\Delta s_v + \Delta s^*)/k \qquad (7.5\text{-}11)$$

The most reliable measurements of self-diffusion in fcc metals show that D_0 generally ranges between 0.1 and 1.0 cm^2 sec^{-1}. This corresponds to an entropy factor $\exp(\Delta s_v + \Delta s^*)/k \sim 100$. From such results, it appears that Δs^* as well as Δs_v is positive. This agrees qualitatively with Zener's concept that Δs^* may be calculated from the elastic strain effect [Eq. (7.4-5)]. Values of the activation energy Q for tracer diffusion in metals are listed in Table 7-1. It is noteworthy that Δh_v is generally a little more than half the value of Q. Accordingly, from Eq. (7.5-8), Δh^* is slightly less than half of Q. These values of $\Delta h^* = Q - \Delta h_v$ are also given in Table 7-1.

The case of diffusion in a chemical gradient is much more complicated than tracer diffusion, since in the former case there may be a net flow of vacancies during the diffusion process. In such a situation dislocations may play a role as sources and sinks for vacancies, while if a high supersaturation of vacancies develops, porosity may occur. Because of these complications, the diffusion data usually used to compare with anelastic relaxation times in substitutional alloys are those obtained by tracer methods.

7.6 Nonequilibrium Defects

When diffusion takes place by means of a defect mechanism, the defects contributing are taken to be present in thermal equilibrium, at concentrations given by the equations of Section 7.2. The same may be said for anelastic phenomena which depend on defects. There are anelastic effects, however, which are produced by nonequilibrium defects. Such defects may be introduced by the following four methods[†]:

[†] The present discussion does not do justice to the extensive study of defects produced by each of these methods. For fuller presentations, see the various treatises listed at the end of the chapter.

(a) quenching,
(b) irradiation,
(c) cold working, and
(d) vapor deposition (thin film formation).

Of these methods quenching is the most straightforward; the quenching process simply tends to retain in the crystal a concentration of defects which was in equilibrium at an elevated temperature. If the quenching is completely effective, the enthalpy of formation of the defect may be obtained from the quenched-in concentration as a function of quenching temperature. The most extensive experiments of this type have been carried out for gold (generally, using resistivity measurements). The value of the enthalpy of formation of a vacancy Δh_v obtained by quenching is 0.98 ± 0.03 eV, which is in excellent agreement with the value obtained from at-temperature thermal expansion measurements [utilizing Eq. (7.2-3)]. It would also appear that annealing of the quenched-in effect at relatively low temperatures should permit one to obtain the activation energy for the migration of single vacancies. Experiments on gold and other metals indicate, however, that association of single vacancies to form divacancies takes place rapidly. Since the activation energy for divacancy migration is lower than that for single vacancy migration, the divacancy motion tends to dominate the annealing process.

Irradiation offers the opportunity to introduce point defects whose energies of formation may be so high that their equilibrium concentrations, even at the melting point, are negligible. Many different particles have been used to produce "radiation damage," including neutrons, electrons, γ rays and deuterons. The simplest possibility is the creation of a Frenkel (vacancy plus interstitial) pair. There are two classes of such pairs. In the first, the interaction between the vacancy and interstitial is strong enough that they may be considered as bound. These defects are termed "close pairs." The second class comprises a Frenkel pair in which there is no binding, so that when the interstitial becomes mobile (assuming $\Delta h_i^* < \Delta h_v^*$), its movement is random. More complex defect clusters may also form, especially with neutron irradiation. An important method of deducing which defects are formed is by studying the annealing kinetics of a suitable physical property (e.g., electrical resistivity) at successively increasing temperatures. In this way a series of annealing stages is obtained. In the much studied case of metallic copper irradiated at low temperatures ($<20°$K), e.g., there are three annealing stages found below room temperature. Stage I occurs below 60°K and is, in fact, made up of a group of substages, while stage II is broad and relatively poorly defined, falling between 60–220°K. Finally, stage III (between 220 and 330°K) is a relatively well-defined stage with an activation energy close to 0.7 eV which often shows second-order kinetics. It has been shown that stage I includes substages due to various types of close pairs, as well as at least one substage involving long-range defect migration (presumably of an interstitial defect of some sort). The major controversy has centered about stage III, which has been attributed by different authors to the migration of vacancies, of divacancies, and of interstitials, and by still others to the release of interstitials from traps or the break-up of di-interstitials.

Plastic deformation or "cold working" may produce point defects by a mechanism which will be discussed in Section 12.3. The complication here is that, in addition to the point defects generated, a complex network of dislocations is also formed. Accordingly, the annealing stages are not so well defined as those following irradiation. Finally, crystals in the form of thin films produced by vacuum evaporation methods are generally known to possess high concentrations of point defects. There has, however, not yet been a significant attempt to study defects in such films by the use of anelasticity.

PROBLEMS

7-1. Taking the enthalpy of formation of a vacancy in copper to be 1.0 eV and the vibrational entropy $\Delta s_v = 1.5k$, and for the corresponding values for the self-interstitial, $\Delta h_i = 4$ eV and $\Delta s_i = 0$, calculate the vacancy and interstitial concentrations in equilibrium at 1350 (the melting point), 1000, 500, and 300°K.

7-2. Assuming that the free energy Δg_2 due to the strain field about a defect is proportional to an average shear modulus G and that the corresponding enthalpy and entropy Δh_2 and Δs_2, respectively, are both independent of temperature, obtain Eq. (7.4-5).

General References

ADDA, Y., and PHILIBERT, J. (1966). "La Diffusion dans les Solides." Presses Univ. de France (in 2 vols.).
BILLINGTON, D. S., and CRAWFORD, J. H. (1962). "Radiation Damage in Solids." Oxford Univ. Press, London and New York.

CORBETT, J. W. (1966). "Electron Radiation Damage in Semiconductors and Metals." Academic Press, New York.

COTTERILL R. M. J., *et al.*, eds. (1965). "Lattice Defects in Quenched Metals." Academic Press, New York.

DAMASK, A. C., and DIENES, G. J. (1963). "Point Defects in Metals." Gordon and Breach, New York.

DIENES, G. J., and VINEYARD, G. H. (1957). "Radiation Effects in Solids." Wiley (Interscience), New York.

GIRIFALCO, L. A. (1964). "Atomic Migration in Crystals." Blaisdell, New York.

HASS, G., and THUN, R. E., eds. (1963–1964). "Physics of Thin Films," Vols. 1, 2. Academic Press, New York.

HOWARD, R. E., and LIDIARD, A. B. (1964). *Rep. Progr. Phys.* **27**, 161.

KELLY, B. T. (1966). "Irradiation Damage to Solids." Pergamon Press, New York.

KRÖGER, F. A. (1964). "Chemistry of Imperfect Crystals." North-Holland Publ., Amsterdam.

LIDIARD, A. B. (1957). *In* "Encyclopedia of Physics," Vol. XX. Springer, Berlin.

MANNING, J. R. (1968). "Diffusion Kinetics for Atoms in Crystals." Van Nostrand, Princeton, New Jersey.

SCHULMAN, J. H., and COMPTON, W. D. (1962). "Color Centers in Solids." Pergamon, Oxford.

SHEWMON, P. G. (1963). "Diffusion in Solids." McGraw-Hill, New York.

SWALIN, R. A. (1962). "Thermodynamics of Solids," Chaps. 13–15. Wiley, New York.

U. S. Department of Commerce (1967). Nat. Bur. Std. Misc. Publ. 287, Calculation of the Properties of Vacancies and Interstitials, U. S. Government Printing Office, Washington, D. C.

VAN BUEREN, H. G. (1961). "Imperfections in Crystals." North-Holland Publ., Amsterdam.

Chapter 8 / Theory of Point-Defect Relaxations

In Chapter 5, we introduced the concept of a set of internal variables which are influenced by stress as the physical basis for anelastic relaxation. In that treatment, there were no restrictions placed on the nature of the internal variables. In the present chapter, the internal variables are related to the concentrations of point defects on various crystallographic sites. In dealing with this more specific type of internal variable, we shall find that the theory (both thermodynamic and kinetic) can be developed much further than for the completely general case. To begin with, we must remind the reader about some aspects of crystal symmetry, and then introduce the notion of defect symmetry. We will then introduce a tensor which characterizes a point defect in its interaction with an applied stress field. With these basic concepts, it becomes possible to develop the thermodynamic and kinetic theories of anelastic relaxation due to point defects.

8.1 Crystal and Defect Symmetry

The symmetry of a perfect crystal is most fully defined by its space group, which is the collection of symmetry operations that takes the atomic arrangement into an identical (indistinguishable) one. The space groups (of which there are 230) include symmetry elements defining lattice translations or rotations (proper and improper),[†] as well as elements which combine rotations and translations, such as screw axes. For present purposes, we are interested only in the rotational type of symmetry operations and not in translations. The reason for this choice is that the applied stress is always taken to be homogeneous, so that only the type of site on which a defect is situated (and not its exact location) is important as far as response to stress is concerned. The collection of symmetry operations of a crystal excluding translations form the so-called

---

[†] These include mirror planes and centers of inversion as special cases.

"crystal class" or "point group" of the crystal (of which there are 32). The space group and the crystal class of most of the common crystals are given in standard references.[†] Each crystal class belongs to one of the seven crystal *systems* (cubic, tetragonal, hexagonal, trigonal, ortho-rhombic, monoclinic, and triclinic).

We turn now to the case of a crystal which contains just one point defect. This defect may be as simple as an extra or missing atom, or as complex as a cluster of several foreign or displaced atoms extending over several lattice sites. The presence of the defect destroys the translational symmetry of the crystal, and the resultant crystal may be thought of as a large molecule. For brevity, the point-group symmetry of this defective crystal is called the *defect symmetry*. The defect symmetry may be lower than or equal to that of the perfect crystal; clearly the presence of the defect cannot increase the symmetry. We will see that if the defective crystal has a lower symmetry than the perfect crystal (i.e., than the crystal class), there must exist more than one distinguishable configuration or "orientation" of the defect. We use the symbol n_d for this number of distinct defect orientations.[‡] The defect symmetry also belongs to one of the seven symmetry systems.[§]

It is easiest to consider defect symmetries by discussing separately the two types of defects defined in Section 7.1. First there is the elementary point defect, which consists of either a single substitutional atom, a vacancy, or an interstitial atom. In this case, it is easy to see that the defect symmetry is simply the site symmetry of the defect.[||] The term *site symmetry* denotes the point symmetry of the perfect crystal at the site at which the defect is created. The site symmetry, which is generally different for different points in the unit cell of the crystal, depends on the space group of the crystal and is conveniently given in the *International Tables for X-ray Crystallography* (Int. Union of Crystallogr., 1952) for all possible sites in all of the 230 space groups. Therefore, the defect

---

[†] See, e.g., Taylor and Kagle (1963) as well as the comprehensive treatise by Wycoff (1963).

[‡] If h_x is the number of symmetry operations in the crystal class (i.e., the order of the point group of the crystal) and h_d the corresponding number in the point group of the crystal containing one defect, then it is easy to show (Nowick and Heller, 1965) that $n_d = h_x/h_d$.

[§] In this case, the common term "crystal system" would be a misnomer.

[||] This statement follows from the fact that, once an elementary point defect is present, the only symmetry elements possible are those (axes and planes) which pass through the defect. However, the statement is not valid if a further lowering of symmetry occurs through readjustment of the surrounding lattice (see the end of this section).

symmetry can be obtained immediately for any elementary point defect in any crystal. We will illustrate this shortly with a simple example.

The second type of point defect is the composite defect, made up of more than one foreign, extra, or missing atom. For such a defect, the symmetry can be lower than or equal to the site symmetry. It is useful to concentrate here on the important case of a pair, consisting of two members which are either alike or unlike. For the like pair, or "dumbbell," the appropriate site from which to survey the symmetry of the surrounding lattice is clearly the midpoint of the pair. The following symmetry elements, if they exist as part of the site symmetry, are completely compatible with the presence of the dumbbell: (a) an n-fold rotation (or rotation–inversion) axis coincident with the dumbbell axis (with $n = 2$, 3, 4, or 6), (b) a two-fold rotation axis perpendicular to the dumbbell axis, (c) mirror planes containing or perpendicular to the dumbbell axis, (d) a center of inversion. All of these elements clearly take the dumbbell into itself. Thus, if any of these elements are part of the site symmetry, they also belong to the defect symmetry. Any other symmetry element which may belong to the site symmetry does not take the dumbbell into itself and therefore cannot be included in the defect symmetry. For the case of an unlike pair, the appropriate site from which to survey the symmetry of the surrounding lattice is any point on the pair axis. The unlike pair is compatible only with the following symmetry elements: (a) an n-fold rotation or rotation inversion axis parallel to the pair, (b) a mirror plane containing the pair axis. Only these elements, when present in the site symmetry, also belong to the defect symmetry.

The above considerations are readily generalized (Nowick and Heller, 1965) to the statement that the defect symmetry is specified by the group of elements which is *common both to the defect when isolated from the crystal, and to the site on the perfect crystal about which the defect is built.*

We now consider a simple example designed to illustrate both elementary defects and pairs. The cube face of a simple cubic lattice is chosen, as illustrated in Fig. 8-1. Sites of different symmetry types are indicated and labeled with letters, following the "Wycoff notation" used by the *International Tables for X-ray Crystallography*. (The absence of some letters is a result of confining ourselves to points which lie on a cube face.) Site a, at a cube corner, has full cubic symmetry, O_h (m3m),[†] while site c, at a face center, has full tetragonal symmetry

---

[†] We will give symmetry classes first in the Schoenflies notation, then in the international notation, for the benefit of the reader who is more familiar with one of these than the other.

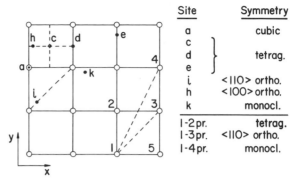

Site	Symmetry
a	cubic
c	
d	tetrag.
e	
i	<110> ortho.
h	<100> ortho.
k	monocl.
I-2 pr.	tetrag.
I-3 pr.	<110> ortho.
I-4 pr.	monocl.

FIG. 8-1. The sites that can occur in the cube face of a simple cubic lattice, as well as some possible pairs.

D_{4h} (4/mmm) with the tetragonal axis perpendicular to the page. Site d, on an edge center, also has D_{4h} symmetry, but now the tetragonal axis is parallel to the y axis. On the other hand, site e an arbitrary point on the cell edge, also has tetragonal symmetry but of a lower class C_{4v} (4mm) (the y axis is four-fold and there are two mirror planes containing that axis). The site i on the face diagonal is orthorhombic, class C_{2v} (mm2). Here the C_2 axis is along [110] and the two mirror planes are (1$\bar{1}$0) and (001). Because of the occurrence of ⟨110⟩-type directions and planes this defect is described, briefly, as having ⟨110⟩ orthorhombic symmetry. Site h is also of C_{2v} symmetry but with planes and axes parallel to the three cube directions; it is therefore described as ⟨100⟩ orthorhombic. Even the arbitrary point k in this plane has symmetry C_s (m), i.e., it lies on the (001) mirror plane. Of course, there always exists a completely arbitrary point at coordinates x, y, z which has no symmetry at all (i.e., a triclinic site symmetry).

Now, let us illustrate what occurs when pairs are created on such a lattice. First, consider a like pair (e.g., two vacancies or two substitutional atoms of the same kind) placed at points 1 and 2 of Fig. 8-1. Such a defect has a site (i.e., the midpoint) equivalent to point d; furthermore, the defect symmetry is the same as the site symmetry, since the tetragonal symmetry of site d lies along the axis of the pair and is, therefore, compatible with it. Similar remarks apply to an unlike pair at points 1 and 2, for which the defect symmetry is the same as that of the site e. But now, consider a like pair at 1 and 3. The site symmetry is of type c, but a four-fold axis perpendicular to the page is incompatible with the pair (since a rotation through $\pi/2$ would take pair 1–3 into pair 2–5). Therefore, the defect symmetry is D_{2h} (mmm), and in fact of the ⟨110⟩ orthorhombic type. Similarly, a dumbbell at positions 1 and 4 has site symmetry of type d, but the overall defect symmetry is only the (001) mirror plane.

In this case, the site symmetry excludes a rotational axis along the pair, while the pair excludes those axes provided by the site; therefore, only the mirror plane remains.

It should be emphasized that for purposes of determining the possibility of anelastic behavior, only knowledge of the symmetry *system* (tetragonal, orthorhombic, etc.) to which the defect symmetry belongs is of importance. The symmetry system is much more easily determined by inspection than the complete symmetry group, as is readily seen from the examples discussed in connection with Fig. 8-1.

The reader may wonder about the effect on symmetry of the readjustment[†] of the surrounding lattice atoms to the presence of the extra or missing atoms which constitute the defect. The fact is that such readjustment often occurs with no change in symmetry of the defect, since it usually takes place in a manner which is symmetrical both with respect to the atoms comprising the defect, and to the site about which they are situated. On the other hand, there exists the possibility that a postulated configuration for a defect is unstable, i.e., that it represents a local energy *maximum* rather than a minimum energy position. In this case, further lowering of symmetry can occur through readjustment. Important examples are the split or dumbbell interstitial in fcc metals (Section 11.2) and impurities which manifest the Jahn–Teller effect (Section 11.1).

As already mentioned, if the symmetry of the crystal containing a defect is lower than the crystal symmetry, then $n_d > 1$, i.e., there is more than one equivalent but distinguishable orientation of the defect. We illustrate this point with Fig. 8-1. For point a, $n_d = 1$. For point c, $n_d = 3$, i.e., there is a point of type c which lies in each of the three cube faces. For the unlike pair at positions 1 and 2, we have $n_d = 6$, since the pair may be arranged along 1–2, 2–1, 2–3, 3–2 as well as two equivalent orientations which lie normal to the plane of the page.

8.2   Concept of an "Elastic Dipole"

The insertion of a point defect into a crystal produces local elastic distortions. As a result of these distortions, there will be an interaction between the defect and a homogeneous stress applied to the crystal. In

---

[†] Often, the term "relaxation" is used to describe this process in the literature. We prefer the term "readjustment" to avoid confusion with the entirely different concept of "relaxation" as used throughout this book.

some ways this interaction is analogous to the interaction of an electric dipole with an applied electric field. Accordingly, a defect which produces local distortions has been called an elastic dipole (Kröner, 1958). A major difference is that, whereas an electric dipole is characterized by a vector quantity (the "dipole moment") which determines its interaction with the (vector) electric field, an elastic dipole is characterized by a second-rank tensor since it interacts with a stress field. A convenient characterization of the elastic dipole is contained in the following equation (Nowick and Heller, 1963) which describes the change in strain of a crystal when defects are introduced

$$\varepsilon_{ij}^{d} - \varepsilon_{ij}^{0} = \sum_{p=1}^{n_d} \lambda_{ij}^{(p)} C_p \qquad (8.2\text{-}1)$$

Here ε_{ij}^{d} and ε_{ij}^{0} refer, respectively, to the tensor components[†] of strain of a crystal with and without defects $(i, j = 1, 2, 3)$, p is the index denoting one of the n_d possible equivalent orientations of the defect, and

$$C_p \equiv N_p/N_\mu = v_0 N_p \qquad (8.2\text{-}2)$$

is the mole fraction of defects in orientation p. Here N_p and N_μ are, respectively, the number of defects in orientation p and the number of molecules per unit volume, and v_0 is the molecular volume. Equation (8.2-1) defines a second-rank tensor $\lambda_{ij}^{(p)}$ which characterizes the elastic dipole, whose components are given by

$$\lambda_{ij}^{(p)} \equiv \partial \varepsilon_{ij}/\partial C_p \qquad (8.2\text{-}3)$$

The quantity $\lambda_{ij}^{(p)}$ is therefore the strain (component ij) per unit mole fraction of defects all having the same orientation p. The six coefficients $\lambda_{ij}^{(p)}$ may be regarded as a simple generalization of the notion of the "size factor" of an impurity in a cubic crystal. (The size factor is $a^{-1} \, da/dC$ where a is the lattice parameter and C the molar concentration of the impurity). The present generalization is based on the recognition that a collection of defects all in the same orientation will, in general, give rise to a distortion requiring all six strain components for its description. We will later see that this λ tensor completely determines the interaction of a defect with a stress field, and therefore, the behavior of a defect as an elastic dipole.[‡]

[†] Note that here we use the two-index tensor notation for the components of strain. These are related to the one-index notation used in Chapter 6 in the footnote on p. 131.

[‡] Clearly only the λ tensor for one orientation p is independent, since the coefficients $\lambda_{ij}^{(q)}$ are obtainable from $\lambda_{ij}^{(p)}$ by carrying out the symmetry operation that takes defect p into defect q.

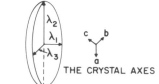

THE STRAIN ELLIPSOID

THE CRYSTAL AXES

FIG. 8-2. The strain ellipsoid of the λ tensor for a particular defect orientation in the crystal.

Since the tensor $\lambda_{ij}^{(p)}$ represents a strain tensor, it must be symmetric ($\lambda_{ij}^{(p)} = \lambda_{ji}^{(p)}$) and therefore can be characterized by a strain ellipsoid with three mutually perpendicular principal axes, as shown in Fig. 8-2. When expressed in the coordinate system of the principal axes, the λ tensor becomes diagonal, of the form

$$\begin{pmatrix} \lambda_1 & 0 & 0 \\ 0 & \lambda_2 & 0 \\ 0 & 0 & \lambda_3 \end{pmatrix} \tag{8.2-4}$$

The importance of the quantities λ_1, λ_2, and λ_3, which are called the *principal values*, is that they are independent of the orientation p. This statement follows from the fact that all of the n_d orientations of the defect are crystallographically equivalent; therefore, while each strain ellipsoid may differ in orientation from the others, the three principal values of all must be the same.

To relate the components $\lambda_{ij}^{(p)}$, which are expressed in terms of axes fixed in the crystal, to the principal values λ_m, we use the standard equation for the transformation of a second-rank tensor (Nye, 1957) to obtain

$$\lambda_{ij}^{(p)} = \sum_{m=1}^{3} \alpha_{im}^{(p)} \alpha_{jm}^{(p)} \lambda_m \tag{8.2-5}$$

where the index m runs over the three principal values, while $\alpha_{im}^{(p)}$ is the direction cosine between the fixed axis i and the mth principal axis for the dipole of orientation p.

The right-hand side of Fig. 8-2 is meant to illustrate the fact that, in general, there is no simple relation between the crystal axes and the principal axes of the λ tensor. However, when the defect possesses symmetry, the strain ellipsoid must indeed reflect the symmetry of the defect which it represents. This requirement restricts the orientation of the principal axes to lie along the symmetry axes of the defect and also, in some cases, decreases the number of independent principal values from three to either one or two. The effect of symmetry on a second-order symmetric tensor is given in standard treatises (see e.g., Nye, 1957) where it is shown that the form of the tensor is determined completely by the symmetry *system*. In the present case, the tensor in question is the λ tensor and the symmetry is that of the defect. Table 8-1 summarizes the effect of symmetry on the principal axes and principal values of the λ tensor. For a cubic defect, all principal values are equal, i.e., the strain ellipsoid is a sphere. In this case, there is only one independent coefficient of the λ tensor. For a defect of tetragonal, hexagonal, or trigonal symmetry, the λ tensor takes the form (8.2-4) with two principal values equal to each other, while the third principal axis lies along the major symmetry axis of the defect. In this case, the distortion about the defect is isotropic in the plane perpendicular to the major symmetry axis and there are only two independent components of the λ tensor. In all the remaining systems there are three independent principal values. In the orthorhombic case, all of the principal axes are symmetry axes, but for the monoclinic

TABLE 8-1

EFFECT OF DEFECT SYMMETRY ON PRINCIPAL VALUES AND PRINCIPAL AXES
OF THE λ TENSOR

Defect symmetry	Principal values	Principal axes	No. of independent λ components
Cubic	$\lambda_1 = \lambda_2 = \lambda_3$	Arbitrary	1
Tetragonal, hexagonal, and trigonal[a]	$\lambda_1 \neq \lambda_2 = \lambda_3$ or $\lambda_1 = \lambda_2 \neq \lambda_3$	Axis 1 along major symmetry axis or Axis 3 along major symmetry axis	2
Orthorhombic	$\lambda_1 \neq \lambda_2 \neq \lambda_3$	Along the three symmetry axes	3
Monoclinic	$\lambda_1 \neq \lambda_2 \neq \lambda_3$	Axis 1 or 3 along the symmetry axis	4
Triclinic	$\lambda_1 \neq \lambda_2 \neq \lambda_3$	Unrelated to crystal axes	6

[a] Two different conventions are used. When the defect is in a cubic crystal, it is conventional to take the unique principal value as λ_1, while in crystals which themselves have a unique axis (along x_3), the unique value is taken as λ_3.

case only one principal axis is a symmetry axis. In this latter case, therefore, an additional direction cosine must be specified in order to define the λ tensor completely; thus there are four independent components of the λ tensor, as listed in the last column. In the triclinic case, of course, all six components are independent.

The fact that the form of the λ tensor is determined only by the symmetry *system* of the defect has important consequences. It means that more than one distinct defect orientation can give rise to the same λ tensor.[†] The most common example of this situation occurs when two defects differ in orientation by 180°. It is clear that the tensor ellipsoid of Fig. 8-2 has inversion symmetry even though the defect may not. Thus, referring again to Fig. 8-1, the tetragonal defect consisting of an unlike pair on positions 1 and 2 must give rise to the same λ tensor as the reversed pair (on positions 2 and 1). For both cases, the unique principal value of the λ ellipsoid must lie along the y axis and the distortion in the x-z plane will be isotropic. In this case, therefore, while the number of distinct defect orientations is six, the number of independent λ tensors is only three. In general, we define the number of independent λ tensors by the symbol n_t. Since the tensor symmetry is equal to or greater than the defect symmetry, we have $n_t \leq n_d$, where the symbol $<$ here means "equal to a submultiple."

It has been emphasized earlier that the interaction of a defect with a stress field (and, therefore, the behavior of the defect as an elastic dipole) is determined entirely by its λ tensor. Accordingly, two defects which differ in orientation but which give rise to the same λ tensor are indistinguishable in terms of their behavior under stress. It is therefore clear that n_t is an important quantity for the characterization of the anelastic behavior of a crystal containing defects. If $n_t = 1$, all defects look alike to a stress field. If $n_t > 1$, an arbitrary stress field will interact differently with defects having different λ tensors such that one is energetically favored over the others. This gives rise to a redistribution of defects and, as we shall see in Section 8.3, to anelasticity. The criterion for the occurrence of anelasticity due to point defects is then simply that $n_t > 1$.

Values of n_t are given in Table 8-2 for all possible defects in the various crystal classes. Classification of the defects is by symmetry system only.

[†] This statement can also be expressed by saying that the symmetry of the λ tensor (i.e., of the strain ellipsoid) may be higher than that of the defect which gives rise to it. In this form, the statement is merely another example of the well-known Neumann principle (Nye 1957).

TABLE 8-2

THE QUANTITY n_t FOR VARIOUS CRYSTAL AND DEFECT SYMMETRIES

Crystal	Defect				
	Tetragonal	Trigonal	Ortho-rhombic	Monoclinic	Triclinic
Cubic (upper) (O_h, T_d, O)	3	4	6	12	24
Cubic (lower) (T_h, T)	—	4	3	6	12
Hexagonal (upper) (D_{6h}, D_{3h}, C_{6v}, D_6)	—	1	3	6	12
Hexagonal (lower) (C_{6h}, C_{3h}, C_6)	—	1	—	3	6
Trigonal (upper) (D_{3h}, C_{3v}, D_3)	—	1	—	3	6
Trigonal (lower) (S_6, C_3)	—	1	—	—	3
Tetragonal (upper) (D_{4h}, D_{2d}, C_{4v}, D_4)	1	—	2	4	8
Tetragonal (lower) (C_{4h}, C_4, S_4)	1	—	—	2	4
Orthorhombic (all)	—	—	1	2	4
Monoclinic (all)	—	—	—	1	2

It is clear from Table 8-2, as well as from the preceding discussion, that the criterion for anelasticity may also be stated as follows: *Anelastic relaxation can be produced only by a defect whose symmetry system is lower than that of the crystal.* In applying this rule, the systems in descending order of symmetry are cubic, hexagonal–trigonal, tetragonal, orthorhombic, monoclinic, and triclinic. (Note that hexagonal and trigonal are taken together, since $n_t = 1$ for a trigonal defect in a hexagonal crystal.) This rule does not say how large or small the relaxation effect may be. For example, in some cases the relaxation strength may be too small to be observable, yet relaxation is not ruled out by the above symmetry requirements. (The quantitative aspects of the problem are dealt with in Section 8.3.)

Before closing this section, it is important to note that the λ tensor is not the only method for characterizing the behavior of a defect in the presence of stress. Kröner (1958), who first used the term "elastic dipole" to describe a point defect which is capable of interacting with a stress field, introduced a set of quantities $P_{ij}^{(p)}$ to describe this dipole. These quantities are defined as the negative stresses needed to maintain constant strain per unit concentration of defects introduced into orientation p, where the concentration is expressed as the number per unit volume (N_p). Thus,

$$P_{ij}^{(p)} = -\partial\sigma_{ij}/\partial N_p = -v_0(\partial\sigma_{ij}/\partial C_p) \qquad (8.2\text{-}6)$$

Clearly, the quantities $P_{ij}^{(p)}$ have units of energy. These quantities are simply related to the components of the λ tensor through the elastic constants. The reader may show that the relations are

$$P_{ij}^{(p)} = v_0 \sum_{k,l} C_{ijkl}\lambda_{kl}^{(p)} \qquad (8.2\text{-}7)$$

or

$$\lambda_{ij}^{(p)} = v_0^{-1} \sum_{k,l} S_{ijkl}P_{kl}^{(p)} \qquad (8.2\text{-}8)$$

where C_{ijkl} are the elastic moduli, and S_{ijkl} the elastic compliances in the four-index notation.

8.3   Thermodynamics of Relaxation of Elastic Dipoles under Uniaxial Stress

In this section we shall calculate an expression for the relaxation magnitude of a crystal containing a collection of defects which may be represented as elastic dipoles with n_t crystallographically equivalent orientations of the λ tensor. The total molar concentration of defects is taken as C_0, and the conservation condition

$$\sum_{p=1}^{n_t} C_p = C_0 = \text{constant} \qquad (8.3\text{-}1)$$

will be assumed. The quantity C_p is now the mole fraction of defects having λ tensor in orientation p. From the previous section, this may include defects having more than one orientation, since $n_t \leq n_d$. Equation (8.3-1) implies that the total concentration of elastic dipoles cannot change,[†] but only that dipoles of one orientation may go into another orientation. Because of this condition, there are, in fact, only $n_t - 1$ independent internal variables in the problem. Furthermore, since all dipole orientations are crystallographically equivalent, it follows that under equilibrium conditions at zero stress $C_p = C_0/n_t$ for all p.

To simplify the calculation, we will, for the present, consider only a homogeneous uniaxial stress, say σ_{11}, and the corresponding strain component ε_{11} as well as $\boldsymbol{\lambda}$ tensor components $\lambda_{11}^{(p)}$. For simplicity, however, the subscripts 11 will be dropped. Based on these considerations, and the definition given by Eq. (8.2-1), we then have[‡]

$$\varepsilon = J_U \sigma + \sum_{p=1}^{n_t} \lambda^{(p)}[C_p - (C_0/n_t)] \tag{8.3-2}$$

where J_U is the unrelaxed compliance for the crystal orientation parallel to the applied stress. The variables $C_p - (C_0/n_t)$ are then precisely the internal variables ξ_p introduced in Chapter 5, while the summation term in Eq. (8.3-2) represents the anelastic strain. Since $\lambda^{(p)}$ actually designates $\lambda_{11}^{(p)}$, an expression for this quantity in terms of the principal values is readily obtained from Eq. (8.2-5):

$$\lambda^{(p)} = (\alpha_1^{(p)})^2\lambda_1 + (\alpha_2^{(p)})^2\lambda_2 + (\alpha_3^{(p)})^2\lambda_3 \tag{8.3-3}$$

Here $\alpha_1^{(p)}$, $\alpha_2^{(p)}$, and $\alpha_3^{(p)}$ are the direction cosines between the stress axis and the three principal axes of the $\boldsymbol{\lambda}$ tensor for dipoles of orientation p.

To complete the calculation of relaxation strength requires that we determine the equilibrium values of the concentrations C_p for a given stress, and put these values into Eq. (8.3-2). For this purpose we turn to thermodynamic considerations. We again use the Gibbs function per unit volume g as in Section 5.3. The differential form of this function is given by

$$dg = -\varepsilon \, d\sigma - s \, dT - \sum_p A_p \, dC_p \tag{8.3-4}$$

where, as before, s is the entropy per unit volume, and the quantities $A_p = -\partial g/\partial C_p$ are called "affinities." We next define a "free energy

---

[†] Changes in C_0 can only occur through diffusion in and out of the crystal, or by a "reaction" in which one defect species goes into a different species which is not crystallographically equivalent. Both of these possibilities are excluded by Eq. (8.3-1).

[‡] In contrast to Eq. (8.2-1), we here express the strain relative to a reference state for which $\sigma = 0$ and $C_p = C_0/n_t$, i.e., where the defects are in the crystal but randomly distributed.

level" γ_p associated with dipole p by the relation

$$\gamma_p \equiv \partial g'/\partial N_p = v_0\,\partial g'/\partial C_p \qquad (8.3\text{-}5)$$

where N_p is the concentration of dipoles in orientation p expressed as a number per unit volume [see Eq. (8.2-2)], and

$$g' = g + Ts_{\text{cf}} \qquad (8.3\text{-}6)$$

i.e., g' is the function g *minus the configurational entropy contribution* $(-Ts_{\text{cf}})$. The quantity γ_p is then the free energy associated with a single dipole in a specific orientation p.[†]

Since the quantity dg of Eq. (8.3-4) is a perfect differential, we obtain the relation

$$\partial A_p/\partial \sigma = \partial \varepsilon/\partial C_p = \lambda^{(p)} \qquad (8.3\text{-}7)$$

where the last equality follows from Eq. (8.3-2). Further, since $A_p = -\partial g/\partial C_p$, and employing Eqs. (8.3-5) and (8.3-6) (recognizing that the configurational entropy per unit volume s_{cf} depends only on the concentrations C_p but not on σ), we find that

$$\partial \gamma_p/\partial \sigma = -v_0\lambda^{(p)} \qquad (8.3\text{-}8)$$

Equation (8.3-8) is an important thermodynamic reciprocity relation. It states that *a stress σ will give rise to a change in free-energy level for dipole p if and only if the presence of such dipoles gives rise to the conjugate strain* (i.e., $\lambda^{(p)} \neq 0$). Further, it gives a quantitative relation between the stress dependence of the free-energy level and the appropriate component of the $\boldsymbol{\lambda}$ tensor. Integrating Eq. (8.3-8) for small values of the stress, we obtain

$$\gamma_p = -v_0\lambda^{(p)}\sigma \qquad (8.3\text{-}9)$$

In carrying out this integration we might also have added terms in the various concentration differences $C_q - (C_0/n_t)$ as well as an arbitrary constant. Omission of terms in C_q implies that the free-energy levels depend only on stress and not on the concentrations. Such an assumption

---

[†] γ_p therefore includes the vibrational entropy associated with a dipole p. These quantities are analogous to the free energy of formation of a defect (Section 7.2), which are also defined so as to exclude the configurational entropy.

should be valid for defect concentrations which are small enough that defect interactions do not take place.[†] On the other hand, omission of a constant term in Eq. (8.3-9) is only a matter of definition, i.e., γ_p is chosen to be zero in the absence of stress. Figure 8-3 illustrates schematically the splitting of free-energy levels by an applied stress.

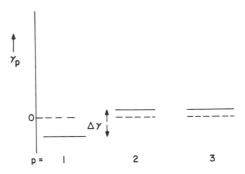

FIG. 8-3.   Schematic illustration of the splitting of the free energy levels by stress for a set of three equivalent dipoles. Dashed lines: before application of stress; solid lines: after stress is applied.

To calculate the equilibrium values $\bar{C}_p$ for the concentrations at any given stress and temperature, one has only to employ Boltzmann statistics, i.e., to set the occupation of dipole orientation p proportional to $\exp(-\gamma_p/kT)$. In other words, once the levels shown in Fig. 8-3 are split by stress, they will subsequently be repopulated in accordance with the Boltzmann distribution law. Thus,

$$\frac{\bar{C}_p}{C_0} = \frac{\exp(-\gamma_p/kT)}{\sum_q \exp(-\gamma_q/kT)} \simeq \frac{1}{n_t}\left[1 - \frac{\gamma_p}{kT} + \frac{1}{n_t}\sum_q \frac{\gamma_q}{kT}\right] \quad (8.3\text{-}10)$$

where the last term is obtained by expanding the exponentials under the assumption that $\gamma_q/kT \ll 1$ (an assumption which is surely valid for sufficiently small stress). When Eq. (8.3-9) is substituted into (8.3-10) for γ_p and γ_q, we obtain

$$\bar{C}_p - \frac{C_0}{n_t} \simeq \frac{C_0 v_0 \sigma}{n_t kT}\left[\lambda^{(p)} - \frac{1}{n_t}\sum_q \lambda^{(q)}\right] \quad (8.3\text{-}11)$$

Equation (8.3-11) shows that the deviation of $\bar{C}_p$ from the random value

[†] The effect of defect interactions is considered in Section 8.10.

C_0/n_t is proportional to the stress and to the total concentration C_0. This redistribution of dipoles to a new set of equilibrium values under an applied stress is often referred to as *stress-induced ordering*. There are some cases (in which optical absorption or spin resonance are employed, rather than anelasticity) where stress-induced ordering is carried out at sufficiently high stress that the exact Boltzmann relation of Eq. (8.3-10) is required. For application to anelasticity, however, the linear approximation given by Eq. (8.3-11) is sufficient. In this case, we substitute the results of Eq. (8.3-11) into (8.3-2) to obtain the relaxation of the compliance

$$\delta J = \frac{\bar{\varepsilon}^{an}}{\sigma} = \frac{C_0 v_0}{n_t k T} \left[\sum_p (\lambda^{(p)})^2 - \frac{1}{n_t} \left(\sum_p \lambda^{(p)} \right)^2 \right] \qquad (8.3\text{-}12)$$

where $\bar{\varepsilon}^{an}$ is the equilibrium anelastic strain (i.e., as obtained from the last term of Eq. (8.3-2) by substituting $\bar{C}_p$ for C_p).

The present derivation of Eq. (8.3-12) does not, in fact, require that the applied stress be of the uniaxial type. The reader will note that we have assumed only that σ and ε are conjugate stress and strain, and that $\lambda^{(p)}$ is the component of the λ tensor which corresponds to ε. Thus, the same relation is valid for relaxation under any simple stress system, e.g., hydrostatic stress, or a simple shear stress. It will be shown later[†] (see Problem 8-12) that for pure shear $\sum \lambda^{(p)} = 0$, i.e., the last term of Eq. (8.3-12) vanishes, so that the final result takes on the simpler form $\delta J \propto \sum (\lambda^{(p)})^2$. For hydrostatic stress, on the other hand, it can be shown (Problem 8-3) that $\delta J = 0$ as a consequence of Eq. (8.3-1).

To complete the solution to the problem of calculating the relaxation magnitude, we may now substitute into Eq. (8.3-12) the expression for $\lambda^{(p)}$ in terms of the principal values of the λ tensor. For the case of a uniaxial stress, the appropriate relation is Eq. (8.3-3). In a more general case, Eq. (8.2-5) must be used. With this substitution the general treatment is completed. We may now profitably turn to the consideration of some specific examples. Although we will illustrate the application of the theory of this section with examples for the case of cubic crystals, it will become clear that the results are equally well applied to other crystal systems (particularly with the aid of the equations in Section 6.4).

[†] Actually, this statement is strictly correct for stress of type II and therefore applies to all pure shears only for crystals which are higher than monoclinic in symmetry.

8.4 Some Examples in Cubic Crystals

In this section, we shall always take σ to represent a uniaxial stress and J a reciprocal Young's modulus. In view of Eqs. (6.4-1) and (6.4-2) and the fact that $\delta(S_{11} + 2S_{12}) = 0$ (Problem 8-3), it is only necessary to consider stress as applied along the $\langle 100 \rangle$ and $\langle 111 \rangle$ directions. In this way, we obtain the magnitude of the two independent shear relaxations, since $\delta E_{\langle 100 \rangle}^{-1} = \frac{2}{3}\, \delta(S_{11} - S_{12})$ and $\delta E_{\langle 111 \rangle}^{-1} = \frac{1}{3}\, \delta S_{44}$. For any other orientation of the stress axis, the relaxation δJ must involve the magnitudes of both shear relaxations.

The examples which will be considered involve the three highest defect symmetries which give rise to anelasticity in cubic crystals. These symmetries are of special importance, since they include most of the point defects which have been studied to date.

A. THE TETRAGONAL DEFECT

A tetragonal defect must have its first principal axis (i.e., the one having principal value λ_1) along one of the three cube axes, while for the other two axes $\lambda_2 = \lambda_3$ (see Table 8-1). The strain ellipsoid is then an ellipsoid of revolution. Consider first a uniaxial stress applied along the [100] direction. The three possible orientations of the tetragonal (λ_1) axis, denoted by $p = 1, 2, 3$, are along the [100], [010], and [001] directions, respectively. The calculation of the direction cosines is then trivial, as shown in Table 8-3, which also includes the value of $\lambda^{(p)}$

TABLE 8-3

DIRECTION COSINES AND $\lambda^{(p)}$ VALUES FOR TETRAGONAL DIPOLES AND [100] STRESS

p	Tetragonal axis	$\alpha_1^{(p)}$	$\alpha_2^{(p)}$	$\alpha_3^{(p)}$	$\lambda^{(p)}$
1	[100]	1	0	0	λ_1
2	[010]	0	1	0	λ_2
3	[001]	0	0	1	λ_2

obtained from Eq. (8.3-3). Finally, substituting these $\lambda^{(p)}$ values into Eq. (8.3-12), and making use of Eq. (6.4-1) we obtain

$$\delta E_{\langle 100 \rangle}^{-1} = (2/3)\, \delta(S_{11} - S_{12}) = (2/9)(C_0 v_0/kT)(\lambda_1 - \lambda_2)^2 \qquad (8.4\text{-}1)$$

in terms of the two independent principal values of the λ tensor. This result shows that $\delta E^{-1}_{\langle 100 \rangle}$, and therefore $\delta(S_{11} - S_{12})$, is proportional to the total defect concentration C_0 and to the square of the ellipticity or *shape factor* of the strain ellipsoid [†] $\lambda_1 - \lambda_2$. An anelasticity experiment can, therefore, only give $| \lambda_1 - \lambda_2 |$ if the concentration C_0 is independently known; to obtain the sign of this "shape factor" would require additional information.

Next, we could do the same calculation for a stress applied in a $\langle 111 \rangle$ direction, to obtain $\delta E^{-1}_{\langle 111 \rangle}$ or δS_{44}. However, the fact that the three possible tetragonal axes (i.e., the three cube axes) make equal angles with the [111] direction assures us that a stress along [111] cannot produce splitting of the free-energy levels among the three dipole orientations. Therefore,

$$\delta E^{-1}_{\langle 111 \rangle} = \tfrac{1}{3} \delta S_{44} = 0 \qquad (8.4\text{-}2)$$

B. The Trigonal Defect

A defect in a cubic crystal possesses trigonal symmetry when one of the $\langle 111 \rangle$ axes of the crystal remains a three-fold rotation axis of symmetry in the presence of the defect. Here $n_t = 4$ (see Table 8-2), corresponding to the trigonal axis located along [111], [$\bar{1}$11], [1$\bar{1}$1], or [11$\bar{1}$]. In accordance with Table 8-1, we again choose λ_1 as the principal value along the trigonal axis and $\lambda_2 = \lambda_3$, so that the strain ellipsoid is again an ellipsoid of revolution, but with its unique principal axis now along a $\langle 111 \rangle$ direction. In this case, a stress applied along a $\langle 100 \rangle$ direction makes equal angles with all four $\langle 111 \rangle$-type orientations. Accordingly,

$$\delta E^{-1}_{\langle 100 \rangle} = \tfrac{2}{3} \delta(S_{11} - S_{12}) = 0 \qquad (8.4\text{-}3)$$

We then turn to the case of a stress applied along the [111] direction. As before, it is helpful to construct a table of direction cosines $\alpha^{(p)}_m$ between the stress axis and the three principal axes, from which we calculate $\lambda^{(p)}$ from Eq. (8.3-3). This is carried out in Table 8-4. In order to be specific, we have made definite choices for the second and third principal axes, although, as already mentioned, the choice is not unique. Substituting these $\lambda^{(p)}$ values into Eq. (8.3-12) finally gives

$$\delta E^{-1}_{\langle 111 \rangle} = (1/3)\,\delta S_{44} = (4/27)(C_0 v_0 / kT)(\lambda_1 - \lambda_2)^2 \qquad (8.4\text{-}4)$$

[†] The term "shape factor" refers to the shape of the distortion pattern created by the defect, by analogy to the "size factor," which refers to the volume change.

TABLE 8-4

DIRECTION COSINES AND $\lambda^{(p)}$ VALUES FOR TRIGONAL DIPOLES AND [111] STRESS

p	Principal axes	$\alpha_1^{(p)}$	$\alpha_2^{(p)}$	$\alpha_3^{(p)}$	$\lambda^{(p)}$
1	$[111]$, $[1\bar{1}0]$, $[11\bar{2}]$	1	0	0	λ_1
2	$[\bar{1}11]$, $[110]$, $[1\bar{1}2]$	$1/3$	$2/\sqrt{6}$	$2/3\sqrt{2}$	$(\lambda_1 + 8\lambda_2)/9$
3	$[1\bar{1}1]$, $[110]$, $[\bar{1}12]$	$1/3$	$2/\sqrt{6}$	$2/3\sqrt{2}$	$(\lambda_1 + 8\lambda_2)/9$
4	$[11\bar{1}]$, $[1\bar{1}0]$, $[112]$	$1/3$	0	$4/3\sqrt{2}$	$(\lambda_1 + 8\lambda_2)/9$

This result differs from Eq. (8.4-1) for the tetragonal defect only in the numerical factor. Again, anelasticity is capable of furnishing only the absolute quantity $\mid \lambda_1 - \lambda_2 \mid$ if the concentration of defects C_0 is known independently.

C. THE $\langle 110 \rangle$ ORTHORHOMBIC DEFECT

For our third example, we choose one which gives rise to both shear relaxations $\delta(S_{11} - S_{12})$ and δS_{44}. This is the example of the ortho-rhombic defect in a cubic crystal, where the three symmetry axes are typically along [110], [1$\bar{1}$0], and [001]. Here λ_1, λ_2, and λ_3 are, in general, all unequal (see Table 8-1), and $n_t = 6$. Beginning with a stress along [100], we may again set up a table of direction cosines analogous to Tables 8-3 or 8-4. (We leave this as an exercise for the reader, Problem 8-6.) When the values of $\lambda^{(p)}$ are inserted into Eq. (8.3-12), we obtain

$$\delta E_{\langle 100 \rangle}^{-1} = (2/3)\, \delta(S_{11} - S_{12}) = (2/9)(C_0 v_0/kT)\{[(\lambda_1 + \lambda_2)/2] - \lambda_3\}^2 \tag{8.4-5}$$

Similarly for a [111] stress axis,

$$\delta E_{\langle 111 \rangle}^{-1} = (1/3)\, \delta S_{44} = (1/9)(C_0 v_0/kT)(\lambda_1 - \lambda_2)^2 \tag{8.4-6}$$

It should be noted that in this case we have three independent principal values, but that anelasticity gives only the two quantities, viz., $\mid \frac{1}{2}(\lambda_1 + \lambda_2) - \lambda_3 \mid$ and $\mid \lambda_1 - \lambda_2 \mid$.

D. GENERAL REMARKS

The results obtained for the three defect symmetries considered in this section show certain features which are common to all expressions for the magnitude of relaxation due to point defects. First, in each case δJ is proportional to the total defect concentration C_0, for reasons which are obvious. Second, δJ varies inversely as kT. This result comes from the Boltzmann statistics, viz., that whereas stress produces a small splitting $\Delta\gamma$ of the free energy levels (as in Fig. 8-3), the equilibrium degree of reorientation is proportional to $\Delta\gamma/kT$. Finally, δJ varies as the square of some difference in principal values of the λ tensor. We may, therefore, express δJ in the form

$$\delta J = \beta(C_0 v_0/kT)(\delta\lambda)^2 \tag{8.4-7}$$

where β is a numerical factor of the order of unity and $\delta\lambda$ is the appropriate difference in principal values. It is useful to carry out a rough calculation for the case of $C_0 \sim 10^{-4}$ (i.e., 0.01% defects) to provide a "rule of thumb" for knowing when a relaxation will be detectable as an internal friction peak. Inserting typical values, $v_0 \sim 10^{-23}$ cm³, $T \sim 600°$K, $J \sim 10^{-12}$ cm² dyne^{-1} and assuming a barely detectable internal friction peak height of $\phi_m \sim 5 \times 10^{-5}$ (so that $\Delta = \delta J/J \sim 10^{-4}$) we obtain as a criterion for detectability: $| \delta\lambda | \gtrsim 0.1$. This result may be thought of as a shape factor of 10%, i.e., a difference in strain per unit concentration of defects in two principal directions being equal to 10%. Of course, smaller values of $\delta\lambda$ can be detected if a smaller peak can be detected, or if C_0 is larger, or if the relaxation appears at a substantially lower temperature than 600°K.

The second feature of the above results is the complete absence of any relaxation for certain stresses as a consequence of the defect symmetry. This is illustrated by Eqs. (8.4-2) and (8.4-3) which, in fact, represent the only examples of such "zeros" for shear relaxations due to defects in cubic crystals. On the other hand, there are many more examples of such null effects in crystals of lower-than-cubic symmetry. Such absences of relaxation effects as a consequence of defect symmetry are known as the "selection rules" for relaxation, which provide an important basis for the identification of the symmetry of an unknown defect in a given crystal. These selection rules are presented and discussed in the next section.

8.5   Generalization of the Thermodynamic Theory: The Selection Rules

In Section 8.2 we found as a criterion for anelastic relaxation that n_t must be greater than 1. We also found that a more useful form of this criterion was simply that the defect symmetry must belong to a lower system than the crystal symmetry. In Chapter 6, we have seen, however, that there exist several different elastic compliances which can undergo relaxation. To know merely that anelastic relaxation does or does not occur in a given crystal is, therefore, not the whole story. We also need to know which of the various compliances undergo relaxation and which do not. Such information constitutes the *selection rules*.

The first step in the development of the selection rules is the following theorem (relevant to the distinction between compliances of types I and II made in Section 6.3): *When defects of only a single species are present,*[†] *so that the conservation condition* (8.3-1) *applies, only compliances of type II may undergo relaxation*, i.e., $\delta J = 0$ for any compliance of type I. For a cubic crystal this theorem implies that $\delta(S_{11} + 2S_{12}) = 0$, a result which was proved in Problem 8-3. The general proof of the theorem follows along similar lines. The reader should recall (Section 6.3) that a strain of type I is one which does not lower the symmetry of the crystal. When the stress and strain are of type I, the corresponding component $\lambda^{(p)}$ of the $\boldsymbol{\lambda}$ tensor is also of type I. This means that the symmetry operation which takes p into q leaves $\lambda^{(p)} = \lambda^{(q)}$ (i.e., invariant). But if $\lambda^{(p)}$ is independent of p, it is easy to see from Eq. (8.3-12) that $\delta J = 0$.

Since $\delta J = 0$ for a compliance of type I, only compliances of type II (i.e., the shear compliances listed in Table 6-2) need be considered. In order to find out which of these compliances undergoes relaxation for a given defect symmetry, we reexamine Eq. (8.2-1) in the light of symmetry considerations. Specifically, this equation may be rewritten in terms of the symmetrized stresses and strain (see Section 6.3) and the similarly symmetrized linear combinations of the concentrations. The basic principle involved is that a given symmetrized coordinate of concentration can only give rise to strain of a type which transforms in the same manner under the symmetry operations of the crystal (i.e., which belongs to the same "symmetry designation"; see Section 6.3). The problem of determining the number of linear combinations of concentrations belonging to each symmetry designation is a straightforward one in terms of group

---

[†] The theorem still applies when more than one species of defect is present if no two species are interconvertible. Thus, if one defect species is interstitial carbon and the other is interstitial nitrogen, the theorem applies. But, if one species is carbon on one type of interstitial site and the other is carbon on a crystallographically inequivalent site, the theorem does not apply, since then Eq. (8.3-1) is not separately valid for each species of defect.

TABLE 8-5

SELECTION RULES FOR ANELASTICITY

Crystal	Compliance	Defect						
		Tetragonal	Trigonal	Orthorhombic $\langle 100 \rangle$	Orthorhombic $\langle 110 \rangle$	Monoclinic $\langle 100 \rangle$	Monoclinic $\langle 110 \rangle$	Triclinic
Cubic	$S_{11} - S_{12}$	1	0	2	1	2	1	2
	S_{44}	0	1	0	1	1	2	3
						[001]	$\langle 100 \rangle$	$\langle 110 \rangle$
Tetragonal	$S_{11} - S_{12}$	0	—	1	0	1	1	0	1
	S_{66}	0	—	0	1	1	0	1	1
	S_{44}	0	—	0	0	0	1	1	2
						[001]	[100]	
Hexagonal	$S_{11} - S_{12}$	—	0	1		2	1	2
	S_{44}	—	0	0		0	1	2
Trigonal	$S_{11} - S_{12}$ $\left. \begin{array}{c} \\ S_{44} \\ S_{14} \end{array} \right\}$	—	0	—			1	2

representation theory[†] (see Nowick and Heller, 1965). Since this theoretical background is beyond the scope of the present book, however, we will simply present the results for the major crystal types in tabular form. These are given in Table 8-5, which is called the selection-rule table, since it shows which compliances (of type II) can and which cannot undergo relaxation for a defect of a given symmetry. The table lists the various crystal systems,[‡] and for each, the possible defect symmetry

[†] One uses the original set of concentrations as the basis for an n_d-dimensional representation of the crystal group. This representation can then be reduced to its simplest (i.e., irreducible) form, making it possible to determine the irreducible representations to which the symmetry coordinates of concentration belong. The above principle then implies that, if there is a symmetry coordinate of strain belonging to the same irreducible representation as one of the symmetry coordinates of concentration, the corresponding compliance will undergo relaxation.

[‡] The cubic, tetragonal, hexagonal, and trigonal systems refer only to the higher symmetry classes within these systems (i.e., the upper classes of Table 8-2).

systems. It also gives the type II compliances for each crystal system. When the listed defect system is incompatible with the crystal system, a dash appears in the table. For example, there cannot be a defect of tetragonal symmetry in a hexagonal crystal, or one of trigonal symmetry in a tetragonal crystal. When there are two or more inequivalent ways of producing a given defect symmetry in the crystal, we designate the distinguishing direction under the defect system. Thus, for cubic crystals, a defect can be orthorhombic either with principal axes typically represented by the set [100], [010], and [001] or by the set [110], [1$\bar{1}$0], [001]. These two sets represent different (i.e., crystallographically inequivalent) defect species. For brevity, we call them the $\langle 100 \rangle$ orthorhombic and $\langle 110 \rangle$ orthorhombic defects, respectively.

An entry of zero in the table means that the relaxation of that particular compliance is prohibited for the crystal and defect in question. Such entries constitute the heart of the selection rules. A numerical entry other than zero signifies that relaxation is not ruled out by symmetry considerations. The specific meaning of entries 1, 2, and 3 will be discussed later in Section 8.9 on kinetics.

For the case of cubic crystals, the material in Table 8-5 is in accord with what we already found in Section 8.4, namely, that for a tetragonal defect $\delta S_{44} = 0$, and for a trigonal defect $\delta(S_{11} - S_{12}) = 0$, while for all defects of lower symmetry both relaxations are permitted.

As discussed in the previous section, the fact that relaxation is permitted in a particular case means only that it is not ruled out by symmetry considerations. Nothing is said here about the magnitude of the relaxation, which may in fact be too small to be observable experimentally. Thus, if we postulate that a defect possesses a certain symmetry, the failure to observe a relaxation when the selection rules show it to be allowed could mean either that the postulated symmetry is wrong, or that $C_0(\delta\lambda)^2$ (see Section 8.4D) is too small to permit detection of the relaxation. On the other hand, the observation of a relaxation when the selection rules predict its absence is conclusive proof that the postulated defect symmetry is incorrect.

The information listed in Table 8-5 centers about the theoretical ("symmetrized") compliances of type II. As discussed in Section 6.4, the symmetrized stresses and strains which are involved are generally not conveniently obtained experimentally. The usefulness of Eqs. (6.4-1)–(6.4-27) then becomes apparent. These equations present the relationship between various "practical" moduli and the corresponding symmetrized compliance or stiffness constants. Furthermore, we have restricted ourselves in these equations to those practical moduli which are related at most to one symmetrized modulus of type II. In view of our general theorem that a single species of defect can give rise *only* to relaxation of a type II modulus, all of the equations of Section 6.4 lead to very simple relations for the relaxation. For example, from Eq. (6.4-1), since $S_{11}+2S_{12}$ is of type I, $\delta E^{-1}_{\langle 100\rangle} = \tfrac{2}{3}\,\delta(S_{11} - S_{12})$, a relation which we have used extensively in Section 8.4. Similarly, for tetragonal crystals, the three relations

$$\delta E^{-1}_{\langle 100\rangle} = \tfrac{1}{2}\,\delta(S_{11} - S_{12}), \qquad \delta E^{-1}_{\langle 110\rangle} = \tfrac{1}{4}\,\delta S_{66}, \qquad \text{and} \qquad \delta G^{-1}_{[001]} = \delta S_{44}$$

provide simple ways to measure relaxations of the three theoretical compliances of type II.

*8.6   Generalization of the Thermodynamic Theory: Expressions for the Relaxation Magnitudes

The form of the thermodynamic theory of relaxation due to point defects developed in Section 8.3, which regards the applied stress as uniaxial (or at least, of a simple type) leads to Eq. (8.3-12) for the relaxation magnitude. This equation is applicable to a variety of problems, as shown by the calculations for various defect symmetries in cubic crystals (Section 8.4), and is readily extended to other crystals as well. However, it is not easy to obtain the relaxation magnitudes for all of the symmetrized (type II) compliances by this method. Accordingly, it is advantageous to utilize a more general approach, which makes full use of the concept of defect symmetry and the power of group theoretical methods, to attack the problem. In order to do this, it is first desirable to develop an alternative method of handling the thermodynamics to that of Section 8.3. The method used in Section 8.3 was really a mixed thermodynamic and statistical approach, with Boltzmann statistics being used to obtain the equilibrium concentrations, Eq. (8.3-10). This method has the advantage of providing the helpful picture of the splitting of free-energy levels by stress (e.g., Fig. 8-3), as well as of providing an expression for the stress-induced ordering of dipoles which is valid even for relatively large stresses. On the other hand, for purposes of generalization, a purely thermodynamic method, which does not require application of Boltzmann statistics, is advantageous. This method is also instructive since it is analogous to that used in Sections 5.3 and 6.6 where the nature of the internal variables was unspecified.

The purely thermodynamic method starts from the differential form of the Gibbs function, Eq. (8.3-4), and the integrated quadratic form of this function as follows

$$g - g_0 = -\tfrac{1}{2}J_U\sigma^2 - \alpha\, \Delta T\sigma - \sigma \sum_p \lambda^{(p)}c_p + (n_t kT/2C_0v_0) \sum_p c_p^2 \qquad (8.6\text{-}1)$$

In this equation, ΔT is the difference between the temperature T and a selected reference temperature, and the variables

$$c_p \equiv C_p - (C_0/n_t) \qquad (8.6\text{-}2)$$

are zero at equilibrium under zero stress, and therefore correspond to the internal variables ξ_p of Section 5.3. The quantity g_0 is the value of g when $\sigma = 0$ and $c_p = 0$ for all p (i.e., when the distribution of dipoles is random). Equation (8.6-1) is similar to Eq. (5.3-10) except that $\chi_p = 0$ and the coefficients β_{pq} are given in an explicit form.[†] The significance of the first three terms in the right-hand side of Eq. (8.6-1) is best shown by obtaining the strain

$$\varepsilon = -(\partial g/\partial\sigma) = J_U\sigma + \alpha\, \Delta T + \sum_p \lambda^{(p)}c_p \qquad (8.6\text{-}3)$$

which is the same as Eq. (8.3-2), except for the term $\alpha\, \Delta T$ (which allows for thermal expansion if the temperature is changed). Thus, in Eq. (8.6-1), the first term on the right-hand side is the purely elastic contribution, the second is the thermal expansion term and the third is the anelastic term. The fourth term comes from the configurational entropy s_{cf} per unit volume (see Problem 8-9). It is also possible to have further quadratic terms in the concentrations, viz. a term of the form $\sum b_{pq}c_p c_q$ as in Eq. (5.3-10). It is easy to show however (see Problem 8-10) that to neglect such terms is precisely the same as neglecting terms in c_q in integrating Eq. (8.3-8) to obtain Eq. (8.3-9). We have already noted that this is equivalent to the neglecting of defect interactions. From Eq. (8.6-1) together with (8.3-4) we have, for the affinities,

$$A_p = -(\partial g/\partial C_p) = \lambda^{(p)}\sigma - (n_t kT/C_0v_0)c_p \qquad (8.6\text{-}4)$$

The condition for equilibrium would appear to be obtained by setting $A_p = 0$, to meet the condition that $dg = 0$ for arbitrary dc_p. This would

---

[†] It should be recalled that the terms in χ_p allowed for the possibility that the equilibrium values of the internal variables at zero stress may be a function of temperature [see, e.g., Eq. (5.3-11)]. In the present case, $\bar{c}_p = 0$ for $\sigma = 0$ at all temperatures.

be the correct procedure if all the c_p were independent variables; however, here we have an auxiliary (conservation) condition which may be written [from Eqs. (8.6-2) and (8.3-1)]

$$F(c_p) \equiv \sum_p c_p = 0 \qquad (8.6\text{-}5)$$

so that there are really only $n_t - 1$ independent variables. The problem of minimizing the g function subject to Eq. (8.6-5) is handled in the usual way[†] by introducing a Lagrange multiplier L and setting $A_p +L(\partial F/\partial c_p) = 0$. If we carry out these steps and solve for c_p (now $\bar{c}_p$, to denote equilibrium) we obtain (Problem 8-11)

$$\bar{c}_p = (C_0 v_0/n_t kT)(\lambda^{(p)}\sigma + L) \qquad (8.6\text{-}6)$$

Finally, summing this result over p and setting it equal to zero in accordance with Eq. (8.6-5) gives

$$L = -(\sigma/n_t)\sum_p \lambda^{(p)} \qquad (8.6\text{-}7)$$

Combining Eqs. (8.6-6) and (8.6-7) gives (8.3-11), the result derived by the previous method. Thus the expression (8.3-12) for δJ is equally well derived by the present purely thermodynamic method.

We now turn to the problem of generalizing this treatment to calculate the magnitude of relaxation for symmetrized compliances of type II for any crystal and defect symmetry. This problem has been solved (Nowick and Heller, 1965) using the above purely thermodynamic theory with the aid of the methods of group representation theory. The thermodynamic equations may all be expressed in terms of symmetry coordinates of defect concentrations and the symmetrized stresses and strains. The equations then separate out according to the various possible symmetry designations γ (see Section 6.3). In many cases the resulting equation for the relaxation of the symmetrized compliance S_γ' can be expressed in the form

$$\delta S_\gamma' = (C_0 v_0/n_t kT)\lambda_\gamma'^2 \qquad (8.6\text{-}8)$$

where λ_γ' is the symmetrized component of the $\boldsymbol{\lambda}$ tensor for the designation γ. This result differs from (8.3-12) in two ways. First, the last term of Eq. (8.3-12) is missing. This term automatically vanishes for a

[†] This method is covered in most books on mechanics and statistical mechanics. (See, e.g., Hill, 1960, Appendix III.)

compliance of type II (see Problem 8-12). Second, the sum $\sum(\lambda^{(p)}_\gamma)^2$ of Eq. (8.3-12) is now replaced by a single term λ'^2_γ This is the major simplification obtained in working with symmetrized quantities.[†]

The quantity λ_γ' can be expressed in terms of the components $\lambda^{(p)}_{ij}$ of the $\boldsymbol{\lambda}$ tensor for one value of p (Nowick and Heller, 1965). We shall not go into the details here but give only final equations obtained for the magnitude of relaxation of the type II shear compliances in terms of the $\lambda^{(p)}_{ij}$ components, arranged by crystal system. (In these equations, the superscript p has been dropped from all components $\lambda^{(p)}_{ij}$ for convenience, but may be thought of as $p = 1$ throughout.)

Cubic

$$\delta(S_{11} - S_{12}) = (C_0 v_0/6kT)[(\lambda_{11} - \lambda_{22})^2 + (\lambda_{11} - \lambda_{33})^2 + (\lambda_{22} - \lambda_{33})^2]$$
$$\delta S_{44} = (4C_0 v_0/3kT)[\lambda^2_{23} + \lambda^2_{31} + \lambda^2_{12}] \qquad (8.6\text{-}9)$$

Hexagonal

$$\delta(S_{11} - S_{12}) = (C_0 v_0/4kT)[(\lambda_{11} - \lambda_{22})^2 + 4\lambda^2_{12}]$$
$$\delta S_{44} = (2C_0 v_0/kT)[\lambda^2_{23} + \lambda^2_{31}] \qquad (8.6\text{-}10)$$

Tetragonal

$$\delta(S_{11} - S_{12}) = (C_0 v_0/2kT)(\lambda_{11} - \lambda_{22})^2$$
$$\delta S_{66} = (4C_0 v_0/kT)\lambda^2_{12}$$
$$\delta S_{44} = (2C_0 v_0/kT)(\lambda^2_{23} + \lambda^2_{31}) \qquad (8.6\text{-}11)$$

Trigonal

$$\delta(S_{11} - S_{12}), \qquad \delta S_{44} \quad \text{(same as hexagonal)}$$
$$\delta S_{14} = (C_0 v_0/2kT)[\lambda_{23}(\lambda_{11} - \lambda_{22}) + 2\lambda_{13}\lambda_{12}] \qquad (8.6\text{-}12)$$

Orthorhombic

$$\delta S_{66} = (4C_0 v_0/kT)\lambda^2_{12}$$
$$\delta S_{55} = (4C_0 v_0/kT)\lambda^2_{31}$$
$$\delta S_{44} = (4C_0 v_0/kT)\lambda^2_{23} \qquad (8.6\text{-}13)$$

[†] Actually Eq. (8.6-8) does not apply in all cases. For certain defects of low symmetry (specifically, those for which an entry of 2 or 3 appears in Table 8-5), Eq. (8.6-8) should be replaced respectively, by a sum over two or three terms of the same symmetry designation. Compare Eq. (6.6-15). Even in these cases, the group theoretical treatment provides a considerable simplification in obtaining the general result.

Equations (8.6-9)–(8.6-13) are applicable for defects of *any* allowed symmetry in the corresponding crystal. To use these formulas in specific cases, we may substitute for $\lambda_{ij}^{(1)}$ in terms of the principal values, using Eq. (8.2-5). In Table 8-6 this has been done for the most important

TABLE 8-6

EXPRESSION FOR $\lambda_{ij}^{(1)}$ IN TERMS OF PRINCIPAL VALUES FOR VARIOUS CRYSTAL
AND DEFECT SYMMETRIES

Crystal	Defect	$\lambda_{11}^{(1)}$	$\lambda_{22}^{(1)}$	$\lambda_{33}^{(1)}$	$\lambda_{23}^{(1)}$	$\lambda_{31}^{(1)}$	$\lambda_{12}^{(1)}$
Cubic	Tetragonal	λ_1	λ_2	λ_2	0	0	0
	Trigonal	λ_a	λ_a	λ_a	$\lambda_c/3$	$\lambda_c/3$	$\lambda_c/3$
	$\langle 100 \rangle$ orthorhombic	λ_1	λ_2	λ_3	0	0	0
	$\langle 110 \rangle$ orthorhombic	λ_b	λ_b	λ_3	0	0	$\lambda_c/2$
Tetragonal	$\langle 100 \rangle$ orthorhombic	λ_1	λ_2	λ_3	0	0	0
	$\langle 110 \rangle$ orthorhombic	same as cubic					
	[a][001] monoclinic	λ_d	λ_e	λ_3	0	0	$(\alpha\beta)^{1/2}\lambda_c$
	[a]$\langle 100 \rangle$ monoclinic	λ_1	λ_f	λ_g	λ_k	0	0
	[a]$\langle 110 \rangle$ monoclinic	λ_h	λ_h	λ_g	$\lambda_k/\sqrt{2}$	$-\lambda_k/\sqrt{2}$	λ_l
Hexagonal	Orthorhombic	λ_1	λ_2	λ_3	0	0	0
	[001] monoclinic	same as tetragonal					
	$\langle 100 \rangle$ monoclinic	same as tetragonal					
Trigonal	Monoclinic	same as tetragonal $\langle 100 \rangle$ monoclinic					

$\alpha \equiv \cos^2 \theta$	$\lambda_c \equiv \lambda_1 - \lambda_2$	$\lambda_g \equiv \lambda_2\beta + \lambda_3\alpha$
$\beta \equiv \sin^2 \theta$	$\lambda_d \equiv \lambda_1\alpha + \lambda_2\beta$	$\lambda_h \equiv (\lambda_1 + \lambda_f)/2$
$\lambda_a \equiv (\lambda_1 + 2\lambda_2)/3$	$\lambda_e \equiv \lambda_1\beta + \lambda_2\alpha$	$\lambda_k \equiv (\alpha\beta)^{1/2}(\lambda_2 - \lambda_3)$
$\lambda_b \equiv (\lambda_1 + \lambda_2)/2$	$\lambda_f \equiv \lambda_2\alpha + \lambda_3\beta$	$\lambda_l \equiv (\lambda_1 - \lambda_f)/2$

[a] Convention for choice of principal axes for monoclinic defects: For [001] monoclinic, choose λ_3 along [001] and let θ be the angle between [100] and the first principal (λ_1) axis; for $\langle 100 \rangle$ and $\langle 110 \rangle$ monoclinic, choose λ_1 along the symmetry axis and θ between [001] and the λ_3 axis.

defect symmetries among the cubic, tetragonal, hexagonal, and trigonal crystal systems. The values in this table may then be substituted into Eqs. (8.6-9)–(8.6-13) to obtain the specific expressions for these symmetrized compliances for the various defect symmetries. The results for some of the higher defect symmetries are as follows:

For Tetragonal Crystals

$\langle 100 \rangle$ orthorhombic defect:

$$\delta(S_{11} - S_{12}) = (C_0 v_0 / 2kT)(\lambda_1 - \lambda_2)^2 \qquad (8.6\text{-}14)$$

$\langle 110 \rangle$ orthorhombic defect:

$$\delta S_{66} = (C_0 v_0 / kT)(\lambda_1 - \lambda_2)^2 \qquad (8.6\text{-}15)$$

For Hexagonal Crystals

Orthorhombic defect:

$$\delta(S_{11} - S_{12}) = (C_0 v_0 / 4kT)(\lambda_1 - \lambda_2)^2 \qquad (8.6\text{-}16)$$

[001] monoclinic defect:

$$\delta(S_{11} - S_{12}) = (C_0 v_0 / 4kT)(\lambda_1 - \lambda_2)^2 \qquad (8.6\text{-}17)$$

[100] monoclinic defect:

$$\delta(S_{11} - S_{12}) = (C_0 v_0 / 4kT)(\lambda_1 - \lambda_2 \cos^2 \theta - \lambda_3 \sin^2 \theta)^2$$
$$\delta S_{44} = (2C_0 v_0 / kT)(\lambda_2 - \lambda_3)^2 \cos^2 \theta \sin^2 \theta \qquad (8.6\text{-}18)$$

For Trigonal Crystals

monoclinic defect: same as Eqs. (8.6-18)

For cubic crystals, the results are the same as those already obtained by the earlier method, Eqs. (8.4-1) and (8.4-4)–(8.4-6).

With the aid of these expressions for the relaxation of the symmetrized compliances, one can then obtain δE^{-1} or δG^{-1} for any orientation in these crystals by using the appropriate equations in Section 6.2 or 6.4. This provides an alternative to the method of Section 8.3, which calculates δE^{-1} directly for appropriate orientations. In that case, only the component $\lambda_{11}^{(p)}$ in the direction of the uniaxial stress was required, but for all values of p. Here the complete set of components $\lambda_{ij}^{(1)}$ are needed, but only for one orientation, e.g., $p = 1$.

*8.7 Information Obtainable from Lattice Parameters

It is noteworthy that in all of the results of Sections 8.4 and 8.6, the number of parameters obtainable from anelastic measurements is less than the number of independent components of the λ tensor (Table 8-1).

Thus, for a tetragonal or trigonal defect in a cubic crystal, Eq. (8.4-1) or (8.4-4) gives one parameter, namely $|\lambda_1 - \lambda_2|$ while the defect is described by both λ_1 and λ_2. Similarly, for the orthorhombic defect, for which there are three independent coefficients, only two parameters are obtained via anelasticity [Eqs. (8.4-5) and (8.4-6)]. For the hexagonal or tetragonal crystals, it is easily verified that anelasticity gives at least *two* parameters fewer than the number of independent λ components. Some of the missing parameters can, in fact, be obtained from the changes in the lattice parameters of a crystal due to the presence of a collection of randomly oriented defects. The basis for this statement is the fact that a set of randomly distributed defects ($C_p = C_0/n_t$), can only give rise to strains of type I, i.e., such that there is no change in crystal symmetry. Nevertheless, such strains do give rise to changes in the lattice parameters relative to those of a perfect crystal.

In the case of cubic crystals, for example, the type I strain is purely hydrostatic. From the definition of the $\lambda_{ij}^{(p)}$ coefficients, Eq. (8.2-3), we obtain, for the hydrostatic strain per unit concentration of defects

$$\lambda_{11}^{(p)} + \lambda_{22}^{(p)} + \lambda_{33}^{(p)} = 3a^{-1}(da/dC_0) = \lambda_1 + \lambda_2 + \lambda_3 \qquad (8.7\text{-}1)$$

where the last equality follows from the invariance of the trace (i.e., the diagonal sum) of a strain tensor to a rotation of the axes. Equation (8.7-1) shows that the fractional change in lattice parameter a per unit concentration of defects is equal to $\frac{1}{3}(\lambda_1 + \lambda_2 + \lambda_3)$. This equation thus constitutes another independent relation involving the principal values of the λ tensor.

The cases of tetragonal, hexagonal, and trigonal crystals may all be considered together. Here there are two strains of type I, viz., uniaxial deformation along the c axis, and isotropic deformation within the basal plane (see Table 6-1). This leads to the following relations for the change of the lattice parameters a and c per unit defect concentration C_0

$$\begin{aligned} a^{-1}(da/dC_0) &= \tfrac{1}{2}(\lambda_{11}^{(p)} + \lambda_{22}^{(p)}) = \tfrac{1}{2}(\lambda_1 + \lambda_2) \\ c^{-1}(dc/dC_0) &= \lambda_{33}^{(p)} = \lambda_3 \end{aligned} \qquad (8.7\text{-}2)$$

where $\lambda_{33}^{(p)}$ and $\lambda_{11}^{(p)} + \lambda_{22}^{(p)}$ are each invariant quantities (independent of p). For these crystals, there are, therefore, two equations which relate the principal values of the λ tensor to the changes in lattice parameters.

Similar expressions for lower symmetry crystals are given by Nowick and Heller (1965).

8.8   Kinetics of Point-Defect Relaxations: An Example

Whereas the thermodynamic problem of point-defect relaxation consists in expressing the relaxation magnitudes in terms of appropriate components of the $\boldsymbol{\lambda}$ tensor, the kinetic problem seeks an expression for each relaxation time in terms of appropriate rate parameters. In this section, we illustrate the kinetic calculation for the special case of a tetragonal defect in a cubic crystal. This calculation can then serve as a basis for the complete generalization of the problem in the next section.

The tetragonal dipole in a cubic crystal gives rise to relaxation only of the shear modulus $S_{11} - S_{12}$. It therefore responds to a uniaxial stress in a [100] direction. Such a stress splits the free energy levels of the defects such that the dipole for which $p = 1$ (i.e., tetragonal axis parallel to [100]) is split apart from the other two ($p = 2$ and 3) by an amount $\Delta\gamma$, as shown in Fig. 8-3. The kinetic equation which describes the rate of change of the number per unit volume N_1 of dipoles in the orientation $p = 1$ is then

$$dN_1/dt = -N_1(v_{12} + v_{13}) + N_2 v_{21} + N_3 v_{31} \qquad (8.8\text{-}1)$$

where v_{pq} is the probability per second for reorientation of a dipole from p to q. Similar equations apply to dN_2/dt and dN_3/dt. Now, *in the absence of stress* all such reorientation frequencies are the same,

$$v_{12} = v_{21} = v_{13} = v_{31} = v_{23} = v_{32} \equiv v \qquad \text{(zero stress)} \quad (8.8\text{-}2)$$

This follows not only from the fact that there is no splitting at zero stress, but also because, for the tetragonal defect, all reorientations (1–2, 2–3, and 1–3) are crystallographically equivalent.[†] The quantity v may be expressed in terms of the theory of rate processes (Section 7.3) in the form

$$v = v_0 \exp(-\Delta\gamma^*/kT) \qquad (8.8\text{-}3)$$

where $\Delta\gamma^*$ is the free energy of activation.

It is then readily seen from Fig. 8-4 (also see Problem 8-14), that in the presence of stress

$$v_{12} = v_0 \exp[-(\Delta\gamma^* + \tfrac{1}{2}\Delta\gamma)/kT] \simeq v[1 - (\Delta\gamma/2kT)] \quad (8.8\text{-}4)$$

[†] For lower symmetry defects, e.g., $\langle 110 \rangle$ orthorhombic, this crystallographic equivalence is no longer valid as we shall see in the next section. Then there is more than one independent quantity v_{pq} for zero stress.

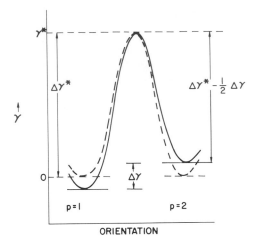

FIG. 8-4.   Illustrating the activation barriers before (dashed lines) and after (solid lines) the splitting of free-energy levels by stress.

when $\Delta\gamma/2kT \ll 1$. Similarly,

$$\nu_{21} \simeq \nu[1 + (\Delta\gamma/2kT)] \qquad (8.8\text{-}5)$$

When these equations are substituted into Eq. (8.8-1), and after multiplying through by the molecular volume to convert from concentrations per unit volume N_p to mole fractions C_p, we obtain

$$\dot{C}_1 = -2C_1\nu[1 - (\Delta\gamma/2kT)] + (C_2 + C_3)\nu[1 + (\Delta\gamma/2kT)] \qquad (8.8\text{-}6)$$

Finally, using the conservation condition, $C_2 + C_3 = C_0 - C_1$, and regrouping terms, Eq. (8.8-6) becomes

$$\dot{C}_1 = -3\nu C_1 + \nu C_0[1 + \tfrac{2}{3}(\Delta\gamma/kT)] \qquad (8.8\text{-}7)$$

[In obtaining Eq. (8.8-7), the product $C_1 \Delta\gamma$ is set equal to $C_0 \Delta\gamma/3$ so as to retain only first-order terms in small quantities, e.g., $\Delta\gamma$ and $C_1 - (C_0/3)$.] Since $\dot{C}_1 = 0$ at equilibrium, it is clear that the last term of Eq. (8.8-7) is $3\nu\bar{C}_1$.[†] Equation (8.8-7) may then be written

$$\dot{C}_1 = -3\nu(C_1 - \bar{C}_1) \qquad (8.8\text{-}8)$$

which is the equation for a simple (exponential) relaxation, with relaxation rate τ^{-1} given by

$$\tau^{-1} = 3\nu \qquad (8.8\text{-}9)$$

[†] This result may also be verified by comparison with Eq. (8.3-10).

The rate of defect relaxation, which is also the relaxation rate (at constant stress) for anelastic behavior (see Problem 8-15), is therefore given simply by 3ν, where ν is the reorientation rate between any two orientations at zero stress.

It is important to note that the term $\varDelta\gamma$ enters only into $\bar{C}_1$ and not into the expression for the relaxation time. Thus, the same τ value is obtained in an aftereffect experiment where σ (and therefore $\varDelta\gamma$) is zero, as is obtained in a creep experiment. This observation is simply a special case of the principle derived from the formal theory (Chapter 2), that the same relaxation spectrum can be obtained from creep as from elastic aftereffect experiments. In generalizing the present results to other defects and crystals (Section 8.9) it is therefore unnecessary to assume a splitting of the type shown in Figs. 8-3 and 8-4. Rather, one may simplify the kinetic calculation by considering only an aftereffect experiment where the free-energy levels remain equal. (See Problem 8-15b.)

It is important to emphasize that the result of our present calculation, Eq. (8.8-9), is not really the end of the problem. Equation (8.8-9) express τ^{-1} in terms of the *reorientation rate* ν and is valid for *any* tetragonal defect in a cubic crystal. However, in an actual defect problem, we prefer to express τ^{-1} in terms of specific *atom jump rates* w_i relevant to the defect in question. Since such atom jump rates may be quite different for different examples of tetragonal defects in cubic crystals, this step must be carried out by examining the model of the specific defect in question. The conversion of the expression 3ν into the appropriate atom jump rates, however, can usually be carried out by inspection. This will be illustrated when we come to discuss specific tetragonal defects in Chapters 9 and 11. The importance of an expression such as Eq. (8.8-9) is first that obtaining it represents the major part of the kinetic calculation, and second that the form of the expression depends only on the *symmetry*, and not on the detailed structure of the defect. Accordingly, we proceed in the next section to obtain similar expressions for a wide range of defect and crystal symmetries.

*8.9 Kinetics of Point-Defect Relaxations: General Theory

In Section 5.2, the kinetic problem was discussed for arbitrary internal variables ξ_p. The solution involved finding the "normal internal variables" each of which obeys a simple first-order kinetic equation, uncoupled from the other normal internal variables and involving a single relaxation time. In the present case, the variables ξ_p become the concentration differences $c_p = C_p - (C_0/n_t)$, but there is more involved than a mere change in symbol. In Section 5.2, equivalence of the different variables ξ_p was not required, but in the present case, elastic dipoles of different indices p an q represent crystallographically equivalent states. This requirement greatly simplifies the problem of finding the normal coordinates and the relaxation times.

By analogy to Eq. (8.8-1), the basic kinetic equation for point-defect relaxation may be written as

$$dN_p/dt = -N_p \sum_{q \neq p} v_{pq} + \sum_{q \neq p} v_{qp} N_q \qquad (8.9\text{-}1)$$

(one such equation for each value of p) where N_p is the number of dipoles of orientation p per unit volume, and v_{pq} is the probability per second for a dipole in orientation p to go into orientation q. The same equation can be written in terms of C_p and C_q by multiplying through by the molecular volume v_0, since $C_p \equiv N_p v_0$. It is sufficient to solve Eqs. (8.9-1) under zero stress, i.e., to obtain the elastic aftereffect, as discussed in the previous section. Under this condition we have the benefit of the relation

$$v_{pq} = v_{qp} \qquad (8.9\text{-}2)$$

since the dipoles in states p and q are equivalent. Finally, if we define a quantity v_{pp} by

$$v_{pp} \equiv - \sum_{q \neq p} v_{pq} \qquad (8.9\text{-}3)$$

so that $\sum_q v_{pq} = 0$, Eq. (8.9-1) becomes

$$dC_p/dt = \sum_q v_{pq}[C_q - (C_0/n_t)] \qquad (8.9\text{-}4)$$

Equation (8.9-4) is like (5.2-3) except for a change of sign (i.e., v_{pq} may be written as $-\omega_{pq}$). Since the eigenvalues of the matrix ω_{pq}, which are the set of relaxation rates τ_r^{-1} of Eq. (5.2-5), have been shown to be positive, it follows that the eigenvalues of v_{pq} are negative; therefore, there exist "normal coordinates" of the concentrations C_r' which are linear combinations[†] of the C_p's and obey the equations

$$dC_r'/dt = -\tau_r^{-1}(C_r' - \bar{C}_r') \qquad (8.9\text{-}5)$$

[†] The symmetry coordinates (discussed in Section 8.5) are also linear combinations of the concentrations which transform according to the scheme of a particular symmetry designation γ. The main difference between these and the normal coordinates is that the

where the quantities τ_r are all real and positive. In Section 5.2, where the internal coordinates were completely general, one could only discuss the *existence* of a transformation [Eq. (5.2-4)] to normal internal coordinates. Here, because of the crystallographic equivalence of all the dipole orientations, one can make full use of group-theoretical methods to find the normal coordinates and to obtain the relaxation times τ_r in terms of the coefficients v_{pq} of Eq. (8.9-4), i.e., to solve the secular determinant, Eq. (5.3-16). This has been done by Nowick (1967) for various crystal and defect symmetries. To review the method used would take us outside the scope of this book. However, we shall attempt to give the reader some idea of the concepts involved before quoting the results for the more important cases.

First, to each normal coordinate there corresponds a *relaxational normal mode* which comes about when that normal coordinate has a finite value while all the others are zero [see Eq. (5.2-6)]. Since the normal coordinate C_r' can always be chosen so as to form an orthogonal set, it is, in fact, possible to introduce one normal coordinate at a time (i.e., to set $C_s' = 0$ except for $s = r$). Second, it should be recalled, from Section 6.6, that each normal mode can only be excited by a component of stress belonging to the same symmetry designation. In a general case, there may be some normal modes belonging to a symmetry designation for which there is no stress component. Such a normal mode is said to be *mechanically inactive*, since it is incapable of being excited by any combination or stresses. The converse situation, in which there is a stress component σ_r' but no corresponding normal coordinate for symmetry designation γ represents the case for which a particular stress combination produces no relaxation. It is just this case for which a zero appears in the selection-rule table. To better illustrate some of these points, we will present the normal coordinates for the case of one particular defect symmetry ($\langle 100 \rangle$ monoclinic) in a tetragonal crystal, in the next subsection.

An important qualitative result of the kinetic analysis appears in Table 8-5. The reader should recall that in this table the presence of a zero implies that the relaxation of that particular compliance does not occur for the specified defect and crystal symmetry. When relaxation *does* occur, however, a number (1, 2 or 3) is given in the table. This number tells

---

symmetry coordinates may not completely diagonalize the v_{pq} matrix. For high symmetry defects the normal coordinates are the same as the symmetry coordinates; at worst they are linear combinations of two or more symmetry coordinates belonging to the same γ.

how many distinct relaxation times the designated (type II) compliance will manifest, for the specified defect and crystal symmetry.

With this information on how many relaxation times correspond to each compliance, it remains to give explicit formulas for these τ values in terms of the v_{pq}. The paper by Nowick (1967) shows how to express each τ value in terms of the set of v_{pq} *for only one value of p*. To be explicit, let us call this value $p = 1$. Furthermore, wherever dipoles q and q' bear the same geometrical equivalence[†] to dipole number 1, it follows that $v_{1q} = v_{1q'}$. Since not all v_{1q} are independent, the final formulas need only be expressed in terms of the independent reorientation frequencies v_{1q}. When there is more than one independent v_{1q}, however, it is necessary to specify a numbering system for the dipoles. For this purpose a stereographic-projection diagram provides the most compact method. Such a diagram is particularly simple for crystals which have a major axis of symmetry (i.e., tetragonal, hexagonal, and trigonal crystals). In these cases, the diagram is drawn such that the major symmetry axis comes out of the page and shows for each dipole orientation, the position where a given principal axis intersects the reference sphere.[‡] We take the results for each of the above-named crystal systems in turn, then finally turn to those for cubic crystals.

A. Tetragonal Crystals

Figure 8-5 shows the projection diagrams for the various defect symmetries in a tetragonal crystal. In these diagrams, a filled circle is used when the principal axis emerges on the horizontal plane perpendicular to the major symmetry axis, while an open circle represents an intersection at a point above this horizontal plane. In both cases, the intersection of the same principal axis on the diagonally opposite side of the reference sphere (below the horizontal plane) is not shown to avoid counting a given orientation of the axis twice. The choice of the one principal axis which uniquely determines the dipole orientation may be illustrated for the $\langle 100 \rangle$ monoclinic dipole as follows. From Table 8-1, the principal axes are clearly of the type [100], [0uw] and [0rt], with $ur + wt = 0$. The other three equivalent sets of directions which are

---

[†] This means that there exists a symmetry operation of the crystal which takes the pair 1, q into either the pair 1, q' or q', 1. It is easy to check for such equivalence of pairs using the "dot product" method (see Problem 8-17).

[‡] In almost all cases, it is possible to define the λ tensor orientation uniquely by designating the orientation of one particular principal axis.

TETRAGONAL CRYSTALS

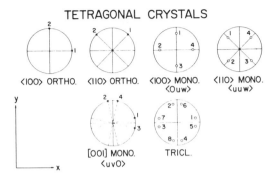

FIG. 8-5. The numbering convention for defects in tetragonal crystals, showing the possible orientations of the principal axis of the defect in a stereographic projection.

consistent with the tetragonal symmetry of the crystal are as follows: [100], [0$\bar{u}w$], [0$\bar{r}t$]; [010], [u0w], [r0t]; and [010], [$\bar{u}$0w], [$\bar{r}$0t]. Clearly, specifying the first principal axis, of the type $\langle 100 \rangle$ (which lies along the symmetry axis), does not uniquely determine the orientation of the strain ellipsoid; on the other hand, the second axis, of the type $\langle u0w \rangle$, is sufficient. It is therefore this second axis that is used in Fig. 8-5 to define the four orientations of the $\langle 100 \rangle$ monoclinic dipole.

Figure 8-5 establishes a numbering convention. From this figure it is possible to see immediately which orientations bear the same geometrical equivalence to defect number 1 and therefore, for which cases $\nu_{1q} = \nu_{1q'}$. (Thus, e.g., for the $\langle 100 \rangle$ monoclinic defect, $\nu_{12} = \nu_{14}$ but $\neq \nu_{13}$.) The expressions for the reciprocal relaxation times associated with the various type II compliances may now be given in terms of the independent reorientation frequencies ν_{1q}. (Note that in each case the number of relaxation times for each compliance is the same as that listed for the corresponding defect in a tetragonal crystal in Table 8-5.)

$\langle 100 \rangle$ orthorhombic defect

$$\tau^{-1}(S_{11} - S_{12}) = 2\nu_{12} \tag{8.9-6}$$

$\langle 110 \rangle$ orthorhombic defect

$$\tau^{-1}(S_{66}) = 2\nu_{12} \tag{8.9-7}$$

$\langle 100 \rangle$ monoclinic defect

$$\tau^{-1}(S_{11} - S_{12}) = 4\nu_{12}$$
$$\tau^{-1}(S_{44}) = 2\nu_{12} + 2\nu_{13} \tag{8.9-8}$$

$\langle 110 \rangle$ monoclinic defect

$$\tau^{-1}(S_{66}) = 4\nu_{12}$$
$$\tau^{-1}(S_{44}) = 2\nu_{12} + 2\nu_{13}$$

$$(8.9\text{-}9)$$

[001] monoclinic defect

$$\tau^{-1}(S_{11} - S_{12}) = 2(\nu_{12} + \nu_{14})$$
$$\tau^{-1}(S_{66}) = 2(\nu_{12} + \nu_{13})$$

$$(8.9\text{-}10)$$

Triclinic defect

$$\tau^{-1}(S_{11} - S_{12}) = 4\nu_{12} + 2\nu_{16} + 2\nu_{18}$$
$$\tau^{-1}(S_{66}) = 4\nu_{12} + 2\nu_{15} + 2\nu_{17}$$
$$\tau^{-1}(S_{44}) = (2\nu_{12} + 2\nu_{13} + \nu_{15} + \nu_{16} + \nu_{17} + \nu_{18})$$
$$\pm [(\nu_{15} - \nu_{17})^2 + (\nu_{16} - \nu_{18})^2]^{1/2}$$

$$(8.9\text{-}11)$$

This last example of the triclinic defect is the only one in tetragonal crystals for which two different relaxation times appear for the same compliance S_{44} as already indicated in Table 8-5.

For the purpose of illustrating the concept of relaxational normal modes, we will give the normal internal coordinates C_r' for the particular case of the $\langle 100 \rangle$ monoclinic defect, for which the numbering is in Fig. 8-5 and the relaxation times are given in Eq. (8.9-8). These coordinates are presented in Table 8-7 with the corresponding symmetry designation and the stress components belonging to each symmetry designation, taken from Tables 6-1 and 6-2. The latter table also shows the corresponding compliance constants. The coordinate belonging to the type I

TABLE 8-7

NORMAL COORDINATES FOR $\langle 100 \rangle$ MONOCLINIC DEFECT IN A TETRAGONAL CRYSTAL

Symmetry designation	Symmetrized stress	Normal coordinate of concentration
A	$(\sigma_1 + \sigma_2)$; σ_3	$\frac{1}{2}(C_1 + C_2 + C_3 + C_4) = C_1'$
B$_1$	$\sigma_1 - \sigma_2$	$\frac{1}{2}(C_1 - C_2 + C_3 - C_4) = C_2'$
B$_2$	σ_6	—
E	σ_4	$(1/\sqrt{2})(C_1 - C_3) = C_3'$
	σ_5	$(1/\sqrt{2})(C_2 - C_4) = C_4'$

designation A involves the sum of all four concentrations which is equal to C_0, the total defect concentration. By virtue of the conservation condition, Eq. (8.3-1), however, this coordinate is constrained to remain unchanged. Therefore, no relaxation of any of the compliances of type I (Table 6-1) is permissible, in agreement with the theorem already proved in Section 8.5. Of the remaining three coordinates C_2', C_3', C_4', the first belongs to the designation B_1, as does the stress $\sigma_1 - \sigma_2$, and the other two to the two-fold degenerate designation E, to which also belongs the pair of stresses σ_4 and σ_5. Note from Table 8-7 that the matrix B_{rp} of the transformation to the normal coordinates $C_r' = \sum B_{rp} C_p$ is an orthogonal matrix. This ensures that all but one normal coordinate may be set equal to zero to produce the corresponding relaxational normal mode. To illustrate, let us obtain the relaxational normal mode for designation B_1. Setting $C_1' = C_3' = C_4' = 0$, one readily obtains $C_1 = C_3 = -C_2 = -C_4$ as the condition for the normal mode. This means that, in the appropriate diagram of Fig. 8-5, excitation of the B_1 mode involves increasing C_1 and C_3 by, say, an amount δ over the random value $C_0/4$, while C_2 and C_4 are correspondingly decreased by δ. Once such a mode is excited (presumably, by the shear stress $\sigma_1 - \sigma_2$), the decay rate back to the random state takes place with a frequency $\tau^{-1} = 4\nu_{12}$ given by Eq. (8.9-8). The reader may easily verify this result.

B. HEXAGONAL CRYSTALS

In a similar way, Fig. 8-6 shows the projection diagrams for the various defect symmetries in a hexagonal crystal. The following formulas give the reciprocal relaxation times for defects other than triclinic:

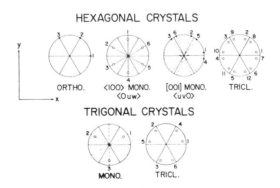

FIG. 8-6. The numbering convention for defects in hexagonal and trigonal crystals.

Orthorhombic defect

$$\tau^{-1}(S_{11} - S_{12}) = 3\nu_{12} \tag{8.9-12}$$

[100] monoclinic defect

$$\tau^{-1}(S_{11} - S_{12}) = 3(\nu_{12} + \nu_{13})$$
$$\tau^{-1}(S_{44}) = \nu_{12} + 3\nu_{13} + 2\nu_{14} \tag{8.9-13}$$

[001] monoclinic defect

$$\tau^{-1}(S_{11} - S_{12}) = (3\nu_{12} + \nu_{14} + \nu_{15} + \nu_{16})$$
$$\pm[(2\nu_{14} - \nu_{15} - \nu_{16})^2 + 3(\nu_{15} - \nu_{16})^2]^{1/2} \tag{8.9-14}$$

C. TRIGONAL CRYSTALS

In the case of trigonal crystals, there are three compliances which show relaxation, but since all three belong to one symmetry designation, they all have the same relaxation times (see Table 8-5). Figure 8-6 shows the appropriate projection diagrams, while the formulas for the relaxation rates are

Monoclinic defect

$$\tau^{-1} = 3\nu_{12} \tag{8.9-15}$$

Triclinic defect

$$\tau^{-1} = (3\nu_{12} + \nu_{14} + \nu_{15} + \nu_{16})$$
$$\pm\tfrac{1}{2}[(\nu_{14} - 2\nu_{15} + \nu_{16})^2 + 3(\nu_{14} - \nu_{16})^2]^{1/2} \tag{8.9-16}$$

D. CUBIC CRYSTALS

For cubic crystals, the projection diagrams are more difficult to understand. Therefore, we will find it more convenient to establish a numbering convention by designating the principal axis of interest in the usual $[uvw]$ notation for each of the p values. There are two compliances which undergo relaxation, viz., $S_{11} - S_{12}$ and S_{44} (see Table 8-5).

The tetragonal dipole may be designated by $p = 1, 2,$ or 3 according as the tetragonal axis is along the x, y, or z axis, respectively. Clearly, here, $\nu_{12} = \nu_{13}$. The relaxation rate τ^{-1} for this defect is

Tetragonal defect

$$\tau^{-1}(S_{11} - S_{12}) = 3\nu_{12} \tag{8.9-17}$$

This is the same result as was obtained in Section 8.8 [Eqs. (8.8-9) and (8.8-2)]. Similarly, for the trigonal dipole, we designate $p = 1, 2, 3$, or 4 according as the trigonal axis is [111], [$\bar{1}$11], [1$\bar{1}$1], or [11$\bar{1}$], respectively. For this case, $\nu_{12} = \nu_{13} = \nu_{14}$ so that ν_{12} is again the only independent reorientation frequency. The result is

Trigonal defect

$$\tau^{-1}(S_{44}) = 4\nu_{12} \tag{8.9-18}$$

The $\langle 110 \rangle$ orthorhombic dipole with principal axes of the type [110], [1$\bar{1}$0], [001], may be designated by the orientation of its first principal axis.[†] For $p = 1, 2, \ldots, 6$ we choose this principal axis as [110], [1$\bar{1}$0], [011], [01$\bar{1}$], [101], [10$\bar{1}$], respectively. Then $\nu_{13} = \nu_{14} = \nu_{15} = \nu_{16}$ (see Problem 8-17) and the τ values, expressed in terms of the two independent frequencies ν_{12} and ν_{13}, are

$\langle 110 \rangle$ orthorhombic defect

$$\tau^{-1}(S_{11} - S_{12}) = 6\nu_{13}$$
$$\tau^{-1}(S_{44}) = 2\nu_{12} + 4\nu_{13} \tag{8.9-19}$$

In the case of the $\langle 100 \rangle$ orthorhombic dipole, with its three principal axes of the type [100], [010], [001], we can clearly see that the designation of any *one* principal axis does not uniquely define the defect. Therefore, for this case, the orientations of the first two principal axes must be specified. We choose as $p = 1, 2, \ldots, 6$, the cases where these two axes, respectively, lie along x and y, x and z, y and z, y and x, z and x, z and y. From Table 8-5, we see that for this defect there is no S_{44} relaxation but that there are two τ's for $S_{11} - S_{12}$. Recognizing that $\nu_{13} = \nu_{15}$ and that all the other ν_{1q} are unequal, we obtain

$\langle 100 \rangle$ orthorhombic defect

$$\tau^{-1}(S_{11} - S_{12}) = (\nu_{12} + 3\nu_{13} + \nu_{14} + \nu_{16})$$
$$\pm [\nu_{12}^2 + \nu_{14}^2 + \nu_{16}^2 - \nu_{12}\nu_{14} - \nu_{12}\nu_{16} - \nu_{14}\nu_{16}]^{1/2} \tag{8.9-20}$$

The monoclinic cases have also been worked out. We give here the more important case of the $\langle 110 \rangle$ monoclinic for which the first two principal axes are typically of the type [110], [$u\bar{u}w$]. The first axis alone does not uniquely specify the defect (since [110], $\bar{u}uw$ is different from

---

[†] Often this is a defect consisting of an atom pair. The "first" principal axis is then most conveniently taken as the pair axis.

[110], [$u\bar{u}w$]), but the second axis is unique. For $p = 1, 2, \ldots, 12$, we now choose for this second axis, respectively, the following orientations: [$u\bar{u}w$], [$\bar{u}uw$], [$uu\bar{w}$], [$uu\bar{w}$], [$wu\bar{u}$], [$w\bar{u}u$] [wuu], [$\bar{w}uu$], [$uw\bar{u}$], [$\bar{u}wu$], [uwu], [$u\bar{w}u$]. It then follows (Problem 8-17) that $\nu_{13} = \nu_{14}$, $\nu_{15} = \nu_{18} = \nu_{1\,10} = \nu_{1\,11}$, $\nu_{17} = \nu_{19}$, and $\nu_{16} = \nu_{1\,12}$. The results are

⟨110⟩ Monoclinic defect

$$\tau^{-1}(S_{11} - S_{12}) = 3(2\nu_{15} + \nu_{16} + \nu_{17})$$

$$\tau^{-1}(S_{44}) = (\nu_{12} + 3\nu_{13} + 5\nu_{15} + \tfrac{3}{2}\nu_{17})$$

$$\pm[(\nu_{13} - \nu_{12} - \nu_{15} + \tfrac{1}{2}\nu_{16} + \tfrac{1}{2}\nu_{17})^2 + 2(\nu_{16} - \nu_{17})^2]^{1/2}$$

$$(8.9\text{-}21)$$

Equations (8.9-6)–(8.9-21) give expressions for each τ value in the relaxation spectrum of the theoretical (type II) compliances listed in Table 8-5. In view of the discussion given earlier, it is clear that all of these results are applicable also to "practical moduli" of the type which are related only to one of the type II compliances. Such practical moduli are those listed in Section 6.4. On the other hand, if deformation corresponding to an arbitrary modulus is studied (e.g., Young's modulus in a single crystal of arbitrary orientation, or a polycrystal), then the relaxation spectrum includes all of the τ values for that defect and crystal symmetry. For example, in a cubic crystal, a defect which is ⟨110⟩ orthorhombic gives rise to a single relaxation time for the Young's modulus $E_{⟨100⟩}$ namely that corresponding to $S_{11} - S_{12}$ in Eq. (8.9-19) and a different single relaxation time for $E_{⟨111⟩}$ (i.e., that for S_{44}), while a polycrystalline sample shows a two-line spectrum made up of both of these relaxation times. We see, therefore, that for the kinetics as well as the thermodynamics of relaxation, the use of single crystals subjected to simple deformations, as given in Section 6.4, greatly simplifies the results.

E. The "Frozen-Free Split" Phenomenon

Inspection of the formulas for τ^{-1} given above shows that in many cases a given defect can give rise to two or more relaxation times which differ considerably from each other. This situation can occur whenever there is more than one independent reorientation frequency of the type ν_{1q}. It is then quite possible that one of these frequencies will be substantially greater than the others, but yet will not appear in all the expressions for τ^{-1}. In such a case two (or more) relaxation times may be very widely resolved, i.e., decades apart in their magnitudes. As an example, consider the case of a $\langle 100 \rangle$ monoclinic defect in a tetragonal crystal, for which the independent frequencies are ν_{12} and ν_{13}. From the expressions in Eq. (8.9-8), it is clear that if ν_{12} is the dominant (i.e., the much greater) frequency, the two τ values will differ by only a factor of 2. On the other hand, if ν_{13} is dominant, $\tau^{-1}(S_{44})$ may be orders of magnitude greater than $\tau^{-1}(S_{11} - S_{12})$, since ν_{13} does not appear in the expression for the latter quantity. From symmetry alone one cannot say which of these two frequencies is dominant; one can only say that they are different. Which is dominant depends on the detailed atomic structure about the actual defect in question.

We may think of widely resolved relaxations as occurring either on a time (or frequency) scale, or else (in the usual case of thermally activated atom movements) on a temperature scale. Since temperature is most commonly varied when one wishes to explore a wide range of relaxation times, we shall continue this discussion from the viewpoint of a temperature scale. The occurrence of widely resolved relaxations means, therefore, that a polycrystalline or arbitrarily oriented single-crystalline sample will show one or more relaxations at relatively low temperature while the remainder appear at much higher temperatures. This situation is shown schematically in terms of the internal friction in Fig. 8-7. In the region between the two loss peaks in this figure, the rate ν_{1q} which gives rise to the low-temperature relaxation is high relative to the applied frequency, i.e., that reorientation occurs freely. On the other hand, the rates of reorientation required to produce the high-temperature relaxation are much lower than the applied frequency, i.e., these reorientations are essentially frozen. Accordingly, we refer to such a wide separation of relaxations as a "frozen-free split."

It can be shown that a frozen-free split occurs when the elastic dipole in question does not have access to all of its n_t equivalent orientations via

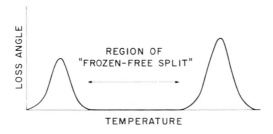

FIG. 8-7. Schematic illustration of a frozen-free split.

the dominant reorientation frequency. In such a case, the dominant frequency is capable of taking a dipole only among a subset of all of its possible orientations. This limited reorientation then gives rise to the low-temperature relaxation, while motion between equivalent subsets (which is much slower) gives rise to the high-temperature relaxation. The effect is to give the high-temperature relaxation the appearance of a higher symmetry defect (e.g., see Problem 8-19). On the other hand, the low temperature relaxation, if taken by itself, may not even obey the selection rules for any defect symmetry (Nowick, 1967). Examples of the frozen-free split phenomenon will be given when specific point defects are discussed (in Chapter 11).

8.10   Limitations of the Simple Theory

The thermodynamic and kinetic theories presented in this chapter apply to a relatively simple situation in which: (a) only one species (crystallographically equivalent set) of defects is present (viz., absence of "reactions"); and (b) the defects are dilute enough so that the probability that a defect is in a given orientation depends only on the applied stress field and not on the orientations of other defects (viz., absence of "interactions").

Let us consider what occurs when we drop the second restriction. The presence of defect interactions manifests itself in the thermodynamic theory by the occurrence of an extra term in the free-energy expression. Note that Eq. (8.6-1) has a term in $\sum c_p{}^2$ which comes from the entropy of mixing. This form can be generalized by adding a term (Nowick and Heller, 1963):

$$- \tfrac{1}{2} v_0^{-1} \sum_{p,q} b_{pq} c_p c_q$$

where the b_{pq} are called "interaction coefficients." It is easier to appreciate the effect of this term in the expression for the free energy level γ_p. In fact (8.3-9) must become

$$\gamma_p = -v_0 \lambda^{(p)} \sigma - \sum_q b_{pq} c_q \qquad (8.10\text{-}1)$$

where c_p is defined by Eq. (8.6-2). Equation (8.10-1) states that, in general, γ_p depends not only on σ, but also on the populations in all of the orientations. The effect of inclusion of the b_{pq} terms is dealt with in some detail by Nowick and Heller (1963). For present purposes, we illustrate the type of results obtained by making the simplifying assumption that γ_p depends only on c_p but not on the other c_q's, or $b_{pq} = b\delta_{pq}$ where δ_{pq} is the Kronecker delta.[†] The fact that all terms b_{pp} must be the same (therefore, written as just b) follows from the equivalence of all the defect orientations. Under this assumption, Eq. (8.10-1) then simplifies to

$$\gamma_p = -v_0\lambda^{(p)}\sigma - bc_p \qquad (8.10\text{-}2)$$

If we now substitute Eq. (8.10-2) into (8.3-10), we readily obtain the same result as Eq. (8.3-11) except that instead of $\bar{c}_p$ being proportional to $1/kT$, it now comes out proportional to $1/k(T - T_c)$, where

$$kT_c \equiv C_0 b/n_t \qquad (8.10\text{-}3)$$

Similarly, Eq. (8.3-12) is modified such that $\delta J \propto (T - T_c)^{-1}$ (see Problem 8-20). Equation (8.10-3) defines a temperature T_c which is proportional both to the interaction coefficient b and to the total concentration C_0. The meaning of T_c may be deduced by returning to Eq. (8.10-2). This equation shows that the existence of a state of order can, in itself, result in a change of γ_p, i.e., a splitting of the free-energy levels. At low enough temperatures, we may expect to reach a point where, due to these interactions, the defects would all spontaneously align themselves into a single orientation if the necessary atom movements could occur. T_c is the critical temperature for such a "self-induced ordering." The situation is analogous to the onset of ferromagnetism below a Curie temperature, while the $1/(T - T_c)$ dependence of δJ is analogous to the Curie–Weiss law for the paramagnetic susceptibility above the Curie temperature. Since $T_c \propto C_0$, this effect is only important when the point-defect concentration becomes relatively high. Some examples of the $1/(T - T_c)$ behavior will be mentioned in the following chapters. In most cases, however, the interaction term can be neglected.

Second, let us consider the effect of dropping restriction (a), that only one equivalent set of defects is present, and allow a "reaction" $A \rightleftharpoons B$ whereby a defect species denoted by A and having n_A dipole orientations, may be converted into a species B which is not crystallographically

---

† This assumption is intended merely to illustrate the effect of introducing interactions in the simplest way. It leads to a critical temperature T_c which is independent of the type of stress employed or the orientation of the sample. Under more general considerations, it can be shown that different T_c values are obtained for the different symmetrized stresses of type II.

equivalent to A, and has n_B orientations. The simplest example occurs for defect pairs where A is a nearest-neighbor (nn) pair and B a next-nearest-neighbor (nnn) pair. In the fcc lattice A has six equivalent orientations (along $\langle 110 \rangle$ directions) while B has three (along $\langle 100 \rangle$ directions). Nowick and Heller (1963) and more recently Nowick (1970b) have considered the effect of such reactions in some detail. They find that the existence of reactions makes possible the relaxation of compliances of type I, which show no relaxation when a single defect species is present (Section 8.5). The most useful application is to axial crystals (hexagonal, tetragonal, trigonal), where a net defect reaction under uniaxial stress along the major crystal axis (#3) gives rise to relaxation of the type I compliance S_{33}, the magnitude of which is given by

$$\delta S_{33} = \frac{v_0 C_A{}^0 C_B{}^0}{(C_A{}^0 + C_B{}^0)kT} (\lambda_{33,A} - \lambda_{33,B})^2 \qquad (8.10\text{-}4)$$

Here $C_A{}^0$ and $C_B{}^0$ are the equilibrium concentrations of species A and B in the absence of stress, while $\lambda_{33,A}$ and $\lambda_{33,B}$ are the respective components of the $\boldsymbol{\lambda}$ tensor (using the two-index notation λ_{ij} as in Section 8.2). The observation of the relaxation of such a type I compliance is an excellent way to prove that a reaction is occurring. Note that the form of Eq. (8.10-4) is the usual one of type (8.4-7), with an effective concentration $C_A{}^0 C_B{}^0/(C_A{}^0 + C_B{}^0)$; thus if $C_B{}^0 \ll C_A{}^0$, the effective concentration is $C_B{}^0$, i.e., the smaller of the two values. It is therefore apparent that the relaxation will only be appreciable if the energy difference involved in the reaction $A \rightleftharpoons B$ is small, so that $C_B{}^0$ and $C_A{}^0$ are roughly comparable in value.

Turning now to the behavior of a system involving a defect reaction subjected to a stress of type II, we find that in this case each defect species is redistributed among its various orientations independently of the other, in the manner already treated here. The expressions for the relaxation magnitudes in the presence of a reaction are therefore the sum of those for the two defect species taken separately. The kinetics, on the other hand, may be drastically affected by the existence of a reaction. Specifically, the τ values may each involve, not only reorientation jumps of each species, but also jump frequencies which take species A into B and vice versa. This problem has been attacked for specific defects by Franklin (1963) and Dreyfus and Laibowitz (1964), and in a general way by Chang (1964), Povolo and Bisogni (1966), and Nowick (1970a). The latter paper shows that the kinetic theory presented in Section 8.9

may, in fact, be further generalized to include reactions. For the purposes of this book, however, we will give the results only for specific cases of defect reactions as we come to them in the subsequent chapters.

As a final remark, we must note that the entire theory presented in this chapter treats a classical problem in which each defect species is confined to a set of equivalent minimum energy sites separated by relatively large potential barriers. As the barrier height decreases, however, one may imagine approaching, in the limit, the case of a free rotation, which may be treated either classically or quantum mechanically. Such a problem, involving a weak potential barrier, has been studied by Welsh (1969) who calculated the relaxation δJ and found results differing in two ways from the ones presented in this chapter: (1) A failure of the selection rules is predicted, approaching the limiting case of an isotropic δJ for a completely free rotator. (2) Under quantum mechanical considerations, δJ is no longer proportional to $1/T$ but shows saturation at low temperatures where the system goes into its lowest quantum state. The scope of application of these considerations is not yet clear, but they may be expected to apply in cases where high defect mobility persists to very low temperatures.

PROBLEMS

8-1. What are the symmetries of the various sites in Fig. 8-1 if this is the basal plane of a simple tetragonal crystal?

8-2. Explain why Eq. (8.3-9), as an approximation valid for small stress, is a better approximation than the last term of Eq. (8.3-10); consequently, explain why it is correct to substitute Eq. (8.3-9) into the exact (Boltzmann) form of Eq. (8.3-10) when relatively high stresses are employed.

8-3. For the case in which σ and ε (as well as $\lambda^{(p)}$) refer to hydrostatic stress and strain, respectively, show that $\delta J = 0$ in Eq. (8.3-12). [Hint: Note that $\lambda^{(p)}$, in this case, is independent of p.]

8-4. Carry out a calculation similar to the one which led to Eq. (8.4-1) for stress applied in a $\langle 111 \rangle$ direction for the tetragonal dipole in a cubic crystal to show that $\delta S_{44} = 0$ [Eq. (8.4-2)].

8-5. Obtain the table of direction cosines and $\lambda^{(p)}$ values for a trigonal dipole and [100] stress and verify Eq. (8.4-3). For the same defect and [111] stress axis, verify Table 8-4.

8-6. Work out the direction cosines and $\lambda^{(p)}$ for the $\langle 110 \rangle$ ortho-rhombic defect in a cubic crystal for both $\langle 100 \rangle$ and $\langle 111 \rangle$ stresses, and verify Eqs. (8.4-5) and (8.4-6).

8-7. Obtain Eqs. (8.6-14) and (8.6-15) by the method of Section 8.4 with the aid of Eqs. (6.4-17) and (6.4-18) and the theorem (Section 8.5) that compliances of type I do not undergo relaxation.

8-8. Obtain Eqs. (8.6-16) and (8.6-17) by the method of Section 8.4 with the aid of Eq. (6.4-9) and the theorem that compliances of type I do not undergo relaxation.

8-9. Calculate the configurational entropy term (i.e., the last term) in Eq. (8.6-1) in the usual way from the number of ways of dividing N_0 objects into sets $p = 1, 2, \ldots, n_t$, with N_p in the pth set. Apply Stirling's approximation, express in terms of the quantities c_p, and expand, keeping only up to quadratic terms in c_p.

8-10. Show that inserting an extra term of the form $-\sum_{p,q} b_{pq} c_p c_q$ into Eq. (8.6-1) is equivalent to inserting terms in c_q when integrating Eq. (8.3-8) to obtain (8.3-9), i.e., to introducing defect interactions.

8-11. Carry out the steps required to obtain Eq. (8.6-6).

8-12. If $\lambda^{(p)}$ represents a component of the λ tensor for dipole p which is of type II, (Section 6.3), show that $\sum_p \lambda^{(p)} = 0$. (Hint: Use the theorem in Section 8.7 that a set of randomly oriented defects can only give rise to strains of type I.) Also show that for the splitting of free energy levels under a stress of type II, $\sum_p \gamma_p = 0$. This also means that for such a stress, the condition (8.6-5) that $\sum \bar{c}_p = 0$ is automatically satisfied and therefore that the Lagrange multiplier L is zero.

8-13. Verify the entries in Table 8-6 under hexagonal crystals, and substitute these results into Eqs. (8.6-10) to obtain Eqs. (8.6-16)–(8.6-18).

8-14. Show that Eqs. (8.8-4) and (8.8-5) follow if one takes the activated state for the reorientation ν_{12} at γ_0^* in the absence of stress, and at $\gamma_0^* + (\Delta\gamma)/2$ in the presence of stress (where $\Delta\gamma = \gamma_2 - \gamma_1$ is the stress splitting), see Fig. 8-3. Thus, it is not necessary to assume that the two levels are displaced by equal and opposite amounts from the zero position, as indicated for simplicity in Fig. 8-4.

8-15. In the problem of Section 8.8, (a) show that the anelastic strain relaxes with the same kinetics as the concentration C_1, as given in Eq. (8.8-8); (b) rederive Eq. (8.8-9) for the case of zero stress, i.e., for the case of an aftereffect experiment.

8-16. Follow the same method as in Section 8.8 for trigonal defects in cubic crystals, introducing a uniaxial stress along the [111] direction, to obtain Eq. (8.9-18).

8-17. A convenient method exists for determining the equivalence of two reorientation frequencies v_{1q} and $v_{1q'}$ when the defect orientation can be uniquely defined by the direction of one of its axes in the crystal. (As pointed out in the text, this condition is satisfied for all defects except the $\langle 100 \rangle$ orthorhombic in the cubic crystal.) The method is simply to check whether defects q and q' make the same angle with defect number 1. This test is best carried out by taking simple dot products of the directions of type $\langle uvw \rangle$ for the unique axes of the defects. Use this method to verify that $v_{13} = v_{14} = v_{15} = v_{16}$ for the $\langle 110 \rangle$ orthorhombic defect in the cubic crystal [Eq. (8.9-19)] as well as the various equalities for the $\langle 110 \rangle$ monoclinic defect [Eq. (8.9-21)].

8-18. Verify Eq. (8.9-19) for the $\langle 110 \rangle$ orthorhombic defect in a cubic crystal starting from Eq. (8.9-1) for the case of zero stress, i.e., for the aftereffect experiment. Note that the relaxational normal mode involving the compliance $S_{11} - S_{12}$ is excited by prior application of stress along the direction $\langle 100 \rangle$, which produces splitting such that $C_1 = C_2 = C_5 = C_6$ and $C_3 = C_4$ [in terms of the numbering convention given above Eq. (8.9-19)]. On the other hand the mode involving S_{44} is excited by a stress along $\langle 111 \rangle$, for which the splitting is $C_1 = C_3 = C_5$ and $C_2 = C_4 = C_6$. Use the equalities $v_{13} = v_{14} = v_{15} = v_{16}$ and the conservation condition (8.3-1).

8-19. Consider the case of a frozen-free split for the $\langle 100 \rangle$ monoclinic defect in a tetragonal crystal in which $v_{13} \gg v_{12}$. What is the apparent symmetry of the defect in the region of the high-temperature relaxation; in the region of the low-temperature relaxation?

8-20. Verify that Eq. (8.10-2) leads to $\delta J \propto 1/(T - T_c)$ where $kT_c = C_0 b / n_t$.

General References

Nowick, A. S. (1967). *Advan. Phys.* **16**, 1.
Nowick, A. S., and Heller, W. R. (1963). *Advan. Phys.* **12**, 251.
Nowick, A. S., and Heller, W. R. (1965). *Advan. Phys.* **14**, 101.

Chapter 9 / The Snoek Relaxation

The term *Snoek relaxation* refers to the anelastic relaxation produced by interstitial solutes in dilute solution in the body-centered cubic (bcc) metals. Passing over some historically interesting early work (reviewed by Zener, 1948), the studies which led to our present understanding of the Snoek relaxation began with the discovery by Richter (1938a,b) of an elastic aftereffect in carbonyl iron. The anelastic nature of the aftereffect was promptly recognized by Snoek (1939), who showed that similar material exhibited an internal friction peak located near room temperature at low vibration frequencies (<1 Hz). A major step forward was made when Snoek found that the virtual elimination of carbon and nitrogen from his samples by heat treatment in a wet hydrogen atmosphere removed the relaxation. The relaxation reappeared when small amounts of either carbon or nitrogen were separately reintroduced into a purified sample. The key to the origin of the relaxation was thus traced to the presence of these interstitial impurities. A good example of the Snoek peak due to C in α-Fe, taken from the work of Wert and Zener (1949), is shown in Fig. 3-9 for several frequencies of vibration.

The theory proposed by Snoek (1941, 1942a,b) to account for the relaxation was subsequently elaborated by Polder (1945) and strongly substantiated experimentally by Dijkstra (1947). The essence of the theory is the recognition that an interstitial solute atom in a bcc metal constitutes an elastic dipole of tetragonal symmetry, and can thus produce anelastic relaxation via the process of stress-induced ordering. As would be expected from this idea, in addition to iron several other bcc metals (e.g., Ta, Nb, Cr, V) are now known to exhibit the Snoek relaxation. The list of solute elements known to produce the relaxation in one or more of these metals now includes H, O (and possibly B), in addition to C and N.

9.1   Theory of the Snoek Relaxation

The specific model proposed by Snoek for the relaxation due to C or N in α-Fe is based upon the premise that these solute atoms occupy the octahedral interstitial sites of the bcc host lattice. Unfortunately, the direct experimental determination of the location of such light atoms by x-ray diffraction is a difficult problem because of their dilute concentration and low atomic scattering factor. However, x-ray evidence in favor of Snoek's assignment was subsequently obtained for the case of carbon in ferrite by Williamson and Smallman (1953). As shown in Fig. 9-1,

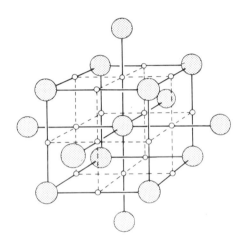

FIG. 9-1.   The location of the octahedral sites (small circles) in the bcc lattice. All these sites are crystallographically equivalent to each other.

the octahedral sites are located at all positions midway along the edges of the two interpenetrating simple cubic lattices which together make up the bcc structure. These positions are known as the octahedral sites for the reason made clear by Fig. 9-2, namely that each site is surrounded by an octahedral array of host atoms. The octahedron is not geometrically regular, since it is built-up from four atoms which are $a/\sqrt{2}$ from the center octahedral site and two atoms which are only $a/2$ from the center. The octahedron is therefore shorter along its major axis than a regular octahedron of the same square cross section. It is easily verified by inspection that the point symmetry of the octahedral site is not cubic but tetragonal, with the single four-fold symmetry axis lying along the major axis of the octahedron. It therefore follows from Section 8.1 that interstitial atoms occupying such sites are defects of tetragonal symmetry. Since, depending on the particular site considered, the tetragonal axis may lie along any one of the cube axes x_1, x_2, or x_3, the octahedral sites

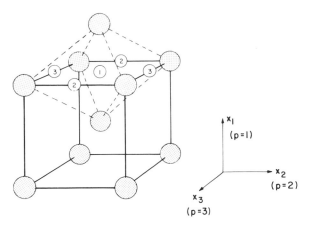

FIG. 9-2. The broken lines indicate the octahedral grouping of host atoms around the site labeled 1. In this drawing, the sites are numbered with the index $p = 1, 2$ or 3 to indicate the direction of their tetragonal axes with respect to the axes x_1, x_2, x_3.

may be subdivided into three groups of crystallographically equivalent sites. All those sites which have their tetragonal axis parallel to x_1 may be tagged with the orientation index $p = 1$, with a corresponding identification applying to $p = 2$ and 3 (cf. Fig. 9-2).

With the identification of the defect symmetry as tetragonal, and thus the identification of the defect behavior under stress as that of a tetragonal elastic dipole, we need only refer to Chapter 8 for expressions which describe both the thermodynamics and kinetics of the Snoek relaxation. For uniaxial stress, the relaxation magnitudes are given by Eqs. (8.4-1) and (8.4-2), repeated here:

$$\delta E^{-1}_{\langle 100 \rangle} = \delta S'/3 = (2/9)(C_0 v_0/kT)(\lambda_1 - \lambda_2)^2 \qquad (9.1\text{-}1)$$

$$\delta E^{-1}_{\langle 111 \rangle} = \delta S/3 = 0 \qquad (9.1\text{-}2)$$

where C_0 is the mole fraction of solute, v_0 is the volume per atom of the host crystal, and λ_1 and λ_2 are the two independent principal values of the $\boldsymbol{\lambda}$ tensor. In addition, the shorthand notations $S \equiv S_{44}$ and $S' \equiv 2(S_{11} - S_{12})$ have been adopted for the two shear compliances in the cubic crystal.

The solution for the kinetics of the relaxation has also been given [Eqs. (8.8-2) and (8.8-9)] as

$$\tau^{-1} = 3\nu_{12} \qquad (9.1\text{-}3)$$

which relates the relaxation time (at constant stress) τ to the rate ν_{12}

at which an interstitial atom located in a site for which $p = 1$ makes a transition to any of the sites for which $p = 2$. It is now desirable to relate the reorientation rate v_{12} to the specific atom jump rates appropriate to the Snoek relaxation. It has generally been assumed that jumps occur between neighboring octahedral sites only. Let us designate the jump rate between specific neighboring sites as w. Inspection of Fig. 9-2 shows that this type of jump inevitably leads to reorientation of the defect. Further, it is evident that the reorientation to $p = 2$ from a particular $p = 1$ site can be achieved via a nearest-neighbor jump in just two ways. Thus we have the result that

$$v_{12} = 2w \qquad (9.1\text{-}4)$$

Inserting Eq. (9.1-4) into (9.1-3) gives the final result[†]

$$\tau^{-1} = 6w \qquad (9.1\text{-}5)$$

We may also relate the relaxation time to the diffusion coefficient for the interstitial solute atoms. To do this, we substitute Eq. (9.1-5) into Eq. (7.5-5), and insert $\alpha = \frac{1}{6}$ to obtain

$$D = a^2/36\tau \qquad (9.1\text{-}6)$$

It is clear from either Eq. (9.1-5) or (9.1-6) that the activation energy which governs τ is simply that for the migration of the interstitial solute. As we shall see in the next section, this fact has been used quite extensively for determining the activation energies of interstitial migration.

The theory of the Snoek relaxation has been developed thus far on the basis that interstitial atoms occupy the octahedral lattice sites. In a bcc metal, the largest spherical interstitial voids are not at the octahedral sites, however, but rather at the so-called *tetrahedral sites*. Such sites have atomic coordinates of the type $(\frac{1}{2}, 0, \frac{1}{4})$, etc., and occur at all points midway between neighboring octahedral sites. The sites are called tetrahedral because each one is enclosed by a tetrahedral array of host atoms, as shown in Fig. 9-3. The tetrahedron is not regular, since two of its edges are of length a while the remaining four are of length $a\sqrt{3}/2$. The symmetry system of the tetrahedral sites, like that of

[†] An expression for τ^{-1} has often been written in terms of the mean jump rate Γ [Eq. (7.5-4)]. Since from Fig. 9-2 an atom may leave a given site in a total of four ways (again assuming only nearest-neighbor jumps), $\Gamma = 4w$ and Eq. (9.1-5) becomes $\tau^{-1} = 3\Gamma/2$.

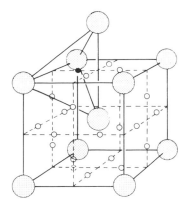

FIG. 9-3. Location of the tetrahedral sites (small circles) in the bcc lattice. The tetrahedral grouping of host atoms around the darkened site is outlined.

the octahedral sites, is tetragonal, although the actual point group symmetry (belonging to the class D_{2d} or $\overline{4}2m$) is lower than that for the octahedral sites.[†] Thus, if solute atoms were to occupy the tetrahedral sites, they would again produce tetragonal elastic dipoles obeying Eqs. (9.1-1) and (9.1-2). Measurements of the anisotropy of the relaxation strength therefore cannot distinguish between tetrahedral and octahedral occupancy. On the other hand, it is possible that a distinction can be made on the basis of the absolute magnitude of the shape factor $|\lambda_1 - \lambda_2|$ of the strain ellipsoid, which will be different for the two cases. While Dijkstra (1947) had suggested that $|\lambda_1 - \lambda_2|_{\text{tet}} \ll |\lambda_1 - \lambda_2|_{\text{oct}}$, this question has been reopened by Beshers (1965), who has attempted (using an approximate elastic model) to assess the relative values of $|\lambda_1 - \lambda_2|$ for octahedral and tetrahedral occupancy, and also to estimate the site energies for the two cases. Beshers concluded that the difference between the relative shape factors is by no means as large as Dijkstra had suggested, and that $|\lambda_1 - \lambda_2|_{\text{tet}}$ is probably only $\frac{1}{2}$ to $\frac{1}{3}$ smaller than $|\lambda_1 - \lambda_2|_{\text{oct}}$. Beshers' calculations also indicate that the assumption of octahedral occupancy for all known cases of the Snoek relaxation may be incorrect. Specifically, he has predicted that nitrogen and carbon in vanadium, and oxygen and nitrogen in tantalum and niobium all occupy the tetrahedral sites. In contrast, the more detailed calculations of Johnson et al. (1964), conducted so far only for nitrogen in vanadium and carbon in iron, predict occupation of the octahedral sites in both systems.

A second possible method of distinguishing between octahedral and tetrahedral occupancy may be provided by a comparison of the diffusion

[†] Accordingly, there are six equivalent defect orientations ($n_d = 6$) but only three independent $\boldsymbol{\lambda}$ tensors ($n_t = 3$). See Section 8.2.

coefficient computed from the Snoek relaxation rate with values obtained directly from diffusion experiments. The point is that the formula used in calculating D from τ^{-1} involves an assumption as to the type of jump(s) involved. For example, suppose we assume tetrahedral occupancy, and consider only the jump (of rate w_t, say) between nearest-neighbor tetrahedral positions. In this case, d^2 in Eq. (7.5-4) has the value $a^2/8$ and the value of α in Eq. (7.5-5) becomes $1/12$. The reader may verify from Fig. 9-3 that $v_{12} = 2w_t$ (and hence $\tau^{-1} = 6w_t$), so that Eq. (7.5-5) now yields

$$D = a^2/72\tau \tag{9.1-7}$$

Since Eqs. (9.1-6) and (9.1-7) differ by a factor of two, comparison of precise anelastic and diffusion data may serve to indicate which of the models is more nearly correct. It should be noted, however, that in reality a more complicated situation may exist than either of these simple alternatives. For example, Condit and Beshers (1967) have hypothesized that for C in α-Fe, where a discrepancy exists between low-temperature anelastic and high-temperature diffusion data, the interstitial atoms may be partitioned between the octahedral and tetrahedral sites and be capable of making octahedral–tetrahedral, tetrahedral–tetrahedral, and tetrahedral–octahedral jumps. Another alternative (Nowick, 1967) for the explanation of this discrepancy is the introduction of jumps between next-nearest-neighbor octahedral sites (see Problem 9-3).

9.2   Experimental Investigations of the Snoek Relaxation

A. Anisotropy and Concentration Dependence of the Relaxation Strength in Single Crystals

One of the earliest and most important investigations of the Snoek relaxation was carried out by Dijkstra (1947) on single crystals of iron containing small amounts of added carbon or nitrogen. Dijkstra was the first to test the linear concentration dependence predicted by Eq. (9.1-1), and the prediction that $\delta E^{-1}_{\langle 111 \rangle} = 0$, Eq. (9.2-2). The internal friction experiments were performed in flexure on nitrided or carburized strip samples (containing up to 0.1 at. % solute) of $\langle 100 \rangle$ and $\langle 111 \rangle$ orientations. The orientations (relative to the axis of the strip) were deduced by magnetic measurements rather than by x-ray methods. The amount of solute introduced by a given carburizing or nitriding treatment was

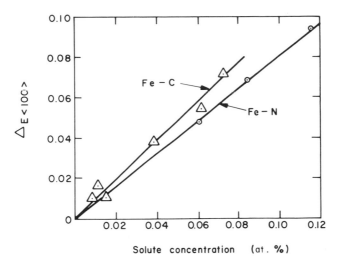

FIG. 9-4.   The concentration dependence of the relaxation strength $\Delta_{E\langle 100\rangle}$ for Fe–C and Fe–N alloys, as measured by Dijkstra (1947).

obtained from the change in the electrical resistance of the sample.[†] The results for the $\langle 100 \rangle$ orientation, shown in Fig. 9-4, confirm the predicted linear concentration dependence and the inherent concept that *each* interstitial solute atom creates an elastic dipole. With regard to the anisotropy of the relaxation, Dijkstra found that the value of $\Delta_{E\langle 100\rangle}$ was much larger than $\Delta_{E\langle 111\rangle}$. (The ratio was 17 : 1 for the carburized samples and 14 : 1 for the nitrided samples.) Allowing for errors in orientation and the presence of a small quantity of misoriented grains, this result can be regarded as a highly indicative, though not totally satisfactory, check that $\delta E_{\langle 111\rangle}^{-1} = 0$. Note from the selection rules, Table 8-5, that in cubic crystals this result is unique to the tetragonal dipole. In view of the importance of this point, it is perhaps surprising that many years elapsed before the anisotropy of the Snoek relaxation was examined in more detail. Interestingly, the next investigation of the anisotropy (Hoffman and Wert, 1966) was not performed with iron but with specimens of niobium, which (from studies on polycrystalline samples over the intervening years) was then known to exhibit Snoek peaks due to both O and N. Actually, on testing single crystal rods

---

[†] Separate measurements were performed on larger samples to determine the variation of resistance with solute concentration. The concentration of these samples was determined from the weight increase produced by the solute addition.

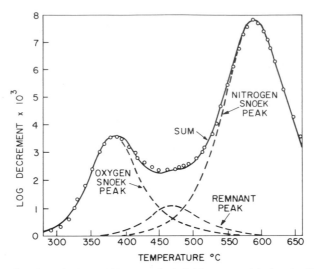

FIG. 9-5.   Snoek peaks in a ⟨100⟩ crystal of niobium, tested in longitudinal vibration at 80 kHz. (From Hoffman and Wert, 1966.)

prepared by the floating zone technique, Hoffman and Wert obtained evidence (Fig. 9-5) of a third relaxation peak lying between the oxygen and nitrogen peaks. The anisotropy results are plotted in Fig. 9-6 as the peak heights versus the orientation factor Γ. The curves show the orienta-

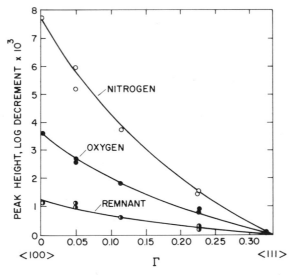

FIG. 9-6.   Anisotropy of Snoek relaxations in niobium, as shown by single crystal samples in longitudinal vibration. (From Hoffman and Wert, 1966.)

tion dependence calculated from the formal theory for the case of a tetragonal dipole, and pinned to the data for the $\langle 100 \rangle$ crystal. Despite some scatter, attributable to difficulties in obtaining the same solute content in all the crystals, the data present convincing proof that each relaxation vanishes for the $\langle 111 \rangle$ orientation, and therefore, that each is produced by a species of tetragonal dipole. Gibala and Wert (1965) have suggested that the remnant peak is due to the presence of a third interstitial impurity, namely, carbon.

More recently, further work has been performed on the anisotropy of the Snoek relaxation in Fe–C and Fe–N alloys. In contrast to the flexural mode of vibration employed by Dijkstra, use was made of torsional vibrations. It should be noted that in torsion the sense of the anisotropy is reversed from that under uniaxial stress (see Problem 9-1). Specifically, it can be seen from the equation

$$\delta G^{-1} = 2 \, \delta S' \Gamma \qquad (9.2\text{-}1)$$

that the largest relaxation in torsion occurs for a $\langle 111 \rangle$ orientation ($\Gamma = \frac{1}{3}$), while the null orientation becomes $\langle 100 \rangle$ ($\Gamma = 0$). Strong support for the conclusion that $\delta G^{-1}_{\langle 100 \rangle} = 0$, and therefore that C and N in α-Fe are tetragonal elastic dipoles, has been given by Ino et al. (1967) and particularly by Swartz et al. (1968), whose results are shown in Fig. 9-7. These investigators point out that the failure of their curves to pass exactly through the origin at $\Gamma = 0$ can be accounted for by the retention of a few small misoriented grains in their samples.

In addition to their use in establishing the tetragonal symmetry of the interstitial defects producing the Snoek relaxation, measurements on single crystals of known orientation and composition are of great value because they permit calculation of the magnitude of the dipole shape factor $|\lambda_1 - \lambda_2|$. The reader should verify that the slopes of the lines in both Figs. 9-4 and 9-7 are proportional to $(\lambda_1 - \lambda_2)^2$. Values of $|\lambda_1 - \lambda_2|$, as determined from measurements on single crystals, are listed in Table 9-1. In the case of the Fe–C and Fe–N alloys, greater weight should be given to the values of Swartz et al. In visualizing the significance of these values, it is well to recall that a $|\lambda_1 - \lambda_2|$ value of unity means, for example, that if it were possible to introduce 0.1 at. % solute solely into sites of a single orientation, a unit cube of bcc Fe would distort into a tetragonal block whose long and short sides would differ in length one from another by 0.1%. For iron, it is in fact possible to check this prediction, since this type of structure (tetragonal martensite) is produced by quenching Fe–C and Fe–N alloys from the austenitic phase. Values of λ_1 and λ_2 deduced from the concentration dependence of the a and c lattice parameters of tetragonal martensite are included in Table 9-1. The values of $\lambda_1 - \lambda_2$ obtained by subtraction are seen to be in good agreement with those calculated from the anelastic data. This agreement is generally regarded as satisfactory proof that, at least for α-Fe, C and N

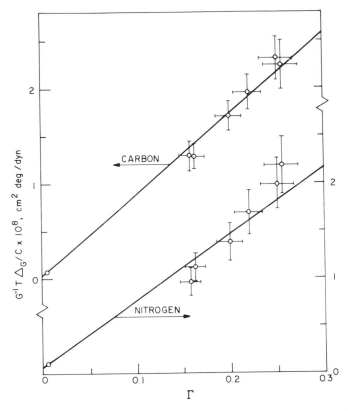

FIG. 9-7.   Anisotropy of the Snoek relaxations due to C and N in α–Fe, as shown by single crystal samples in torsional vibration. (From Swartz *et al.*, 1968.)

indeed occupy the octahedral sites. It should be noted that the x-ray measurements on martensite establish that λ_1 is positive, in confirmation of the expectation that insertion of an interstitial atom into an octahedral site causes the two nearest-neighbor iron atoms to move apart. The small negative value of λ_2 corresponds to a small inward movement of the four next-nearest neighbors.

TABLE 9-1

SINGLE CRYSTAL MEASUREMENTS OF $|\lambda_1 - \lambda_2|$ FOR THE SNOEK RELAXATION IN VARIOUS ALLOYS AND RELATED DATA FOR TETRAGONAL IRON MARTENSITES

Alloy	From anelastic data $|\lambda_1 - \lambda_2|$	From martensite data[a]		
		λ_1	λ_2	$\lambda_1 - \lambda_2$
Fe–C	0.87[a] 1.06[b]	+0.86	−0.08	0.94
Fe–N	0.80[a] 0.97[b]	+0.83	−0.07	0.90
Nb–O	0.54[c]	—	—	—
Nb–N	0.66[c]	—	—	—

[a] Swartz et al. (1968). [b] Dijkstra (1947).
[c] Values quoted by Gibala and Wert (1965) from the data of Hoffman and Wert (1964).

B. THE RELAXATION STRENGTH OF POLYCRYSTALLINE ALLOYS

Many studies of the Snoek relaxation have been performed on polycrystalline wires, with the aid of torsion pendulum apparatus. For many purposes, the polycrystalline nature of a specimen presents no disadvantage. For example, provided the grain structure has been stabilized by an adequate preparatory anneal, one given specimen, progressively loaded with solute, can be used to verify and measure the proportionality between solute content and relaxation strength.[†] Such measurements have been made for example on Fe–N alloys by Rawlings and Tambini (1955) and by Fast and Verrijp (1955), on Nb–N alloys by Ang and Wert (1953), on Nb–O alloys by Powers and Doyle (1959a), and on Ta–O alloys by Powers and Doyle (1956). As for single crystal specimens, the experiments generally involve introducing the interstitial solute into a previously purified wire by heating the wire to an elevated temperature in an appropriate gaseous atmosphere. Subsequently, the specimen is usually quenched (often the solute level introduced exceeds the solubility limit at lower temperatures) and is then mounted in the internal friction apparatus for measurement of the peak. In some cases measurements

[†] As will be pointed out in Section 11.4, this proportionality can become invalid at high solute concentrations due to pairing or clustering of the interstitial atoms.

near and above the peak temperature should be made as quickly as possible, since loss of solute by precipitation may occur at an appreciable rate and cause a decline in the strength of the peak. Various methods of obtaining the solute content of a doped specimen have been used, including (a) direct measurement of the amount of gas absorbed, (b) gas extraction analysis, and (c) resistivity measurements in conjunction with a previously established resistivity-composition curve.

Experiments of the type described above have provided values of the strength parameter Δ_G per atomic percent solute for various polycrystalline materials. The data shown in Table 9-2 are taken mainly from

TABLE 9-2

SNOEK RELAXATION PARAMETERS FROM POLYCRYSTALLINE SAMPLES

System	Δ_G per at. % solute	T°K	G [dyn cm^{-2} $\times 10^{-12}$ (solvent)]	$\delta S'$ per at. % solute	$\|\lambda_1 - \lambda_2\|$	τ_0^{-1} (10^{14} sec^{-1})	Q (eV)
V–N	0.12	540	0.47	0.64	0.72	3.6	1.48
V–O	0.55	455		2.9	1.35	5.1	0.87
Fe–C	0.43	308	0.75	1.43	0.87	1.8	0.835
Fe–N	0.40	290		1.33	0.83	1.9	0.796
Nb–N	0.10	559	0.36	0.70	0.67	2.7	1.52
Nb–O	0.09	418		0.63	0.55	7.0	1.17
Ta–C	0.4	623		1.5	1.03	2.0	1.67
Ta–N	0.23	616	0.68	0.85	0.78	1.7	1.64
Ta–O	0.17	415		0.63	0.55	1.5	1.11

a compilation by Powers and Doyle (1959a).[†] Several authors have suggested that the magnitude of the strength parameter is affected by the grain size of the aggregate, due to grain boundary absorption and immobilization of solute atoms. As pointed out by Swartz (1969a), it seems probable that such an effect is apparent rather than real, and actually reflects a correlation of crystallographic texture (preferred orientation) with grain size. Certainly there is no doubt that texture is the primary

[†] Care has been needed in some cases to identify the particular interstitial solute responsible for a given Snoek peak. The peak claimed by Kê (1948d) to be the carbon peak in Ta was later shown by Powers (1955) to be due to oxygen.

structural factor which affects the strength per unit concentration of a polycrystalline sample. Consideration has been given to this effect by a number of workers [see, e.g., Ino et al. (1967)]. Unfortunately, a rigorous evaluation of the dipole shape factor $| \lambda_1 - \lambda_2 |$ cannot be made from polycrystalline data, since even with the assumption of a completely random sample the averaging problem is tractable only with the further idealized assumption of either a uniform stress or a uniform strain in the sample. We shall estimate $| \lambda_1 - \lambda_2 |$ by employing the Reuss averaging method, Eq. (6.2-14), which assumes both a random grain distribution and uniformity of stress. With these assumptions, we may write

$$\Delta_G/G = \delta G^{-1} = 2 \, \delta S' \bar{\Gamma} = 2 \, \delta S'/5 \qquad (9.2\text{-}2)$$

using the result of Problem 6-8. The values of the shear modulus G shown in Table 9-2 have been calculated using this value of $\bar{\Gamma}$ and the room temperature single crystal elastic constants for the metals in question. The values of $\delta S'$ per atomic percent solute obtained from Eq. (9.2-2) give the calculated values of $| \lambda_1 - \lambda_2 |$ entered in Table 9-2. It is noteworthy that, where comparison is possible with Table 9-1, the agreement is surprisingly good. With the exception of the vanadium alloys, Table 9-2 reveals that for each solvent metal the value of $| \lambda_1 - \lambda_2 |$ is smaller in the sequence C→N→O. This is the sequence to be expected from size considerations. It may be seen further from Table 9-2 that the largest and smallest values of $| \lambda_1 - \lambda_2 |$ do not differ by more than a factor of three, and that none of the values is less than one-half of those for C and N in α-Fe. This rough similarity and overall high value of the shape factors appears to favor a belief that, in metals other than iron, interstitial atoms also enter the octahedral sites.

In addition to the systems listed in Table 9-2, there are several others for which Snoek peaks are known or suspected. These include V–C (Powers and Doyle, 1958; Klein, 1967), Nb–C (Powers and Doyle, 1957), Cr–N (De Morton, 1962), and W–C (Schnitzel, 1965). At present, evidence for the relaxation in molybdenum alloys is uncertain (Schnitzel, 1964). The possibility that boron may dissolve interstitially in iron, and hence give rise to a Snoek peak, has prompted investigations by a number of workers. Thomas and Leak (1955a), and more recently Tavadze et al. (1967), have claimed that such a peak exists, in close proximity to the carbon peak. On the other hand, work by Strocchi et al. (1967) and Hayashi and Sugeno (1970) makes it seem probable that the observed peak originates from residual carbon impurity, and that boron is essentially a substitutional solute in iron.

C. Temperature Dependence of the Relaxation Strength

To date, the temperature dependence of the Snoek relaxation strength has received comparatively little attention. This dependence is of interest since it is capable of yielding information on the extent of the interaction between solute atoms. As explained in Section 8.10, such an interaction would be manifest by a nonzero value of T_c, the critical temperature for self-induced ordering. Two investigations (Kê, 1948d; Powers and Doyle, 1959a) have been made of the temperature dependence of Δ_G in essentially the same alloy, namely Ta containing ~ 0.6 at. % oxygen. The results do not agree with each other. Kê concluded that $T_c = 0°K$, whereas Powers and Doyle found $T_c = 77°K$. A further complication is that at the relatively high oxygen content employed, an appreciable pairing of oxygen atoms occurs, to an extent which varies with temperature. This not only means that the concentration of single oxygen atoms changes with temperature, but that the Snoek peak is subject to an apparent distortion in height and shape due to the existence of an overlapping peak caused by the stress-induced reorientation of oxygen atom pairs (Section 11.4). Corrections for these effects do not appear to have been made in either investigation, so that the significance of both results is open to question.

D. Kinetics of the Relaxation

In view of the fact, noted earlier, that the activation energy of the Snoek relaxation corresponds to the activation energy for interstitial solute migration, a substantial amount of work has been done in many systems to determine the activation energy Q and the corresponding pre-exponential frequency factor τ_0^{-1} with considerable precision. Values of these quantities are shown in Table 9-2. The activation energies are probably accurate to about 0.02 eV or better, while most τ_0^{-1} values are probably correct to ± 20–50%. With the exception of the systems Fe–C and Fe–N, the data shown in Table 9-2 were obtained by Powers and Doyle (1959a) by both elastic aftereffect and low-frequency internal friction measurements. Their experimental results for nine different alloys are shown in Fig. 9-8, which illustrates the excellent fit obtained to the Arrhenius equation over a range of nearly five decades in τ. Powers and Doyle have also shown that at very dilute solute concentrations, where the Snoek peak is not subject to an apparent distortion by an overlapping interstitial solute pair relaxation, the activation energy cal-culated from the width of the Snoek peak via Eq. (3.5-7) checks very well with the values obtained from Fig. 9-8, thus verifying the existence of essentially only a single relaxation time. The values of τ_0^{-1} and Q entered in Table 9-2 for Fe–C and Fe–N are those obtained by Lord and Beshers (1966) from a compilation of data from many sources, including their own work at 7 MHz. At this frequency the peak due to nitrogen, for example, appears near 325°C, i.e., roughly 300°C above its location for a frequency of 1 Hz. The Lord and Beshers value of Q for C

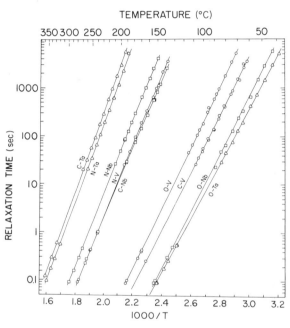

FIG. 9-8. Temperature dependence of the Snoek relaxation time in several alloys. (From Powers and Doyle, 1959a.)

in α-Fe is slightly but significantly lower than the value 0.874 eV obtained from the earlier compilation by Wert (1950a). Wert's value was determined from the slope of the best single straight line fitting a plot of $\log D$ versus $1/T$, which combined with the results of direct diffusion measurements at high temperatures (>500°C), with the D values obtained from the Snoek relaxation (below 200°C) via Eq. (9.1-6). From their own more extensive compilation (see Fig. 9-9) Lord and Beshers point out that direct diffusion measurements above 500°C appear to be governed by an activation energy substantially greater than that for the anelastic data in the range -40 to $+360$°C. On the other hand, this discrepancy

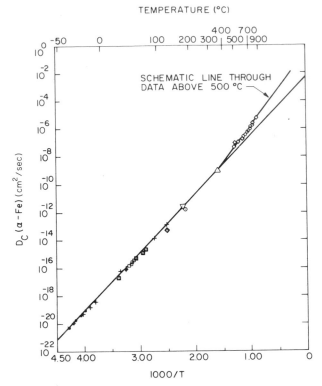

Fig. 9.9. Lord and Beshers' (1966) compilation of data for the diffusion of C in
α-Fe. Snoek relaxation data (below 400°C) have been converted to D_c via Eq. (9.1-6).
The plot includes data from Guillet and Hocheid (1956), Hasiguti and Kamoshita (1954),
Lord and Beshers (1966), Maringer (1960, 1964), Rathenau (1958), Smith (1962),
Stanley (1949), and Thomas and Leak (1954).

does not appear in the corresponding compilation of data for the Fe–N
alloys. The reason for the difference between the two alloy systems is
uncertain. Possibly it may indicate, as mentioned in Section 9.1, that
alternative diffusion paths become significant for carbon in iron at high
temperatures.

Before leaving Table 9-2, it may be noted that the value of τ_0^{-1} for the
Snoek relaxation is rather constant, with most values lying in the range
1.5–3.6×10^{11} sec^{-1}. From this result, and Eqs. (9.1-5) and (7.3-1), it
can be seen that $w_0 \exp(\Delta s^*/k)$ is in the range 0.25–0.60×10^{11} sec^{-1}.
Consequently, if w_0 is taken to be $\simeq 10^{13}$ sec^{-1}, $\Delta s^*/k$ lies in the range
0.9–1.8. This range of values is in satisfactory agreement with the range
of values $(1.6$–$2.6)$ calculated from Zener's theory, Eq. (7.4-5).

Another point of interest in connection with the kinetics of the Snoek relaxation is the dependence of the relaxation rate on hydrostatic pressure. From Eqs. (7.4-1) and (7.4-6) it follows that

$$\partial(\ln \tau^{-1})/\partial P = -\Delta v^*/kT \qquad (9.2\text{-}3)$$

where the quantity Δv^* is the activation volume for diffusion. Physically, Δv^* represents the volume expansion of a sample when a single atom is conveyed from an equilibrium site to the saddle point position of a diffusion jump. Bass and Lazarus (1962) and Tichelaar et al. (1961) have obtained values of Δv^* for the Snoek relaxation in Fe–C, V–N, and V–O alloys from the slopes of curves of $\ln \tau^{-1}$ versus P. In confirmation of the work of Bosman et al. (1960), Δv^* for C in Fe was found to be immeasurably small; in molar units $\Delta V^* \equiv N_A \, \Delta v^* \leq 0.1$ cm³, where N_A is Avogadro's number. (For comparison, the volume change on introducing a mole of interstitial solute is 6.2 cm³.) On the other hand, ΔV^* for O and N in V are quite large, 1.7 and 1.1 cm³, respectively. There is thus a striking difference between C in Fe, as compared with O or N in V. Interestingly enough, just such a difference is predicted by the machine calculations of Johnson et al. (1964).

E. Snoek Peaks Produced by Hydrogen

The Snoek relaxation caused by the lightest element hydrogen (or its isotopes) is of special interest because of the possible importance ot quantum-mechanical tunneling as an athermal migration mechanism which may at low temperatures compete with or even short circuit the classical activated jump mechanism (Heller, 1961). The effect of tunneling should be manifest initially as a deviation from linearity in the $\ln \tau^{-1}$ versus $1/T$ Arrhenius plot. The sense of the deviation is toward higher rates at larger values of $1/T$. The deviation will therefore become more marked as the frequency is lowered to move the peak to lower temperatures. At sufficiently low temperatures, the tunneling rate may completely dominate the relaxation, and τ^{-1} would then become a constant, independent of T. The ability to observe the relaxation as a function of temperature would then disappear, and the existence of the relaxation could then only be revealed by measurements made as a function of frequency.

As yet, it appears that evidence for tunneling is available only for iron alloys. At a frequency of 10 MHz, Lord (1967) has shown that the hydrogen Snoek peak in iron appears at 120°K (Fig. 9-10), which within

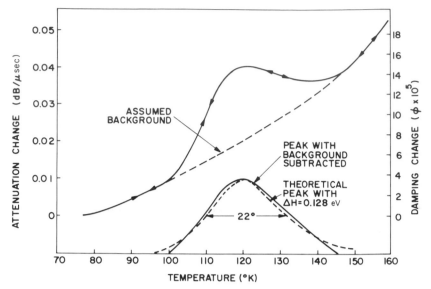

Fɪɢ. 9-10.   The hydrogen Snoek peak in iron, as measured at 10 MHz by Lord (1967).

experimental error is the location estimated by extrapolation using the Q of 0.130 eV obtained from high temperature diffusion measurements. On the other hand, at 1 Hz, Heller (1961) has obtained evidence that the peak is not at the similarly estimated location of 47°K, but at a significantly lower temperature (30°K), indicative of tunneling. In samples charged with the heavier deuterium isotope, the peak is reported at 35°K. This significant shift toward the extrapolated value of 47°K is very much larger than would be expected from classical considerations (where the vibration frequency w_0 of the interstitial atom of mass m in a parabolic potential well is proportional to $m^{-1/2}$), and suggests that the predominant effect may be a reduction in the rate of tunneling. Since Heller's observations suggest that tunneling effects can be observed, further investigations to verify and extend his work would be well worthwhile.

In addition to the work on iron, very well-defined hydrogen Snoek peaks have been found by Cannelli and Verdini (1966) in both Ta and Nb, following electrolytic charging. These workers studied the change of peak temperature with frequency, with the results shown in Fig. 9-11. The data are most complete for the case of Ta, where the frequency was varied from 70 kHz down to 300 Hz. Though this curve largely follows a simple Arrhenius relationship (yielding $Q = 0.12$ eV and

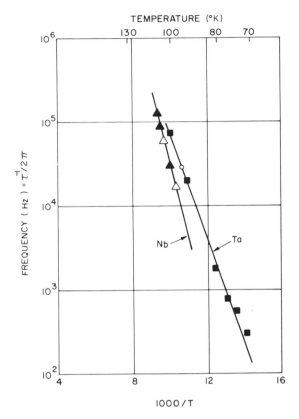

FIG. 9-11. Arrhenius plots for the hydrogen Snoek peak in Nb and Ta. (From Cannelli and Verdini, 1966.)

$\tau_0 = 1.6 \times 10^{-12}$ sec), there is a suggestion of an upward deviation from linearity in the last two points. However, extension of the data to even lower frequencies would be needed to ascertain if this effect is real and represents the onset of a deviation due to tunneling.

9.3 Applications of the Snoek Relaxation

Applications of the Snoek relaxation can be divided into two main categories, in which use is made of either (a) the rate of the relaxation or (b) the relaxation strength. Item (a) is concerned with the determination of the interstitial diffusion coefficient D (as a function of temperature). Since this application has been covered in the previous section, only item (b) will be considered below. The utility of the relaxation strength centers about the established fact that the peak height is proportional to the concentration of solute *in solution*. This proportionality between peak height and dissolved solute concentration makes the Snoek peak an excellent tool for solubility and precipitation studies. It should be borne in mind that the magnitude of the proportionality factor is strongly crystallographically anisotropic in single crystals and is therefore texture-dependent in polycrystals. This constant should therefore be determined individually for each polycrystalline specimen whenever absolute measurements are desired; it is not required, however, for relative measurements. The procedure for the investigation of precipitation kinetics and the solubility of a precipitate phase typically involves the following steps:

(i) Introduction of a known or determinable solute concentration into a specimen at some high temperature T_Q where the solid solubility is appreciable.

(ii) Quenching the specimen rapidly to retain the solute in super-saturated solid solution.

(iii) Warming the specimen to the temperature T_P of the Snoek peak, for measurement of the peak height.

(iv) Heating the specimen to a selected aging temperature T_A to allow precipitation to proceed.

At suitable intervals the aging is interrupted by quenching, and the specimen returned to T_P so that the kinetics of precipitation can be obtained from the variation of peak height with aging time at the temperature T_A. The final steady value of peak height achieved by aging at T_A is the required index of the solute concentration in equilibrium with the phase that has precipitated out. To obtain the solubility curve, and the temperature dependence of the precipitation kinetics and of the precipitate solubility, the above experiments must of course be repeated for a series of different temperatures T_A. A variation of the above procedure is to approach the equilibrium solubility at T_A from an under-saturated rather than a supersaturated condition. In this case the specimen is first treated so as to contain an excess of precipitate, and the growth of the Snoek peak is then monitored after up-quenching to T_A. A study of Fe–C alloys by this method led to the discovery of an interesting transient overshooting of the equilibrium solubility (Keefer and Wert, 1959).

The solubility of Fe_4N in α-Fe was studied first by Dijkstra (1949) and later by Fast and Verrijp (1955) and Rawlings and Tambini (1956). More recently, Bunn and Wert (1964) have determined the solubility of tantalum nitride (presumably Ta_2N) in Ta. The Snoek relaxation has also been used to study the solubility of Fe_3C (cementite) in α-Fe by a number of workers, including Wert (1950b), Lindstrand (1955), Stark et al. (1958), and Swartz (1967, 1969c). There is general agreement on an enthalpy of solution close to 0.55 eV. Swartz (1967) has pointed out that this value refers to self-stressed cementite and gives 0.64 eV for the stress free condition. In later work, Swartz (1969c) has determined the solubility of elemental graphite in iron by the procedure of equilibrating a sample with respect to a gaseous carburizing atmosphere of known thermodynamic activity relative to graphite. This work is significant in two respects. First, it illustrates a method of some generality for studying the solubility of phases other than those obtainable in precipitate form. Second, the data obtained by Swartz have essentially resolved an earlier long-standing discrepancy between the observed solubility of cementite in iron and that calculated from graphite solubility data and the formation energy of cementite.

The kinetics of precipitation during quench aging of supersaturated solid solutions of carbon and nitrogen in iron have been studied in some detail, notably by Dijkstra (1949) and by Wert (1949, 1950c, 1954). Dijkstra was able to conclude that two nitrides can precipitate from Fe–N alloys. The nitride appearing last was readily identified as Fe_4N; that precipitating first has since been identified as Fe_8N (or $Fe_{16}N_2$) for which the corresponding solubility curve has been reported by Wert (1954) and Kamber et al. (1961).

In addition to its use in studies of precipitation during quench aging, the Snoek relaxation also finds application to the investigation of strain aging (see Chapter 12) in samples which have been cold worked after quenching. The relatively rapid decay of the Snoek peak observed in such samples can be explained by the segregation of solute atoms to dislocations generated by the plastic deformation. (A solute atom near a dislocation core is presumed not to contribute to the Snoek peak, either because it is "locked" by the dislocation stress field or because of actual precipitation at the dislocation.) Many workers [see, e.g., Thomas and Leak (1955b), Wepner (1957), and Szkopiak and Eliaz (1966)] have found consistency with the $(time)^{2/3}$ kinetic law originally derived by Cottrell and Bilby (1949) for the start of strain aging, and from which an estimate of the dislocation density can be made. For longer aging times, a semiempirical logarithmic modification of this relation was successfully employed by Harper (1951). Ham (1959) later criticized the theoretical foundation of Harper's equation, and developed an analysis which showed that at long aging times the free solute concentration should decay in a simple exponential fashion with time. A similar conclusion was also reached by Bullough and Newman (1962a) and Meisel (1967) for the case of segregation without precipitation. Evidence that such a dependence may in fact be observable in Fe–C alloys has been reported by Oren and Stephenson (1970). Progress in understanding why the Harper equation appears to work well in some circumstances was made by Bullough and Newman (1962b), who extended their analysis to include the effect of precipitation of a second phase at the dislocations. They were able to show that if the precipitates form as discrete widely spaced particles, a simple exponential decay of the free-solute concentration should still be expected. On the other hand, where the precipitates form as a more or less continuous rod around the dislocation core, their calculations justify the Harper equation. Dollins and Wert (1969) have reported experiments on Nb–N alloys where they were able to vary the mode of precipitation and show that the aging kinetics changed in accord with these predictions.

PROBLEMS

9-1. Using the fact that the Snoek effect produces relaxation of the compliance S' only, verify from Chapter 6 that the following equations express the orientation dependence of the Snoek relaxation in tension and torsion

$$\delta E^{-1} = \delta S'(1 - 3\Gamma)/3, \qquad \delta G^{-1} = 2\,\delta S'\Gamma$$

where $\delta S' \equiv 2\,\delta(S_{11} - S_{12})$.

Make a plot which shows how δE^{-1} and δG^{-1} vary with Γ. Prove that $\delta G^{-1}_{\langle 110\rangle}/\delta E^{-1}_{\langle 110\rangle} = 6$.

9-2. Using a hard ball model of the bcc structure, show that the diameter of the spherical voids centered about the octahedral and tetrahedral sites are $0.134a$ and $0.252a$ respectively, where a is the lattice parameter.

9-3. If interstitial atoms jump directly between specific nearest neighbor octahedral sites at a rate w, and between specific next-nearest octahedral sites at a rate w', show from Eq. (9.1-5) that the Snoek relaxation rate is given by

$$\tau^{-1} = 6w + 12w'$$

Also, show [by generalizing Eq. (7.5-4)] that the diffusion coefficient is given by

$$D = (a^2/6)(w + 4w')$$

and thus that τ^{-1} and D are not strictly proportional to each other in this case.

Chapter 10 / The Zener Relaxation

It was discovered by Zener (1943) that a single crystal of 70 : 30 α-brass exhibits a well-defined internal friction peak near 400°C for a frequency of 620 Hz. Zener estimated the activation energy of the relaxation from the shape of the peak (assuming the existence of only a single relaxation time), and obtained a figure of 1.5 eV. The relaxation strength was quoted as 0.025. A few years later, without the benefit of any further experiments on the effect, Zener (1947b) proposed the "pair-reorientation" model which triggered off further experiments and a general interest in the phenomenon. It is a tribute to Zener's insight that the evidence which has since accumulated shows only the need for an elaboration rather than a basic revision of his model. One of the predictions of the model is that the relaxation behavior of the type found in the α-brass crystal is a quite general property of substitutional solid solutions. Indeed, examples of the relaxation are now known in over 20 alloy systems and for all three of the common metallic structures (fcc, hcp, and bcc) as well as in an ionic solid solution. It has become customary to refer to this relaxation as the Zener relaxation. A good example is found in the Ag–Zn primary solid solutions, as shown in Fig. 10-1. It is noteworthy that the low damping reached on the high-temperature side of these peaks is achieved only by the use of single-crystal samples. With polycrystalline samples, a grain boundary peak (Chapter 15) present at temperatures above the Zener peak impairs the resolution of the Zener peak. An example of the overlap between the Zener and the grain-boundary peak in a polycrystalline sample of α-brass is shown in Fig. 10-2.

10.1 Zener's Pair Reorientation Theory

The key point in this theory is the proposal that the relaxation is due to a stress-induced reorientation of solute atom pairs present in the solid solution in a nearest-neighbor configuration (Zener, 1947b). In order to be able to consider solute pairs as individual or isolated defects, it is

clear that this theory confines us to consider only dilute solutions, where
the number of solute pairs is relatively small. An example of such a pair,
and the atomic displacements produced around it, is shown schematically
for the fcc lattice in Fig. 10-3. It is easily found by inspection that such
a pair constitutes a $\langle 110 \rangle$ orthorhombic elastic dipole (Section 8.4C),

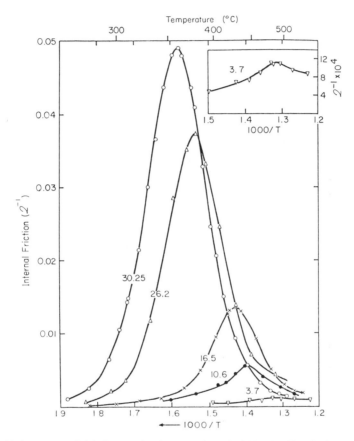

FIG. 10-1. Internal friction peaks for a series of $\langle 110 \rangle$ Ag–Zn single crystals, as
measured in flexure at approximately 500 Hz. The number labeling each curve is the
atomic percent of Zn. (From Seraphim and Nowick, 1961.)

since it possesses three mutually perpendicular two-fold rotation axes,
two of which lie along directions of the $\langle 110 \rangle$-type (the directions of
the arrows in Fig. 10-3). With this identification, expressions for the
relaxations of the two shear compliances $S_{44} \equiv S$ and $2(S_{11} - S_{12}) \equiv S'$
are obtained immediately from Eqs. (8.4-5) and (8.4-6), which are

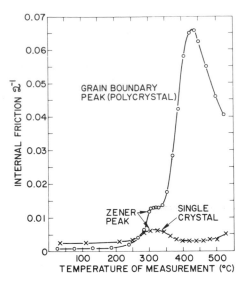

FIG. 10-2.   Variation of internal friction with temperature in polycrystalline and single-crystal specimens of α-brass. The measurements were made in torsional vibration at approximately 0.5 Hz. (From Kê, 1948c.)

repeated here for convenience

$$3 \, \delta E_{\langle 100 \rangle}^{-1} = \delta S' = (2C_0 v_0/3kT)[\tfrac{1}{2}(\lambda_1 + \lambda_2) - \lambda_3]^2 \qquad (10.1\text{-}1)$$

$$3 \, \delta E_{\langle 111 \rangle}^{-1} = \delta S = (C_0 v_0/3kT)(\lambda_1 - \lambda_2)^2 \qquad\qquad (10.1\text{-}2)$$

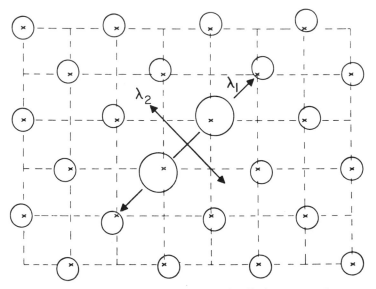

FIG. 10-3.   Schematic illustration of the atomic displacements about a pair of oversized solute atoms, in the (100) plane of the fcc lattice. The crosses denote the atomic positions in the undistorted lattice.

In a bcc crystal, on the other hand, a nearest-neighbor solute pair constitutes a trigonal dipole and the corresponding expressions (8.4-3) and
(8.4-4) are

$$3 \, \delta E^{-1}_{\langle 100 \rangle} = \delta S' = 0 \tag{10.1-3}$$

$$3 \, \delta E^{-1}_{\langle 111 \rangle} = \delta S = (4 C_0 v_0 / 9kT)(\lambda_1 - \lambda_2)^2 \tag{10.1-4}$$

As originally pointed out by Zener, and also given in Section 8.4B, the
result expressed by Eq. (10.1-3) is easily anticipated from the fact that a
$\langle 100 \rangle$ uniaxial stress makes equal angles with all pair orientations (all
four of the $\langle 111 \rangle$ directions), and hence the stress cannot split the free-
energy levels of the different pair orientations.

For future reference it is desirable to express the relaxation magnitudes
for cubic crystals of arbitrary orientation. Such expressions have, in fact,
already been given in Eqs. (6.5-1) and (6.5-2), and are repeated here for
convenience, but now in terms of S and S' as defined above, and S''
$\equiv S_{11} + 2 S_{12}$:

$$\delta E^{-1} = [(\delta S' + \delta S'')/3] - (\delta S' - \delta S)\Gamma \tag{10.1-5}$$

$$\delta G^{-1} = \delta S + 2(\delta S' - \delta S)\Gamma \tag{10.1-6}$$

These expressions are obtained from the formal theory, and are more
general than Eqs. (10.1-1)–(10.1-4), where the hydrostatic relaxation
$\delta S''$ was taken equal to zero under the assumption that only a single
defect species is present. (See Problem 8-3.)

We consider now what the Zener pair model predicts for the variation
of relaxation strength with composition. It is apparent from Eqs. (10.1-1)–
(10.1-6) that the relaxation strength for any specified orientation is proportional to C_0, the mole fraction of solute pairs. What is required,
therefore, is the relation between C_0 and the mole fraction of solute X.
This relation is analogous to that for divacancy formation, Eq. (7.2-5),
and may be written

$$C_0/(X - 2C_0)^2 = (z/2) \exp(\Delta g_\mathrm{b}/kT) \equiv K(T) \tag{10.1-7}$$

where $X - 2C_0$ is the concentration of unpaired solute atoms. There
are two ranges of Eq. (10.1-7) which are of interest. If the binding free
energy of a pair Δg_b is small, and recognizing that $X \ll 1$ since we are
considering only dilute alloys, it follows that $C_0 \propto X^2$ and therefore that
the relaxation magnitude δJ is given by

$$\delta J \propto C_0/kT = [K(T)/kT]X^2 \tag{10.1-8}$$

This is the case of nearly random formation of solute pairs. In the other extreme of nearly complete association, Δg_b (and therefore K) is large, and therefore $C_0 \simeq X/2$, or $\delta J \propto X$. In view of the fact that strong solute association is not anticipated for dilute solid solutions, the square-law dependence of Eq. (10.1-8) is most reasonably anticipated.

Another prediction of the theory concerns the temperature dependence of the relaxation strength. Equations such as (10.1-1)–(10.1-4) suggest an inverse temperature dependence. As noted in Eq. (10.1-8), however, there is also the possibility of a dependence of C_0 on temperature through the constant $K(T)$ of Eq. (10.1-7). This contribution is only negligible if $\Delta g_b \simeq 0$. It is also assumed in Eqs. (10.1-1)–(10.1-4) that defect interactions are negligible. If the concentration of defects is high enough that such interactions must be considered, δJ may then be anticipated to be of the form (see Section 8.10)

$$\delta J \propto C_0/k(T - T_c) \tag{10.1-9}$$

Here T_c is a critical temperature for self-induced ordering below which, if there were sufficient atomic mobility, the solute pairs would become spontaneously aligned. The critical temperature T_c is itself proportional to C_0.

So far, we have considered only the thermodynamic aspects of the pair reorientation theory. Actually, it was not these aspects, but rather the kinetics of the relaxation, that first drew the attention of numerous workers. The reason was that the relaxation appeared to provide a tool for the study of atomic mobility in substitutional alloys at temperatures much lower than possible by diffusion methods. Expressions for the relaxation times for various defect and crystal symmetries have already been given in Section 8.9. For the important case of nearest-neighbor pairs in fcc crystals, which are of $\langle 110 \rangle$ orthorhombic symmetry, the two relaxation times are [Eq. (8.9-19)]

$$\tau^{-1}(S') = 6\nu_{13}, \qquad \tau^{-1}(S) = 2\nu_{12} + 4\nu_{13} \tag{10.1-10}$$

Here ν_{12} and ν_{13} are the reorientation rates at which a pair along [110] goes into [1$\bar{1}$0] and [011] orientations, respectively. To convert Eq. (10.1-10) into its most useful form, we introduce the appropriate atom jump rates. In the simplest approximation, we introduce only the jump rate w_1 which is the rate at which either member of the pair makes a jump that retains the pair. From examination of the fcc model, e.g., see Fig. 10-4, it becomes clear, since either member of the pair can make

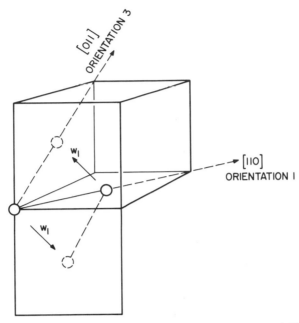

FIG. 10-4.   Diagram to illustrate that $\nu_{13} = 2w_1$ for the nearest-neighbor pair in the fcc lattice.

one jump that takes the pair from [110] to [011] (i.e., from orientation 1 to 3), that $\nu_{13} = 2w_1$. Further, since no nearest-neighbor jump can take the defect from [110] to [1$\bar{1}$0], we conclude that ν_{12} is negligible. Accordingly, Eqs. (10.1-10) become

$$\tau^{-1}(S') = 12w_1, \qquad \tau^{-1}(S) = 8w_1 \qquad (10.1\text{-}11)$$

The first of these τ values is the relaxation time under a $\langle 100 \rangle$ uniaxial stress and the second is that under $\langle 111 \rangle$ stress. These two relaxation times are, therefore, in the ratio 2 : 3. This result was first derived by LeClaire (1951).

As already mentioned, Eq. (10.1-11) must be regarded as a highly simplified approximation. A more complete calculation would have to take into account atom jumps to and from next-nearest-neighbor (nnn) positions, as well as those producing dissociation and association of solute atom pairs. So far, a general solution to the problem is not available. However, two approaches have been used to remove some of the restrictions imposed in the derivation of Eqs. (10.1-11). On the one hand,

Haven (1968) has derived expressions analogous to Eqs. (10.1-11), taking the dissociation of nearest-neighbor pairs into account, but assuming that all pair configurations beyond the nearest-neighbor pair have zero dipole strength. Equations (10.1-11) then become[†]

$$\tau^{-1}(S') = 12w_1 + 12.74w_2, \qquad \tau^{-1}(S) = 8w_1 + 12.78w_2 \qquad (10.1\text{-}11a)$$

where w_2 is the rate of the specific jump producing dissociation of a nearest-neighbor pair. On the other hand, a calculation that considers only first and second neighbors but not dissociation has been carried out for fcc crystals by Chang (1964) and gives

$$\tau^{-1}(S') = 6w_1 + 4w_3 + 2w_4 \pm [(6w_1 - 4w_3 + 2w_4)^2 + 8w_3w_4]^{1/2}$$
$$(10.1\text{-}12)$$

$$\tau^{-1}(S) = 8w_1 + 4w_4 \qquad (10.1\text{-}13)$$

where w_3 is the specific rate of the nnn $\rightarrow$ nn jump, w_4 that of the nn $\rightarrow$ nnn jump, and w_1 has the same meaning as above (i.e., nn $\rightarrow$ nn). It should be noted that Eqs. (10.1-12) and (10.1-13) provide two relaxation times for the S' shear and one for the S shear. This is consistent with the fact that we now have two defects, the nn pair which is $\langle 110 \rangle$ orthorhombic, and the nnn pair which is tetragonal. Because two defects are present, a relaxation time for a hydrostatic mode is also given; the magnitude of this relaxation, however, is probably small. In the simple case in which all jump frequencies are the same, i.e., $w_1 = w_3 = w_4 \equiv w$, Eqs. (10.1-12) and (10.1-13) reduce to

$$\tau^{-1}(S') = 2(6 \pm \sqrt{6})w, \qquad \tau^{-1}(S) = 12w \qquad (10.1\text{-}14)$$

Thus, the S' relaxation consists of a close pair of relaxation times centered at $\tau^{-1} = 12w$ which is the same as $\tau^{-1}(S)$. In other words, to this approximation the relaxation time is *isotropic*, in contrast to the result of Eq. (10.1-11). Still better approximations have not yet been developed.

For the bcc lattice, a nearest-neighbor jump which preserves the nn pair is not possible. Using the results of Chang (1964), the approximation analogous to Eq. (10.1-14) is

$$\tau^{-1}(S') = 6w, \qquad \tau^{-1}(S) = 16w \qquad (\text{bcc}) \qquad (10.1\text{-}15)$$

In the hcp case there are two nonequivalent types of nn pairs. From the results of Povolo and Bisogni (1966) the approximation equivalent to

[†] Haven's expressions also contain a correlation factor which is omitted here.

Eq. (10.1-11) (i.e., nn's only and all w's the same) turns out to be

$$\tau^{-1}(S_{11} - S_{12}) = (10 \pm 2)w, \qquad \tau^{-1}(S_{44}) = 10w \qquad \text{(hcp)} \qquad (10.1\text{-}16)$$

so that here τ is essentially isotropic.

Although all of the above results are approximations, for present purposes the important result is that by measuring τ for relaxation, we are obtaining an appropriate jump rate w, and therefore, by Eq. (7.5-5), a diffusion coefficient D. Because an anelastic creep experiment, for example, only requires a time of the order of w^{-1}, while a conventional diffusion experiment requires at least $10^{11}w^{-1}$ (Nowick, 1953), it is apparent that anelastic experiments may be conducted in a much lower temperature range than conventional diffusion experiments. Accordingly, it would appear possible, by combining diffusion and anelastic data, to extend the Arrhenius plot by many decades, as was done for the case of the Snoek relaxation (e.g., in Fig. 9-9). As we shall see, however, the situation is more complex in the case of the Zener relaxation for reasons which will be discussed later.

10.2 Results for Dilute Alloys

It was pointed out in the previous section that Zener's model is only clearly appropriate to dilute alloys where the concept of individual solute pairs is meaningful. Unfortunately, data on the relaxation in dilute alloys is extremely sparse. The reason is that, although many concentrated alloys show quite large Zener peaks, the relaxation strength drops rapidly as the alloy is made more dilute (cf. Fig. 10-1). The only dilute alloy on which any detailed measurements appear to have been made is Al–1.8 at. % Cu (Berry and Nowick, 1958; Berry, 1961). This alloy (better known as Al–4 wt. % Cu) is familiar to metallurgists as one of the classic alloys used in the study of precipitation hardening. To dissolve the copper, the alloy is solution treated at about 525°C, and then quenched. After this treatment, the Zener peak can be observed at about 180°C (for 1 Hz) by rapidly reheating the specimen to about 200°C and taking measurements on cooling back to room temperature.[†] Due to the low solubility of Cu in Al in the temperature range where the peak occurs, the peak is not stable and decreases in height as the exposure at

[†] A brief exposure to 200°C constitutes a reversion treatment for this alloy; it has the effect of redissolving solute clusters (G. P. [1] zones) formed at lower temperatures.

temperatures near the peak is prolonged. Fortunately, however, measurements can be made quickly enough that an essentially constant condition can be maintained during a run. Various experiments are discussed in turn below, with particular reference to how the observations relate to the pair reorientation theory.

A. THE CONCENTRATION DEPENDENCE OF THE RELAXATION STRENGTH

The fact that Al–1.8 at. % Cu is a precipitation alloy made it possible to determine the concentration dependence of the relaxation strength in an especially convenient manner upon a single specimen. The procedure simply involved equilibrating the specimen in turn at selected tempera-

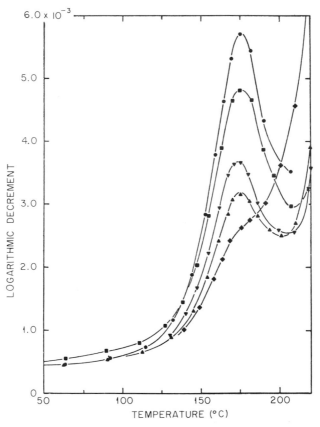

FIG. 10-5.   Internal friction of polycrystalline Al–4 wt. % Cu after quenching from 525°C and from four temperatures [525°C (●), 488°C (■), 477°C (▼), 464°C (▲), 427°C(◆)] below the phase boundary following an anneal to establish equilibrium. Measurements were made in torsion at 0.90 Hz. (From Berry and Nowick, 1958.)

tures below the solvus line on the phase diagram and then quenching; the copper content remaining *in solution* could then be obtained from the known solubility data. Internal friction peaks following various equilibration treatments are shown in Fig. 10-5. The peak heights (taken as a relative measure of the relaxation strength) are shown plotted in Fig. 10-6 against the square of the copper concentration in solution. It is evident from the straight line so obtained that the observations support the concentration dependence predicted by Eq. (10.1-8).

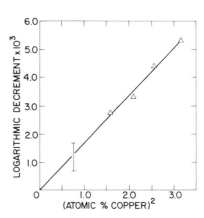

FIG. 10-6.   Peak heights of Fig. 10-5, plotted against the square of the atomic percentage of copper remaining in solution. (From Berry and Nowick, 1958.)

B. ANISOTROPY OF THE RELAXATION

The procedure used to investigate the anisotropy of the relaxation was largely dictated by the fact that the long single crystal wires were not available in other than a $\langle 100 \rangle$ orientation (i.e., $\Gamma = 0$). Accordingly, measurements were made in both a torsion pendulum and a flexure pendulum apparatus to determine the relaxation strengths $\Delta_{G\langle 100 \rangle}$ and $\Delta_{E\langle 100 \rangle}$, respectively. Using Eqs. (10.1-5) and (10.1-6) for the case $\Gamma = 0$, we find

$$\Delta_{G\langle 100 \rangle}/G_{\langle 100 \rangle} = \delta S \qquad (10.2\text{-}1)$$

and

$$\Delta_{E\langle 100 \rangle}/E_{\langle 100 \rangle} = (\delta S' + \delta S'')/3 \qquad (10.2\text{-}2)$$

The peaks observed in torsion and in flexure are compared in Fig. 10-7. The large anisotropy is quite evident. From these results, and other data on the elastic compliances, the following numerical values are obtained via Eqs. (10.2-1) and (10.2-2)

$$\delta S = 1.9 \times 10^{-15} \quad \text{cm}^2 \ \text{dyn}^{-1}$$

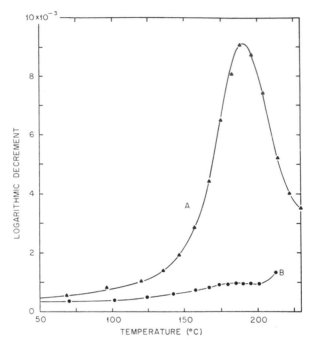

F IG. 10-7. Internal friction of single crystal Al–4 wt. % Cu wires oriented with $\langle 100 \rangle$ nearly parallel to the specimen axis. Curve A shows results for a pair of specimens tested together in flexure at 2.8 Hz; curve B shows results for one member of the pair tested in torsion at 1.4 Hz. (From Berry, 1961.)

and

$$\delta S' + \delta S'' = 35 \times 10^{-15} \quad \text{cm}^2 \, \text{dyn}^{-1}$$

To proceed further, it is necessary to make the assumption that the hydrostatic relaxation $\delta S''$ can be neglected in relation to $\delta S'$. (In the two concentrated alloy systems where experimental information is available on this point, Section 10.3, this assumption turns out to be well justified.) Thus we obtain (Al–1.8 at. % Cu)

$$\delta S'/\delta S \simeq 18.5 \qquad (10.2\text{-}3)$$

This result may now be examined in terms of the pair reorientation theory. Taking the ratio of Eqs. (10.1-1) and (10.1-2) for the $\langle 110 \rangle$ orthorhombic dipole, we have

$$\delta S'/\delta S = 2 \{[(\lambda_1 + \lambda_2)/2] - \lambda_3\}^2/(\lambda_1 - \lambda_2)^2 \qquad (10.2\text{-}4)$$

Equation (10.2-4) can be rearranged as a quadratic equation in the quantity $(\lambda_3 - \lambda_1)/(\lambda_1 - \lambda_2)$, which expresses the ratio of the dipole ellipticities in the two principal planes containing the pair axis.[†] The two solutions of the equation are

$$(\lambda_3 - \lambda_1)/(\lambda_1 - \lambda_2) = [-1 \pm (2\,\delta S'/\delta S)^{1/2}]/2 \qquad (10.2\text{-}5)$$

Upon inserting the experimental result given in Eq. (10.2-3), we obtain

$$(\lambda_3 - \lambda_1)/(\lambda_1 - \lambda_2) = +2.6 \quad \text{or} \quad -3.6 \qquad (10.2\text{-}6)$$

To avoid making assumptions about the signs and relative magnitudes of the λ's, both of these solutions can be covered by the approximation

$$|\lambda_3 - \lambda_1|/|\lambda_1 - \lambda_2| \simeq 3 \qquad (10.2\text{-}7)$$

In words, we have the result that if the relaxation takes place by the reorientation of dipoles consisting of nerarest-neighbor pairs, then the dipole ellipticity in the plane containing λ_1 and λ_3 is about three times that in the plane containing λ_1 and λ_2. Thus, for example, we must exclude the possibility that λ_1 is the dominant component of the $\boldsymbol{\lambda}$ tensor, since this is not compatible with Eq. (10.2-7). [More dramatically, it can be seen from Eq. (10.2-4) that if $|\lambda_1| \gg |\lambda_2|$ and $|\lambda_3|$, then $\delta S'/\delta S \simeq \frac{1}{2}$. This anisotropy is opposite in sense to that observed.] On the other hand, the result expressed by Eq. (10.2-7) could come about if $|\lambda_3|$ is appreciably greater than either $|\lambda_1|$ or $|\lambda_2|$. DeJong (1962) has suggested this possibility, on the grounds that the $\langle 100 \rangle$ directions are not close packed and hence may suffer the greatest atomic displacements when the pairs are introduced into the lattice. However, this interpretation is not unique. For example, the result expressed by Eq. (10.2-7) could also be interpreted as indicating that λ_1 and λ_2 are practically equal, though both may be comparable in magnitude to λ_3.

So far, we have discussed the anisotropy result [Eq. (10.2-3)] solely from the viewpoint of what it implies if Zener's nearest-neighbor (nn) pair model is assumed to be correct. It is, however, possible to place quite a different interpretation on Eq. (10.2-3), namely that it reflects a substantial contribution to the relaxation from the reorientation of next-nearest-neighbor (nnn) pairs (Seraphim and Nowick, 1961). The

---

[†] In accord with the convention adopted in Section 8.4, for the $\langle 110 \rangle$ ortho. defect, λ_1 is related to the strain along the pair axis, e.g., along [110], λ_2 is related to the strain in the perpendicular $\langle 110 \rangle$ direction, e.g., [1$\bar{1}$0], and λ_3 is related to the strain in the third symmetry direction, e.g., [001].

defect symmetries for nn and nnn pairs in both the fcc and bcc lattices are as follows:

	nn	nnn
fcc	$\langle 110 \rangle$ orthorhombic	tetragonal
bcc	trigonal	tetragonal

Since in both structures the nnn pairs possess tetragonal symmetry, such pairs contribute to $\delta S'$ but not to δS. Hence, such a contribution would raise the ratio $\delta S'/\delta S$ to larger values than would be the case if the relaxation were due only to nearest-neighbor pairs. Unfortunately, there seems to be no way at present of deciding for the fcc Al–Cu alloy, what are the relative contributions made to the relaxation by nearest-neighbor and next-nearest-neighbor pairs. On the other hand, a much more definitive situation exists for an alloy having the bcc structure. Here, reference to Eqs. (10.1-3) and (10.1-4) reminds us that the nearest-neighbor pair causes a relaxation of the S compliance, but not of S'. For the next-nearest-neighbor pair (a tetragonal dipole) exactly the reverse situation obtains. Thus in the bcc case, the ratio $\delta S'/\delta S$ is a direct indication of the relative magnitudes of the next-nearest neighbor and the nearest-neighbor contributions, respectively. Though such measurements have not yet been performed on a really dilute bcc alloy, the measurements of Boesono et al. (1967) on Fe–8 at. % Si indicate a $\delta S'/\delta S$ ratio greater than 8, while in the concentrated bcc alloy Li–57 at. % Mg, Seraphim and Nowick (1961) found the ratio to be as high as 27. In view of these numbers, the possibility cannot be ignored that an appreciable relaxation from next-nearest neighbors may be a quite general feature of the Zener relaxation.

C. THE KINETICS OF RELAXATION

The best values of the activation energy and frequency factor for the Zener relaxation in the Al–Cu alloy are apparently those given by Entwistle and Fitzpatrick (1965):

$$Q_r = 1.32 \pm 0.08 \quad \text{eV}, \qquad \tau_0^{-1} = 10^{15.6 \pm 1} \quad \text{sec}^{-1}$$

Fortunately, the diffusion of Cu in Al has been measured very precisely (Peterson and Rothman, 1970) to give an activation energy Q_{Cu} of 1.40 $\pm$ 0.01 eV and a D_0 value of 0.65 cm^2 sec^{-1}. The value of Q_r thus appears to be lower than Q_{Cu}. Using Eqs. (7.5-5), (7.5-9), and (7.5-11), a value for the product $fW_0 = 4 \times 10^{14}$ sec^{-1} is obtained. If n is the average number of jumps needed to produce relaxation, we may write

$$\tau = n\Gamma_r^{-1} = n(zw_r)^{-1} \qquad (10.2\text{-}8)$$

as the relation between τ and the mean rate of atom migration, Γ_r, producing the relaxation. Here w_r is the appropriate jump rate between specific sites, given by

$$w_r = W_{r0} \exp(-Q_r/kT) \qquad (10.2\text{-}9)$$

as in Section 7.5, and W_{r0} is a frequency factor which includes both the atomic vibration frequency and the entropy factor [Eq. (7.5-9)]. Thus we finally obtain

$$\tau_0^{-1} = \Gamma_{r0}/n = zW_{r0}/n \qquad (10.2\text{-}10)$$

Assuming that the value of W_0 obtained from the diffusion experiments is the same as W_{r0} in Eq. (10.2-10), taking f to be $\lesssim 1$, and utilizing the experimental value for τ_0^{-1} given above, we obtain the result that $n \simeq 1$. This result is in reasonable agreement with the prediction that $n \simeq 1$ from Eq. (10.1-11) or Eq. (10.1-14), representing two different degrees of approximation to the kinetic problem.

The data on the Al–Cu alloy, as shown in Fig. 10-7, also offer the opportunity to test the anisotropy of the relaxation time predicted by Eq. (10.1-11) and (10.1-14). The result is

$$\tau(S')/\tau(S) = 0.94 \pm 0.15$$

Within the estimated error, therefore, τ appears to be more isotropic than predicted by the nn approximation Eq. (10.1-11) but in good agreement with Eq. (10.1-14) which includes nn $\leftrightarrow$ nnn jumps. Similar results have also been obtained for a concentrated Ag–Zn alloy by Seraphim et al. (1964).

Another comparison between relaxation and diffusion data has been made for dilute (Ag–Zn) alloys, by a more indirect procedure (Seraphim et al., 1964). This procedure was to obtain the variation of Q_r with composition over a range from 33 at. % Zn down to 3.7 at. % Zn, and then to extrapolate the (linear) plot so obtained to 0 % Zn. The intercept value, $Q_r(0) = 1.70 \pm 0.04$ eV, is thus the relaxation activation energy for an infinitely dilute alloy. This value is distinctly lower than $Q_{Zn}(0)$, the activation energy for diffusion of Zn into pure Ag, which is 1.81 ± 0.01 eV. In this case the difference between $Q_r(0)$ and $Q_{Zn}(0)$ is not hard to understand in qualitative terms. In the infinitely dilute alloy, where the ratio of Zn–Zn pairs to single Zn atoms is very small, the value $Q_{Zn}(0)$ relates almost exclusively to the motion of an isolated Zn atom (i.e., one surrounded entirely by Ag atoms). On the other hand, since only pairs give rise to relaxation, $Q_r(0)$ must involve the jump of a Zn atom which is close to another Zn atom. Clearly, these two quantities need not be the same. In fact, since diffusion measurements of radio-tracer Zn in various Ag–Zn alloys show that Q_{Zn} decreases with increasing Zn content, it is reasonable to regard that Zn atoms diffuse faster when adjacent to other Zn atoms. Accordingly, it seems reasonable that $Q_r(0) < Q_{Zn}(0)$.

In summary, it appears from the evidence presented in this section that the pair reorientation theory does provide a base for understanding the Zener relaxation in dilute alloys. At the same time, however, the evidence does provide a strong indication that the model could be usefully improved by also taking next-nearest-neighbor pairs into account. Perhaps the most pressing need at the moment is for theoretical calculations which enable numerical values of the components of the λ tensors appropriate to both nearest and next-nearest-neighbor pairs to be predicted.

10.3   The Zener Relaxation in Concentrated Alloys

Most studies of the Zener relaxation have been made on alloys containing solute contents in excess of 10 at. %, where the proportion of solute to solvent atoms is so large that a description of the alloy in terms of single and paired solute atoms dispersed throughout the lattice of the solvent is surely unrealistic. In view of the absence of a simple theory for concentrated alloys, we begin with a summary of the major experimental observations, and then consider the theoretical side in Section 10.4.

A.   THE RELAXATION STRENGTH OF VARIOUS BINARY ALLOYS

A list of alloys in which the Zener relaxation has been observed is given in Table 10-1. For the most part, these alloys are fcc terminal solid solutions. There are, however, several examples of bcc alloys (including the intermediate phase β-Cu–Zn), and one example of an hcp alloy (Mg–Cd). In addition to the many metallic alloys listed, a Zener peak in the ionic solid solution NaCl : KCl has been reported by Laibowitz and Dreyfus (1965). Studies of the Zener relaxation in ternary metallic alloys have been made by Pirson and Wert (1962), Coleman and Wert (1966) and

TABLE 10-1

THE RELAXATION STRENGTH Δ OF THE ZENER RELAXATION IN BINARY ALLOYS

Alloy[a]	Structure	Temp. (°C)	Δ ($\times 10^3$) Obs.[b]	Δ ($\times 10^3$) Estim. for $X = 0.1$	Reference
Ag–0.25 Au	fcc	400	2.8	0.64	Turner and Williams (1963)
Ag–0.31 Cd	fcc	210	15.5	2.75	Shtrakhtman and Piguzov (1964)
Ag–0.18 In	fcc	230	15.0	5.6	Williams and Turner (1968)
Ag–0.063 Sb	fcc	260	11.9	27.6	Williams and Turner (1968)
Ag–0.081 Sn	fcc	285	5.25	7.7	Williams and Turner (1968)
Ag–0.24 Zn	fcc	240	77	18.8	Berry and Orehotsky (1968a)
Al–0.018 Cu	fcc	170	4.2	107	Berry and Nowick (1958)
Al–0.06 Mg	fcc	150	1.1	2.8	Nilson (1961)
Au–0.3 Ni	fcc	380	88	16.2	Ang *et al.* (1955)
Au–0.15 Zn	fcc	250	66	33	Pirson and Wert (1962)
Cd–0.1 Mg	hcp	10	5	5	Lulay and Wert (1956)
Cd–0.29 Mg	hcp	20	270	—	
Cu–0.15 Al	fcc	380	17.6	8.8	Childs and LeClaire (1954)
Cu–0.16 Ga	fcc	330	14	6.3	Rotherham and Pearson (1956)
Cu–0.16 Mn	fcc	420	9	4	Wert (1953)
Cu–0.32 Ni	fcc	570	1.47	0.25	Roberts and Barrand (1969a)
Cu–0.15 Zn	fcc	380	5.8	2.9	Childs and LeClaire (1954)
Cu–0.45 Zn	bcc	300	1.4[c]	0.185[c]	Artman (1952)
Fe–0.15 Al	bcc	520	11	5.5	Fischbach (1962)
Fe–0.24 Cr	bcc	575	7.7	1.9	Barrand (1967)
Fe–0.08 Si	bcc	525	8.8[c]	13[c]	Boesono *et al.* (1967)
Fe–0.20 V	bcc	620	20	6.3	Stanley and Wert (1961)

TABLE 10-1 (*Continued*)

Alloy[a]	Structure	Temp. (°C)	Δ ($\times$ 10^3) Obs.[b]	Δ ($\times$ 10^3) Estim. for $X = 0.1$	Reference
Li–0.57 Mg	bcc	115	23[c]	3.0[c]	Seraphim and Nowick (1961)
Na–0.30 Rb	bcc	−90	1.1	0.2	Gulden and Shyne (1968)
NaCl–0.014 KCl	NaCl	380	0.087[c]	3.65[c]	Laibowitz and Dreyfus (1965)
Ni–0.20 Zn	fcc	550	14.3	4.5	Coleman and Wert (1966)

[a] Solute content expressed as mole fraction X.

[b] Values given are the torsional relaxation strength of polycrystalline samples except where otherwise noted.

[c] Values of the tensile relaxation strength of $\langle 100 \rangle$ oriented single crystals.

Shtrakhman (1967). In order to assess roughly the relative magnitude of the relaxation strength shown by different alloys, it is necessary to make allowance for differences in composition. Accordingly, Table 10-1 also contains estimates of Δ_G for an arbitrarily selected reference composition of $X = 0.1$, using Eq. (10.1-8) where necessary to estimate this value from a value of Δ_G observed at some other composition. On this basis, notably strong relaxations occur in Al–Cu, Au–Zn, Cd–Mg, and Ag–Zn alloys.

From surveys of the type shown in Table 10-1, attempts have been made from time to time to find a correlation between the strength of the Zener relaxation and other alloy parameters. The first correlation suggested (Zener, 1947b) was between the relaxation strength and the size difference of the solute and the solvent. From a survey by Nowick and Seraphim (1961), however, no such correlation is apparent. In terms of elastic dipole theory, this cannot be regarded as too surprising since the size factor expresses a dilational effect whereas the relaxation strength is governed by differences between distortions in different directions. By extending an argument proposed by LeClaire and Lomer (1954), Nowick and Seraphim were led to look for a correlation between relaxation strength and a parameter containing the square of the deviation from Vegard's law. In this case, from information on a total of nine Ag–base and Cu–base alloys, a rough correlation appears to exist. As yet, however, there appears to be no simple means of predicting with any certainty how large a Zener relaxation can be expected from an arbitrarily selected solid solution.

B. THE TEMPERATURE DEPENDENCE OF THE RELAXATION STRENGTH

Detailed measurements to determine the temperature dependence of the relaxation strength have been performed only for concentrated Ag–Zn alloys. Results obtained by Li and Nowick (1961) for three different compositions are shown in Fig. 10-8. For each composition, all the data were obtained upon just one polycrystalline sample, so as to avoid the anisotropy effect which would cause specimens of different textures to show different relaxation strengths. It is apparent that the reciprocal relaxation strength Δ_G^{-1} varies linearly with temperature, and becomes

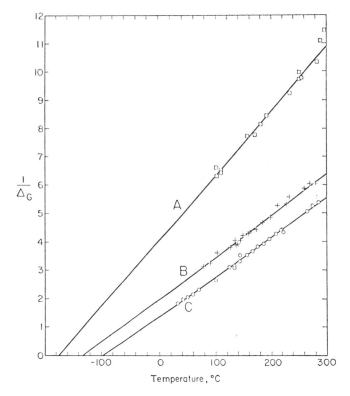

FIG. 10-8.   Variation of reciprocal of the relaxation strength with temperature for three polycrystalline Ag–Zn specimens of different compositions. Specimen: A, 24.2 at. % Zn; B, 30.2 at. % Zn; C, 33.5 at. % Zn. (From Li and Nowick, 1961.)

zero at a finite temperature (T_c) which is, respectively, 97, 140, and 175°K for the 24.2, 30.2, and 33.5 at. % Zn alloys. The straight lines drawn through the data points correspond to an analogous relation to Eq. (10.1-9), namely,

$$\Delta_G = T_0/(T - T_c) \tag{10.3-1}$$

where the parameter T_0 depends on both concentration and orientation. As discussed in Section 8.10, a nonzero value of T_c means that the free-energy levels depend not only on the stress but also on the existing state of order in the alloy. It is obvious from Fig. 10-8 that the interaction effect, which is represented in Section 8.10 by the matrix of interaction coefficients b_{pq}, is indeed significant in these concentrated alloys. In discussing their results, Li and Nowick made the simplifying assumption of neglecting the off-diagonal terms of this matrix. This procedure has already been discussed in Section 8.10, where it was shown that this assumption leads to the prediction that T_c should vary as C_0, and that it should be independent of the mode of deformation (and therefore of the texture of a polycrystalline sample). While Li and Nowick's results supported the first prediction (in that T_c was found to be proportional to X_{Zn}^2), no experiments were performed to test the independence of T_c on the texture. Limited evidence on that point is now available from equivalent measurements on the Ag–24 at. % Zn alloy by Berry and Orehotsky (1968a). These workers obtained a value of $T_c = 150°$K as against the value of 97°K of Li and Nowick. The corresponding values of T_0 of the two samples involved were also substantially different, indicating that the samples differed in texture. It thus appears probable that the neglect of off-diagonal terms in the matrix b_{pq} is not justified. A fuller investigation using single-crystal specimens would be most desirable.

C. The Concentration Dependence of the Relaxation Strength

Childs and LeClaire (1954) investigated a series of polycrystalline α-Cu–Zn alloys containing up to 29 at. % Zn, and found the simple relation $\Delta_G \propto X_{Zn}^2$ to be a quite adequate description of their data over the whole range. There is thus no evidence here of any major change in the behavior of concentrated versus dilute alloys (see Fig. 10-6). The same conclusion is true of a more detailed study made on $\langle 100 \rangle$ single crystals of α-Ag–Zn alloys (Seraphim and Nowick, 1961). These results are shown in Fig. 10-9. Within the precision of the data, the observed

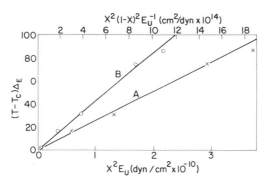

FIG. 10-9. The concentration dependence of the Zener relaxation strength for $\langle 100 \rangle$ oriented single crystals of α-Ag–Zn. The quantity $(T - T_c) \Delta_E$ is plotted against $X^2(1 - X)^2 E_U^{-1}$ in curve A, and against $X^2 E_U$ in curve B. (From Seraphim and Nowick, 1961.)

variation fits equally well any of the relations

$$(T - T_c) \Delta_E \propto X^2(1 - X)^2 E_U^{-1} \tag{10.3-2}$$

or

$$(T - T_c) \Delta_E \propto X^2 E_U \tag{10.3-3}$$

or simply, $\Delta_E \propto X^2$. Equations (10.3-2) and (10.3-3) each have theoretical justification [Eq. (10.3-2) in terms of the LeClaire–Lomer theory, Section 10.4, and Eq. (10.3-3) in terms of the pair reorientation theory]. In both cases, the dependence of E_U on composition is allowed for explicitly.

In some instances, observations have been made on the concentration dependence of Δ in alloy phases which show an order–disorder transformation near a stoichiometric composition. Data for Mg–Cd alloys (Lulay and Wert, 1956) covering a range which includes the composition $MgCd_3$, are shown in Fig. 10-10. In this system the internal friction peaks occur close to room temperature (for a frequency of ~ 1 Hz), whereas $MgCd_3$ orders in the range 80–94°C. The strong suppression of the Zener relaxation near the stoichiometric composition is evident. Similar results have been obtained in the Fe–Al system near the composition Fe_3Al (Fischbach, 1962). The indication that the Zener relaxation should be absent in a perfectly ordered alloy is not hard to understand, since all order parameters then take on their extreme values and become unaffected by the application of stress. Somewhat different evidence which bears on the same point has been obtained in Cu_3Au

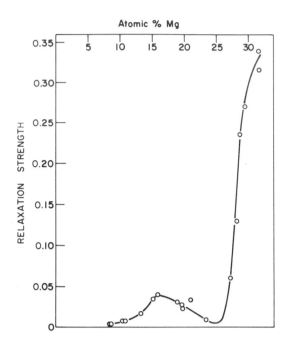

FIG. 10-10.   Relaxation strength as a function of concentration for Mg–Cd alloys. (From Lulay and Wert, 1956.)

(Goering and Nowick, 1958) and in β-brass (Artman, 1952). Here, the Zener peaks were observed in a temperature range where the degree of long-range order changes fairly rapidly with temperature. Under these conditions it was found that the peaks were distorted in just the manner expected if a higher degree of long-range order causes a reduction in the strength of the relaxation.

D. ANISOTROPY OF THE ZENER RELAXATION IN CONCENTRATED ALLOYS

Seraphim and Nowick (1961) have performed experiments on Ag–Zn alloys of various compositions up to 30% Zn, and also on the bcc alloy Li–57 at. % Mg. In addition, they were able to deduce some information on the relaxation anisotropy in β-brass by reinterpreting some earlier measurements by Artman (1952). An example of their results has been presented in Figs. 6-2 and 6-3 to illustrate the formal theory [Eqs. (6.5-1) and (6.5-2)]. The linear nature of the plots of δE^{-1} and δG^{-1} versus Γ in Fig. 6-2 makes it a straightforward matter to extrapolate to the limits $\Gamma = 0$ and $\frac{1}{3}$ to obtain the intercepts. (Note that this is not so easily done for the plots of Δ_E and Δ_G versus Γ, which exhibit considerable curvature.) The intercepts of Fig. 6-2 can, in principle, be used to obtain the three relaxations δS, $\delta S'$, and $\delta S''$. Within experimental error, however, the value $3\,\delta E^{-1}_{\langle 111 \rangle}$ $(= \delta S'' + \delta S)$ turned out to be the same as $\delta G_{\langle 100 \rangle}$ $(= \delta S)$, which means that $\delta S''$ was too small to be detected. In the Li–Mg alloy, on the other hand, a definite hydrostatic relaxation was observed, the value of $\delta S''$ being more than twice that of δS. Data on a representative Ag–Zn alloy and the Li–Mg alloy are given in Table 10-2.

TABLE 10-2

ZENER RELAXATION MAGNITUDES FOR TWO CONCENTRATED ALLOYS

Alloy	$\delta S''$	$\delta S'$	δS	Ratio $\delta S'/\delta S$
	$(10^{-13}\ \mathrm{cm^2\ dyn^{-1}})$			
Ag–26.1 at. % Zn (at 350°C)	$\leqslant 0.1$	17.1	0.5	34
Li–57 at. % Mg (at 115°C)	0.43	4.55	0.17	27

The very large values of the anisotropy ratio $\delta S'/\delta S$ are most striking. More recently Boesono *et al.* (1967) have found the same type of anisotropy for the bcc alloy Fe–8 at. % Si. Their observations, which can be expressed in the form $(\delta S' + \delta S'')/(\delta S + \delta S'') \simeq 8$, show that the behavior of the Li–Mg alloy is not unique. The results for the bcc alloys emphatically contradict the prediction $\delta S' = 0$ made by both the theories of Zener and of LeClaire and Lomer (see Section 10.4). As was mentioned in the previous section, if a simple pair model has any validity for a concentrated alloy, the above result implies that the dominant relaxation mechanism is the reorientation of next-nearest-neighbor pairs, rather than that of nearest-neighbor pairs. It is also tempting to infer that next-nearest neighbors may also be important for the Ag–Zn alloys, since the values of $\delta S'/\delta S$ for these alloys are even higher than for Li–Mg.

Although the application of the pair model to concentrated alloys is, conceptually at least, an overextension of the theory, it can be seen from the results given so far in this section that there is nothing in the presently available evidence to indicate at what point a serious modification is needed. We have seen (Fig. 10-9) that the concentration dependence of the relaxation strength follows the square law, or a reasonable modification of it, up to large concentrations (30 at. % solute), and that the composition dependence of T_c can also be accounted for on the pair model. Further, judging from a comparison of the dilute Al–Cu and concentrated Ag–Zn alloys, there is no marked change in anisotropy of the relaxation magnitude in going from a dilute to a concentrated alloy. It thus appears that an "improved" theory of the Zener relaxation in concentrated alloys must turn out to give much the same results for the thermodynamics of the relaxation as the simple pair model.

E. Kinetics of the Zener Relaxation in Concentrated Alloys

The activation energy Q_r governing the rate of the Zener relaxation has been determined for a number of concentrated alloys. Many of these values are probably subject to an error of several percent, due to the small temperature range over which the relaxation time was determined. Thus, the calculated value of the preexponential constant τ_0^{-1} in the relation $\tau^{-1} = \tau_0^{-1} \exp(-Q_r/kT)$ often cannot be relied on to better than a decade. Actually, there appear to be only two alloys in which Q_r is known to within 1 or 2% (and the corresponding log τ_0^{-1} to about ± 0.2), and for which comparative tracer diffusion data exist for both components. These are the Cu–Zn and Ag–Zn alloys listed at the top of Table 10-3. The Zener relaxation in each of these alloys has been studied by both quasi-static and dynamic methods to give Arrhenius plots extending over nine and seven decades in τ, respectively. In these two cases, Q_r cannot be identified within experimental error with either Q_A or Q_B, the activation energies for solvent and solute self-diffusion. Rather, it is found that $Q_r < Q_B < Q_A$ for both alloys. Listed next in Table 10-3 is the alloy Ag–32% Cd, studied over four decades in τ by Turner and Williams (1962). A range of Ag–Cd solid solutions were subsequently examined by Shtrakhman and Piguzov (1964) and by Turner et al. (1968). Taken together, these later results indicate, as noted for the Ag–34% Cd alloy, that Q_r is systematically smaller than Q_{Cd} by about 0.05 eV (which in turn, is smaller than Q_{Ag} by about the same amount). The same general conclusion is obtained from similar work on Ag–In alloys by Finkelshteyn and Shtrakhman (1964) and Williams and Turner (1968). The last entry in Table 10-3 concerns two Ag–Au alloys of essentially the same composition. The earlier anelastic investigation (Turner and Williams, 1962), covering four decades in τ, gave a Q_r of 1.92 eV, a value which lies between Q_A and Q_B. The later investigation (Turner and Williams, 1963) employed data obtained over only 1.3

TABLE 10-3

COMPARISON OF TRACER DIFFUSION AND ZENER RELAXATION DATA

Alloy A	B	Q_r (eV)	Q_A (eV)	Q_B (eV)	D_{A0} (cm² sec⁻¹)	D_{B0} (cm² sec⁻¹)	$\log \tau_0^{-1}$ Γ^{-1} or τ in sec	$\log \Gamma_{A0}$	$\log \Gamma_{B0}$	Reference
Cu–31 %	Zn	1.64	1.82	1.77	0.34	0.73	15.1	15.47	15.80	Hino *et al.* (1957)
Ag–30 %	Zn	1.39	1.56	1.53	0.29	0.46	14.6	15.33	15.53	Seraphim *et al.* (1964)
Ag–32 %	Cd	1.52	1.58	1.52	0.14	0.30	15.6	15.0	15.3	Turner and Williams (1962)
Ag–33 %	Cd	1.49					15.3			Turner *et al.* (1968)
Ag–44 %	Au	1.92	1.88	1.99	0.205	0.26	15.6	15.17	15.27	Turner and Williams (1962, 1963)
Ag–46 %	Au	1.79					14.5			

decades, but was smoothed by taking into account results for alloys of other compositions. This work gave a Q_r value at the same composition which is 7% lower than the previous figure and a τ_0^{-1} value which is smaller by a full order of magnitude. In view of the fact that it is uncertain as to which of the two procedures provides a more reliable value for Q_r, it appears that too fine a comparison between the anelastic and the diffusion data for Ag–Au would be inappropriate at this time.

In discussing the activation energies determined from tracer diffusion and anelastic measurements, it has often been pointed out that the temperatures at which diffusion measurements are carried out are higher than those used in anelastic studies. This leads to the possibility that part of the difference between Q_r and Q_A or Q_B may arise from a temperature dependence of the activation energy. The most extensive data which can be inspected for such an effect are those of Hino et al. (1957), These workers obtained excellent straight line diffusion plots over the range 600–900°C and an Arrhenius plot for anelastic data over the range 580–170°C. Though the plot is certainly well fitted by a straight line, the possibility of a slight curvature is not entirely eliminated, due to the paucity of experimental points above 230°C. In early work on Ag–Zn alloys, Nowick (1952a) obtained data indicating (over seven decades in τ) a detectable curvature of the Arrhenius plot, with Q_r becoming larger at higher temperatures. This is just the curvature which would be needed to improve the correlation between Q_r and Q_{Zn} or Q_{Ag}. However, a later study of the alloy Ag–24 at. % Zn (Berry and Orehotsky, 1968a) failed to confirm this result, as is shown in Fig. 10-11. Taken as a whole, therefore, there appears to be little evidence to support the idea that a temperature dependence of the activation energy can be used to bring a better reconciliation between Q_r and Q_A or Q_B.

From the evidence presented above it appears that, as in the case of dilute alloys, the activation energy Q_r for the atom movements involved in the Zener relaxation must be accepted as a distinct and individual quantity, which cannot be thought of in general as being identical to either Q_A or Q_B. Thus Γ_r, the mean rate of atom migration producing the relaxation, which is related to τ by Eq. (10.2-8) is given by

$$\Gamma_r = zw_r = \Gamma_{r0} \exp(-Q_r/kT) \qquad (10.3\text{-}4)$$

where the frequency factor Γ_{r0} is related to τ_0^{-1} by Eq. (10.2-10). In a corresponding manner, we may write for the mean jump rate Γ_A

$$\Gamma_A = \Gamma_{A0} \exp(-Q_A/kT) = zW_{A0} \exp(-Q_A/kT) \qquad (10.3\text{-}5)$$

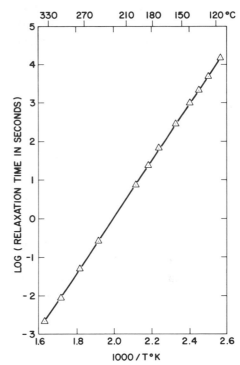

FIG. 10-11. Temperature dependence of the Zener relaxation time for the alloy Ag–24 at. % Zn. $Q = 1.45$ eV, $\tau_0^{-1} = 10^{14.6}$ sec^{-1}. (From Berry and Orehotsky, 1968a.)

and similarly for Γ_B. The quantities Γ_{A0} and Γ_{B0} are related to the corresponding quantities D_{A0} and D_{B0} obtained from diffusion measurements by combining Eqs. (7.5-9) and (7.5-11) with Eq. (10.3-5). Values of Γ_{A0} and Γ_{B0} so obtained are listed in Table 10-3. To evaluate the quantity n in Eq. (10.2-10), we observe first from Table 10-3 that the values of Γ_{A0} and Γ_{B0} are, for each alloy, quite close to one another. It seems reasonable then to assume that Γ_{r0} will also have a similar value, and for want of a better procedure, Γ_{r0} will be taken as their geometric average. From this assumption, and the corresponding value of τ_0^{-1}, the data on the Cu–Zn and Ag–Zn alloys indicate that n has a value of the order of 1–10, which is not much different from the dilute Al–Cu alloy. Though the data are less precise, a similar conclusion can be obtained for a variety of other alloys.

F. THE DISTRIBUTION OF RELAXATION TIMES

The final topic to be discussed in this section is concerned with the distribution of relaxation times associated with the Zener relaxation. In a dynamic experiment, the existence of such a distribution is revealed by the fact that the internal friction peaks are ~20% wider than a simple Debye peak; the corresponding situation in a quasi-static experiment is that the response function is more smeared (faster at short times and slower at long times) than a simple exponential curve. Nowick and Berry (1962) have shown that the assumption of a lognormal distribution of relaxation times fits data on the Zener relaxation very well. A typical value of the distribution parameter β (Section 4.5) is unity or somewhat less, which means that the width of the distribution is less than a decade in τ. The existence of a distribution of relaxation times shows that the rate of atom migration producing the Zener relaxation is different at different points in the sample, a situation readily attributable to fluctuations in the local atomic arrangement and/or composition. It is interesting that while it is undoubtedly true that both Γ_A and Γ_B (corresponding to the diffusion coefficients D_A and D_B) are also distributed quantities, there appears to be no comparable method in use for analyzing diffusion data to obtain the dispersion exhibited by these quantities.

Returning to the Zener relaxation, it is of interest to establish to what extent the distribution in $\ln \tau$ stems from a distribution in $\ln \tau_0$, and to what extent it is due to a distribution in Q_r. This question has been considered in Section 4.8. The basic point is that a distribution in $\ln \tau_0$ causes a temperature independent contribution to β while a distribution in Q_r produces a temperature dependent contribution. For what seems to be the most reasonable physical case, namely where $\ln \tau_0$ and Q_r are correlated with each other through their dependence on a single internal variable, β is given by Eq. (4.8-3). The best available data for β as a function of temperature have been given in Fig. 4-13. This figure shows that the dispersion of relaxation times arises mainly from a distribution in the activation energy Q_r. Since this in turn can be expected to arise in part at least from fluctuations in local composition, it might be anticipated that rather narrow Zener peaks would be shown by those systems in which Q_r varies slowly with composition. Such a situation occurs for the system Ag–Au, where Turner and Williams (1963) have reported the Zener peaks to have essentially the simple Debye form.

10.4   Theory of the Zener Relaxation in Concentrated Alloys

In order to make the transition from simple solute pairs at low solute concentrations to the more complex case of concentrated alloys, LeClaire and Lomer (1954) introduced a theory which treats the two components

A and B in a symmetrical manner (i.e., with no distinction between "solute" and "solvent"). Instead of solute pairs we now deal with short-range order parameters. LeClaire and Lomer consider nearest-neighbor order only. Instead of the usual short-range order parameter, however, they introduce a set of $z/2$ parameters, one for each nearest-neighbor direction in the crystal. Each of these parameters is assumed to be capable of changing independently of the others. Thus, whereas for zero stress (or purely hydrostatic stress) the short-range order parameters are the same for all nearest-neighbor directions, application of a shear stress changes the equilibrium value of the parameter in one direction relative to that in another direction, thereby producing anelastic relaxation. Figure 10-12 illustrates this concept of "directional short-range order" for a simple square lattice.

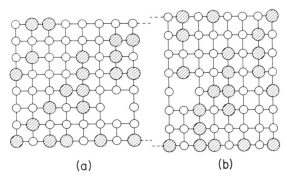

(a)   (b)

FIG. 10-12. Schematic illustration of the concept of directional short-range order in a simple square lattice. In (a) the numbers of horizontal and vertical bonds between nearest-neighbor shaded atoms are equal, corresponding to zero directional order. In (b) there are more bonds of this type in the vertical than in the horizontal direction, corresponding to a finite degree of directional order, which is accompanied by an overall distortion of the lattice.

As a measure of the short-range order in direction p ($p = 1, 2, \ldots,$ $z/2$), it is convenient to use the parameter $\varkappa_p$, the fraction of bonds which are of type AA in that direction. In equilibrium at zero stress all $\varkappa_p$ are taken equal to $\varkappa_0$. (The fractions of BB and of AB bonds are expressible in terms of $\varkappa_p$.) The theory is then analogous to Section 8.3 where $\varkappa_p - \varkappa_0$ replaces $C_p - (C_0/n_{\mathrm{t}})$, except that there is no constraint on $\sum_p \varkappa_p$ analogous to Eq. (8.3-1). The parameter $\lambda^{(p)}$ is here defined by

$$\lambda^{(p)} = (\partial \varepsilon / \partial \varkappa_p)_{\sigma, T} \tag{10.4-1}$$

We may also define an ordering free energy γ_p as in Eqs. (8.3-5) and (8.3-8). In the present case, it is simpler to neglect any vibrational contribution by using an energy u_p. The relation of the equilibrium order parameter to the ordering energy u_p may be obtained by using the quasi-chemical approach[†] in which changes in the numbers of bonds are treated as a "reaction":

$$2AB \rightleftharpoons AA + BB, \qquad \text{for any } p \qquad (10.4\text{-}2)$$

with the mass action equation

$$[AA][BB]/[AB]^2 = \bar{x}_p(1 - 2X + \bar{x}_p)/(X - \bar{x}_p)^2$$
$$= \exp(-u_p/kT) \qquad (10.4\text{-}3)$$

where X is the mole fraction of A in the alloy, and $\bar{x}_p$ is the equilibrium value of x_p (see Problem 10-2). In this equation the concentrations [BB] and [AB] have been expressed in terms of x_p. The ordering energy u_p is the energy of the reaction (10.4-2), or

$$u_p = u_{AA,p} + u_{BB,p} - 2u_{AB,p} \qquad (10.4\text{-}4)$$

expressed in terms of the individual bond energies. These bond energies are different for different directions p only in the presence of a shear stress. When Eq. (10.4-3) is expanded for small departures from $x_p = x_0$ and $u_p = u_0$ (where x_0 and u_0 are values for zero stress), we obtain (see Problem 10-3)

$$\bar{x}_p - x_0 = -[f(x_0, X)/kT]X^2(1 - X)^2(u_p - u_0) \qquad (10.4\text{-}5)$$

For present purposes it suffices to note that $f(x_0, X)$ is a function of x_0 and X which is unity for complete randomness (i.e., when $x_0 = X^2$) and is zero for a complete long-range order, e.g., of the AB or A_3B type. Equation (10.4-5) replaces (8.3-10). When the relaxation magnitude is then calculated as in Section 8.3, the result

$$\delta J = [v_0 f(x_0, X)X^2(1 - X)^2/kT] \sum_p (\lambda^{(p)})^2 \qquad (10.4\text{-}6)$$

is obtained. This equation has many interesting features. First, it shows a dependence on the state of order through the function $f(x_0, X)$ such that δJ goes to zero for complete order. Second, for a nearly random alloy, it shows a symmetrical composition dependence: $\delta J \propto X^2(1-X)^2$,

[†] See, e.g., Fowler and Guggenheim (1949, Chapter XIII).

which goes, in the limit of low concentration, to a square-law dependence at either end of the phase diagram where the "solute pair" concept would apply. Finally, δJ shows a $1/T$ dependence.

In order to obtain the orientation dependence of δJ, LeClaire and Lomer make another approximation, namely, that u_p *depends only on the interatomic spacing in the direction p*, and that the change in u_p with stress is related to its change with dimensions through the appropriate elastic constant. In this way, using Eq. (8.3-8), they write

$$-v_0 \lambda^{(p)} = \partial u_p / \partial \sigma \simeq M_U^{-1}(du_p/da_p)(da_p/d\varepsilon) \qquad (10.4\text{-}7)$$

where a_p is the interatomic spacing in direction p. Further, du_p/da_p is independent of p, and will be called η. They then obtain

$$\sum_p (\lambda^{(p)})^2 = \beta \eta^2 a_0^2 / v_0 \qquad (10.4\text{-}8)$$

where a_0 is the interatomic spacing in the absence of stress and

$$\beta \equiv (1/a_0^2) \sum_p (da_p/d\varepsilon)^2 \qquad (10.4\text{-}9)$$

The quantity β is a dimensionless geometrical parameter which depends only on the nature of the strain imposed on the crystal. Values of β for the important cases of fcc and bcc lattices turn out as follows:

$$\text{fcc} \begin{cases} \text{for } J = S, & \beta = 1/2 \\ \text{for } J = S', & \beta = 1/4 \end{cases}$$

$$\text{bcc} \begin{cases} \text{for } J = S, & \beta = 4/9 \\ \text{for } J = S', & \beta = 0 \end{cases}$$

For hydrostatic stress, Eq. (10.4-9) yields $\beta = z/18$, applicable to all cubic crystals.

The anisotropy ratio $A \equiv \delta S'/\delta S$ is thus predicted to be $\frac{1}{2}$ for the fcc and zero for the bcc case.

The major strengths of the theory are: (a) the prediction of a hydrostatic relaxation for cubic crystals, or more generally, of a type I relaxation (see Section 6.3) for all crystals; (b) the prediction of a strong dependence of δJ on order, and a value of zero for perfect long-range order; (c) the symmetrical concentration dependence given by eq. (10.4-6). All of these points agree qualitatively or semiquantitatively with the results for concentrated alloys summarized in the previous section. The major weaknesses of the theory are: (a) its failure to predict the large values of the anisotropy ratio A actually observed in fcc and bcc alloys; (b) the $1/T$ dependence of δJ, rather than the Curie–Weiss or $1/(T - T_c)$ dependence.

It is quite clear, particularly for the bcc case, that the failure to predict the anisotropy correctly is largely due to the restriction to a nearest-neighbor approach. Accordingly Welch and LeClaire (1967) have abandoned the quasi-chemical description of short-range order and used in its place the well-known Cowley short-range order parameters. This approach takes into account first and second nearest-neighbor interactions and order parameters out to the eighth nearest neighbor. The relaxation strength is then expressed in terms of the Cowley parameters and ordering energies. Unfortunately, it is not possible to write an expression for the relaxation strength in an analytic form. It is necessary to have the complete set of experimentally determined order parameters for the alloy of interest. Such parameters have been measured for the alloy Cu_3Au. In the absence of order parameters for α-Ag–Zn (for which the best anelastic data are available), Welch and LeClaire were forced to assume that these parameters are the same as those for Cu_3Au in order to obtain numerical estimates. They also predict the Curie–Weiss type of temperature dependence with a value of T_c which is anisotropic (cf. Section 10.3B).

A somewhat different approach is to recognize that the major weaknesses of the LeClaire–Lomer theory are not only the neglect of second nearest-neighbor effects, but also the approximation involved in Eq. (10.4-7). [The latter is equivalent to taking only one principal value for the λ tensor in the pair reorientation theory, namely, that along the pair axis (see Problem 10-4). The study of point-defect relaxations shows that such an assumption is not justified.] Accordingly, we return to Eq. (10.4-6) as the basic relation, and further, introduce next-nearest-neighbor order parameters $\varkappa_q'$ as well as the nearest-neighbor parameters $\varkappa_p$. (The index q runs over the number of nnn orientations, which in general, is different from the number of nn orientations $z/2$.) Correspondingly, we define parameters $\lambda'^{(q)}$ analogously to Eq. (10.4-1) with $\varkappa_q'$ replacing $\varkappa_p$. Thus, Eq. (10.4-6) becomes

$$\delta J = [v_0 X^2 (1 - X)^2/kT]\left[f(\varkappa_0, X) \sum_p (\lambda^{(p)})^2 + f'(\varkappa_0', X) \sum_q (\lambda'^{(q)})^2 \right]$$

$$(10.4\text{-}10)$$

in which $f'(\varkappa_0', X)$ is the function for nnn order, analogous to $f(\varkappa_0, X)$. In this way, the directional ordering theory is a natural extension of the pair-reorientation model, particularly because at low solute concentrations $\lambda^{(p)}$ and $\lambda'^{(q)}$ as defined by Eq. (10.4-1) go into the corresponding quantities given by Eq. (8.2-3). Also, for small X, the functions f', f, and $(1 - X)^2$ all go to unity. The only missing feature in such a theory is the Curie–Weiss temperature dependence. This can be obtained by introducing interaction coefficients, as for isolated point defects (see Section 8.10), which then justifies replacing T by $T - T_c$ in Eq. (10.4-10).

In summary, the basic concept of the directional order theory of LeClaire and Lomer seems to be valid for describing the Zener relaxation in concentrated solutions. Simplifying approximations are needed, however, to obtain explicit expressions for the relaxation strength.

Turning now to the question of the kinetics of the relaxation, we find that a satisfactory theory for concentrated solutions is still lacking. The first suggestion (Nowick, 1952a) was that the activation energy for relaxation in a concentrated alloy should be comparable to the self-diffusion activation energy of the *slower* moving component, i.e., to the higher of the two values Q_A and Q_B. The reason is qualitatively as follows. Suppose that A is the faster diffusing atom. In a high concentration alloy, other A atoms are usually present as nearest neighbors to a given atom. Accordingly, lattice vacancies will diffuse primarily along networks of A atoms. Such vacancy movements, although they produce diffusion, do not give rise to relaxation since the local order is unaffected. Only a B atom jump leads to a change in local order which contributes to relaxation. The experimental results quoted in the previous section (Table 10-3) do not support this prediction. Rather, it appears that Q_r tends to be somewhat less than either Q_A or Q_B.

Two explanations have been advanced for this discrepancy. The first, by LeClaire (1962), relates the differences to the temperature dependence of the correlation factor f, for diffusion in an alloy. The reader should recall that in an alloy f is in general a function of temperature, as, for example, in Eq. (7.5-6). Accordingly, the temperature dependence of f can contribute to the effective activation energy for diffusion. LeClaire showed that df/dT is of the correct sign to account for the fact that Q_r is lower than either Q_A or Q_B. The second explanation by Seraphim *et al.* (1964) is based on an extension of the interpretation for very dilute alloys (Section 10.2) according to which diffusion is due to the motion of isolated solute atoms while relaxation is due to solute pairs. As generalized to concentrated alloys this suggestion states that (in view of the statistical distribution of local environments that exist in an alloy) different weight must be given to atom jumps in different environments in the two types of measurements.

Welch (1969) has derived an expression for the kinetics of the Zener relaxation in concentrated solution which utilizes the framework of the theory of order–disorder kinetics developed by Vineyard (1956) and extended by Kidin and Shtremel (1961). The result includes both the effect of the temperature dependence of the correlation factor and the different weights assigned to jumps in different environments. Quantitative estimates, which can be compared with experiments, are difficult to make, however.

10.5   Applications of the Zener Relaxation

As for the Snoek relaxation, applications of the Zener relaxation can be based either on the utilization of the relaxation strength or the relaxation time. In the first category, the sensitivity of the relaxation strength to changes in either composition, degree of order, or crystallographic texture is of interest. To date, comparatively little use has been made of these first two features, while the last (which has application to the investigation of annealing textures) does not appear to have been used at all. Ang et al. (1955) and Berry and Nowick (1958) have, however, applied the concentration dependence of the relaxation to obtain information on the kinetics of precipitation in Au–Ni and Al–Cu alloys, respectively. Wert (1953) has also reported on the use of the relaxation strength to follow the long-range ordering process in Mg–Cd alloys on annealing below the critical temperature.

Turning to the kinetics of the relaxation, it is already clear that the relaxation provides its own "Zener-averaged" measure of the rate of atom migration in an alloy, a corresponding activation energy Q_r and frequency factor τ_0, and information on the distributed nature of each of these quantities. The fact that such measurements are made at lower temperatures than conventional diffusion measurements has considerable utility. First, despite the small differences which exist between the activation energies for the Zener relaxation and for tracer diffusion (Table 10-3), it is possible to convert the Zener τ value to an effective diffusion coefficient (using a relationship of the type $D = Ba^2/\tau$, where B is a constant selected for best fit), to provide a low-temperature extension of actual diffusion data. The work of Stanley and Wert (1961) provides an interesting case in which diffusion and anelastic measurements were so combined to reveal the effect of spin-ordering on atomic mobility in the ferromagnetic alloy Fe–18%V. Their results, shown in Fig. 10-13, show that the buildup of a spontaneous magnetization on cooling below the ferromagnetic Curie temperature T_c is associated with a gradual suppression of D which amounts to about two decades at temperatures where spin ordering is essentially complete. While a quantitative explanation of this effect is not available, the absence of a corresponding effect for the interstitial diffusion of carbon in Ni (Section 11.4B) suggests that a coupling exists between the saturation moment and the equilibrium vacancy concentration in the alloy.

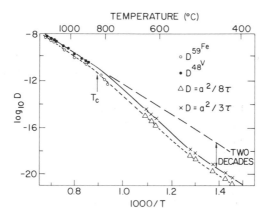

FIG. 10-13. Composite plots of $\log D$ versus $1/T$ for the alloy Fe–18% V. The open and filled circles show tracer diffusion coefficients for Fe and V, respectively. The anelastic data can be joined smoothly with either set of diffusion data by appropriate choice of the proportionality constant between D and τ (see key). T_c is the ferromagnetic Curie temperature. (From Stanley and Wert, 1961.)

The use of the Zener relaxation for studying the defect-controlled nature of the atomic mobility in solid solutions probably constitutes its most important application. Indeed, this use of the Zener relaxation provided one of the earliest and most striking demonstrations in support of a vacancy mechanism of atom migration in fcc substitutional alloys (Nowick, 1951b). It has since yielded quantitative information on various important parameters characterizing the behavior of vacancies in such alloys. The approach usually followed has been to study changes in the rate of the Zener relaxation in specimens for which the vacancy concentration had been enhanced by quenching. When atomic migration is due only to the presence of single vacancies, the average atom jump rate w_r appropriate to the Zener relaxation can be written as the product of the vacancy concentration C_v and the mean rate w_v at which specific atom–

vacancy interchanges occur. [See Eq. (7.5-7).] Accordingly, Eq. (10.2-8) becomes

$$\tau^{-1} = (z/n)C_v w_v \qquad (10.5\text{-}1)$$

For a sample containing the equilibrium vacancy concentration at a temperature T, C_v is given by [Eq. (7.2-1)]

$$\bar{C}_v = A \exp(-\Delta h_v/kT) \qquad (10.5\text{-}2)$$

where A represents the preexponential term containing the formation entropy of a vacancy, and Δh_v is the enthalpy of formation of a vacancy. It is important to observe that Eq. (10.5-1) is valid regardless of whether or not C_v has its equilibrium value $\bar{C}_v$. When equilibrium is achieved, τ^{-1} of course has a unique and constant value at the particular temperature considered. On the other hand, if C_v is a nonequilibrium "quenched-in" vacancy concentration, which changes with time towards the equilibrium value, τ^{-1} is time dependent in a corresponding manner. Consider now an experiment in which a specimen is equilibrated at a temperature T_q and quenched to a temperature T_a. If the quench is so rapid that no appreciable annealing takes place during the quench, it is easily seen that

$$\ln[\tau^{-1}(\infty, T_q)/\tau^{-1}(0, T_a)] = (\Delta h^*/k)(T_a^{-1} - T_q^{-1}) \qquad (10.5\text{-}3)$$

and that

$$\ln[\tau^{-1}(0, T_a)/\tau^{-1}(\infty, T_a)] = (\Delta h_v/k)(T_a^{-1} - T_q^{-1}) \qquad (10.5\text{-}4)$$

where $\tau^{-1}(\infty, T_a)$ and $\tau^{-1}(\infty, T_q)$ represent the equilibrium relaxation rates at T_a and T_q, respectively, and $\tau^{-1}(0, T_a)$ is the instantaneous value of τ^{-1} immediately after the quench. Berry and Orehotsky (1968a, b) have used Eqs. (10.5-3) and (10.5-4) to obtain values of Δh_v and Δh^* for Ag–Zn solid solutions containing 24–33 at. % Zn. The measurements were made using a novel "delayed-creep" technique which permitted both the determination of the initial value $\tau^{-1}(0, T_a)$ and the subsequent variation in τ^{-1} due to vacancy annealing. Their results can be summarized by the statement $\Delta h_v = 0.6Q_r$ and $\Delta h^* = 0.4Q_r$, with the annealing experiments providing an independent check on the value of Δh^*. These authors have discussed some of the complicating factors which caused earlier workers to report lower values of Δh_v and higher values of Δh^* (Nowick and Sladek, 1953; Roswell and Nowick, 1953; Cost, 1963). The Zener relaxation has also been utilized for vacancy studies in quenched Au–Ni and Cd–Mg alloys by Cost (1965a,b).

PROBLEMS

10-1. Obtain Eq. (10.2-5) from Eq. (10.2-4).

10-2. Express the concentrations of BB and AB pairs in a given orientation in terms of the fraction $\varkappa_p$ of AA pairs in that orientation, to obtain the result given by Eq. (10.4-3).

10-3. Verify Eq. (10.4-5) and show that

$$f(\varkappa_0, X) = \varkappa_0(X - \varkappa_0)(1 + \varkappa_0 - 2X)/X^2(1 - X)^2(X + \varkappa_0 - 2X^2)$$

10-4. Show that the approximation involved in the LeClaire–Lomer theory, Eq. (10.4-7), is equivalent to taking only one principal value for the λ tensor in the pair orientation model.

10-5. Derive Eqs. (10.5-3) and (10.5-4).

Chapter 11 / Other Point-Defect Relaxations

The first two sections of this chapter are devoted to elementary defects, namely single substitutionals (designated s for brevity), vacancies (v), or interstitials (i). In the latter category, we shall exclude the impurity interstitial in the bcc lattice, since this was treated separately in Chapter 9. The examples discussed should serve to emphasize the basic fact that simple "monatomic" defects only produce relaxation if they occupy a site which is already of lower symmetry than that of the crystal, or if their introduction into the crystal produces a spontaneous lowering of local symmetry. Among the higher symmetry crystals, this requirement limits the number of cases in which the elementary s, v, or i defects produce relaxation behavior.

The later sections of this chapter deal with composite defects, mainly those of the paired type such as i–i and s–v pairs. Here, the existence of a defect symmetry which is lower than that of the host crystal is the rule rather than the exception, and a rich variety of relaxations attributable to paired defects will be reviewed.

Some relaxations have been reported which are apparently due to point defects, but are still unidentified. These relaxations are discussed at the end of the chapter (Section 11.6) under the headings of the materials in which they occur.

11.1   Substitutionals and Vacancies

There are a number of ways in which a simple substituted atom or ion, or a vacancy, can give rise to anelastic relaxation. The simplest category is that in which the site symmetries of the atoms in the crystal are relatively low (see Part A of this section). Another case involves substitution of a radical for a single ion in the original crystal (Part C). In addition to these possibilities, there are a number of cases (Parts B, D, and E) which may be grouped under the heading of "spontaneous symmetry reduction." By this we mean that the substitutional atom or vacancy is unstable in the symmetric lattice position. Instead, a position of minimum energy is arrived at by a local rearrangement of atoms adjacent to the defect in such a way that the local point symmetry is reduced. To determine whether a given symmetric position for a defect is actually one of minimum or maximum energy requires a detailed calculation in each case taking into account the various interatomic interaction potentials. For one type of substitutional ion, however, the occurrence of spontaneous symmetry reduction can be anticipated based on a general principle (see Part E on the Jahn–Teller defects).

A. CASE OF LOW SITE SYMMETRY

It is often stated that a single substitutional atom or vacancy cannot give rise to anelasticity. From the theory of Section 8.2, however, we have seen that the requirement for point defects to give rise to anelasticity is that the defect symmetry belong to a lower system than the crystal symmetry. Clearly, then, a single vacancy or substitutional atom *can* produce anelasticity, provided only that its site symmetry belongs to a lower system than that of the crystal. The statement that vacancies and substitutionals cannot produce relaxation is therefore incorrect, in general. It is, however, valid for many of the common crystal structures such as fcc, bcc, hcp, diamond cubic, NaCl, CsCl, and CaF_2, where the sites of the atoms or ions belong to the same symmetry system as the crystal. On the other hand, there are many crystal structures for which one or both of the atomic (or ionic) sites do belong to a lower system than the crystal. Some examples are: α-quartz, SiO_2 (both sites); rutile, TiO_2 (both sites); spinel, $MgAl_2O_4$, (Al and O sites); $PbCl_2$ (both sites); cuprite, Cu_2O (Cu sites). Thus far, however, a clear example of such a simple relaxation phenomenon has not been obtained experimentally.

B. Li$^+$ in KCl

We consider here a specific example representing the case of a substitutional ion which spontaneously lowers its symmetry by moving to an off-center position from the symmetric substitutional site. The site of the K$^+$ ion in KCl possesses full cubic symmetry. However, Lombardo and Pohl (1965) have suggested that, when the small Li$^+$ ion is substituted for K$^+$, it locates itself in an off center position within the cation site.

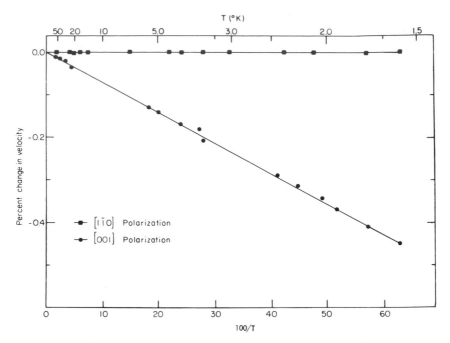

FIG. 11-1.   Temperature dependence of the velocity of ultrasonic (30 MHz) waves in KCl doped with 100 ppm Li$^+$. Propagation direction is [110]. (From Byer and Sack, 1966.)

The anelastic behavior of this defect was studied by Byer and Sack (1966, 1968a) using 10–150 MHz ultrasonic velocity measurements at low temperatures. They studied the two sound velocities $v_{[1\bar{1}0]}^{[110]}$ and $v_{[110]}^{[001]}$ for both pure and Li$^+$ doped KCl, with results as shown in Fig. 11-1. The former of these two velocities, which measures the shear modulus $C_{11} - C_{12}$ [see Eq. (6.4-6)] shows no change to within 0.001% due to the Li$^+$. The velocity $v_{[110]}^{[001]}$, which measures C_{44}, however, shows a linear decrease with $1/T$ down to 1.6°K. In both cases, the attenuation was low and independent of frequency. These results suggest that the relaxed modulus $(C_{44})_R$ is being measured at all temperatures in the doped sample.

From these measurements it may be concluded that:

1. Li$^+$ in KCl forms a trigonal dipole (i.e., the off-center displacement is along a $\langle 111 \rangle$ direction).

2. The relaxation time for reorientation is very rapid ($\tau \lesssim 10^{-9}$ sec) even at 1.6°K. If it obeys an Arrhenius equation, the activation energy

must be very small ($<10^{-3}$ eV); more likely, quantum-mechanical tunneling may occur among the stable sites (see Section 7.3).

3. If the lowering of the velocity $v_{[110]}^{[001]}$ due to Li$^+$ is treated as proportional to a relaxation δC_{44} which varies as $1/T$, a value of $|\lambda_1 - \lambda_2|$ $= 0.066$ is obtained from Eq. (8.4-4). This value is small compared to those of other point defects, as might have been expected.

Theoretical calculations first suggested an off-center displacement of the Li$^+$ along $\langle 100 \rangle$ (Dienes *et al.*, 1966), but more refined calculations (Wilson *et al.*, 1967) show that the $\langle 111 \rangle$ displacement actually occurs. These authors also obtain the displacements of the six neighboring Cl$^-$ ions, from which Byer and Sack (1968a) have estimated the shape factor $\lambda_1 - \lambda_2$ by an approximate method due to Känzig (1962). Excellent agreement with the above experimental value is obtained.

The Li$^+$ defect in KCl constitutes not only an elastic dipole but also an electric dipole. Dielectric relaxation due to this defect has been observed by Sack and Moriarty (1965).

C. RADICALS SUBSTITUTING FOR A SINGLE ION

Another way to produce an off-site symmetry is to substitute an unsymmetrical radical onto a single lattice site. Several such examples are known for the alkali halides on the anion (halogen) sites, namely, OH$^-$, CN$^-$, and NO$_2^-$. Most of these radicals have been studied by low-temperature dielectric measurements (e.g., Sack and Moriarty, 1965; Känzig *et al.*, 1964; Bosshard *et al.*, 1965). In some cases, the evidence indicates the presence either of tunneling or of a very low activation barrier; in other cases however, the motion does freeze at temperatures of several °K, giving rise to a peak in the dielectric loss angle.

Some anelastic measurements have been made on such materials. The earliest are the measurements of Brugger and Mason (1961) who found a peak in the ultrasonic attenuation of NaCl crystals (which had been grown in air) in the temperature range 2–3°K. The activation energy is ~ 0.001 eV. Unfortunately, the impurity present in the crystal is not well established; presumably it is the OH$^-$ ion. Using different directions of propagation and polarization of the ultrasonic waves, Brugger and Mason show that those waves involving only C_{44} shear give no attenuation peak. Accordingly, it must be concluded that the defect in question is tetragonal. A fuller account is given by Brugger *et al.* (1967), in which relaxations attributed to (H$_2$O)$^-$ as well as OH$^-$ are reported.

Anelastic measurements on alkali halides doped with CN^- made by Byer and Sack (1968b) give evidence for more complex behavior, in that both the $C_{11} - C_{12}$ and C_{44} shear moduli show relaxation behavior, and also the dependence on CN^- concentration is quadratic. These results then suggest that CN^- clusters, rather than the single ions, give rise to the observed behavior.

Another radical of interest is the O_2^- molecule ion which also substitutes for a halide ion in the alkali halides. This defect in KCl, KBr, and KI has been studied by Känzig (1962) and Silsbee (1967), using paramagnetic resonance in combination with an applied uniaxial stress in various directions in the crystal. These studies show that the defect is $\langle 110 \rangle$ orthorhombic and that its motion does not freeze even at temperatures below $4.2°K$. A study of this defect by elastic constant and internal friction measurements has, thus far, not been carried out.

D. Vacancies in Germanium

An example of an "off-center" vacancy, analogous to the case of Li^+ in KCl, has been considered in calculations by Scholtz and Seeger (1963) for germanium. It is assumed that covalent bonds which are broken to form a vacancy are reformed between pairs of atoms which are nearest neighbors to the vacancy. Thus, although the site of each Ge atom is cubic, the defect so formed has lower than cubic symmetry. Anelastic relaxation is predicted in the vicinity of liquid hydrogen temperature. Such an effect may be difficult to observe unless some method for introducing an appreciable vacancy concentration in Ge becomes available. (Quenching is not likely to be effective, since even at the melting point the concentration of vacancies in Ge is small.)

E. Jahn–Teller Defects

There is one situation where the occurrence of spontaneous symmetry reduction can be anticipated based on a general principle. This is the case where the lowest electronic state of the defect is orbitally degenerate, and the principle involved is called the *Jahn–Teller rule*. Such defects, which involve mainly substitutional transition metal ions, will be termed Jahn–Teller defects.

The rule which Jahn and Teller have demonstrated (see, e.g., Dunitz and Orgel, 1957) deals with the case of a nonlinear molecule for which the electronic ground state shows orbital degeneracy. The rule then states the corresponding atomic configuration is unstable with respect to one of lower symmetry which does not give rise to an orbitally degenerate ground state, and therefore spontaneously undergoes distortion to the lower symmetry state. In crystals, this rule has been applied mainly to transition metal ions in cubic environments. In a simplified form, the situation is as follows. The isolated transition-metal atom has five orbitals for its d electrons, all orbitals having the same energy. (The fact that two spins are allowed in each orbital explains why there is a maximum of ten d electrons.) A cubic environment in a crystal may be of octahedral or tetrahedral symmetry. In an octahedral site, the five d orbitals are split into a triplet (called t_{2g}) and a pair (called e_g) with the first set having lower energy than the second, as shown in Fig. 11-2a. The magnitude of the splitting depends, of course, on the strength of the crystal field. For the tetrahedral environment the order of the separation is reversed, as shown in Fig. 11-2b. [†] The separation of the levels is also generally smaller in this case.

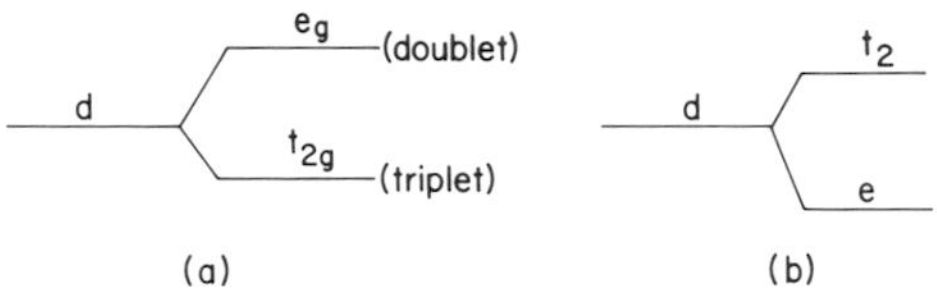

FIG. 11-2. Crystal field splitting of d orbital energy levels: (a) in an octahedral field, (b) in a tetrahedral field.

Returning to the octahedral case, which is of greater interest, the first three d electrons clearly go into the t_{2g} orbitals. Beyond this point there are two possibilities. On the one hand, due to the exchange forces, the energy is lowest when as many spins as possible are parallel (Hund's rule). This requires putting the next two electrons into the e_g state, because of the Pauli exclusion principle which does not allow two electrons of the same spin in the same orbital state. On the other hand, the crystal field splitting of the t_{2g} and e_g states favors keeping the next electrons in the t_{2g} states with (necessarily) opposite spin. Which effect prevails depends on the magnitude of the crystal field, a weak field favoring parallel spins and a strong field forcing the pairing of spins. For the strong field case, for example, there is no orbital degeneracy for an ion with three, six, eight, and, of course, ten d electrons (i.e., when each level is empty or exactly filled with spins of one or both signs).

[†] The use of t_2 and e for the tetrahedral case, without the subscript g (for "gerade" or "even") is due to the absence of a center of symmetry in this case.

For all other numbers of d electrons, there would be orbital degeneracy of the lowest state according to the diagram of Fig. 11-2a. Then, by the Jahn–Teller rule, the degeneracy is eliminated by a further splitting which comes from a spontaneous symmetry reduction. The type of distortion which commonly occurs is to a tetragonal configuration along any one of the three cube axes. The defect is then tetragonal and shows the same anelastic relaxation (i.e., of the $S_{11} - S_{12}$ compliance) as do all tetragonal defects.

Examples of acoustic effects observed in the 1 MHz range and attributed to Jahn–Teller defects have been reported by Gyorgy et al. (1965) for Ni^{3+} and Mn^{3+} ions in garnet crystals and in Al_2O_3. (Additional references to earlier publications are given in this paper.) Both of these ions enter octahedral sites in the crystal. The Ni^{3+} has seven d electrons and is believed to be in a strong-field state $(t_{2g})^6(e_g)$ while the Mn^{3+} with four electrons is in the weak-field state $(t_{2g})^3(e_g)$, so that each has a single electron occupying the degenerate e_g orbital pair.[†] Both ions should then constitute Jahn–Teller defects. Gyorgy et al.

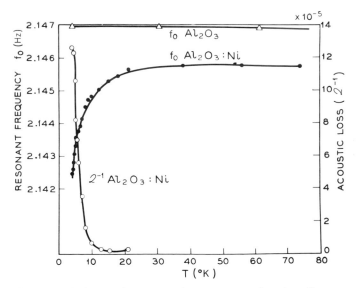

FIG. 11-3.   Acoustic loss and resonant frequency as a function of temperature for Al_2O_3 undoped and containing 0.004% Ni^{3+}. (From Gyorgy et al., 1965.)

[†] The crystal Al_2O_3 is actually trigonal but may be regarded as a trigonally distorted cubic crystal with the three cube axes remaining equivalent after the distortion. Such a trigonal distortion affects only the t_{2g} and not the e_g orbitals.

observe a large acoustic loss and a reduction in sound velocity at low temperatures for these ions, as shown, e.g., in Fig. 11-3 for the case of Ni^{3+} in Al_2O_3. Doping with Cr^{3+}, Co^{3+} or Fe^{3+}, each of which is expected to show no Jahn–Teller effect in the ground state, gives no unusual acoustic loss or modulus defect.

The clearest demonstration that the effect is indeed a relaxation phenomenon was obtained by the same group of authors (Sturge *et al.*, 1967) making observations on Ni^{3+} doped Al_2O_3 at considerably higher frequencies (~ 260 MHz). At these frequencies, the data for internal friction (attenuation) versus T pass through a maximum near 14°K. From such data results are obtained for the relaxation time as a function of temperature as shown in Fig. 11-4. At the higher temperatures τ obeys the Arrhenius equation with $\tau_0 = 5 \times 10^{-14}$ and $Q = 0.011$ eV. At low temperatures, however, there is a strong departure from the Arrhenius plot where τ^{-1} varies approximately linearly with temperature.

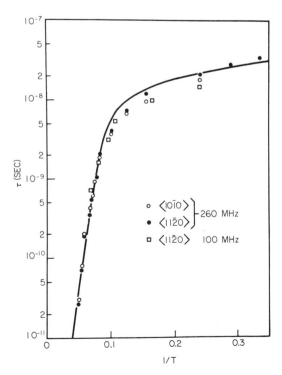

FIG. 11-4. Dependence of relaxation time τ on T^{-1} for Ni^{3+} doped Al_2O_3, deduced from attenuation of longitudinal waves at 260 and 100 MHz in various crystallographic directions. (From Sturge *et al.*, 1967.)

This low temperature behavior, which is of the form predicted for phonon assisted tunneling, is the reason that an internal friction peak (versus $1/T$) could not be obtained at the lower frequencies (as in Fig. 11-3). The relaxation time is interpreted as the time for the Jahn–Teller distorted defect to relax among the various possible directions of the distortion. It is not surprising that, for such a small energy barrier, quantum-mechanical tunneling should be rate determining at the lowest temperatures.

11.2   Interstitials

This heading includes the case of the Snoek relaxation, which was covered in Chapter 9. Of the two new examples considered below, one is again concerned with an interstitial impurity, while the other deals with self-interstitials. Apart from the Snoek relaxation, the case of oxygen in silicon appears to be the only other known example in which relaxation is produced by an interstitial impurity occupying a lower symmetry site. It is however interesting to note that calculations by Weiser (1962) suggest that certain fast-diffusing interstitial elements (lithium and copper) may also occupy lower symmetry (hexagonally coordinated) sites in silicon. However, for Li^+ in silicon, the experimental evidence of Berry (1970) strongly indicates that isolated Li^+ ions must in fact occupy the tetrahedral interstitial sites of cubic symmetry, where they are not susceptible to stress-induced ordering.

In spite of the sparcity of known examples of interstitial relaxations, this category is potentially a very important one, since many crystal structures do offer interstitial sites of relatively low symmetry. It can therefore be expected that as future work extends to a wider range of crystals, more examples of relaxation due to isolated interstitial impurities will be found.

A.   INTERSTITIAL OXYGEN IN SILICON

Silicon crystals which have been pulled from silica crucibles contain oxygen as an impurity at concentration levels of up to about 10^{-5} mole fraction (5×10^{17} atoms cm^{-3}). Southgate (1957, 1960) has observed that such samples exhibit an internal friction peak which can be explained in terms of the stress-induced ordering of the oxygen atoms among a set of interstitial sites. The peak occurs at a high temperature ($\sim$1000°C for a frequency of 100 kHz) and is located above another peak of electronic origin (discussed in Chapter 19). Though the relaxation strength is quite small ($\Delta_{E\langle 111\rangle} \simeq 10^{-4}$), the remarkably low background damping exhibited in this elevated temperature range permits excellent resolution of the peak. From the shift of the peak with vibration frequency, the activation energy Q and frequency factor τ_0^{-1} were found to be 2.5 eV and 5×10^{13} sec^{-1}, respectively. With these values, the peak shape is very well fitted by the Debye equation, indicating the existence of a single relaxation time.

As would be expected if oxygen were the cause of the relaxation, the peak is virtually eliminated in samples of substantially lower oxygen content prepared by the floating zone technique. Further, in contrast to the crucible grown samples of $\langle 111\rangle$ orientation, no peak was detected in similar samples of $\langle 100\rangle$ orientation. This observation implies that the defect responsible for the relaxation is of trigonal symmetry. At first sight, this may appear to conflict with the configuration of the interstitial oxygen atoms as deduced from infrared absorption studies (Kaiser *et al.*, 1956; Hrostowski and Kaiser, 1957). These studies indicate that the oxygen bonds preferentially with two silicon atoms to form a non-collinear Si–O–Si configuration with a bond angle of about 100°, as shown in Fig. 11-5a. The symmetry of such oxygen sites is much lower than trigonal (it is in fact monoclinic). However, without breaking either nearest-neighbor bond, the oxygen atom has access to a set of six equivalent sites, located in circular arrangement around the $\langle 111\rangle$ axis (Fig.

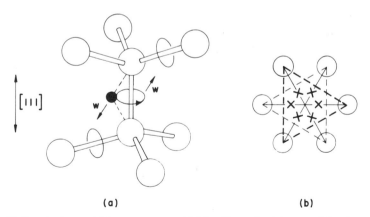

(a)   (b)

FIG. 11-5. An interstitial oxygen atom (●) in silicon. In (a), two of the six possible translational jumps (of frequency w) are indicated by arrows: these produce the same reorientation of the elastic dipole. The circular motion of the oxygen atom involves hopping between a ring of six sites shown by the crosses in (b), which represents a view along the [111] direction.

11-5b). Since the energy barrier between these sites will be very small compared with that for a translational jump which involves breaking one of the nearest-neighbor bonds, it follows that before reaching temperatures high enough to permit rapid translational jumps, an oxygen atom will already be in rapid motion by hopping among the ring of six sites. Accordingly, this is an example of a frozen-free split as described in Section 8.9. As both Haas (1960) and Nowick and Heller (1963) have pointed out, the hopping motion has the effect of raising the effective symmetry of the defect to trigonal, the symmetry consistent with Southgate's observations. From Eq. (8.4-4), the relaxation strength $\Delta_{E\langle 111\rangle}$ for trigonal defects in a cubic crystal is

$$\Delta_{E\langle 111\rangle} = (4C_0 v_0 E_{\langle 111\rangle}/27kT)(\lambda_1 - \lambda_2)^2 \qquad (11.2\text{-}1)$$

Based on the information that 2×10^{17} atoms cm^{-3} of oxygen produce a $\Delta_{E\langle 111\rangle}$ of 0.96×10^{-4}, Eq. (11.2-1) gives 0.77 for the absolute value of the dipole shape factor, $|\lambda_1 - \lambda_2|$. This is in good agreement with the separate estimate of $\lambda_1 - \lambda_2 = 0.71$, obtained from the experiments of Corbett and Watkins (1961) on the polarization of the 9 μ infrared absorption band due to stress-induced ordering of oxygen at 400°C. The dipole shape factor is thus quite large, and comparable to the magnitude of the values associated with interstitial impurities in bcc metals. The positive sign of $\lambda_1 - \lambda_2$, as given by the work of Corbett and Watkins, shows that the dominant distortion around the defect corresponds to the pushing apart along the $\langle 111\rangle$ direction of the two silicon neighbors which form the Si–O–Si bridge.

With the model given above, the activation energy for the relaxation corresponds to that for the migrational jump shown in Fig. 11-5. To obtain the rate of relaxation τ^{-1} in terms of the rate w for a specific nearest-neighbor jump, we start from the relationship [Eq. (8.9-18)], appropriate to the trigonal dipole in a cubic crystal

$$\tau^{-1} = 4v_{12} \qquad (11.2\text{-}2)$$

where v_{12} is the rate at which a defect in a specified site of orientation 1 (e.g., along [111]) can reorient to any site of orientation 2 (e.g., along [$\bar{1}$11]). In taking the defect symmetry as trigonal, we have ignored the complications which arise if the defect symmetry is taken to be monoclinic and full consideration is given to the frozen-free split associated with both the jumping and hopping motions of the defect. Thus, while Eq. (11.2-2) is appropriate to the high-temperature relaxation observed by Southgate, it is also possible that this defect may exhibit a low-temperature relaxation governed by the rate of hopping (Nowick, 1967). As is evident from Fig. 11-5, a change from orientation 1 to 2 can be accomplished by either one of two nearest-neighbor migrational jumps (of rate w), so that

$$\tau^{-1} = 8w \tag{11.2-3}$$

It is also of interest to relate τ^{-1} to the diffusion coefficient D. Using the relationship (Haas, 1960) (see Section 7.5B)

$$D = a^2 w/8 \tag{11.2-4}$$

we obtain

$$D = a^2 \tau^{-1}/64 \tag{11.2-5}$$

Though the evidence is less certain, it is possible that a small peak detected in germanium by Southgate (1958) may also be produced by interstitial oxygen via the mechanism described above.

B. Self-Interstitials in Metals

The stable configuration of the self-interstitial defect in metals, and particularly in copper (fcc structure), has been the subject of several theoretical investigations. Huntington and Seitz (1942) and Huntington (1953) were the first to calculate that for copper the two alternative configurations shown in Fig. 7-2 were of roughly equal energy. In Fig. 7-2a, the interstitial defect is shown as an extra atom occupying the body-centered cubic position in the fcc structure. This is the configuration that suggests itself from size considerations based on simple inspection of the geometry of a hard ball model. The alternative arrangement shown in Fig. 7-2b is known as the ⟨100⟩ split or dumbbell interstitial configuration. It consists of a pair of atoms centered about an empty lattice site, with the pair axis along a ⟨100⟩ direction. Using variously constructed potentials and different approximations, several calculations have since been performed to establish which configuration is the more stable (Gibson et al., 1960; Seeger et al., 1962; Johnson and Brown, 1962; Johnson 1969). The overall result is that the split configuration appears to be the stable one, but since the energy difference between this and the body-centered configuration is small, it may be unwise to assert that theory has established the stability of the split configuration beyond reasonable doubt, or that the split configuration is necessarily common to all fcc metals.

Inspection of Fig. 7-2 shows that whereas the body-centered self-interstitial constitutes a defect of cubic symmetry which is therefore incapable of stress induced ordering under shear, the split interstitial is of tetragonal symmetry and is therefore capable of producing relaxation of the $S_{11} - S_{12}$ compliance. The two factors which principally determine whether the relaxation will be of perceptible strength are C_0 (the concentration of defects) and the shape factor $\lambda_1 - \lambda_2$. Two theoretical estimates of $\lambda_1 - \lambda_2$ for the split interstitial in copper have been given by Huntington and Johnson (1962) and Seeger *et al.* (1962). Nowick and Heller (1963) have discussed the procedure and results of these calculations. From Huntington and Johnson's calculation, Nowick and Heller estimate $\lambda_1 - \lambda_2 = -0.025$ and emphasize the extreme sensitivity of the result to a parameter appearing in the exponential atomic repulsion potential. The result obtained by Seeger *et al.* is almost an order of magnitude larger, $\lambda_1 - \lambda_2 = -0.21$, and is much less sensitive to the parameter mentioned above. Substitution of the numerical values show that experimental observation of the relaxation can be expected for a reasonable concentration of defects ($C_0 \sim 10^{-5}$) only if $\lambda_1 - \lambda_2$ has a value as high as that calculated by Seeger *et al.*

Apart from establishing the anisotropy of the relaxation strength, the tetragonal symmetry of the $\langle 100 \rangle$ split interstitial is also important in considering the kinetics of the relaxation. For this defect symmetry in a cubic crystal, the rate of relaxation is given by Eq. (8.9-17) as $\tau^{-1} = 3\nu_{12}$ where ν_{12} is the total rate at which a defect in a chosen orientation 1 (e.g., parallel to the x axis in Fig. 11-6) can reorient to orientation 2 (e.g., along the y axis). Figure 11-6 shows the two types of jump which produce reorientation of the $\langle 100 \rangle$ split interstitial. One of these is a

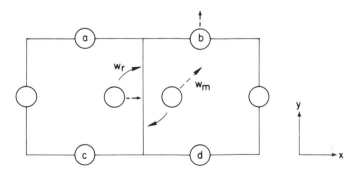

FIG. 11-6.   The dumbbell interstitial defect in the fcc structure, as seen in the (100) plane at $z = \frac{1}{2}$. The solid circular arrows indicate a rotational jump of frequency w_r; the broken straight arrows indicate a migrational jump of frequency w_m.

rotational jump (through 90°), which does not shift the site of the defect and therefore cannot produce translation of the defect. If the rate of a specific rotational jump is w_r, the rotational contribution to ν_{12} is $2w_r$, since the rotation can proceed in either a clockwise or counterclockwise manner. The second type of motion, indicated by the dotted lines in Fig. 11-6, is the translation of the defect by the movement of one atom into the vacant site between the pair, while the other displaces a neighboring atom from a lattice point to form the new member of the split configuration. If the rate of such a migration jump is w_m, then the contribution to ν_{12} is $4w_m$, since (with reference to Fig. 11-6) reorientation from the x to the y axis can occur by the left hand atom of the pair displacing either atom a or c, or the right hand atom displacing either atom b or d. The total rate of relaxation thus becomes

$$\tau^{-1} = 6w_r + 12w_m \tag{11.2-6}$$

Assuming that the preexponential frequency factors are not greatly different, it follows from Eq. (11.2-6) that relaxation will occur mainly by rotational jumps if Q_r, the activation energy for rotation, is less than the activation energy for migration Q_m.

From an experimental viewpoint, a search for a relaxation due to split-interstitials requires attention to a number of factors. Due to their high energy of formation (e.g., >3 eV in copper), an appreciable concentration of defects can be produced only by cold-working or by irradiation. Since the defects tend to anneal out (either at dislocations or by re-combination with vacancies) with an activation energy which cannot be greater than Q_m, it follows that the experiments must be performed rapidly and over as low a range of temperature as possible (see Problem 11-1). For this reason, extensive use has been made of low-frequency torsion pendulum apparatus. It should be noted that the ability to observe the peak before it anneals away will be aided if Q_r happens to be less than Q_m. Information on the magnitude of these quantities comes mainly from theoretical calculations and from the interpretation of annealing experiments following radiation damage. According to some calculations (e.g., Johnson and Brown, 1962), Q_m for the split interstitial in copper is only 0.1 eV, which would imply that the appropriate range to search for the peak would be between the temperatures of liquid helium and liquid nitrogen. On the other hand, the calculations of Seeger et al. (1962) favor much higher rotation and migration energies, such that for copper the peak should appear somewhat below (and for nickel somewhat above) room temperature. These larger values ($Q_m = 0.7$ eV for Cu and 1 eV for Ni) are consistent with the school of opinion which assigns Stage III of radiation damage annealing experiments to the migration of interstitials, a view which has recently been strengthened by the dislocation pinning experiments of Thompson *et al.* (1967) and Thompson and Buck (1967).

The first experimental work based on the realization that anelastic measurements may provide evidence for split-interstitials was carried out by Seeger *et al.* (1960). These workers studied both cold-worked and neutron irradiated nickel of 99.9% purity using both internal friction and magnetic disaccommodation measurements. [†] The magnetic measurements revealed the existence of a process governed by an activation energy of about 0.8 eV, and whose relaxation time was about 100 sec at room temperature. The 1-Hz internal friction behavior, observed on heating above room temperature revealed two small maxima ($\delta_{max} \sim 1 \times 10^{-3}$) near 70 and 110°C, superimposed on a rather large background (see Schiller *et al.*, 1962). Later experiments by Turner and de Batist (1964) gave evidence for a similar double maximum in the heating curve of deformed 99.88% Ni, whereas for 99.999% Ni only the higher temperature maximum was thought to be present. The interpretation of such maxima requires considerable caution. It is not possible to conclude immediately that they represent internal friction peaks, for a maximum may also result from the onset of an annealing process leading to recovery of the background internal friction. To substantiate that a maximum seen on heating represents a true internal friction peak rather than an annealing maximum, it is also necessary to carry out measurements during cooling. Although Berry (1962) failed to find evidence of a peak on cooling, Wagner *et al.* (1964), using specimens of 99.999% purity and smaller deformations (15% elongation in tension), were able to obtain curves which gave a definite indication of a small peak at 70°C for a frequency of 1 Hz. Consequently, this lower (70°C) maximum must be attributed to a true relaxation effect. [‡] Their results, when combined with a new set of magnetic measurements on electron irradiated samples, yielded an activation energy of 0.84 eV and $\tau_0^{-1} = 5 \times 10^{12}$ sec^{-1}. As this energy is significantly smaller than the value of 1.05 eV assigned to the

[†] Magnetic disaccommodation refers to a decrease of initial permeability with time, resulting from the stabilization of the position of domain walls due to directional ordering of point defects (see Section 18.5).

[‡] Seeger and Wagner (1965) later reported that the higher temperature maximum seen in the heating curves is an annealing effect and not a true relaxation peak.

migration of interstitial atoms, it was inferred that the kinetics of the relaxation were governed by rotational rather than migrational jumps.

Following this work, Seeger and Wagner (1965) performed torsion pendulum measurements on $\langle 100 \rangle$ and $\langle 111 \rangle$ oriented single crystal wires to determine the anisotropy of the relaxation. Owing to the tetragonal symmetry of the $\langle 100 \rangle$ split interstitial, it would be predicted that the maximum relaxation should be seen for the $\langle 111 \rangle$ orientation, whereas $\Delta_{G\langle 100 \rangle}$ should be strictly zero. Their results, shown in Figs. 11-7 and

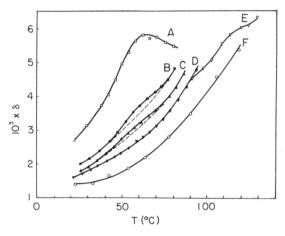

FIG. 11-7. Internal friction of a $\langle 100 \rangle$-oriented single crystal nickel wire, tested in torsion at 0.53 Hz after the following cumulative treatments: (A) 15% elongation at 20°C, (B) $\frac{1}{2}$ hr at 80°C, (C) $\frac{1}{2}$ hr at 85°C, (D) $\frac{1}{2}$ hr at 95°C, (E) extension of curve D to higher temperatures, (F) 10 min at 127°C. (From Seeger and Wagner, 1965.)

11-8, reveal that there is in fact considerable similarity between the $\langle 100 \rangle$ and $\langle 111 \rangle$ samples. On first heating, both samples exhibit a relatively large maximum, which is much reduced in the second heating curve and which then declines more slowly on further aging. Seeger and Wagner have suggested that the initial large maximum, which is believed to be too large to be accounted for by simple interstitial reorientation, arises from a dislocation–interstitial interaction (see Schiller, 1964). The strong reduction in damping after the first heating excursion is attributed to the onset of dislocation pinning via the migration of interstitial atoms to dislocations. The anisotropy of the relaxation arising from any residual isolated interstitials will then be revealed only after sufficient pinning has taken place to completely suppress the dislocation contribution. Seeger and Wagner point out that while the peak has disappeared in the

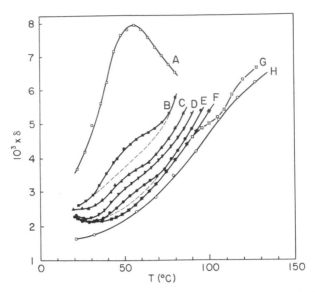

FIG. 11-8.   Internal friction of a ⟨111⟩ oriented single crystal nickel wire, tested in torsion at 0.3 Hz after the following cumulative heat treatments: (A) 13% elongation at 20°C, (B) ½ hr at 80°C, (C) ½ hr at 85°C, (D) ½ hr at 90°C, (E) ½ hr at 95°C, (F) ½ hr at 100°C, (G) upward excursion from 90°C, (H) 10 min at 120°C. (From Seeger and Wagner, 1965.)

⟨100⟩ sample after 30 min at 90°C, a small residual peak still persists in the ⟨111⟩ sample both after this treatment and the following one at 95°C (cf Figs. 11-7 and 11-8). On this basis, it is claimed that the measurements reveal the tetragonal symmetry to be expected from the ⟨100⟩ split interstitial. It seems, however, that this evidence hardly offers a conclusive proof, since it must be borne in mind that the kinetics of annealing are being compared on samples which have been deformed in very different orientations, so that they cannot be regarded as identically prepared samples. It would seem that a more conclusive result could be obtained from a comparison of single crystals which have been irradiated, rather than cold-worked, so as to eliminate dislocation effects.

To summarize the work on nickel, it can be said that a good deal of evidence can be fitted together to support the claim that the anelastic and magnetic effects discussed above are connected with the presence of interstitial defects. However, it has not yet been experimentally demonstrated beyond reasonable doubt that the isolated defects (free of interaction with dislocations) have either been detected anelastically, or that they possess the tetragonal symmetry required of the ⟨100⟩ split configuration. Turning to other materials, Völkl and Schilling (1963) and Walz (1964) have studied a peak in deformed copper which possesses an activation energy of ~0.7 eV and which may therefore be controlled by the migration of interstitials. As discussed in Section 13.3, however, the experimental evidence again suggests that the mechanism involved here is predominantly if not exclusively connected with an interstitial–dislocation interaction.

The possibility of split-interstitial configurations is not limited to fcc metals. In bcc iron, for example, Vineyard (1963) has calculated that the stable interstitial has the split configuration shown in Fig. 11-9. The

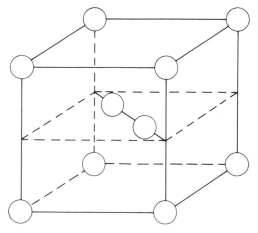

FIG. 11-9. A possible configuration for the self-interstitial defect in a bcc metal.

symmetry of this defect is $\langle 110 \rangle$ orthorhombic, and therefore the defect is in principle detectable by internal friction measurements. Hivert *et al.* (1970) have observed a peak near 126°K for a frequency of ~0.5 Hz in both electron and neutron irradiated iron, which may be due to this defect. The activation energy of the relaxation (0.25 eV) is the same as that with which the peak anneals away, indicating that the condition $Q_r \geq Q_m$ applies in this case.

C. INTERSTITIALS AND THE GORSKY RELAXATION

One of the earliest contributions to the theory of anelastic relaxation processes concerned the long-range diffusion of point defects in a sample subject to an inhomogeneous dilatational stress. This model was proposed and worked out in detail by Gorsky (1935), for the case of a beam specimen subject to bending. Such a deformation produces a uniaxial strain (with an associated dilatational component) which varies linearly across the depth of the specimen. If the specimen contains defects whose introduction produced dilatation, bending will induce a spatial gradient in the chemical potential of the defects. Relaxation will then occur by long-range diffusion, so as to establish a concentration gradient in the direction of the stress gradient. It is noteworthy that, in contrast to examples of defect *reorientation* (which involve the ellipticity or shape factor of the defect), the Gorsky relaxation involves the *migration* of defects and has a relaxation strength which depends on the size factor of the defect.

The mathematical treatment of the Gorsky relaxation is in many ways similar to the more familiar theory of thermoelastic relaxation in flexed bars (see Sections 17.2 and 17.3). For example, the relaxation time τ for a specimen of rectangular section is given by Eq. (17.4-9):

$$\tau = d^2/\pi^2 D \tag{11.2-7}$$

where d is the thickness of the specimen and D is now the diffusion coefficient of the defect involved. It can be understood from Eq. (11.2-7) why extensive use has not been made of the Gorsky relaxation. At reasonable temperatures, the relaxation time even for a rather thin sample is usually impractically long, particularly where the motion of substitutional atoms is considered. Consequently, rapidly moving interstitial defects provide the best opportunity for observing the relaxation. Schaumann *et al.* (1968) have observed the Gorsky relaxation due to interstitial hydrogen (and deuterium) in niobium, utilizing elastic aftereffect measurements on coiled wire samples. The extremely rapid diffusion rate of hydrogen at room temperature can be appreciate from the fact that the relaxation time was only 160 sec for a sample of 1.25-mm diameter! For hydrogen, measurements made over a range of temperature gave $D_0 = 5.4 \times 10^{-4}$ cm^2 sec^{-1} and $Q = 0.110 \pm 0.005$ eV. For deuterium, D_0 was the same within experimental error, but Q was appreciably higher, 0.135 ± 0.005 eV. A discussion of the significance of this isotope effect on the activation energy is included in the paper.

An estimate of the size factor for hydrogen (and deuterium) in niobium can be made from the reported value of the relaxation strength, which was given as 0.016 per atomic percent solute. For a dilute interstitial solid solution, the relaxation strength can be written (Gorsky, 1935; Zener, 1948)

$$\Delta_E = (C_0 v_0 E/9kT\beta)(\text{tr } \boldsymbol{\lambda})^2 \tag{11.2-8}$$

where $(\mathrm{tr}\,\boldsymbol{\lambda})/3$ represents the size factor [Eq. (8.7-1)], and β is the number of interstitial sites per host atom in the lattice. From Eq. (11.2-8), we find that $(\mathrm{tr}\,\boldsymbol{\lambda})/3$ is about 0.1, a result which is surprisingly large when compared to the values 0.2–0.3 estimated for the larger interstitials C and N in Fe (cf. Table 9-1). At high concentrations, the relaxation strength takes the form

$$\Delta_E \propto 1/(T - T_\mathrm{s}) \qquad (11.2\text{-}9)$$

where T_s is a temperature which is closely related to the critical temperature for the condensation of the hydrogen "lattice gas" (Alefeld et al., 1970). A plot of $1/\Delta_E$ versus T then gives T_s from which information on this phase transformation is obtained. For example, for 40 at. % H in Nb, Alefeld et al. obtain $T_\mathrm{s} = 144°\mathrm{C}$.

Recently, the Gorsky relaxation has also been observed in vanadium doped with either hydrogen or deuterium (Cantelli et al., 1970; Völkl et al., 1970). Again the activation energy for deuterium is observed to be significantly higher than that for hydrogen (0.073 versus 0.059 eV according to Cantelli et al.; 0.080 versus 0.050 eV according to Völkl et al.).

11.3 Defect Pairs Containing a Vacancy

A. VACANCY–INTERSTITIAL (V–I) PAIRS

At first sight, the existence of a defect consisting of a vacancy paired to a self-interstitial may seem surprising, since annihilation of the defect could occur by the coalescence of the two parts. However, there is good evidence that such "close pairs" are a feature of low temperature radiation damage (see Section 7.6). The pairs are highly unstable, and their self-annihilation appears to be one of the earliest steps in the recovery process, taking place in the first annealing region (Stage I). The detection of an internal friction peak due to the stress-induced ordering of these defects therefore requires facilities for irradiation and measurement at very low temperatures. This mechanism is thought to provide the explanation of the peak observed near $10°\mathrm{K}$ in proton irradiated copper by Nielsen and Townsend (1968). Di Carlo et al. (1969) claim to have observed a similar peak near $30°\mathrm{K}$ in electron irradiated tungsten, but the evidence seems less conclusive. The peak in copper was observed following irradiation with 9 MeV protons at temperatures below $15°\mathrm{K}$. The measurements were performed in flexural vibration at frequencies between 0.6 and 8 kHz. The peak is small but well resolved, and initially increases linearly with irradiation dose. In a $\langle 111 \rangle$ oriented single crystal, a peak height of 5×10^{-4} (log decrement) is obtained for an irradiation dose of 2×10^{16} protons cm^{-2}. The concentration of pairs producing this peak height was not estimated, but may well be quite small on account of the unusually low peak temperature and the fact that $\delta J \propto T^{-1}$. The activation energy of the peak is 0.015 ± 0.002 eV, and the frequency factor τ_0^{-1} is $8 \times 10^{11 \pm 1}$ sec^{-1}. The width of the peak (about $2°K!$) is broader by about 30% than that calculated from the Debye formula. The peak is stable against annealing up to a temperature of $30°K$, where from other evidence close pair recombination is thought to take place with an activation energy of 0.09 eV. By the use of $\langle 100 \rangle$ and $\langle 111 \rangle$ oriented single crystals, Nielsen and Townsend were able to show that the defect involved was of trigonal symmetry (since no peak was observed in the $\langle 100 \rangle$ specimens). They refrained however from speculating on a specific model for the pair. Nevertheless, it is tempting to remark that the trigonal symmetry is consistent with an interstitial in the body-centered position of the face-centered cube, with the vacancy as a next-nearest neighbor (i.e., on the cube corner).

In addition to i–v defects in which i refers to a self-interstitial, it is also possible to conceive of i–v defects in which i denotes an impurity interstitial. Here again such a configuration is likely to be unstable, collapsing in this case to the substitutional solute atom s. Wagenblast and Swartz (1965) have observed relaxation effects in irradiated Fe–C alloys which may be related to defects of this type.

B. Divacancies (v–v Pairs)

Several unsuccessful attempts have been made to detect an internal friction peak due to the stress-induced ordering of divacancies in fcc metals, particularly gold (Neuman, 1966; Okuda and Hasiguti, 1964). Apart from the obvious difficulty that such a peak is likely to be quite small because of the low defect concentration attainable, the sensitivity of the internal friction behavior to dislocations provides a second factor which complicates the identification of a clear-cut divacancy peak. Recently, however, Franklin and Birnbaum (1971) claim to have observed the divacancy peak in small diameter (0.005 in.) gold wires either gas- or water-quenched from high temperatures. The peak is located at $0°C$ for a frequency of 9 kHz, is governed by an activation energy of 0.65 ± 0.08

eV and a frequency factor τ_0^{-1} of 10^{13} sec^{-1}, and exhibits a width corresponding to a single relaxation time. The peak anneals out slowly near room temperature and more rapidly at $40°$C. During annealing, the peak can first be observed to grow before eventually declining. This behavior can be explained by the partitioning which takes place between the populations of single vacancies and of divacancies. Franklin and Birnbaum find they are able to combine all their observations to form a self-consistent picture in which the divacancy possesses an activation energy of migration equal to that for reorientation (0.65 eV), and has a relatively high binding energy of ≥ 0.35 eV. The single most surprising feature of the relaxation, in terms of the divacancy model, is undoubtedly its relatively large strength (e.g., a logarithmic decrement of 8×10^{-3} for a specimen quenched in water from $1035°$C). Despite arguments to the contrary presented by Franklin and Birnbaum, the observation of a peak of this magnitude does serve to raise the question of whether some form of dislocation enhancement may be involved in the results, e.g., in a similar manner to that proposed by Schoeck to explain the Snoek–Köster relaxation (Section 13.6).

C. The Vacancy–Substitutional Solute (v–s) Pair

Anelasticity which originates in the presence of a v–s pair has been clearly demonstrated in only two cases, both of which involve ionic crystals doped with a cation impurity of a different valence.[†] In these cases, the presence of one vacancy for each impurity ion is required for reasons of charge neutrality or chemical balance, and the close association between the vacancy and the impurity ion arises because of their mutual Coulomb attraction.

The first example is that of ThO_2 doped with CaO, which was first studied by Wachtman (1963). The crystal structure of ThO_2 is the cubic fluorite (CaF_2) structure, part of the unit cell of which is shown in Fig. 11-10. The Ca^{2+} impurity substitutes for the Th^{4+} ion and is electrically and chemically compensated for by a vacancy on an O^{2-} site. Due to a strong Coulomb attraction, it can be expected that at reasonable temperatures the Ca^{2+} ion and the O^{2-} vacancy will be located on adjacent sites. Thus, the vacancy can sit on one of the eight sites shown in Fig. 11-10. The defect so formed is clearly trigonal, and there are four distinct

---

[†] Although the v–s defect is anticipated to be present in a number of metallic systems and anelasticity due to this defect has been sought, a clear demonstration of its presence has not been achieved.

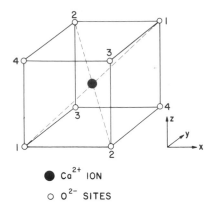

Ca²⁺ ION

○ O²⁻ SITES

Fig. 11-10. Part of the unit cell of the structure of ThO_2, showing the site of a Ca^{2+} impurity ion (●) and the neighboring O^{2-} (○) sites on which a charge-compensating vacancy may reside.

elastic dipole tensors (since two orientations differing by 180° are equivalent in a stress field), as numbered in the figure. By the selection rules (Table 8-5), such a defect is expected to give rise to a relaxation of the shear modulus S_{44}, but not of the modulus $S_{11} - S_{12}$. For single crystals subjected to uniaxial stress, we therefore expect no relaxation for $\langle 100 \rangle$ oriented crystals and a maximum effect for the $\langle 111 \rangle$ orientation (see Section 8.4). The relaxation strength is given by Eq. (8.4-4) in terms of the difference in the two principal values of the λ tensor. Finally, the relaxation time is given by Eq. (8.9-18) as $\tau^{-1} = 4\nu_{12}$, where ν_{12} is the rate of reorientation between orientations 1 and 2. In the present case, it seems reasonable to regard only one ion jump as important, viz., the jump into a vacancy of an O^{2-} ion which is on the one hand nearest to the vacancy, and on the other hand a nearest neighbor to the Ca^{2+} ion. If the rate of such an ion jump between specific sites is denoted by w, it is clear from Fig. 11-10 that $w = \nu_{12}$, so that we obtain for the final result

$$\tau^{-1} = 4w \tag{11.3-1}$$

as the expression for the relaxation rate.

Because of the polarity of the present defect, it is also capable of acting as an electric dipole in the presence of an electric field, i.e., of giving rise to dielectric relaxation. The corresponding relaxation time has been shown (Wachtman, 1963; Nowick, 1967) to be

$$\tau_{\text{diel}}^{-1} = 2w \tag{11.3-2}$$

In a study of polycrystalline ThO_2:CaO, Wachtman has observed both the anelastic and dielectric relaxations, which are located near 240°C for 1400 Hz. Both peaks correspond closely to a simple Debye behavior.

Wachtman measured an activation energy $Q = 0.95$ eV, and $\tau_0 \sim 10^{-13}$ sec. He also showed (for concentrations of CaO up to 1.0 mole %) that the peak height is proportional to the concentration of CaO. The relaxation strength obtained at 1.0 mole % is 4×10^{-4}. Unfortunately, single crystals of this material were not available so that the absence of anelastic relaxation for a $\langle 100 \rangle$ oriented crystal could not be verified. This absence is predicted by the selection rules, and would constitute the strongest verification that the model of Fig. 11-10 is correct. On the other hand, by studying both anelastic and dielectric relaxation, Wachtman was able to check roughly the ratio of τ values predicted by Eqs. (11.3-1) and (11.3-2). More recently, Lay and Whitmore (1971) have carried out the same experiments on the analogous system $CeO_2:CaO$ (also polycrystalline) and verified this 2:1 ratio more precisely. It therefore appears that the model is correct, although a study of single crystals would provide the best check. To obtain a precise value for $|\lambda_1 - \lambda_2|$ using Eq. (8.4-4) also requires single crystal measurements. A completely analogous system is apparently that of CaF_2 (which has the same crystal structure as ThO_2) doped with NaF. Here a F^- vacancy is expected to be present as compensation for each Na^+ ion, to form a s–v pair. The work of Johnson $et\ al.$ (1966) again shows a ratio close to two for τ_{diel}/τ_{anel}. In addition, however, single crystal measurements were reported (Johnson $et\ al.$, 1969) showing that the $S_{11} - S_{12}$ relaxation is absent.

Another material of similar crystal structure to ThO_2 is ZrO_2. Wachtman and Corwin (1965) found an analogous peak to the above in $ZrO_2:CaO$ but also found an additional unsymmetric peak. The doping levels in these samples were quite high (~ 10–20% CaO); thus, it is not surprising that the internal friction behavior is more complex.

The second case for which relaxation due to a v–s defect has been established is that of an alkali halide crystal doped with divalent cation impurities, as e.g., $NaCl:CaCl_2$. In this case, the Ca^{2+} ion substitutes for a Na^+ ion, while charge compensation results in a vacancy on the Na^+ lattice for each Ca^{2+} ion. Again, there is a Coulomb attraction leading to association, since the Ca^{2+} is the center of an excess positive charge, while the Na^+ vacancy is the center of an excess of negative charge. The nearest-neighbor v–s pair constitutes a $\langle 110 \rangle$ orthorhombic defect, for which the strengths are given by Eqs. (8.4-5) and (8.4-6) and the two relaxation times by Eq. (8.9-19). Figure 11-11 shows the possible orientations of this defect, numbered according to the sign convention of Section 8.9 (recognizing that there are only six distinguishable elastic dipoles). If we denote by w_1 the rate of the closest jump which takes

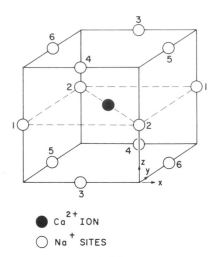

FIG. 11-11.   The NaCl structure, showing the site of a Ca^{2+} ion ($\bullet$) and the twelve nearest-neighbor Na^+ sites ($\bigcirc$) on which a charge-compensating vacancy may reside. The numbering shows the six distinguishable elastic dipoles, according to the convention of Chapter 8 for $\langle 110 \rangle$ orthorhombic defects.

$\bullet$ Ca^{2+} ION

$\bigcirc$ Na^+ SITES

one nearest-neighbor pair into another (as shown in the figure), and regard other jumps as much slower, then clearly $w_1 = v_{13}$ and $v_{12} \approx 0$. Accordingly,

$$\tau^{-1}(S_{11} - S_{12}) = 6w_1$$
$$\tau^{-1}(S_{44}) = 4w_1 \qquad (11.3\text{-}3)$$

This result implies that both $\langle 100 \rangle$ and $\langle 111 \rangle$ oriented samples will show standard-solid behavior under uniaxial stress with a ratio of relaxation times of 2:3.

Dielectric relaxation in crystals like $NaCl:CaCl_2$ has been observed by numerous workers over a period of many years (Dryden and Meakins, 1957). Anelasticity in this crystal was first observed by Dreyfus and Laibowitz (1964). Figure 11-12 taken from their work shows that the predictions based on the simple nearest-neighbor v–s pair are not borne out; rather, a multiple relaxation peak is observed for a $\langle 100 \rangle$ oriented crystal, and a single relaxation for a $\langle 111 \rangle$ oriented crystal. In order to explain this result, it is necessary to introduce the next-nearest as well as the nearest-neighbor v–s pair. That this assumption is not unreasonable is indicated by theoretical calculations which show that the binding energy of this defect in both the nearest and next-nearest positions is not greatly different (both ~ 0.4 eV), while for more separated configurations it is substantially lower. The next-nearest-neighbor pair lies along a $\langle 100 \rangle$ axis and therefore possesses tetragonal symmetry. In thus gives rise only to relaxation of the $S_{11} - S_{12}$ modulus (see Table 8-5). The presence of a single relaxation for the $\langle 111 \rangle$ orientation and a double relaxation for the $\langle 100 \rangle$ is therefore anticipated. Although the *number* of relaxations

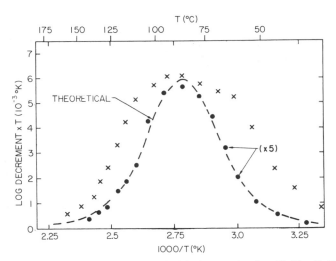

FIG. 11-12. A comparison of internal friction peaks for NaCl: CaCl$_2$ crystals (NaCl : 200 ppm CaCl$_2$) oriented in the $\langle 100 \rangle$ and $\langle 111 \rangle$ directions. $\times$, $\langle 100 \rangle$ at 6.6 kHz; $\bullet$, $\langle 111 \rangle$ at 10 kHz. The curve marked "theoretical" is a single Debye peak for an activation energy of 0.7 eV. Note that the data for the $\langle 111 \rangle$ sample have been multiplied by a factor of five. (From Dreyfus and Laibowitz, 1964.)

from this model can be predicted correctly from the considerations of Chapter 8, the expressions for the relaxation times are more complex, since they now depend on the coupling between the nearest-neighbor (nn) and the next-nearest-neighbor (nnn) pairs, i.e., on jumps which take these two types of pairs into each other. Figure 11-13 shows the

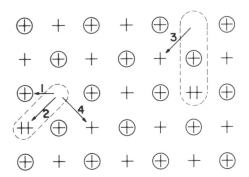

FIG. 11-13. The cation lattice of NaCl showing nearest-neighbor and next-nearest-neighbor vacancy–impurity pairs. Circled positive charges represent Na$^+$ ions lying above and below the plane of the page by one-half of the lattice parameter. The impurity ions (indicated by the double charges) lie in the plane of the uncircled Na$^+$ ions. The rates corresponding to the vacancy jumps 1, 2, 3, and 4 are w_1, w_2, w_3, and w_4, respectively. (From Dreyfus and Laibowitz, 1964.)

possible jumps that have been considered. The rate w_1 is that which has already been defined; w_2 is the rate of interchange of the Ca^{2+} ion with the neighboring vacancy, w_3 is the rate at which a next-nearest-neighbor pair goes into a specific nearest-neighbor pair, while w_4 is the rate of the reverse jump to w_3. The expressions for the relaxation times in terms of these jump frequencies have been worked out by Dreyfus and Laibowitz (1964) and also by Franklin (1963) who used group theoretical methods. The results are

$$\tau^{-1}(S_{11} - S_{12}) = 3w_1 + 2w_3 + w_4 \pm [(3w_1 - 2w_3 + w_4)^2 + 2w_3 w_4]^{1/2} \quad (11.3\text{-}4)$$

$$\tau^{-1}(S_{44}) = 4w_1 + 2w_4 \quad (11.3\text{-}5)$$

which involves two τ values for the $S_{11} - S_{12}$ shear and one for the S_{44}, as already anticipated. It is important to note that the rate w_2, which corresponds to a jump that produces 180° reorientation of the pair, does not enter into any expression for an anelastic relaxation time, since the stress tensor is unable to distinguish orientations which differ by 180°. (The quantity w_2 does, however, enter into the expressions for the dielectric relaxation time.) Finally, since a reaction between nearest- and next-nearest-neighbor pairs is now considered, a hydrostatic relaxation is also anticipated (see Section 8.10). The corresponding relaxation time is given by

$$\tau^{-1}(S_{11} + 2S_{12}) = 4w_3 + 2w_4 \quad (11.3\text{-}6)$$

As already mentioned, the results of Dreyfus and Laibowitz, as e.g., in Fig. 11-12, show a single relaxation for the $\langle 111 \rangle$ orientation and a multiple relaxation for $\langle 100 \rangle$. Analysis of the $\langle 100 \rangle$ data shows that they correspond, in fact, to three (rather than two) Debye peaks, as illustrated in Fig. 11-14. This resolution is obtained by assuming the same activation energy (0.70 eV) for all components of the peak, based on the observation that, upon changing the frequency, the peak shifts without distortion (see Section 4.9). Subpeaks A and B of Fig. 11-14 were associated respectively with the plus and minus signs in Eq. (11.3-4). Peak C, however, was not identified and was therefore attributed to higher-order complexes. (It was not possible to obtain a self-consistent assignment of the subpeaks which includes the hydrostatic relaxation, Eq. (11.3-6), as one of them, and it therefore appears that the hydrostatic relaxation is too weak to be detected.) As a consistency check, the position of the dielectric relaxation could be predicted quite precisely from the anelastic measurements, indicating that the assignments were made correctly. Since there are three peaks (subpeaks A and B for the $\langle 100 \rangle$ orientation and the one peak for the $\langle 111 \rangle$ orientation) and three unknowns (w_1, w_3, and w_4), it is possible to obtain numerical values for these three jump rates. The result is that $w_3 > w_4 > w_1$. This rather surprising result

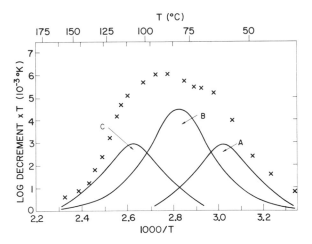

FIG. 11-14. The decomposition of the experimental results for the $\langle 100 \rangle$ sample of Fig. 11-12 into three Debye peaks, based upon the assumption that the component peaks have half-widths given by an activation energy of 0.7 eV. (From Dreyfus and Laibowitz, 1964.)

means that reorientation among nearest-neighbor sites can be accomplished more rapidly when the defect passes through the next-nearest-neighbor configuration, than directly, via the jump of type 1.

Dreyfus and Laibowitz also found similar results for NaCl doped with $MnCl_2$, $MgCl_2$, and $SrCl_2$. A detailed study, however, was only made for the cases of $MnCl_2$ and $CaCl_2$ as dopants.

11.4 Interstitial Impurity (i–i) Pairs and Higher Clusters

A number of relaxation studies have given evidence that interstitially dissolved impurities interact with one another to form other species of defects consisting of pairs of interstitial atoms and higher-order clusters. The most detailed work has been done on the bcc transitional metals, but work on C in both Ni and Co indicate that similar interactions are detectable in fcc interstitial alloys.

A. Relaxations in Body-Centered Cubic Metals

In bcc metals, the dominant relaxation produced by interstitial impurities is the Snoek relaxation (Chapter 9), arising from the stress-induced ordering of individual solute atoms. The first systematic experiments revealing that the Snoek relaxation can be accompanied by satellite relaxations were carried out by Powers (1955) and Powers and Doyle (1956) on Ta alloys containing O and/or N. Figure 11-15 shows a set of their data obtained from Ta–O alloys containing 0.1–1.8 at. % O. As the total oxygen concentration is increased, the measured peak becomes both larger and broader, in a manner indicating the appearance of a rapidly developing satellite peak located above but overlapping the Snoek peak. Up to about 1 at. % oxygen, the observed behavior could be accounted for by the introduction of just one extra peak, located about

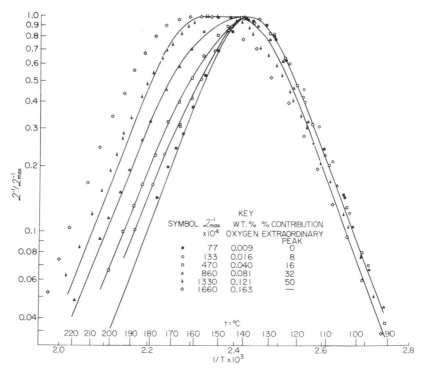

FIG. 11-15. Normalized internal friction peaks in tantalum containing various amounts of oxygen, measured in torsion at 0.6 Hz. The data are fitted by curves formed by the superposition of a second or extraordinary peak on the Snoek peak, with a separation of about 25°C. It can be seen from the key that the relative contribution of the second peak rises rapidly with oxygen content. (From Powers, 1955.)

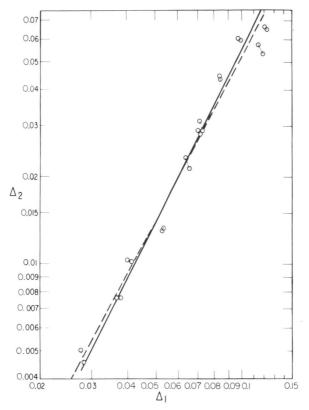

FIG. 11-16.   Log–log plot of data on Ta-O alloys, showing that the strength of the second peak varies as the square of the strength of the Snoek peak. [Least squared slope, 1.89 (– – –); slope of 2 (———).] (From Powers and Doyle, 1959b.)

20°C above the Snoek peak and characterized by a single and concentration-independent relaxation time. (At higher concentrations, an analysis in terms of just two peaks becomes insufficient.) A most significant characteristic of this extra peak is the manner in which its height varies in relation to the height of the Snoek peak as the total oxygen content of the sample is varied. Figure 11-16, taken from a later more extensive study (Powers and Doyle, 1959b) employing elastic aftereffect measurements, shows quite clearly that the relaxation strength Δ_2 of the second peak varies as the square of the strength Δ_1 of the Snoek relaxation. This strongly suggests that the defect responsible for the second peak is a bound interacting pair of interstitial atoms, formed by a reaction of the type

$$i + i \rightleftharpoons ii \qquad\qquad (11.4\text{-}1)$$

where i denotes an isolated or single interstitial atom in the solid solution and ii represents an interstitial pair. Denoting the concentrations of singles and pairs by C_1 and C_2, respectively,[†] the mass-action relation governing Eq. (11.4-1) is analogous to Eq. (7.2-5) for vacancy pairs and has the form

$$C_2/C_1{}^2 = K_2(T) \qquad (11.4\text{-}2)$$

where $K_2(T)$ is the equilibrium constant at the temperature T. If the relaxation strengths Δ_1 and Δ_2 are proportional to the respective concentrations C_1 and C_2, this hypothesis immediately explains the quadratic dependence of Δ_2 on Δ_1, as shown in Fig. 11-16. Powers and Doyle were also able to show that the temperature dependence of the peak heights obeyed the behavior to be expected from mass-action considerations. For the case of a dilute solution of interstitial atoms which occupy the octahedral sites of the bcc lattice (where there are three interstitial sites per lattice site), the equilibrium constant $K_n(T)$ for the formation of a cluster of n atoms is given by

$$K_n(T) = C_n/C_1{}^n = (z_n/3^n)\exp(\Delta g_n/kT) \qquad (11.4\text{-}3)$$

where z_n is the number of equivalent distinguishable orientations the cluster can assume, and Δg_n is the free energy change to dissociate a cluster into well-separated single atoms (Gibala and Wert, 1966b). Splitting Δg_n into an enthalpy (binding energy) and a vibrational entropy term, we obtain

$$K_n(T) = C_n/C_1{}^n = A_n\exp(\Delta h_n/kT) \qquad (11.4\text{-}4)$$

where

$$A_n \equiv (z_n/3^n)\exp(-\Delta s_n/k) \qquad (11.4\text{-}5)$$

For the moment, we shall limit our discussion to the formation of pairs, as given by Eq. (11.4-1), for which Eq. (11.4-4) takes the form

$$K_2(T) = C_2/C_1{}^2 = A_2\exp(\Delta h_2/kT) \qquad (11.4\text{-}6)$$

It is evident from Eq. (11.4-6) that if Δh_2 is positive, a decrease in tem-

---

[†] To avoid possible confusion, it should be noted that in Chapter 8, C_0 was used to represent the total concentration of one given species of defect, and the quantities C_1, C_2, ..., C_n represented the concentrations of this defect in each of the n orientations. In the present case, we use C_1, C_2, ..., C_n to represent the total concentration of each separate defect (of 1, 2, ..., n atoms), and denote their sum by C_0.

perature should serve to increase the proportion of pairs to singles, and hence increase the ratio Δ_2/Δ_1. Powers and Doyle confirmed this behavior, and measured the value of Δh_2 in the manner outlined below. To start with, the proportionality between Δ_1 and C_1 may be written

$$\Delta_1 = a_1 C_1 \tag{11.4-7}$$

The proportionality parameter a_1, expressing the relaxation strength per unit defect concentration, has the disadvantage for future purposes of being a temperature dependent quantity, since it contains implicitly the $1/T$ or $1/(T - T_c)$ term common to all stress-induced ordering phenomena (Chapter 8). Since we are dealing with dilute alloys, we shall assume the case of no interaction ($T_c = 0$) and write a_1 in the form

$$a_1 = (b_1/T)(\delta\lambda)_1{}^2 \tag{11.4-8}$$

where b_1 is now a temperature insensitive parameter and $(\delta\lambda)_1$ is the shape factor for the tetragonal dipoles produced by single atoms. It should be noted that a_1 in Eq. (11.4-7) is not only temperature dependent but also crystallographically anisotropic. The anisotropy inherent in a_1 is thus also present in b_1. For pairs, we may write the corresponding equations[†]

$$\Delta_2 = a_2 C_2 \tag{11.4-9}$$

$$a_2 = (b_2/T)(\delta\lambda)_2{}^2 \tag{11.4-10}$$

Here, $(\delta\lambda)_2$ must be regarded as the effective shape factor of the pair which is appropriate to the particular orientation (or averaged orientation) of the specimen, as contained in the parameter b_2. Substitution of Eqs. (11.4-7)–(11.4-10) into Eq. (11.4-2) gives the result

$$\ln\left(\frac{\Delta_2}{T\Delta_1{}^2}\right) = \frac{\Delta h_2}{kT} + \ln\left(\frac{b_2(\delta\lambda)_2{}^2\Delta_2}{b_1{}^2(\delta\lambda)_1{}^4}\right) \tag{11.4-11}$$

Powers and Doyle's data on the temperature dependence of Δ_1 and Δ_2 for two specimens of slightly different oxygen content are shown plotted in Fig. 11-17 according to Eq. (11.4-11). The slopes of these lines yield the binding energy Δh_2 of a pair as 0.1 eV. It is interesting that this value corresponds quite closely to the difference in the activation energies for

[†] In the past, it has been customary to write Eq. (11.4-9) in the form $\Delta_2 = 2a_2 C_2$, so that a_2 becomes a measure of the relaxation strength per constituent atom of the pair. This practice is not followed here since we shall be more interested in comparisons made on a per defect basis.

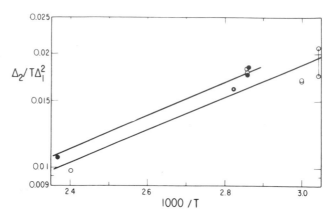

FIG. 11-17.   Data for two Ta–O alloys [(○) Ta–0.44 at. % O, (●) Ta–0.56 at % O] plotted according to Eq. (11.4-10). The slopes of the lines yield a value of 0.1 eV for the binding enthalpy Δh_2 of oxygen atom pairs. (From Powers and Doyle, 1959b.)

the orientation of pairs and singles, suggesting that the reorientation of a pair may require a sequence of jumps involving the break-up and re-formation of the pair.

Measurements of the parameters a_1 and a_2 are of interest for two reasons. First, they may be used to calculate the equilibrium constant $K_2(T)$ from the relation

$$K_2(T) = (a_1{}^2/a_2)(\Delta_2/\Delta_1{}^2) \qquad (11.4\text{-}12)$$

which is obtained by combining Eqs. (11.4-2), (11.4-7), and (11.4-9). Second, the ratio a_1/a_2 may be used to make an estimate of $(\delta\lambda)_1/(\delta\lambda)_2$. To determine a_1 and a_2, Powers and Doyle introduced various total levels of oxygen C_0 into a sample, and determined both the total relaxation strength Δ_0 and the relaxation strength Δ_2 of the contribution due to pairs. Since

$$C_0 = C_1 + 2C_2 \qquad (11.4\text{-}13)$$

and

$$\Delta_0 = \Delta_1 + \Delta_2 \qquad (11.4\text{-}14)$$

we obtain, by making use of Eqs. (11.4-7) and (11.4-9),

$$\frac{C_0}{\Delta_0} = \frac{1}{a_1} + \frac{\Delta_2}{\Delta_0}\left(\frac{2}{a_2} - \frac{1}{a_1}\right) \qquad (11.4\text{-}15)$$

Thus, by plotting C_0/Δ_0 against Δ_2/Δ_0, as shown in Fig. 11-18, it is possible to calculate a_1 and a_2 from the slope and intercept of the data. At

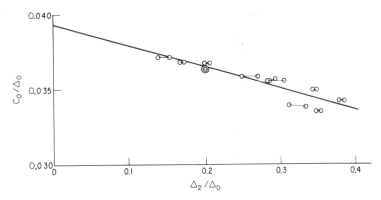

FIG. 11-18. Data for Ta–O alloys, plotted according to Eq. (11.4-15), for the determination of the parameters a_1 and a_2. (From Powers and Doyle, 1959b.)

76°C, it was found that $a_1 = 25.4$, $a_2 = 79.6$, $K_2(T) = 45.3$. To obtain an estimate of $(\delta\lambda)_1/(\delta\lambda)_2$, the best that can be done is to assume that the parameters b_1 and b_2 in Eqs. (11.4-8) and (11.4-10) are roughly equal, so that these equations yield

$$(\delta\lambda)_2/(\delta\lambda)_1 \simeq (a_2/a_1)^{1/2} \tag{11.4-16}$$

As listed in Table 11-1, the estimate of $(\delta\lambda)_1/(\delta\lambda)_2$ obtained from Eq. (11.4-16) for the Ta–O alloys is 1.8. Evidently, therefore, the relative configuration of the two atoms in the pair must be such that the principal distortions produced by each atom are nearly additive. This point will

TABLE 11-1

PARAMETERS FOR INTERSTITIAL CLUSTERS IN BCC METALS[a]

System	Pairs		Triplets		Quadruplets	
	Δh_2	$(\delta\lambda)_2/(\delta\lambda)_1$	Δh_3	$(\delta\lambda)_3/(\delta\lambda)_1$	Δh_4	$(\delta\lambda)_4/(\delta\lambda)_1$
Ta–O	0.1	1.8				
Nb–O	0.07	1.6	0.18	2.2	0.27	2.6
Fe–N	0.07	2[b]	0.22	3[b]		
Fe–C	0.08	2[b]	0.26	3[b]		

[a] Binding energies are in eV/cluster.
[b] Assumed values.

be pursued later when we consider the calculations that have been made to assess the relative stability of various pair configurations.

Following the work of Powers and Doyle, further anelastic studies of clustering in interstitial alloys were taken up by Wert and his colleagues (Keefer and Wert, 1963a, b; Gibala and Wert, 1966a,b,c). Gibala and Wert (1966a,b) studied Nb–O alloys containing up to 1.5 at. % oxygen. Again, a combination of elastic aftereffect and low frequency internal friction measurements was employed. Analysis of the aftereffect data was performed by the "subtraction of tails" method described in Section 3.7, which assumes that the relaxation behavior consists of a super-position of standard anelastic solids (i.e., a discrete spectrum) whose relaxation times differ from one another by about a factor of five or more. The internal friction data were analyzed by a complementary method of "subtraction of peaks," in this case however starting with the largest and fastest component (the Snoek peak) and working through the data in reverse order to that employed for the static measurements. As can be seen from Fig. 11-19, the internal friction data for a Nb–1.1 at. % O

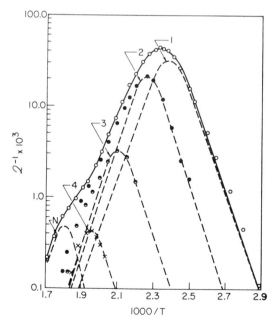

FIG. 11-19. Decomposition of experimental data ($\bigcirc$) for a Nb–1.1 at. % O alloy, $f = 0.82$ Hz, into five subpeaks. The oxygen Snoek peak is labeled 1; peaks 2, 3, and 4 can be associated with different oxygen clusters. The fifth peak (labeled N) is a Snoek peak produced by residual nitrogen. (From Gibala and Wert, 1966a.)

alloy can be represented by a main Snoek peak (labeled 1) and the satellite relaxations 2–4 of progressively diminishing strength and increasing relaxation time. An extensive amount of data (taken on samples of various oxygen content) indicates that the relaxation time of each of the four component relaxations obeys an Arrhenius relationship (Fig. 11-20), though the scatter in the data indicates only moderate success in demonstrating that each τ value should be independent of composition. Based on a mass-action analysis similar to that discussed above, Gibala and Wert found that the relaxation strength of the second, third, and fourth con-

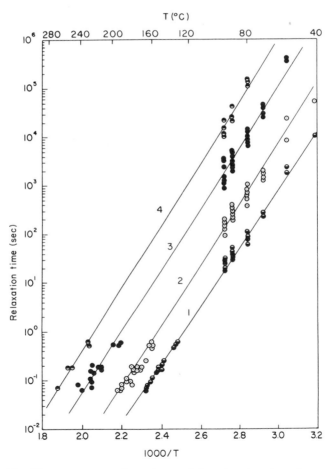

FIG. 11-20.   The temperature dependence of the relaxation times for processes 1–4 in Fig. 11-19. The τ_0 values are all about the same (3×10^{-15} sec); the activation energies are 1.17, 1.24, 1.27, and 1.30 eV for processes 1–4, respectively. (From Gibala and Wert, 1966a.)

tributions varied roughly as the corresponding powers of the first (Snoek) contribution, and thus assigned these contributions to relaxation from clusters of two, three, and four atoms, respectively. That better agreement was not obtained with the mass action principle can be understood in terms of the simplifying assumption that the relaxation spectrum consists of a discrete set of well-separated relaxation times, with just one τ value for each cluster of size n. The actual relaxation spectrum is likely to be much more complicated, since not only may one defect exhibit a spectrum of relaxation times,[†] but different configurations of pairs, triplets, etc. each corresponds to a distinct defect species. Further, interactions among these defects are probably important at the higher concentrations. With these complexities in mind, the analysis procedure of Gibala and Wert should perhaps be thought of primarily as a means of sensing the general trend of the relaxation spectrum. The trend seems clearly to point to the fact that with increasing concentration of interstitial solute, higher-order clusters assume increasing importance in the description of the solid solution.

The values of Δh_n and $(\delta\lambda)_n/(\delta\lambda)_1$ obtained by Gibala and Wert are listed in Table 11-1, along with estimates of the pair and triplet binding energies for nitrogen and carbon clusters in iron as given by Keefer and Wert (1963a,b). It will be seen that for all cases reported, the binding energy per cluster increases significantly with the cluster size. If this were not the case, the number of triplets and quadruplets present would be so small as to escape detection. The binding energy for pairs is apparently largest in the Ta–O system, although the values for the other systems are not greatly different.

As yet, little is known with certainty about the specific arrangement of the interstitial atoms forming the pairs and higher-order clusters discussed above. For pairs, there have been binding energy calculations based on elasticity theory by Fisher (1958) and more refined calculations by Johnson et al. (1964). Fisher's results indicate stability of the third and fifth neighbor pairs (Fig. 11-21), whereas Johnson et al. favor the third neighbor configuration as the most stable. On the other hand, Nowick and Heller (1963) have suggested that the structure of Ta_4O may indicate a preference for the fourth nearest-neighbor pair in the solid solution. It is instructive to examine these configurations in relation to the relatively large values of $(\delta\lambda)_2/(\delta\lambda)_1$ given in Table 11-1, which, as noted

---

[†] For example, a triclinic defect in a cubic crystal gives rise to five τ values which, in general, differ from each other (see Table 8-5).

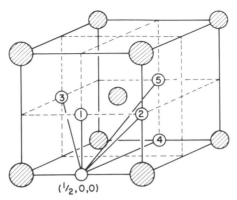

FIG. 11-21. Possible interstitial pair configurations in the bcc lattice. The interstitials labeled 1–5 are the first through the fifth nearest neighbors to the reference interstitial at $(\frac{1}{2}, 0, 0)$.

earlier, suggest that the principal distortions produced by each interstitial atom must be nearly additive. This is most likely to occur when both members of the pair occupy a site of the same orientation. Of the possibilities illustrated in Fig. 11-21, this is the case only for the third and the fourth neighbor pairs. Experiments on the anisotropy of the relaxation in single crystals might be expected to shed considerable light on the relative merits of these suggestions.

B. RELAXATIONS IN FACE-CENTERED CUBIC METALS

In this category, there is evidence for relaxation due to carbon pairs in both Ni and the fcc allotrope of Co, and for oxygen pairs in Ag. The existence of an internal friction peak associated with dissolved C in Ni was first reported by Kê and Tsien (1956). The peak is quite small, having a height of about $\phi = 3 \times 10^{-4}$ for 1 at. % C, and occurs at 250°C for a frequency of 1 Hz. By application of a saturating magnetic field, the existence of the peak was shown to be unrelated to the ferromagnetic nature of the sample. Further, the peak was found to decline in strength as the carbon was precipitated from solid solution. Kê and Tsien point out that unassociated C atoms, located at the body-centered position of the fcc structure and in the equivalent positions midway along the cube edges, could not be responsible for the relaxation, since the symmetry of such defects is cubic. After Tsien (1961) found in later work that the relaxation strength varied essentially as the square of the carbon content in solution, it became evident from the type of mass-action considerations discussed in Section 11.4A that carbon pairs were the responsible defect.

Further experiments were performed by Diamond and Wert (1967), whose analysis of elastic aftereffect data by the subtraction of tails method (Section 3.7) suggests that in addition to pairs, more complex clusters may contribute in smaller measure to the relaxation. By combining several experimental techniques (high and low frequency internal friction measurements, elastic aftereffect and magnetic disaccommodation measurements), Diamond and Wert performed a most elegant study of the kinetics of the relaxation over a wide temperature range spanning the ferromagnetic Curie temperature (320°C). Their data, shown in Fig. 11-22, cover an impressive ten decade range in τ and form an excellent

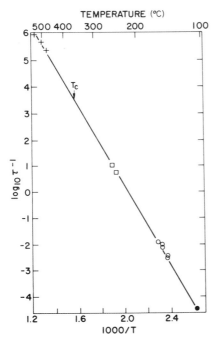

FIG. 11-22. Temperature dependence of the relaxation time for carbon pairs in nickel, as obtained from internal friction data in the region of 100 kHz and 1 Hz ($\times$, $\square$, respectively), elastic aftereffect measurements ($\bigcirc$) and a magnetic disaccommodation measurement ($\bullet$). (From Diamond and Wert, 1967.)

straight line Arrhenius plot conforming to the relationship $\tau^{-1} = 2.8 \times 10^{15} \exp(-1.51/kT)$. From the linearity of the plot, it is evident that for this case of interstitial migration, there is no anomalous behavior of τ associated with the ferromagnetic transition. Accordingly, Diamond and Wert have suggested that in those cases of substitutional or self-diffusion where an anomaly is seen, the effect results from a variation in either the formation or motion energy of a vacancy, rather than from a variation in the elastic constants which would be expected to affect interstitial- as well as vacancy-controlled migration.

The investigation of Co–C alloys by Mah and Wert (1968) contains a number of interesting features. At high frequencies (80 kHz), the location of the "carbon-pair" peak is 570°C, i.e., well above the M_s temperature of 420°C for martensitic transformation from the fcc structure to the low temperature hcp form. At 1 Hz, partially transformed specimens containing a mixture of the fcc and hcp phases exhibit a peak at 270°C which appears to vary as the 5/2 power of the solute content. Since specimens composed almost entirely of the hcp phase showed no well-defined peak, the peak seen at 270°C in the two phase samples appears to originate solely from the presence of the fcc phase. In support of this, the low frequency and high frequency data fit together on an Arrhenius plot, and yield an activation energy of 1.65 eV. The anisotropy of the relaxation was studied from high frequency measurements on single crystals, with the results shown in Fig. 11-23. Since it seems probable

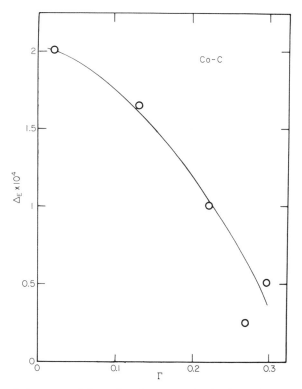

FIG. 11-23. Anisotropy of the relaxation strength Δ_E shown by single crystals of fcc cobalt containing 0.4 wt. % carbon. The data, which refer to a temperature of 565°C, were obtained from measurements in longitudinal vibration at 80 kHz. (From Mah and Wert, 1968.)

that the relaxation strength Δ_E vanishes for the $\langle 111 \rangle$ orientation ($\Gamma = \frac{1}{3}$), the defect model favored by Mah and Wert is the next-nearest-neighbor interstitial pair of tetragonal symmetry.

To conclude the discussion of fcc materials, we note that Papazian (1963) and Papazian and Himmel (1964) have reported that silver–oxygen alloys exhibit internal friction peaks whose origin appears related to interstitial oxygen pairs. Since Swartz (1969b) was unable to reproduce these peaks, however, a clarification of the experimental situation is now needed.

11.5   Interstitial–Substitutional (i–s) Pairs

Anelastic measurements have provided evidence that the defect consisting of an interstitial impurity atom (or ion) bound to a substitutional impurity, forming what we may conveniently call the i–s pair, occurs in a wide variety of materials including semiconductors, insulators, and metals. The reorientation process can be pictured as taking place simply by the jumping of the interstitial, since in all cases this is by far the more mobile member of the pair.

A. Semiconducting and Insulating Crystals

A good example of relaxation produced by i–s pairs is provided by Berry's (1970) work on silicon containing lithium and boron. Lithium is present interstitially in silicon as the Li^+ ion, whereas boron is present substitutionally as the B^- ion. The coulombic attraction between these ions serves to produce Li^+B^- pairs according to the simple reaction

$$Li^+ + B^- \rightleftharpoons Li^+B^-$$

for which the mass action equation is

$$\frac{C_p}{(C_{Li}^0 - C_p)(C_B^0 - C_p)} = A \exp \frac{\Delta h_b}{kT} \qquad (11.5\text{-}1)$$

where C_p is the mole fraction of pairs, C_{Li}^0 and C_B^0 denote the *total* concentrations of lithium and boron,[†] and Δh_b is the binding enthalpy. The preexponential factor A includes, as usual, a configurational constant and a vibrational entropy factor. An example of the relaxation behavior

---

[†] Both species will be assumed to be completely ionized.

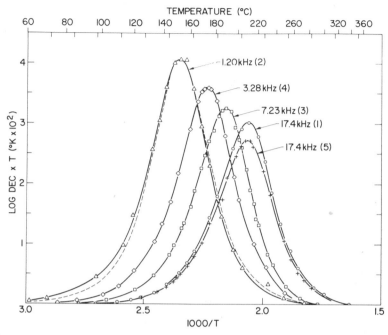

FIG. 11-24.   Internal friction peaks in flexural vibration for a series of vibration frequencies, as shown by a ⟨111⟩ crystal of silicon containing 6.6×10^{18} atoms cm^{-3} of boron and 5.3×10^{18} atoms cm^{-3} of lithium. Note that use of the damping-temperature product for the ordinate makes the peak heights scale as the concentration of defects involved, which is therefore seen to decrease with increasing temperature. This behavior also leads to a skewing of the peak shape, as is evident by reference to the broken curve, which is a symmetrical Debye peak fitted to the height and width of the peak for 1.20 kHz. The numbers in parentheses denote the sequence in which the runs were performed; the difference between runs 1 and 5 reflects a small loss of Li during the measurements. (From Berry, 1970.)

produced by ion pairing is shown in Fig. 11-24. These data were obtained in flexure on a ⟨111⟩ oriented sample containing 6.6×10^{18} atoms cm^{-3} of B and 5.3×10^{18} atoms cm^{-3} of Li. (A peak is not present in samples which contain only Li or B separately.) A notable feature of Fig. 11-24 is the manner in which the peak height falls with increasing temperature. This behavior reflects the dissociation of the pairs in a manner consistent with Eq. (11.5-1). By performing other measurements over a range of boron concentrations, the validity of Eq. (11.5-1) has been verified and the values of the mass action parameters found to be $A = 9$ and $\Delta h_b = 0.28$ eV. Measurements yielding the symmetry of the pair are shown in Fig. 11-25. The fact that only a very small peak is detectable in the

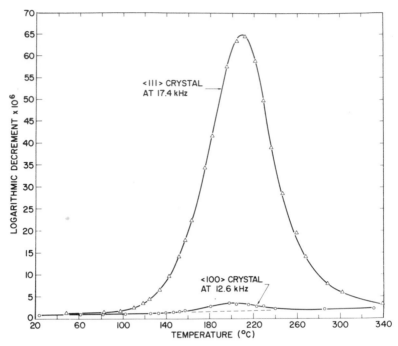

FIG. 11-25.   Internal friction peaks in flexural vibration for $\langle 111 \rangle$ and $\langle 100 \rangle$ oriented silicon rods containing 6.6×10^{18} atoms cm^{-3} of boron and 5.3×10^{18} atoms cm^{-3} of lithium. (From Berry, 1970.)

$\langle 100 \rangle$ sample is a satisfactory indication that the defect symmetry is trigonal.[†] This symmetry is the one obtained by placing the Li^{+} ion in a tetrahedral interstitial site and in a nearest-neighbor position to the B^{-} ion (see Fig. 11-26). The shape factor $|\,\delta\lambda\,|$ of the defect, as calculated from the peak height for a known concentration of pairs, has the value 0.1. The kinetic parameters of the relaxation, as determined from the shift of peak position with frequency, are $\tau_0^{-1} = 5 \times 10^{13}$ sec^{-1} and $Q = 0.83$ eV. This value of Q is significantly higher than the value of 0.65 eV for the migration of free (unassociated) Li^{+}. This can be explained by recognizing that, in order for reorientation to take place, the interstitial must first move away from the boron atom to at least a next-nearest-neighbor position (Fig. 11-26). In view of the binding between the Li^{+}B^{-} pair, the activation energy for this jump can be reasonably expected to be higher than that for the movement of unbound Li^{+}.

[†] The absence of a strict null for $\delta E_{\langle 100 \rangle}^{-1}$ can be explained by the presence of a small fraction of pairs in the next-nearest-neighbor configuration.

FIG. 11-26. The diamond cubic structure of silicon. The sites labeled a, b, c, d
are tetrahedral interstitial sites in nearest-
neighbor positions to the substitutional B^-
ion (shown shaded). These sites are not ac-
cessible to each other by a single jump. A
Li^+ ion leaving site a must first move either
to a next-nearest-neighbor position to the
B^- ion (jumps 1, 2, and 3), or to a third
neighbor position (jump 4).

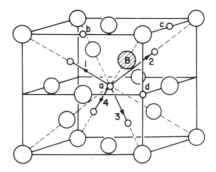

By restricting consideration to only the first three shells of tetrahedral
sites, the kinetics of the relaxation may be approximately treated as
follows. As indicated in Fig. 11-26, there are three ways of moving from
a nn to a nnn position. Denoting the rate of a specific jump of this type
by w, the probability per second of moving from a given nn to any nnn
site is thus $3w$. On the other hand, taking all Li^+ ions which are in nnn
positions to B^- ions, the probability/jump of obtaining a nn pair of a
specified orientation is $\frac{1}{4}$. Consequently, ν_{12} is $3w/4$, and hence, from
Eq. (8.9-18)

$$\tau^{-1} = 3w \qquad\qquad (11.5\text{-}2)$$

Turning now to insulating crystals, Southgate (1966) has reported
relaxation behavior attributable to i–s pairs in yttrium doped crystals of
calcium fluoride. When trivalent Y^{3+} ions replace Ca^{2+} ions in this
crystal, the mode of charge compensation is the introduction of extra
F^- ions, located at interstitial sites (Fig. 11-27).[†] Relaxation is thus

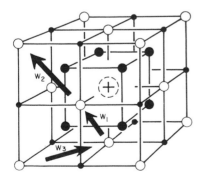

FIG. 11-27. The structure of fluorite, with
a Y^{3+} ion replacing a Ca^{2+} ion at the cube
center. The Ca^{2+} ions (small filled circles) form
an fcc sublattice interpenetrated by F^- ions
(large filled circles). Sites for interstitial F^- ions
are shown as the large open circles. The jump of
rate w_1 reorients a nn Y^{3+}–F^- pair; w_2 produces
dissociation from a nn to nnn pair; and w_3 is the
converse jump to w_2. (From Southgate, 1966.)

[†] This situation presents an interesting contrast with the case of NaF-doped CaF_2
(Section 11.3), where charge compensation of the *lower* valence Na^+ ion is obtained by
the creation of an F^- vacancy.

possible by the reorientation of $Y^{3+}F^-$ bound pairs. Internal friction data obtained using uniaxial stress along $\langle 111 \rangle$ and $\langle 100 \rangle$ directions are shown in Fig. 11-28 for crystals doped with 10^{-5} mole fraction of YF_3. Both peaks have an activation energy of 1.2 eV, a value which is to be associated with the movement of interstitial F^- ions around the substitutional (and essentially immobile) Y^{3+} ions. The simplest interpretation of the data of Fig. 11-28 involves the reorientation of both nn and nnn

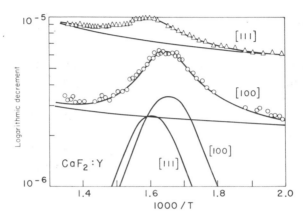

FIG. 11-28.   Internal friction peaks in single crystals of CaF_2 doped with about 10^{-5} mole fraction of YF_3. Measurements in longitudinal vibration at 37.5 and 39 kHz for the $\langle 111 \rangle$ and $\langle 100 \rangle$ crystals, respectively. The two lower curves show the peaks with the background removed. (From Southgate, 1966.)

pairs, in a somewhat similar (but not precisely analogous) manner to that discussed for the case of s–v pairs in calcium-doped NaCl (Section 11.3). As can be seen by inspection of Fig. 11-27, in the present case the nn i–s pair has tetragonal symmetry, while the nnn pair is of trigonal symmetry. An $S_{11} - S_{12}$ shear will therefore produce reorientation of nn pairs only, while an S_{44} shear will produce reorientation of nnn pairs only. Despite this simplification in the relaxation strengths, the kinetics of each relaxation are in general still coupled by the existence of jump paths which can take a nn pair into a nnn pair, and vice versa. The simplest possible rate expressions are obtained by restricting attention only to the three types of jump indicated in Fig. 11-27 [i.e., the "two-shell" model from Chang's (1964) analysis] with the results

$$\tau^{-1}(S_{11} - S_{12}) = 6w_1 + 4w_2 \tag{11.5-3a}$$

$$\tau^{-1}(S_{44}) = 2w_3 \tag{11.5-3b}$$

Application of these results to the data of Fig. 11-28 requires the additional consideration that the uniaxial stress used experimentally contains a dilatational component capable of exciting hydrostatic relaxation by the net reaction of nearest- and next-nearest-neighbor pairs (Section 8.9). With the two-shell model, the rate of this relaxation is given by

$$\tau^{-1}(S_{11} + 2S_{12}) = 4w_2 + 3w_3 \qquad (11.5\text{-}4)$$

Since nothing is known a priori about the three relaxation rates given by Eqs. (11.5-3) and (11.5-4) or of the relaxation strengths associated with them, Southgate set $w_1 = w_2 = w_3$ and showed that a fit to the data could be obtained by suitable choices of the three relaxation strengths. However, since other self-consistent analyses of the data could also be obtained, including some based on a more complex three-shell model, this assignment must not be regarded as unique, or even the most plausible. A more basic question has been raised recently by Franklin and Crissman (1971), who show that these i–s relaxations may actually occur at much lower temperatures than Southgate's peaks.

As a second example involving a dielectric crystal, a number of anelastic relaxations attributed to i–s defects are observed in (trigonal) α-quartz crystals (Fraser, 1964, 1968). [†] Both natural and some synthetic crystals are known to contain Al^{3+} ions in a concentration of at least 50 ppm. These ions are believed to enter the lattice by substituting for a Si^{4+} ion. Charge compensation is then apparently obtained by the presence of a monovalent ion M^+ (e.g., H^+ or an alkali ion), residing in an interstitial site adjacent to the Al^{3+} ion. In natural crystals, Li^+ tends to be the predominant alkali, while in some synthetic crystals it is Na^+. In any case, by application of an electric field along the c axis at elevated temperatures ($\sim$500°C) it is possible to sweep out the monovalent interstitial ions that are present, and, by applying a suitable salt at the positive electrode, to sweep in another alkali to replace it. In this way K^+ ions, which do not occur otherwise, may be introduced into the crystal. Table 11-2 gives a listing of the peaks that have been found below room temperature, all presumed due to associated i–s pairs. The activation energies are calculated using the frequency, the peak temperature, and an assumed τ_0 of $10^{-13.5}$ sec. The fact that there are two peaks for Na-doped quartz

---

[†] Because of its widespread use as a transducer and its low background damping, a wealth of relaxation peaks have been found in crystalline quartz (Frazer, 1968). In particular, a number of relaxation peaks have been observed in irradiated crystals, but the defects which give rise to these peaks have not been established.

indicates that the Al^{3+}–Na^+ defect may be present in two different states of association, i.e., a nn and a nnn configuration. With the aid of both anelastic and dielectric relaxation data, the following conclusions have been drawn (Nowick and Stanley, 1969):

(a) All of the relaxations listed in Table 11-2 result from triclinic defects.

TABLE 11-2

DATA ON Al^{3+}–M^+ (ALKALI–ION) DEFECTS IN α-QUARTZ[a]

M^+	Peak temperature (°K)	Q (eV)
Na^+	50	0.059
Li^+	105	0.125
Na^+	135	0.160
K^+	208	0.246

[a] All measurements in the AT shear mode at 5 MHz.

(b) In each case, the observed relaxation is the low temperature member of a frozen-free split in which the motion of the interstitial ion takes place rapidly. The corresponding high-temperature relaxations, involving substitutional migration, have not been observed.

(c) In the case of the two Na^+ relaxations, the motion of the interstitial Na^+ ion between a pair of nn positions on the one hand, and between nn $\rightleftharpoons$ nnn positions, on the other hand, give rise to the two low temperature relaxations.

B. METALLIC ALLOYS

In alloys, evidence of i–s pairing has been obtained in all three of the common crystal structures (fcc, hcp, and bcc). These are conveniently discussed in two groups, the first containing both the fcc and hcp alloys. Compared to the bcc alloys, the hcp and fcc alloys exhibit a simpler anelastic behavior which is the more clearly revealed because of the absence of a counterpart to the Snoek relaxation. Such an absence is consistent with the belief that the symmetry system of the occupied interstitial sites in these crystals is the same as that of the host crystal. Turning to specific examples, Fig. 11-29 shows, in normalized form, the internal friction peak attributed to the reorientation of O–Zr pairs in an oxygen doped hcp hafnium alloy containing 6 wt. % Zr. These

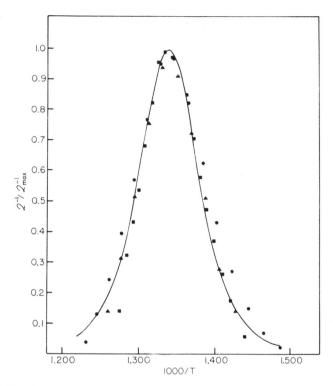

FIG. 11-29.   Normalized internal friction data for a Hf–6 wt. % Zr alloy containing different amounts of interstitial oxygen. The measurements were made in torsional vibration at ∼1 Hz. The solid curve is a Debye peak calculated for an activation energy of 2.52 eV. (From Bisogni *et al.*, 1964.)

data, obtained by Bisogni *et al.* (1964), contain measurements for three different oxygen contents for which the absolute peak height varied from $\phi = 3 \times 10^{-4}$ to $\phi = 11 \times 10^{-4}$. The solid curve, representing a Debye peak governed by an activation energy of 2.52 eV, fits the data quite well. [†] Evidently, therefore, the relaxation can be accounted for with a rather simple model. The model proposed can be understood with reference to

[†] For alloys doped with nitrogen in place of oxygen, Bisogni *et al.* obtained a very similar behavior. However, the reported activation energy for the case of nitrogen is considerably smaller (2.2 eV), even though the temperatures of the peaks for oxygen and nitrogen are nearly the same. As a result, the calculated preexponential factors differ significantly, the one for nitrogen being over two decades smaller than that for oxygen. One may therefore suspect that the disparity between the activation energies is not as great as the reported values suggest.

Fig. 11-30. In the pure host crystal the indicated intertistial sites possess trigonal symmetry and hence their occupancy by single atoms does not create defects capable of producing a shear relaxation. However, if an interstitial atom is paired to a substitutional atom the resulting defect is [100] monoclinic and relaxation of both the S_{44} and $S_{11} - S_{12}$ compliance is possible. The magnitudes of the relaxations are given by Eqs. (8.6-18). The kinetics of the relaxation have been discussed by Povolo and Bisogni

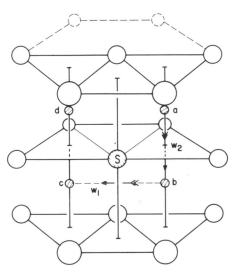

FIG. 11-30.   Illustration of the two types of interstitial jump which produce reorientation of a nearest neighbor i–s pair in the hcp structure. The jump of rate w_1 is parallel to the basal plane (e.g., from b to c) while that of rate w_2 is perpendicular to the basal plane (e.g., a to b, or c to d). Note that only four of the six nearest-neighbor interstitial sites to the solute atom s are shown in the drawing.

(1966) and by Nowick (1967). Two types of jump are likely to be of importance, namely, a jump of rate w_1 parallel to the basal plane, and a jump of rate w_2 perpendicular to the basal plane. In terms of these two jumps, the rates of relaxation are

$$\tau^{-1}(S_{44}) = 3w_1 + 2w_2 \qquad (11.5\text{-}5)$$

$$\tau^{-1}(S_{11} - S_{12}) = 3w_1 \qquad (11.5\text{-}6)$$

In the polycrystalline samples studied, where both compliances would be excited, the observation of a behavior corresponding to only a single relaxation time might therefore suggest that w_1 is the rate-controlling jump. Alternatively, it could be argued, as originally favored by Bisogni *et al.* that $w_2 \gg w_1$, which implies that a split would occur in which the relaxation of the $(S_{11} - S_{12})$ compliance would only be observed at temperatures well above those of the present observations. Nowick (1967) has pointed out that measurements on properly oriented single crystals over an extended temperature range could distinguish between these two possibilities.

Other work on hexagonal crystals has been reported for the case of titanium alloys (Miller, 1962; Pratt *et al.*, 1954; Gupta and Weinig, 1962). Gupta and Weinig's work involved the oxygen doping of Ti containing small ($\sim$0.1 at. %) additions of V, Al, Au, Nb, and Zr. Though no corresponding internal friction peak was observed in high purity binary Ti–O alloys, the dilute ternary alloys were found to exhibit small peaks ($\phi_{max} < 2 \times 10^{-3}$) at a temperature near 450°C (for 1 Hz), with an activation energy (1.96 $\pm$ 0.2 eV) consistent with the movement of oxygen atoms. The most detailed measurements were made on Ti–Zr–O alloys in which the Zr content was varied while the oxygen content was held constant, and vice versa. As would be expected from the mass-action equation for the case of a low concentration of i-s pairs, the peak in samples of constant Zr content (0.06 at. %) was found to increase linearly with oxygen content (up to 4 at. % O). However, for a fixed oxygen content of 2 at. %, additions of Zr beyond 0.06 at. % were found to decrease the peak height. This behavior, which clearly does not conform to simple mass-action considerations, was attributed to an increasing fraction of the oxygen content being gettered by the Zr addition.

Turning to work indicative of i-s pairing in fcc alloys, we may mention first the work of Kê and Tsien (1956) on a number of austenitic chrome–nickel and manganese steels containing carbon as the interstitial impurity. Figure 11-31 shows the peaks found in an Fe–18.5 % Mn steel containing various amounts of carbon. The activation energy of this relaxation, as determined from measurements at different frequencies, is about 1.5 eV, in good agreement with the results of high-temperature carbon diffusion data. Kê and Tsien pointed out that the increase[†] of peak height with carbon content (or with the manganese content) favors a model based on the reorientation of i–s pairs, as is shown in Fig. 11-32.

[†] While the relationship between peak height and carbon concentration is linear for a fixed Mn content, it is not quite a simple proportionality due to the existence of a small intercept on the concentration axis. This suggests that a corresponding amount of carbon is unavailable for participation in the relaxation, as discussed by Kê and Tsien.

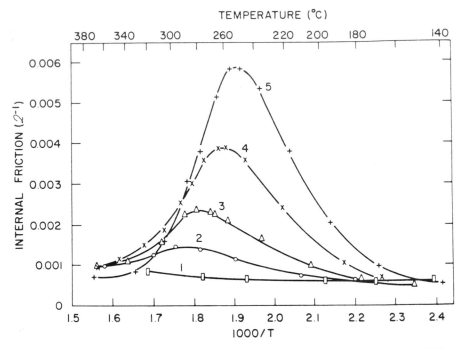

FIG. 11-31.   Internal friction peaks in an 18.5% manganese steel containing 0.12, 0.37, 0.70, 0.95, and 1.34% carbon (curves 1–5, respectively). Measurements in torsional vibration at 2.2 Hz. (From Kê and Tsien, 1956.)

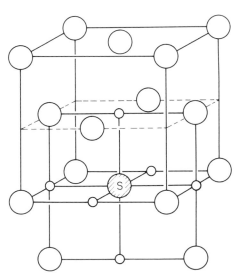

FIG. 11-32.   The set of nearest-neighbor interstitial sites (○) to a substitutional impurity atom s in the fcc lattice.

Here, the interstitial and substitutional atom form a nn pair whose axis lies along a $\langle 100 \rangle$ direction. The symmetry of this defect is tetragonal, so that Eqs. (8.4-1) and (8.9-17) apply for the magnitude and rate of the relaxation. Since there are two ways in which the interstitial may leave one site to achieve another chosen orientation, it is evident that Eq. (8.9-17) becomes

$$\tau^{-1} = 6w \tag{11.5-7}$$

where w is the rate of jumping from one chosen site to another. In the alloys used by Kê and Tsien the substitutional element is present in such high concentration that the isolated i–s pair model of Fig. 11-32 can be regarded as only a zeroth approximation. (Evidence of more complicated interactions is available from Fig. 11-31, which shows a significant dependence of peak position on the C content and a broadened and asymmetrical peak shape.) More recently, Peterson *et al.* (1969) have observed a peak at 210°K (for a frequency of 80 kHz) in a hydrogen charged austenitic steel. This relaxation has an activation energy of 0.5 eV, and was attributed to an i–s pair with hydrogen as the mobile interstitial member. Turning to other fcc materials, Mah and Wert (1964) have found analogous peaks due to oxygen and nitrogen doping of impure (∼99% purity) ytterbium. The peaks are of comparable magnitude to those shown in Fig. 11-31, and occur at 140°C (0.5 Hz) for O and 120°C (1 Hz) for N. Even here, however, based on the reported activation energy of 1.1 eV, the peaks are considerably broader than would be expected from the simple model of Fig. 11-32. Since this model involves a defect of tetragonal symmetry, measurements on the anisotropy of the relaxation strength using single crystal specimens would be illuminating. Such measurements do not appear to have been attempted.

In bcc alloys, even the simplest model of relaxation behavior to be expected from i–s pairs is more complex than for hcp and fcc alloys, owing to the fact that in the bcc lattice an i–s pair cannot reorient to an equivalent configuration by a single nearest neighbor jump of the interstitial atom. From an experimental viewpoint, there is the additional complexity that some of the components of the i–s relaxation may overlap with the Snoek relaxation, making their resolution difficult. The simplest model is based on the assumption that the defect pairs are present only in the nn (tetragonal) and nnn ($\langle 110 \rangle$ orthorhombic) configurations, as shown in Fig. 11-33a. From the selection rules, Table 8-5, we then expect three relaxation peaks, two for the compliance $S_{11} - S_{12}$ and one for S_{44}. Chang (1964) has worked out the problem allowing for various

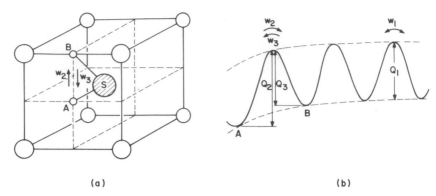

(a)   (b)

FIG. 11-33.   (a) Nearest and next-nearest interstitial–substitutional pairs (AS and BS, respectively) in the bcc lattice. (b) Schematic illustration of the change in potential as an interstitial atom approaches the substitutional atom S. The sites marked A and B correspond to those in (a). The vertical lines indicate the activation energies for the jumps of rates w_1, w_2, and w_3.

types of jumps. It is reasonable, however, to consider as probable only interstitial jumps between closest positions. If such a jump from specific nn $\rightarrow$ nnn positions has a jump rate w_2 and the reverse nnn $\rightarrow$ nn jump has the rate w_3, as noted in Fig. 11-33a, Chang's expressions for the relaxation rates then reduce to

$$\tau^{-1}(S_{11} - S_{12}) = (2w_2+w_3) \pm [(2w_2 - w_3)^2+2w_2w_3]^{1/2} \qquad (11.5\text{-}8)$$

$$\tau^{-1}(S_{44}) = 2w_3 \qquad (11.5\text{-}9)$$

A similar analysis showing three relaxations was given by Meijering (1961). The relative concentrations of defects in equilibrium, under zero stress, in the nn and nnn configurations may clearly be expressed in terms of the two jump rates, as

$$C_0^{\text{nnn}}/C_0^{\text{nn}} = 2w_2/w_3 \qquad (11.5\text{-}10)$$

the factor of two coming from the fact that there are twice as many nnn as nn sites. It is reasonable to expect that $w_3 > w_2$ (i.e., that the pairs are more strongly bound in the nn configuration). Another reasonable approximation is that

$$(w_2w_3)^{1/2} = w_1 \qquad (11.5\text{-}11)$$

where w_1 is the jump rate for the dissociated interstitial, which determines τ^{-1} for the Snoek relaxation. Equation (11.5-11) simply implies that the activation energy for the isolated impurity is the arithmetic average of those for the nn → nnn and nnn → nn jumps (see Fig. 11-33b).

In the limiting case where $w_3 \gg w_2$, Eq. (11.5-8) gives

$$\tau_{(+)}^{-1}(S_{11} - S_{12}) \simeq 2w_3$$
$$\tau_{(-)}^{-1}(S_{11} - S_{12}) \simeq 3w_2$$

$$(11.5\text{-}12)$$

where the subscripts $(+)$ and $(-)$ refer to taking the positive and negative signs in Eq. (11.5-8). Thus, under the assumption made, [i.e., Eqs. (11.5-11) and (11.5-12)], one of the $S_{11} - S_{12}$ relaxations would fall (in temperature) above and the other below the Snoek peak. Also, from Eq. (11.5-9), the S_{44} relaxation would coincide with the lower-temperature peak. However, from Eq. (11.5-10), we see that, if $w_3 \gg w_2$, only a very small fraction of the total defect concentration is to be found in nnn positions. This means that the major defect is the nn (tetragonal) defect, which gives rise to a single $S_{11} - S_{12}$ relaxation. Since such a relaxation can only take place in a temperature range in which nn → nnn jumps are possible, it is clear that the only relaxation having appreciable magnitude is that for which $\tau^{-1} \simeq 3w_2$, i.e., the one that falls above the Snoek peak. The peaks which fall below the Snoek peak may then be expected to be quite small, perhaps negligibly small, in magnitude.

Most of the experimental work on i–s defects in the bcc metals has been concerned with polycrystalline ternary iron-based alloys containing nitrogen in supersaturated solid solution. Historically, the first evidence indicative of i–s pairing, namely, the presence of a satellite relaxation to the Snoek peak, was reported by Fast (1950) for Fe–Mn–N alloys. This work was later extended by Dijkstra and Sladek (1953), who performed a survey of various Fe–N alloys containing 0.5 at. % of the substitutional elements Mn, Cr, Mo, and V. Leak et al. (1955) and Rawlings and Robinson (1961) studied Fe–N alloys containing Si. It was found in all cases that the dominant feature of the results was the appearance of a substantial relaxation component located above the position of the normal Snoek peak. Results on the Fe–V–N ternary alloy are shown in Fig. 11-34. In this case the results on heating a nitrided and quenched sample reveal a Snoek peak at 22°C and a larger, somewhat broadened second peak at 87°C. It will be seen that the results on cooling show a substantial reduction in both peak heights, indicative of a substantial loss of dissolved nitrogen by precipitation. Table 11-3 lists the peak temperatures for the solutes studied by Dijkstra and Sladek, together with the corresponding activation energies obtained by as-

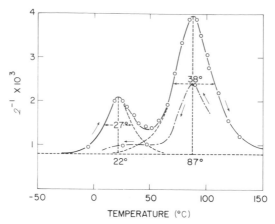

FIG. 11-34.   Internal friction behavior of a nitrided Fe–0.5 at. % V alloy on heating (solid curve) and on subsequent cooling from about 150°C (chain curve). Measurements in torsional vibration at ~1 Hz. (From Dijkstra and Sladek, 1953.)

suming $\tau_0 = 10^{-14.5}$ sec (see Fig. 3-11). The observations on the Fe–V–N alloy were confirmed and extended by Fast and Meijering (1953), who made measurements on samples containing different levels of dissolved nitrogen and studied the aging kinetics in more detail. Perry *et al.* (1966) have taken Fast and Meijering's data on the broadened higher-temperature peak seen on heating, and attempted to analyze it (with only partial success) into a series of subpeaks each governed by a single relaxation time. Owing to the rapidity with which aging occurs, however, it appears

TABLE 11-3

DATA FOR I–S PEAKS IN Fe–N ALLOYS CONTAINING 0.5 AT. % SUBSTITUTIONAL SOLUTE

Substitutional solute	Peak temperature (°C)	Q (eV)
Mn	7	0.785
	32	0.826
Cr	47	0.868
Mo	75	0.945
V	87	0.975

questionable whether the peak shape measured on heating is sufficiently stable to warrant such close scrutiny.[†]

Of the ferrous alloys examined thus far, the Fe–Mn–N alloys appear to be best suited for a detailed experimental study. In these alloys, in contrast to those containing Cr and V (elements that form strongly bound nitrides) precipitation occurs relatively slowly. This behavior, coupled with the fact that the relaxation is completed at lower temperatures, permits measurements to be made under more stable conditions. Enrietto (1962) has studied the behavior of Fe–Mn–N alloys containing 0.02–0.75 wt. % Mn and up to about 0.025 wt. % dissolved nitrogen. For a frequency near 1 Hz, it was found that most (though not all) of the observations could be decomposed self-consistently into three Debye peaks located at 7°, 24°, and 35°C, whose half-widths correspond to activation energies of 0.65, 0.78, and 0.91 eV, respectively. An example of such a decomposition is shown in Fig. 11-35. The 24°C central peak, corresponding to the normal Snoek peak, overlaps with both the small peak at 7°C and the larger one at 35°C. For a fixed Mn content it appears that although the 24 and 35°C peaks increase linearly with the amount of nitrogen in solution, the 7°C peak seems to be of greater relative prominence at lower nitrogen levels. As yet, the cause of this behavior must be regarded as unexplained. Except for this point, the data can be interpreted, at least as a first approximation, by the model discussed earlier in connection with Fig. 11-33. From the activation energies given above and Eq. (11.5-10) one obtains $C_0^{nnn}/C_0^{nn} \simeq 0.07$, which is not so small as to disallow the existence of a satellite relaxation on the low-temperature side of the Snoek peak. Thus far, work on single crystals of Fe–Mn–N alloys, which can give important information on the nature of the i–s defects in this system, has not been carried out.

Recently, there have been significant studies of i-s pairing in other alloys, notably those of Nb containing Zr as the substitutional solute and O and/or N as the interstitial solute. Following the early evidence for i–s cluster formation given by Bunn et al. (1962), the anisotropy of the relaxation in single crystal Nb–Zr–O–N alloys was studied by Miner et al. (1970). Their results on ⟨100⟩ single crystals in longitudinal vibration indicate the presence of five separate peaks, two of which are the normal

---

[†] It may be remarked in passing that, based on a belief that the "anomalous" peak is composed of three subpeaks, Perry et al. proposed the existence of three configurations of i-s cluster, each with its own relaxation time. From the discussion given in Chapter 8, however, it should be evident that a one-to-one correspondence need not be invoked between the number of relaxation times and the number of defect species.

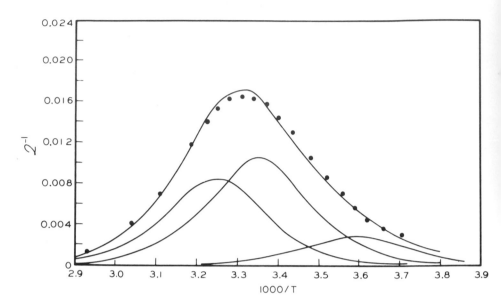

FIG. 11-35.   Decomposition of internal friction data on a nitrided Fe–0.15% Mn alloy into three Debye peaks whose sum is given by the upper curve. Measurements in torsion at ∼1 Hz. (From Enrietto, 1962.)

Snoek peaks due to O and N, while the remaining three peaks appear to be due to i–s defects. A most significant finding was that all the peaks are absent for the ⟨111⟩ orientation, indicating that all the defects must be either of tetragonal or ⟨100⟩ orthorhombic symmetry. With the aid of further results on the concentration dependence of the peak heights, Miner *et al.* have concluded that each of the three i–s peaks is produced by a different type of tetragonal defect. Two of these defects are believed to be the O–Zr and N–Zr nearest-neighbor pairs. The third defect is of composition ZrO_2, and, to obtain tetragonal symmetry, is suggested to have a linear O–Zr–O configuration with the two oxygen atoms diametrically opposite each other and in nearest-neighbor positions to the Zr atom. It is interesting that the earlier but less detailed work of Hashizume and Sugeno (1967) on single crystal Fe–Si–N alloys also revealed a striking anisotropy behavior matching that shown by the niobium alloys.

The formation of i–s defects in polycrystalline Nb–Zr–N alloys has been studied by Mosher *et al.* (1970). A mass-action analysis of the relaxation data indicates that both Zr–N and Zr_2N clusters are formed, with binding enthalpies of 0.31 and 0.46 eV, respectively.

11.6 Defects in Various Other Crystals

In addition to the examples covered so far in this chapter, a number of other relaxations have been observed which probably arise from a point defect mechanism. These have not been discussed in earlier sections owing either to uncertainty is the specific nature of the defect, or to the likelihood that the defect falls outside the scope of the categories listed above. In this section, we therefore discuss these relaxations under the headings of the materials in which they have been observed.

A. RUTILE (TiO_2)

Crystals of rutile, which have a tetragonal (D_{4h} or 4/mmm) structure, have attracted great interest because of the semiconducting properties which they exhibit when prepared in nonstoichiometric (oxygen-deficient) condition. An internal friction peak was discovered in reduced rutile by Carnahan and Brittain (1963) and by Wachtman and Doyle (1964). This peak is absent when the material is in the oxidized condition; therefore, one first tends to attribute it to either an oxygen vacancy or a Ti interstitial. We shall see, however, that the responsible defect is evidently more complex than these two possibilities. This study is of interest in that it provides a beautiful example for the application of some of the theoretical considerations of Chapter 8.

Measurements of internal friction were made on single crystals vibrated longitudinally along $\langle 100 \rangle$, $\langle 110 \rangle$, and [001] directions. The result was that a peak appeared only for the $\langle 100 \rangle$ oriented crystal. Since longitudinal vibration of a tetragonal crystal in the [001] direction does not lower the symmetry of the crystal (i.e., it produces strain of type I only), it cannot give rise to reorientation of defects among an equivalent set of orientations. It can, therefore, only reflect the presence of a "reaction" among two or more defect species [as discussed in Section 8.10, Eq. (8.10-4)]. The failure to observe a relaxation for the [001] case at least encourages us to consider a single species as the responsible defect. A substantial peak is observed for the $\langle 100 \rangle$ orientation (near 120°C for 1800 Hz) as shown in Fig. 11-36 which includes a comparison of reduced and oxidized specimens. For the reduced sample in the $\langle 110 \rangle$ orientation, Wachtman and Doyle claim that the damping is no greater than 3×10^{-5} between 100° and 575°C. Thus, if a peak is present, it must be almost two orders of magnitude smaller for the $\langle 110 \rangle$ than for the $\langle 100 \rangle$ orientation. Carnahan and Brittain also failed to find a $\langle 110 \rangle$

peak. It should be remembered [Eqs. (6.4-17) and (6.4-18)] that a peak for the $\langle 100 \rangle$ direction corresponds to relaxation of the compliance $S_{11} - S_{12}$, while a peak for the $\langle 110 \rangle$ direction relates to the relaxation of S_{66}. The third shear relaxation, that of the shear compliance S_{44}, was unfortunately not looked for in either investigation. (This relaxation would be best observed by torsion of an [001] oriented sample.)

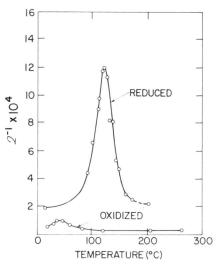

FIG. 11-36.   Internal friction of a [100] oriented rutile single crystal, tested in flexure at 1.8 kHz. (From Wachtman and Doyle, 1964.)

An activation energy of about 1.05 eV was determined by Wachtman and Doyle by treating the peak as due to a standard anelastic solid. Carnahan and Brittain obtained essentially the same value from the peak shift, so that the peak corresponds very nearly to a single relaxation time. A value of $\tau_0 \sim 10^{-17}$ sec, is obtained, however, which is anomalously small. Another complexity is introduced by Carnahan and Brittain's work. These authors vary the oxygen deficiency, using the electrical resistivity as a monitor. They find a peak height proportional to the conductivity, but also find that τ at a given temperature may vary over an order of magnitude with conductivity. This result contradicts the simple idea that changing the amount of reduction simply changes the *number* but not the structure of the defects present, for in that case τ should be independent of the defect concentration (i.e., the conductivity). Finally, later work by Wachtman *et al.* (1966) investigates the effect of doping of the TiO_2 with Ni and Cr. The surprising result is that the 120°C peak is no longer present, but both lower- and higher-temperature peaks are obtained in the doped samples. In spite of these various complexities,[†] attempts have been made by a number of authors to analyze the peak in nominally pure reduced rutile in terms of a well-defined defect.

The first detailed analysis of the possible responsible defect is that given by Wachtman and Doyle who concluded that both the oxygen vacancy and the simple titanium interstitial must be ruled out. The simple interstitial in TiO_2 is believed to be that located at so-called c sites, at coordinates of the type $\frac{1}{2}, 0, 0$ and $\frac{1}{2}, 0, \frac{1}{2}$. These sites, which have four equivalent orientations, are shown as $\times$'s in Fig. 11-37. This simple

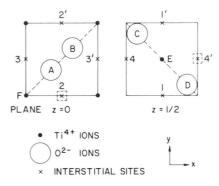

FIG. 11-37. The structure of TiO_2, showing sites for interstitial titanium ions; ($\bullet$) Ti^{4+} ions; ($\bigcirc$) O^{2-} ions; ($\times$) interstitial sites.

defect has [001] monoclinic symmetry and accordingly (see Table 8-5) should give rise to both the $S_{11} - S_{12}$ and S_{66} relaxations, in contradiction to the observations. Nowick and Heller (1965), using symmetry considerations of the type given in Chapter 8, reviewed the situation and arrived at some remarkable conclusions, which we will briefly review here. First, examination of the selection rules (Table 8-5) shows that only for a $\langle 100 \rangle$ orthorhombic or $\langle 100 \rangle$ monoclinic defect will the peak for a $\langle 110 \rangle$ oriented crystal be completely absent. Second, examination of the rutile structure (i.e., the space group) shows that there exists no site within the unit cell with the required $\langle 100 \rangle$ type symmetry. If we recall (from Chapter 8) that the symmetry of a simple defect is the site symmetry and that of a composite defect is a subgroup of the site symmetry, we are forced to conclude that *there is no defect in this crystal for which the $\langle 110 \rangle$ relaxation can be absent.* At this point two alternatives may be

---

[†] Other evidence from electrical conductivity measurements and spin resonance shows that the defect structure of reduced rutile is relatively complex (see, e.g., Hasiguti *et al.*, 1964). Most recently, electron microscopy and diffraction by Bursill *et al.* (1969) show that nonstoichiometry in reduced rutile is accommodated primarily by planes of "crystallographic shear" rather than by isolated point defects.

considered: (a) that the peak is not really absent for the $\langle 110 \rangle$ orientation but only that it is too small to be detected; and (b) that the peak for a $\langle 110 \rangle$ crystal was not observed because it falls in an entirely different temperature range, i.e., a frozen-free split is involved (see Section 8.9E). Wachtman and Doyle argue against alternative (a) under the assumption that the most logical defect is a simple Ti interstitial which has [001] monoclinic symmetry, and for which they make a rough calculation that the $\langle 110 \rangle$ peak should be ~ 0.7 times that for $\langle 100 \rangle$. The fact that the experimental situation indicates that the $\langle 110 \rangle$ peak must be at least 50 times smaller tends to rule out this defect. Nowick and Heller argue that such a small peak for the $\langle 110 \rangle$ crystal could only come about if a principal axis of the $\boldsymbol{\lambda}$ tensor were within $4°$ of the $\langle 100 \rangle$ axis, even though it cannot be exactly along $\langle 100 \rangle$. Examination of the lattice structure makes it difficult to understand how this could come about, although a vague possibility in terms of an electron resonating between an interstitial Ti and an adjacent Ti^{4+} ion of the lattice is suggested. Alternative (b), on the other hand, has led to a number of suggestions worth considering. First, there is a model proposed by Wachtman and Doyle of a pair of interstitials located on the sites marked 2 and $4'$ in Fig. 11-37, with rapid motion primarily along the z axis (so that, simultaneously, $2 \to 1$ and $4' \to 3'$). Such a pair constitutes a triclinic defect of which there are eight possible orientations. If the defect pair orientations are matched to the numbering scheme of Fig. 8-5, the above mentioned rapid motion is found to represent a dominance of v_{18} in Eq. (8.9-11) (Nowick, 1967). In terms of this model, the observed $\langle 100 \rangle$ peak is the low-temperature member of a frozen-free split. The model thus explains the observations, but with an ad hoc assumption that the interstitial pair is strongly bound only at the postulated separation, and consequently is forced to move in such a way as to avoid the formation of a pair having either a closer or further separation.

Because of the complexity and ad hoc nature of this model, other suggestions have been made. Nowick (1967) proposes that a titanium interstitial forms a pair with an unspecified substitutional impurity located on a Ti^{4+} site. Such an impurity atom can be located on site E in Fig. 11-37 with the interstitial ion on sites 1 or 4. Such a defect is of [001] monoclinic symmetry, since both members of the pair lie on the basal (001) plane, which is a mirror plane. If the binding is strong enough, pairs at greater distances would be negligible. The rapid reorientation rate is then v_{14}, since this motion is the only way to maintain the pair with a simple interstitial jump. This defect provides an example of an

[001] monoclinic defect in which ν_{14} dominates, so that the low-temperature relaxation behaves as a $\langle 100 \rangle$ orthorhombic defect [see Eqs. (8.9-10) and (8.9-6)]. Still another suggestion is due to Huntington and Sullivan (1965) who postulate a different interstitial site but with the interstitial again bound to a substitutional impurity ion. The defect then has triclinic symmetry, but again gives rise to a frozen-free split. It is clear from the complexities mentioned earlier that the relaxations in reduced rutile require further investigation before a full understanding can be achieved.

B. MAGNESIUM OXIDE

Southgate (1966) has reported that both chromium and iron at levels of 100 ppm cause an internal friction peak near 850°C in MgO single crystals vibrating at $\sim$50 kHz. The peak is of small magnitude (10^{-4}) and has a height which is proportional to the impurity content. The peak shifts with frequency in a manner yielding an activation energy of 2.1 ± 0.1 eV, and the factor τ_0^{-1} is 3×10^{14} sec^{-1}. The peak is exceptionally broad, and may in fact be resolvable into three overlapping Debye peaks. Measurements on $\langle 111 \rangle$ and $\langle 100 \rangle$ oriented samples do not reveal any striking anisotropy to aid in the interpretation. As Southgate has pointed out, the observations suggest a point defect relaxation involving several modes, some of which may result from reactions between different species of defect. Since the impurity solutes Cr and Fe exist either wholly or partially in the trivalent state, it is possible that these defects consist of various configurations of trivalent ions bound to charge compensating vacancies. However, further work is needed to substantiate this hypothesis.

C. GALLIUM ARSENIDE

Another example of relaxation behavior that is probably caused by the stress-induced ordering of point defects is provided by work on GaAs by Chakraverty and Dreyfus (1966). Single crystal specimens grown by the Czochralski method in a slight overpressure of As vapor were tested in flexural vibration at frequencies in the range 12–26 kHz. Measurements taken on cooling a reheated sample revealed a small peak near 150°C. (Some virgin samples also exhibited a transient peak at a somewhat lower temperature on the first heating run.) The activation energy and τ_0^{-1} value of the relaxation were found to be 0.7 eV and 10^{13} sec^{-1}, respectively. The peak is approximately of the Debye shape and is mildly anisotropic, being about twice as large in a $\langle 111 \rangle$ as in a $\langle 100 \rangle$ oriented sample.

Though the peak height showed no correlation with the level of residual impurities (Al, Si, or O_2), it was found to be dependent on heat treatments designed to change the stoichiometry of the samples. Removal of As by a vacuum anneal at 930°C was found to eliminate the peak, and a partial restoration was obtained by a subsequent heat treatment at 1040°C in As vapor at 1 atm pressure. From these results, it may be reasonably concluded that the relaxation is associated with an intrinsic defect produced by an excess of As above the stoichiometric composition. Although the nature of this defect cannot be regarded as established, Chakraverty and Dreyfus have pointed out that a nearest-neighbor pair of Ga vacancies appears to be the simplest defect which could account for the observed kinetics and anisotropy of the relaxation.

D. Niobium Pentoxide

A brief report of relaxation phenomena in pressed and sintered specimens of α-Nb_2O_5 has been given by Makkay and Fine (1962). At a frequency of 100 kHz, an internal friction peak was observed near 50°C, whose shape and position were affected by long time vacuum anneals at the relatively low temperature of 125°C. This treatment, which was observed to change the electrical conductivity, is thought to produce electrically active oxygen vacancies. As yet, however, there is no clear proof that these defects are involved in the relaxation process.

E. Duralumin and Related Alloys

During low-temperature aging following solution-treatment and quenching, the commercial age-hardening alloy Duralumin develops a small but well-defined internal friction peak at 25°C for a frequency of 1.2 kHz (Entwistle, 1953-54, 1956-57). The peak is characterized by an activation energy of 0.59 eV and a frequency factor τ_0^{-1} of 10^{14} sec^{-1}, and is approximately twice as broad as a Debye peak. Since the peak grows during the stage in which solute clustering takes place, it can be inferred that clusters exhibiting a susceptibility to stress-induced ordering are responsible for the relaxation. To gain more information on the identity of these clusters, Entwistle investigated various binary and ternary alloys with compositions based on the proportions of solute elements (Mg, Cu, Si, Mn, Fe) found in the Duralumin alloy. None of these showed the relaxation behavior. The simplest alloys behaving in a manner similar to Duralumin were found to be the quaternary Al–Cu–Mg–Si alloys. Apparently, therefore, the defect or cluster responsible for the relaxation contains several different species of substitutional atoms. The anisotropy of the relaxation in single crystals has been measured by Elliott and Entwistle (1964), with the result $\delta E^{-1}_{\langle 100 \rangle}/\delta E^{-1}_{\langle 111 \rangle} = 3.8$. Unfortunately, little can be said about the defect symmetry from this result, owing to the possibility that a defect reaction, as well as a reorientation, contributes to the relaxation. If it assumed that a reaction is absent, it would follow that the defect symmetry is orthorhombic or lower. The kinetics of the relaxation present two quite significant features: (a) the activation energy is consistent with that for vacancy motion, and (b) that the relaxation time is independent of the general vacancy concentration in the lattice. Berry (1959) has pointed out that these observations suggest that the relaxation centers contain vacant lattice sites as a part of their structure.

F. ICE

Following the first observation of an anelastic relaxation peak in ice crystals by Kneser *et al.* (1955), more detailed measurements were carried out in the same laboratory by Schiller (1958). The work of Schiller examined crystals of ordinary (hexagonal) ice oriented both parallel and perpendicular to the c axis and in both torsional and longitudinal vibrations. In all cases an internal friction peak corresponding to very nearly a single relaxation time was found at 263°K for a frequency of 4 kHz. The kinetic parameters obtained are $Q = 0.58$ eV, $\tau_0 = 3 \times 10^{-16}$ sec. These parameters are essentially the same as those obtained from a large dielectric relaxation peak which had been found for ice some years prior to the anelastic relaxation. Schiller also found that the anelastic peak height was quite large, $\phi_{max} \sim 10^{-2}$, except for longitudinal vibration of a crystal oriented parallel to the c axis (i.e., under type I stress) for which the peak was about an order of magnitude smaller. Such a large relaxation strength is suggestive of a high degree of disorder in the crystal.

In order to discuss this relaxation, it is necessary to review briefly the structure of ice. (For further details, consult Eisenberg and Kauzmann, 1969.) The ice crystal is an example of a hydrogen bonded structure. The oxygens are arranged according to the hexagonal wurtzite structure; each oxygen atom is surrounded by four others to form a nearly ideal tetrahedron with an O–O distance of 2.76 Å. These pairs of oxygen atoms are linked by hydrogen bonds that obey the following "Bernal–Fowler" rules:

1. On each line connecting an O–O pair there exists one and only one H atom.

2. Of the four H's surrounding a given oxygen atom, two are at a close distance (0.99 Å) while the other two are closer to the neighboring oxygen (i.e., at a distance $2.76 - 0.99 = 1.77$ Å).

The second rule shows that the H_2O molecule is preserved in the structure. However, the rules do not uniquely specify the H positions in the crystal. In fact Pauling (1935) showed that the number of hydrogen configurations consistent with these rules in a crystal containing N molecules is $\frac{3}{2}^N$. The crystal therefore contains a highly disordered hydrogen sublattice. One manifestation of this disorder is the large entropy of the crystal. (Neutron diffraction data show that no ordering occurs on cooling to very low temperatures. Rather, the state of disorder becomes frozen in.)

Examination of the structure shows that each H_2O molecule possesses six equivalent orientations and that there are three distinct orientations of the elastic dipole tensor. Thus, the application of stress should give rise to molecular reorientations. To produce such reorientations without the presence of defects, however, would require the cooperative movements of large numbers of molecules, clearly an event of very low probability. Instead defects which can give rise to such reorientations are believed to be present at low concentrations. These are the *Bjerrum defects*, which violate the first Bernal–Fowler rule. (Other defects can also occur which violate the second rule.) A pair of Bjerrum defects forms when an H atom makes a rotation within its own molecule to a neighboring bond, as shown in Fig. 11-38. In this way, we obtain a doubly occupied bond, O—H—H—O, called a D defect, and a vacant

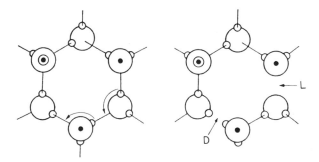

FIG. 11-38.   Schematic representation of the formation and separation of a pair of D and L defects in ice. The c axis is perpendicular to the page. (From Eisenberg and Kauzmann, 1969.)

bond O— — —O, called an L defect, and the migration of either defect produces rotations of H_2O molecules in its path. The D and L defects thus formed may separate by further jumps. The concentrations of such defects are believed to be small ($\sim 10^{-7}$ at $-10°C$) (Gränicher, 1963).

The role of the D and L defects in producing reorientations of the H_2O molecules is analogous to that of vacancies in producing the Zener relaxation in a high-concentration alloy. In both cases, the relaxation occurs because of a change in local atomic order, but the *mechanism* of the relaxation is provided by the presence of defects. The relaxation rate therefore depends on the product of the defect concentration and the defect mobility. The fact that the D and L defects are not the entities which undergo the relaxation in ice is underscored by the large magnitude of the relaxation strength observed.

It is worth emphasizing that the case of ice is somewhat in a different category than most examples considered in this chapter. Here we are dealing with a highly disordered lattice in which the disorder occurs in every molecular position. The concept of relatively isolated point defects developed in Chapter 8 breaks down in such a case.

PROBLEM

11-1. Consider a defect which gives rise to relaxation but which is unstable with respect to annealing, i.e., either it anneals out of the crystal or it undergoes a reaction to form other defects, by a process of migration. Assume that the defect jump which gives rise to reorientation is the same as that for migration. Show that measurement of a relaxation peak due to such an unstable defect must be carried out at a frequency below $\omega \sim N/\Delta t$, where N is the number of defect jumps for appreciable annealing and Δt is the warm-up time of the equipment for an incremental change in temperature. How would this result be changed if reorientation and migration involve different activation energies?

Chapter 12 / Dislocations and Crystal Boundaries

This chapter is intended to provide a review of the material on the theory of dislocations and of crystal boundaries which is essential as background for the next three chapters. It is presented particularly for the benefit of the reader who is not too familiar with dislocation theory. Such a broad topic, however, cannot be treated with any degree of completeness in such a chapter. Accordingly, we direct the reader who wishes to go more deeply into the subject to the general references at the end of the chapter, which is a list of several excellent books and review articles on the subject.

12.1 Definitions, Geometry, and Energetics of Dislocations

In contrast to point defects (Chapter 7) a dislocation is a *line* imperfection, i.e., a defect extending over a macroscopic distance in one dimension. In principle, a dislocation can be created by making a cut in a crystal over a surface S, displacing (or slipping) the part of the crystal above S relative to that below by an amount **b**, and then welding the material back together again (see Fig. 12-1). The slip vector **b** is called the *Burgers vector*. When **b** is a simple lattice translation, the perfect lattice is restored everywhere except at the curve C which bounds the surface S (i.e., which separates the slipped area from the unslipped area). This curve then constitutes the dislocation. Clearly a dislocation must either be a closed curve, or it must terminate on the boundary of the crystal. For a planar dislocation (as in Fig. 12-1), or in general, for any small segment of a dislocation line, we may define the *slip plane* as the plane determined by the dislocation line and the Burgers vector. For example, in the case of the dislocation of Fig. 12-1 the slip plane is the plane of the page.

The two simplest types of straight dislocations are the edge and the screw types. For the *edge dislocation* the surface S can be taken as a portion of a plane bounded by the crystal surfaces on three sides and on the fourth by a straight line extending completely across the crystal

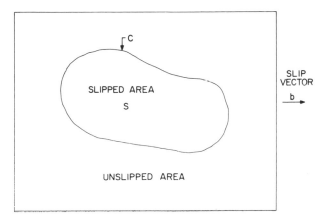

FIG. 12-1. Formation of a dislocation along a curve C by producing slip across an area S. The slip vector **b** is the "Burgers vector."

(see Fig. 12-2). The Burgers vector **b** is perpendicular to this line. The structure of such a dislocation is shown in Fig. 12-3. Part (b) of this figure, which gives a view perpendicular to the dislocation line, shows that one may also conceptually create the edge dislocation by inserting an extra half-plane into the crystal perpendicular to the slip plane. The symbol commonly used for an edge dislocation is ⊥, where the vertical line marks the extra half-plane and the horizontal line designates the slip plane. On a given slip plane the edge dislocation may take on two orientations or "signs," corresponding to whether the extra half-plane lies above or below the slip plane. It is clear that by moving the dislocation line along the slip plane, the slipped area can be made to grow larger or to

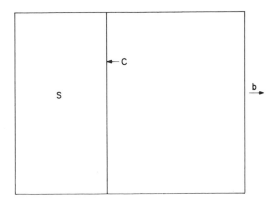

FIG. 12-2. Formation of a straight edge dislocation. The dislocation line is perpendicular to **b**.

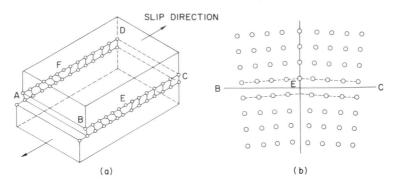

(a)

(b)

FIG. 12-3.   Structure of an edge dislocation in a simple cubic crystal. (a) Slip plane *ABCD* is divided by dislocation line *EF* into slipped region *ABEF* and unslipped region *FECD*. (b) View perpendicular to the line *EF* showing atomic arrangement.

diminish in size. The defining characteristic of an edge dislocation is actually the fact that the dislocation line lies perpendicular to **b**. In order to meet this requirement the dislocation need not be straight; there is more generally the possibility for forming an edge-type dislocation as an irregular curve which lies in a plane perpendicular to **b**.

The *screw dislocation*, by contrast, is defined as one for which the dislocation line is parallel to **b**. In this case the dislocation must be straight. A screw dislocation is illustrated in Fig. 12-4. Figure 12-4a shows the slip plane with dislocation line *EF*, while Fig. 12-4b looks at the atomic arrangement above and below the slip plane. It is interesting to note

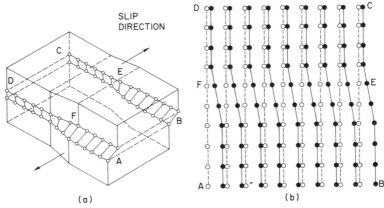

(a)

(b)

FIG. 12-4.   Structure of a screw dislocation. (a) Slip plane *ABCD* is divided by dislocation line *EF* into slipped region *ABEF* and unslipped region *FECD*. (b) View of plane *ABCD* from above, showing atomic arrangement in upper plane (●) and lower plane (○).

that a crystal with a single screw dislocation is no longer made up of parallel atomic planes one above the other, but has become a single atomic plane in the form of a helicoid (spiral ramp). The two possible directions of spiraling (i.e., right-hand and left-hand screws) correspond to the two signs of a screw dislocation. The slip plane of a screw dislocation is not defined since **b** and the dislocation line are parallel to each other and therefore do not define a plane. It is therefore proper to regard any plane through the dislocation as a slip plane.

A general dislocation may be neither of screw nor of edge type since **b** may make an arbitrary angle with the dislocation line. Such an imperfection is often called a mixed dislocation. Also a general dislocation need not be straight. It may therefore have segments which are perpendicular and parallel to **b** and which are then said to have edge or screw character, respectively.

Due to the strain field about a dislocation, energy is required to create it. The energy per unit length of a dislocation line varies in general with the orientation of the dislocation. For an isotropic medium, this energy may be taken as nearly constant, so that, to a first approximation, a dislocation acts like a one-dimensional soap film with line tension γ equal to the energy per unit length. The approximate value of this line tension is

$$\gamma \sim \tfrac{1}{2}Gb^2 \qquad (12.1\text{-}1)$$

where G is the shear modulus and b the magnitude of the Burgers vector. A dislocation in a real crystal does, however, have a preference for certain planes and directions. For example, the dislocation line is much more stable when it lies in a close-packed plane (which constitutes a slip plane) than in an arbitrary direction. A dislocation whose mean direction is not in a slip plane may, therefore, consist of a series of sections located in neighboring slip planes and connected by steps normal to these planes and one interatomic distance in length. Such a step is called a *jog*. Figure 12-5 illustrates edge dislocations on two neighboring planes connected by a jog. Since the entire dislocation line must have the same Burgers vector, the jog is, in fact, also an edge dislocation segment.

In addition to a preference for lying in a close-packed plane, dislocations may also be expected to have a preference for a close-packed direction. The potential energy of such a dislocation line must be a periodic function of its displacement, as shown in Fig. 12-6. Since the original analysis of this potential was given by Peierls, this periodic potential is called the Peierls potential and the low-energy position, a Peierls valley

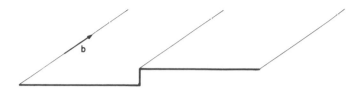

FIG. 12-5.   Illustrating an edge dislocation line (heavy line) which contains a jog. The entire dislocation line is perpendicular to **b**.

or well. Peierls and Nabarro have approximated this potential in the form

$$U(x) = \tfrac{1}{2}U_0[1 - \cos(2\pi x/a)] \qquad (12.1\text{-}2)$$

The quantity U_0 is the difference in energy per unit length for the dislocation at the top and bottom of the well. A dislocation which lies in an arbitrary direction in the slip plane may then be expected to develop a kinked structure as shown in Fig. 12-7, in order to take advantage of the Peierls potential, i.e. of the lower energy per unit length along the close-packed direction. Such kinks on arbitrary oriented dislocations are called *geometrical* (or "built-in") *kinks*, in contrast to those produced by thermal activation on dislocation segments which lie along the Peierls valley. Kinks are not expected to be as abrupt as jogs, but rather are estimated to be about 10–50 atom distances in width.[†] Thus, for a dislocation

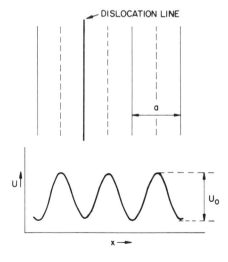

FIG. 12-6.   Upper part shows the location of the Peierls valleys (—) and Peierls hills (---) for a dislocation along a simple crystallographic direction. Lower part shows the form of the potential curve for the dislocation.

[†] The kink width is determined as a compromise, between the dislocation line tension (which tends to make the dislocation straight) on the one hand, and the Peierls potential (which tends to make the transition between valleys abrupt) on the other.

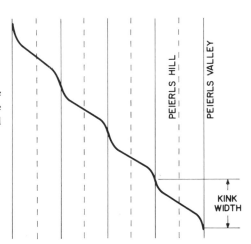

FIG. 12-7. A dislocation line whose average direction lies at an angle to the Peierls valleys, showing the kinked structure.

oriented such that the spacing of the kinks is smaller than the kink width, the kink structure should disappear and the dislocation should become essentially straight.

Up to this point the Burgers vector **b** has always been taken as a lattice vector. If, however, **b** is a displacement which produces a twin orientation, a twinned surface or stacking fault is then created terminating on dislocation lines. Since the stacking fault possesses substantial surface energy, it is usually limited in extent to the area that falls between two parallel dislocation lines called *partial dislocations*. The system of two partial dislocations connected by a stacking fault as illustrated in Fig. 12-8 is called an *extended* dislocation. In such a dislocation the sum of **b**₁ and **b**₂ must be a lattice vector. Since the elastic energy of a dislocation is proportional to b^2 [see Eq. (12.1-1)], the criterion for a dislocation to split into partials is that $b_1^2 + b_2^2 < b^2$.

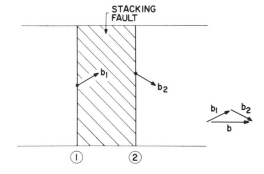

FIG. 12-8. Illustration of a pair of partial dislocations connected by a stacking fault (extended dislocation). The area to the right of dislocation 2 has slipped by a lattice vector **b**, while that between 1 and 2 has slipped by **b**₁.

A real crystal generally contains a network of dislocations where three dislocations join at each node. A convenient measure of the *dislocation density* is Λ, the total length of all dislocation lines in a unit volume. The quantity Λ is clearly expressed in units of cm^{-2}. For the case of an idealized distribution of dislocations in which all dislocation lines are parallel to each other, Λ represents the number of dislocation lines threading through a unit area perpendicular to the dislocations.

12.2 Motion of Dislocations

The existence of a strain field about a dislocation means that when external stresses are applied to the crystal an energy gradient will be created for the dislocation, or a "force" may be said to be exerted on the dislocation line. The direction of this force on a dislocation is perpendicular to the dislocation line, and its magnitude per unit length F_l is given by

$$F_l = \sigma b \qquad (12.2\text{-}1)$$

where b is the magnitude of the Burgers vector and σ is the shear stress acting on the slip plane and in the slip direction. Since b is the same for all segments of a dislocation line, the force F_l has the same magnitude all along the dislocation line. In response to this force the dislocation will attempt to move. There are two basic types of motion. The first, called *glide* (or conservative motion) involves motion in the slip plane. Such motion is nothing more than the enlarging or diminishing of the original slip area associated with the definition of the dislocation. It is easy to see from Figs. 12-3 and 12-4 that only slight readjustment of atoms near the dislocation can produce displacement of the dislocation line by one additional atomic distance. Thus, glide motion is a relatively easy process. The second type of dislocation motion is called *climb* (or nonconservative motion) and involves the movement of the dislocation in a direction perpendicular to its slip plane. This process must be accompanied by dilatational changes, e.g., vacancies or interstitial atoms created or absorbed in the vicinity of the dislocation. This is most easily seen from Fig. 12-3b showing the simple edge dislocation. In order to climb out of its slip plane, this edge dislocation requires either a lengthening or shortening of the extra half-plane. Such a result can only be obtained by diffusing atoms into or out of the region of the dislocation. Similar diffusion is required for the climb of any dislocation with partly edge character. For a screw dislocation, on the other hand, any plane is a glide plane, so that climb does not occur. Clearly climb must be associated with a substantial activation energy, usually equal to that for self-diffusion, since both the formation and migration of defects are involved. The process of climb therefore normally occurs only at elevated temperatures.

Because of the importance of dislocation glide in various internal friction phenomena, we will now discuss this type of dislocation motion in further detail. We first consider the case of a dislocation which lies in a Peierls valley, as shown in Fig. 12-6. In terms of Eq. (12.2-1) and the potential of the form of Eq. (12.1-2), the external stress required to overcome this potential barrier (called the Peierls stress σ_p) is

$$\sigma_p = \pi U_0 / ab \qquad (12.2\text{-}2)$$

where a is the spacing between Peierls valleys, as in Fig. 12-6. For an applied stress lower than σ_p, the dislocation cannot glide as an entity. Nevertheless, glide motion can still take place by a process of kink generation. This involves advancing a length L of dislocation into the next Peierls well by the thermally activated formation of a pair of kinks of opposite sign, as shown in Fig. 12-9. Clearly, the applied stress must

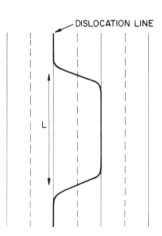

DISLOCATION LINE

FIG. 12-9. A dislocation line advancing a segment L from one Peierls valley to the next by the formation of a pair of kinks of opposite sign.

L

be sufficient to overcome the attractive force between two kinks which attempts to annihilate them and thereby to reduce the dislocation length. An important quantity in the theory of kink-pair generation is the energy of a kink W_k. By solving the differential equation for the shape of a dislocation crossing the Peierls barrier, Seeger (1956) obtained for the relation between W_k and σ_p

$$W_k = (2a/\pi)(2ab\gamma\sigma_p/\pi)^{1/2} \qquad (12.2\text{-}3)$$

where γ is given by Eq. (12.1-1). As we shall see in Chapter 13, the Bordoni relaxation effect appears to offer the most direct way to determine σ_p experimentally via Eq. (12.2-3).

The opposite extreme to the dislocation in a Peierls valley is one at a sufficiently high angle to a close-packed direction that there is no geometrical kink structure, i.e., the dislocation is straight. For such a dislocation, there may be a negligible obstacle to glide motion under stress. On the other hand, there can be a limitation to the motion of such a dislocation if it is a segment which is part of a dislocation network. In this case the dislocation is pinned at nodes (intersection points). Also it can be pinned by impurities or precipitate particles. In any of these cases the effect of an applied stress is to produce a bowing of the dislocation segment between its pinning points (as shown in Fig. 12-10, where

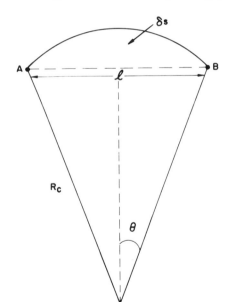

FIG. 12-10. A dislocation segment of length l pinned at points A and B bows into an arc of radius of curvature R_c under an applied stress.

A and B are the pinning points) in a manner analogous to a stretched string of length l. The curvature of such a dislocation segment depends on the balance between the force per unit length due to the applied stress, Eq. (12.2-1), and the line tension (energy per unit length) due to the increase in length of the bowed out segment [Eq. (12.1-1)]. When these two contributions are set equal (Problem 12-1), an expression for the radius of curvature R_c results

$$R_c = \gamma/\sigma b = \tfrac{1}{2}Gb/\sigma \qquad (12.2\text{-}4)$$

The smallest possible value of R_c occurs when the dislocation segment takes the shape of a semicircle. In this case $R_c = l/2$. If the segment bows out beyond this point, R_c increases and a complete dislocation loop can be generated. This is just the "Frank–Read mechanism" for dislocation multiplication. From Eq. (12.2-4) it is clear that the critical stress σ_0 for dislocation multiplication is given by $\sigma_0 \simeq Gb/l$.

Returning to the case of small σ, and therefore small curvature, we can calculate the area δs between the chord and the arc AB in Fig. 12-10 (Problem 12-2)

$$\delta s = (2/3)R_c{}^2\theta^3 \simeq (2/3)R_c{}^2(l/2R_c)^3 = (1/12)(l^3/R_c) \quad (12.2\text{-}5)$$

In order to calculate the strain produced when a dislocation bows out in this manner, we recall that when a dislocation line moves completely across the slip plane it produces slip by an amount b and therefore (for a cube 1 cm on edge) a strain b. The sweeping out of an area δs of the slip plane should therefore give a proportionate amount of strain. If the crystal under consideration had N_v such dislocation segments per unit volume, we obtain for the strain ε_d due to the bowing out of these dislocations under stress

$$\varepsilon_d \simeq b(\delta s)N_v \quad (12.2\text{-}6)$$

The compliance or reciprocal shear modulus may be taken as composed of two parts as follows:

$$\varepsilon/\sigma = G^{-1} + (\varepsilon_d/\sigma) \quad (12.2\text{-}7)$$

where G is the modulus in the absence of dislocations. Since the dislocation contribution to the modulus is usually small, we may write

$$\Delta G/G = -\varepsilon_d G/\sigma \quad (12.2\text{-}8)$$

where ΔG is the difference between the modulus with and without dislocations. Combining Eq. (12.2-8) with Eqs. (12.2-4)–(12.2-6) we obtain

$$\Delta G/G \simeq -\beta N_v l^3 = -\beta \Lambda l^2 \quad (12.2\text{-}9)$$

where β is a numerical constant, here equal to $\tfrac{1}{6}$, and the definition of Λ as the total dislocation length per cm³ (i.e., $\Lambda = N_v l$) has been utilized. Equation (12.2-9) is the expression for the *modulus defect due to dislocations*. It states that the shear modulus of a crystal with dislocations is lower than that of the same crystal without dislocations by an amount proportional to the dislocation density and the square of the loop length. [†] This dislocation anomaly can be quite significant, especially in pure crystals. For example, for typical values $\Lambda \sim 10^8/cm^2$, $l \sim 3 \times 10^{-5}$ cm (i.e., 1000 atom distances) we obtain $\Delta G/G \sim 1\%$. When the pinning of the dislocation lines is by impurities or defects, one expects a distribution in the value of l due to the distribution of pinning points along dislocation lines. The mean value of l is given by $\bar{l} = a/X$, where X is the fraction of sites along the dislocation occupied by impurities and a the atomic spacing. Nevertheless, Koehler (1952) has shown that Eq. (12.2-9) still applies with $\bar{l}$ substituted for l, except for a change in the magnitude of the constant factor β (see Problem 12-4).

The above description of the modulus defect due to dislocations is often referred to as the "string model" because of the analogy between a dislocation line which is pinned at both ends and under constant line tension, and a stretched string. On the other hand, the modulus defect may be calculated from the viewpoint of a model of a dislocation containing geometrical kinks. The results obtained from the kink picture, both for modulus defect and internal friction (see Chapter 14), are not substantially different from those of the string model so long as the dislocation displacements are small. At high amplitudes, or under bias stress, substantial differences appear. The subject of kinks in dislocations has been treated in detail by Seeger and Schiller (1966).

Bradfield and Pursey (1953) have demonstrated the modulus defect due to dislocations in a study of copper-based alloys. Their data, reproduced in Fig. 12-11, show that Young's modulus[‡] for various copper-based alloys, when plotted against concentration of solute, and extrapolated back to zero solute concentration gives essentially the same value; however this value is about 3% higher than that obtained directly on high purity Cu. The discrepancy is attributed to the modulus defect due to dislocations, in accordance with Eq. (12.2-9). The effect of adding solute is to eliminate quickly the dislocation contribution to the modulus because of the pinning of dislocations by impurity atoms (see Section 12.3), which rapidly causes a decrease in the effective value of l. A detailed

---

[†] The fact that $\Delta G/G$ is proportional to Λl^2 can also be obtained by dimensional analysis. A more refined calculation, taking account of the distribution of glide systems, gives Eq. (12.2-9) but with $\beta \simeq 1/20$ (see Friedel *et al.*, 1955).

[‡] Although Eq. (12.2-9) refers to the shear modulus, it should be realized that the effect also occurs for Young's modulus, since longitudinal deformation may be analyzed into pure shear plus hydrostatic deformation (see Problem 12-5).

analysis of this data is given by Friedel (1953). Other manifestations of this dislocation anomaly are shown in the work of Thompson and Holmes (1956) and of Gordon and Nowick (1956). The former authors irradiate high-purity Cu with neutrons and show that the modulus rises to a saturation value for relatively small amounts of radiation. In the latter work freshly cold-worked NaCl crystals were used, and the radiation with x rays was shown to produce a rise in the modulus. In both cases the effects obtained were attributed to the pinning of dislocation loops by the

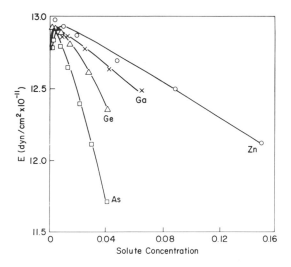

FIG. 12-11.   Variation of Young's modulus with the concentration of solute in various copper-based alloys. (From Bradfield and Pursey, 1953.)

irradiation produced defects.[†] Perhaps the largest modulus defect due to dislocations was that observed by Brouwer (1965) who obtained a value as high as 23%. All of these experiments add up to the rather remarkable fact that if one wishes to measure precisely the shear modulus characteristic of a pure perfect crystal, the very highest purity and well-annealed material should *not* be used. Rather, to obtain the correct value, one must use slightly impure or irradiated material, in order to eliminate the dislocation contribution.

Dislocations which oscillate under an alternating stress also contribute to the internal friction, i.e., to the portion of the strain that is out of phase with the stress. Such contributions will be considered in Chapter 14.

[†] For more quantitative considerations, see Section 14.2.

12.3   Interaction of Dislocations with Other Imperfections

The motion of a dislocation is strongly affected by its interaction with other lattice imperfections, such as other dislocations and point defects. We have already seen that an external stress exerts a force on a dislocation [Eq. (12.2-1)]. Similar effects must, of course, arise due to the internal stresses produced by other dislocations. Diagrams showing the atomic arrangement about dislocations, such as Figs. 12-3 and 12-4, clearly show that there is a stress field about a dislocation. The form of the stress field is easily calculated for simple dislocations only for the case of an isotropic elastic medium. In such a case the stress field varies as $1/r$ for a straight dislocation line in an infinite medium (where r is

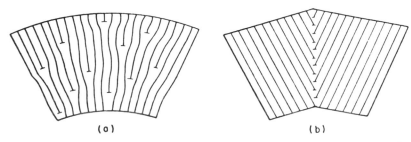

(o)   (b)

FIG. 12-12.   Schematic illustration of (a) edge dislocations in a bent crystal, (b) alignment of edge dislocations to produce a low-angle boundary through dislocation climb (polygonization). (From Washburn and Parker, 1952.)

the radial distance from the dislocation line). As a consequence of this stress field, dislocations interact with each other. For edge dislocations of the same sign, the effect of these dislocation interactions is to tend to produce vertical alignment of the dislocations into walls or low-angle boundaries, as illustrated in Fig. 12-12. This process, called *polygonization*, requires the climb of dislocations in order to bring some of them out of the slip plane of others. Therefore, it takes place during relatively high-temperature annealing.

Probably the most important manifestation of the interaction of dislocations with each other is the shape of the stress–strain curve obtained during the course of plastic deformation. For single crystals of fcc metals, in particular, the stress–strain curve may be divided into three parts, as shown in Fig. 12-13. The first part, region I, is often called the *easy glide* region. Its extent depends strongly on the orientation of the crystal with respect to the stress axis, and it is characterized by relatively un-

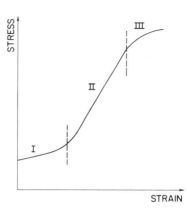

Fig. 12-13.   Schematic diagram of a typical stress–strain curve of an fcc metal crystal.

impeded dislocation motion on only one of the twelve possible {111} ⟨110⟩ glide systems. Region II is the steep, essentially straight line, region involving a high rate of work hardening. The slope of this part of the curve is insensitive to temperature and impurity content. Region II begins when enough dislocation movement has occurred on other than the primary slip system to generate obstructions (particularly the so-called Lomer–Cottrell barriers), and the high rate of work hardening is related to elastic interactions of the primary dislocations with these barriers. Finally, region III, which terminates in facture, shows a continuously decreasing slope and is markedly temperature dependent. It is probably controlled by cross slip of screw dislocations, which is a thermally activated process.

The interaction of dislocations with solute atoms may also be of elastic origin. For an isotropic medium, an oversized or undersized solute atom of radius $r_0(1 + \delta)$, where r_0 is the radius of the solvent, interacts with the hydrostatic component of the stress field of an edge dislocation according to the Cottrell formula for the elastic interaction or binding energy

$$U_b = \alpha G b r_0{}^3 \delta (\sin \theta / R) \qquad (12.3\text{-}1)$$

Here α is a constant ~ 0.2, while R and θ are the polar coordinates of the position of the impurity relative to the edge dislocation line as shown in Fig. 12-14. With decreasing R this equation must break down as $R \to 0$, since the interaction energy must become a constant at about one or two atomic distances from the dislocation core. Equation (12.3-1) shows that an oversized solute atom ($\delta > 0$) is in its most stable position below the extra half-plane of the dislocation, while an undersized atom is incorporated into the extra half-plane, just as one would expect intuitively.

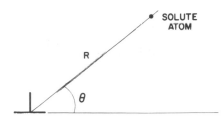

FIG. 12-14. A solute atom in the stress field of an edge dislocation.

The elastic interaction of a solute atom with a screw dislocation in an isotropic medium can occur only for a defect which produces non-spherical distortion, i.e., an elastic dipole, since the stress field of the screw dislocation has no hydrostatic component. A point defect may also interact with a screw dislocation by virtue of the local change in elastic constants which it produces (see Friedel 1964, Section 13.3.3). Also, if a screw dislocation splits into an extended dislocation, each of the partials must have a substantial edge component. Thus for the various reasons given, solute atoms will be attracted to dislocations by virtue of elastic interactions, and will tend to cluster about the dislocation line. There are sources of interaction other than the elastic type, as follows. For extended dislocations, there is the *chemical interaction* which originates in the difference in solute concentration in the stacking fault and in the lattice itself. *Electrical interaction* can also exist depending on the valency of the solute atom. In metals, these electrical interactions are weaker than the elastic interactions; stronger electrical interactions probably exist in ionic crystals.

As a consequence of the existence of a binding free energy g_b between a solute atom and a dislocation,[†] solute atoms in thermal equilibrium will occupy a fraction of sites X on the dislocation given by

$$X \simeq X_0 \exp(g_b/kT) \tag{12.3-2}$$

where X_0 is the average mole fraction of impurity atoms. Equation (12.3-2) is actually valid only for $X \ll 1$, i.e., far from a condition of saturation of the dislocation. The stress required to break away a disloca-tion from an impurity can be estimated with the aid of Eq. (12.2-1). From this equation it is clear that the work required to move a disloca-

---

[†] Actually g_b is a function of position about the dislocation, having positive values on one side of the slip plane and negative values on the other side, for the case of an edge dislocation. Thus, solute atoms form a cloud or "atmosphere" about the dislocation. The value of g_b which appears in Eq. (12.3-2) is then that which applies at favorable sites at the core of the dislocation, where g_b takes on maximum positive values.

tion segment of length l over an interatomic distance a is

$$\text{work} = \sigma bal \tag{12.3-3}$$

In the case of a dislocation pinned by impurities, the average value of the spacing is $\bar{l} = a/X$. Ignoring the fact that l values have a distribution, the critical stress σ_c required to produce breakaway at low temperatures is obtained approximately by setting g_b equal to the work in Eq. (12.3-3), or

$$\sigma_c = g_b X/a^2 b \tag{12.3-4}$$

For typical values of $g_b \sim 0.1$ eV and $X \sim 10^{-3}$, σ_c turns out to be $\sim 10^{-5}G$, where G is the shear modulus. Thus, breakaway may be anticipated for the strain amplitudes used in typical internal friction experiments. At finite temperatures and lower stresses, thermal fluctuations may aid breakaway, the probability for the occurrence of breakaway being proportional to $\exp[-(g_b - \sigma abl)/kT]$.

The phenomenon of *strain aging* is related to the pinning of dislocations by impurities which migrate to them. Annealing of a dilute alloy following deformation results in the reestablishment of impurity atmospheres about the dislocations. This aging process may then lead to recovery of the sharp yield point observed in certain alloys at the beginning of the stress–strain curve.

Vacancies and interstitials are also attracted to dislocations for the same reasons as solute atoms. The main difference between these structural point defects and solute atoms is that the structural defects can be completely absorbed in the extra half-plane of an edge dislocation. The mechanism can be understood in terms of jogs, such as that illustrated in Fig. 12-5. Vacancies arriving at this dislocation can move along the dislocation to the jog and simply displace the jog by one atomic spacing along the dislocation axis. In this way the vacancy is absorbed or annihilated without altering the character of the dislocation. A similar situation applies for the absorption of an interstitial defect, except that the jog shifts in the opposite direction.

The reciprocal process is also possible, i.e., the generation of defects at a jog. This provides one means by which defect equilibrium can be achieved when the temperature is raised. The fact that dislocations serve as sources and sinks for point defects means that the time constant for the establishment of equilibrium is much less than one would anticipate if diffusion to external surfaces were required.

In nonthermal processes, specifically during plastic flow, nonequilibrium point defects can be generated in several ways. Probably the most important of these is by the dragging of a jog on a screw dislocation (such jogs can be formed by dislocation intersections). In the case of a screw dislocation the jog has edge character, since that short segment of dislocation line runs perpendicular to **b**. Motion of such a jog along with the rest of the screw dislocation involves a climb process. At temperatures sufficiently low that no diffusion can take place, the jog may be dragged along with the gliding screw dislocation, leaving behind a row of vacancies or of interstitials.

The annealing out of point defects produced by low-temperature deformation in the noble metals has been studied extensively by means of resistivity measurements. Annealing stages are observed near 150° and 250°K in typical cases. Changes in elastic moduli upon annealing are also observed. These are attributed to the pinning of dislocations by point defects which are generated by the deformation and migrate to the dislocations upon annealing the sample. Some examples of studies of the modulus defect phenomenon following low-temperature deformation are those of Lems (1962, 1964) and of Druyvesteyn *et al.* (1959).

12.4   Grain Boundaries

A boundary between two crystals of the same kind can be defined by the relative angular tilt or twist of the two crystals and by the orientation of the surface between them relative to the axes of one of them. In all, five degrees of freedom are involved. It is convenient to distinguish between *low-angle boundaries* for which the angles of relative tilt or twist are small, and *high-angle boundaries* for which these angles are large. A low-angle boundary or "subboundary" can be described as an array of dislocations. The simplest example is a symmetric tilt boundary, which is equivalent to a row of parallel edge dislocations of spacing h related to the angle of tilt θ by the formula

$$\theta \simeq b/h \qquad (12.4\text{-}1)$$

where b is the magnitude of the Burgers vector. Such a boundary can be produced by polygonization of a bent crystal, as shown in Fig. 12-12. Similarly, a simple twist boundary may be formed by introducing a square network of screw dislocations.

High-angle boundaries may also be described as arrays of dislocations, but the dislocation spacing required is then of the order of the interatomic spacing, and the dislocations lose their individual identity. The properties of the boundary are then not readily calculable from those of the individual dislocations, so that most of the value of the dislocation model is lost. For a rather long period of time, the description of a high-angle grain boundary did not proceed much beyond the self-evident statement that it represented a transition region between two crystals of different orientation. Considerable debate arose on the question of whether this region was so disorganized that it could be regarded as an "amorphous cement" between adjacent grains, as opposed to the view that it possessed a periodicity of structure which could more properly be described as a "transition lattice" between the two crystals. Subsequently, an intermediate view was proposed in Mott's (1948) "island" model. Mott suggested that the boundary may contain areas or islands across which the atoms of the two adjoining crystals showed good matching, surrounded by regions of relatively poor fit. A variety of more recent work has served to emphasize that the degree of disorder present in a high-angle boundary may be very sensitive to the particular orientation relationship between the grains. (For example, a twin boundary is a high-angle boundary of a definite crystallographic nature.) The work of Aust and Rutter (1959) provides clear evidence for the existence of "special" boundaries which have a high rate of migration that is little affected by impurities. These special boundaries have been shown to occur at orientations which permit a high coincidence of sites in the boundary for atoms from the two adjacent crystals (Brandon, 1966; Brandon et al., 1964). Recent work using both electron and field-ion microscopy suggests that a minor misorientation from such a special high-coincidence boundary may be accommodated, as for a low-angle subboundary, by the additional introduction of a grid of dislocations. From the progress made to date (see Aust and Chalmers, 1970 for a recent review) it is already clear that the phrase "high-angle boundary" encompasses a wide range of structures which can exhibit widely different properties.

Impurities may be expected to segregate preferentially to grain boundaries, just as they do to individual dislocations, and for the same reasons (elastic, chemical, and electrical). When the boundary sites are far from saturated, the relative numbers of solute atoms in the boundary and in the lattice are given by

$$N_{gb}/N_l \simeq (6t/L) \exp(W_b/kT) \qquad (12.4\text{-}2)$$

where t is the effective thickness of the boundary, L the grain size, and W_b is the binding energy.

From the viewpoint of anelasticity, the most interesting property of a boundary is its mobility. Two kinds of motion are possible: "migration," which involves motion of the boundary normal to itself, and "shear," involving motion parallel to itself. A small-angle tilt boundary can undergo migration simply through the gliding of the edge dislocations which constitute the boundary. Other boundaries require more complex mechanisms involving vacancy flow, which are not well understood. Migration has been studied extensively during the process of recrystallization upon annealing after severe deformation. The velocity of boundary motion v obeys an equation of the form

$$v = AF \exp(-Q/kT) \qquad (12.4\text{-}3)$$

where A is a constant, F is the force on the boundary (free energy gained per unit displacement), and Q is an effective activation energy. It is found that Q is very sensitive to impurity content, being much less than the self-diffusion activation energy in metals of very high purity.

An important mode of deformation at high temperatures is by a stress-induced diffusion mechanism in which the grain boundaries provide the

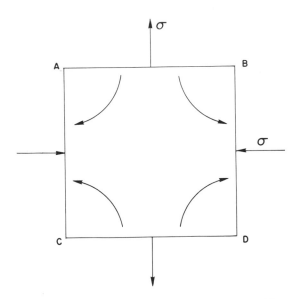

FIG. 12-15.   Illustration of the flow of vacancies between crystal boundaries, induced by a shear stress.

sources and sinks for vacancies. The mechanism, originally proposed by Nabarro (1947) and further developed by Herring (1950) and others, is called *Nabarro–Herring creep*. Figure 12-15 provides the basic picture in which a crystal with boundaries $ABCD$ is subjected to shear consisting of a compressive stress σ in one direction and equal tension in a perpendicular direction. The effect of this stress is clearly to induce a net vacancy flow as shown, with boundaries AB and CD serving as vacancy sources and the side faces as sinks. A straightforward calculation (e.g. see Friedel, 1964, Section 11.3.1) gives a creep rate

$$\dot{\varepsilon} = \alpha D b^3 \sigma / L^2 k T \qquad (12.4\text{-}4)$$

where L is the grain size, D the self-diffusion coefficient and α a numerical coefficient. For equiaxed grains, Herring (1950) obtained a value $\alpha = 25$. Equation (12.4-4) represents a strictly viscous creep flow.

For subboundaries (polygonization walls), or even isolated dislocations, a similar expression is also obtained, but the creep rate is then more rapid due to the smaller distance L involved.

PROBLEMS

12-1. Verify Eq. (12.2-4) for the radius of curvature of a dislocation loop under an applied stress σ by equating the force per unit length to the restoring force which originates in the line tension.

12-2. Verify Eq. (12.2-5) with the aid of Fig. 12-10.

12-3. Show that for a uniform three-dimensional network of dislocations with intersection points spaced at a distance l, $\Lambda l^2 = 3$. Note that from Eq. (12.2-9) with numerical factor $\beta \sim 1/20$ (to allow for the distribution of glide systems), this result corresponds to a modulus defect of $\sim 15\%$.

12-4. Show that solute atoms arranged at random along a dislocation line lead to a probability distribution of free length l given by $P(l)\,dl = (X/a)\exp(-Xl/a)\,dl$, where X is the fraction of occupied sites and a the atomic spacing along the dislocation. Then show that Eq. (12.2-9) is obtained with $\beta = 1$.

12-5. Using Eq. (6.2-12), obtain the Young's modulus defect due to dislocations $\Delta E/E$ in terms of $\Delta G/G$.

General References

AMELINCKX, S., and DEKEYSER, W. (1959). *Solid State Phys.* **8**, 327.

COTTRELL, A. H. (1953). "Dislocations and Plastic Flow in Crystals." Oxford Univ. Press, London and New York.

COTTRELL, A. H. (1964). "Theory of Crystal Dislocations." Gordon and Breach, New York.

FRIEDEL, J. (1964). "Dislocations," Pergamon, Oxford.

HIRTH, J. P., and LOTHE, J. (1968). "Theory of Dislocations." McGraw-Hill, New York.

McLEAN, D. (1962). "Grain Boundaries in Metals." Oxford Univ. Press, London and New York.

NABARRO, F. R. N. (1967). "Theory of Crystal Dislocations." Oxford Univ. Press (Clarendon), London and New York.

READ, W. T., JR. (1953). "Dislocations in Crystals." McGraw-Hill, New York.

SEEGER, A. (1955). *Encycl. Phys.* **7**, 383.

VAN BUEREN, H. G. (1960). "Imperfections in Crystals." North-Holland Publ., Amsterdam.

WEERTMAN, J., and WEERTMAN, J. R. (1964). "Elementary Dislocation Theory." Macmillan, New York.

Chapter **13** | Dislocation Relaxations

The characteristics of dislocations covered in Chapter 12 show that dislocation displacements give rise to shear strain, and correspondingly, that the application of the conjugate shear stress acts to produce dislocation motion. Accordingly, a dislocation displacement meets the conditions of Eqs. (5.1-1) and (5.1-2) for an internal variable that can give rise to anelastic behavior. It is also required, however, that the motion be sufficiently restricted that it will lag behind the applied stress, in accordance with Eq. (5.1-3). Such a restriction may occur when potential barriers or obstacles (e.g., point defects) are present which impede the dislocation motion.

This chapter deals with several relaxation effects, observable as internal friction peaks, which are reasonably well established as due to dislocation motion. In almost all cases, the material must be in a deformed or "cold-worked" state in order that the peak in question can be observed. The cold-worked state is known to possess a very complex defect structure, including the presence of point defects generated by the deformation process as well as many types of complex dislocation configurations. A peak observed in a cold-worked material may then be due to point defects alone, to dislocations alone (one or more of the several types that are present), or to dislocations in combination with point defects (as a consequence of their interactions).

Of all the relaxation peaks observed in cold-worked materials, the one that has attracted the most attention is that originally observed by Bordoni in fcc metals and now called the "Bordoni peak" (Section 13.1). The attractive aspects of this relaxation are primarily related to its reproducibility and its relative stability toward annealing before recrystallization. It has been generally attributed to dislocations alone, yet there has been great difficulty in establishing the exact mechanism of the effect. Some of the numerous theories advanced for this effect are reviewed in Section 13.2. The question of whether materials other than the fcc metals show this same phenomenon has been difficult to answer (Sections 13.4 and

13.5). Other peaks in deformed materials appear to involve interacting combinations of point defects and dislocations. Notable among these are the Hasiguti peaks (Section 13.3) and the Snoek–Köster peak (Section 13.6). In the latter phenomenon, which has been widely investigated, the point defect is an interstitial impurity, such as nitrogen or oxygen.

13.1 Description of the Bordoni Peak in fcc Metals

The appearance of a low-temperature internal friction peak in cold-worked fcc metals was first reported by Bordoni (1949, 1954) for the metals Cu, Pb, Al, and Ag. In each case, the peak appeared, for frequencies of ∼10 kHz, at a temperature about one-third the Debye temperature (e.g., 80°K for Cu). The existence of such a relaxation phenomenon, presumably related to dislocations, attracted considerable attention. Prior to Bordoni's work, dislocation damping was always found to be strongly amplitude dependent, originating in a static hysteresis mechanism rather than in relaxation (see Chapter 14). The Bordoni peak, on the other hand, is essentially independent of strain amplitude over a wide range (Niblett and Wilks, 1957; Caswell, 1958; Paré, 1961). The amplitude independence, plus the fact that the peak is relatively well defined and reproducible, suggests true anelastic behavior. As in all relaxation phenomena, the experimental quantities of interest are the peak height (relaxation strength), the peak position (giving an activation energy and frequency factor), and the peak width and shape. The dependence of each of these quantities on appropriate variables will now be considered in turn. The extent to which the experimental results eliminate certain categories of mechanisms will also be mentioned, in preparation for the detailed discussion of mechanisms in Section 13.2.

That the Bordoni peak is general to all fcc metals is shown by the fact that it has been observed not only in copper and aluminum, on which the most detailed studies have been made, but also in silver, gold, palladium, and platinum (Bordoni, *et al.*, 1960; Okuda, 1963a,b), as well as in lead (Welber and Quimby, 1958), and nickel (Sommer and Beshers, 1966).

A. The Peak Height

The Bordoni peak is absent in a fully annealed material and appears only after some form of cold-working. Although the early work was entirely on polycrystalline samples, it was later shown (Caswell, 1958;

Paré, 1961; Mayadas, 1966; Mecs, 1966) that the peak could be obtained with single crystals as well. Further, impurities are not necessary for the appearance of the peak, which has been observed for 99.999% Cu (Niblett and Wilks, 1956) and for zone-refined aluminum (Sack, 1962). Thus the possibilities that grain boundaries or impurities are responsible are eliminated. The origin of the peak is then narrowed down to defects (dislocations or point defects) generated by the deformation process.

The height of the fully developed peak is quite large (tan $\phi_{max} \sim 1$ to 10×10^{-3}) but appears to be greatest in metals which have a high stacking fault energy (Burdett and Queen, 1970a). In addition, the peak height is very sensitive to material parameters and treatments. For polycrystals, it increases rapidly with the amount of cold-work for deformations $\lesssim 3\%$, and then levels off or goes through a maximum. Figure 13-1 shows the peak in polycrystalline copper as a function of deformation. Apparently, however, the amount of deformation alone does not determine the peak height; rather, it depends significantly on the type of deformation. For example, Caswell (1958) deformed copper single crystals by

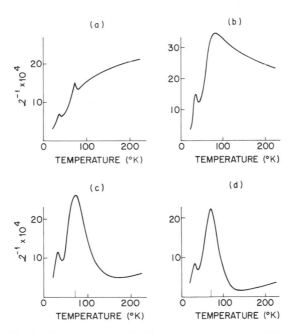

FIG. 13-1. The Bordoni peak and the lower temperature subsidiary peak in pure polycrystalline copper for the following degrees of cold work: (a) 0.1%, (b) 0.5%, (c) 2.2%. (d) 8.4%. The measurements were performed in flexural vibration at 1.1 kHz. (From Niblett and Wilks, 1957.)

rolling and showed that cross rolling is much more effective in producing further peak growth than is the continuation of rolling in the original direction. More detailed information is available from work on single crystals by Mecs (1966), Mecs and Nowick (1968), Mayadas (1966), and by Venkatesan and Beshers (1970). For example, experiments by Mecs on silver single crystals have shown that bending of a crystal, in a direction designed to introduce primarily edge dislocations of one sign, does not produce a detectable Bordoni peak. Further, both Mecs and Mayadas show that the peak is not large or well developed in stage I

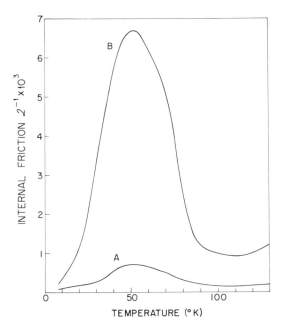

Fig. 13-2.   Comparison of the Bordoni peaks shown by two single crystals of silver deformed in tension at room temperature. Curve A: crystal oriented for easy glide, deformed 29%. Curve B: ⟨111⟩ crystal, deformed 5.4% (a fully developed peak). The shapes of the two peaks are nearly identical. Measurements in flexural vibration at about 600 Hz. (Adapted from Mecs and Nowick, 1968.)

of the strain hardening curve, where "easy glide" on a single slip system takes place (see Section 12.3). On the other hand, the peak grows rapidly in stage II, the region of a high rate of work hardening. Figure 13-2 illustrates this point by comparing the peak in a silver crystal oriented for easy glide and deformed 29%, with a ⟨111⟩ oriented crystal, deformed only 5.4%. The latter crystal, which immediately shows stage II behavior, actually behaves most like a polycrystal in that the peak develops rapidly, then slowly decreases with increasing deformation. In work on nickel single crystals, Venkatesan and Beshers (1970) show that the orientation dependence of the peak height is consistent with the hypothesis that dislocations on the primary slip system are responsible for the peak throughout stages I and II.[†]

Small amounts of impurities substantially reduce the peak height obtained for the same amount of cold work. An illustration of this point is given in Fig. 13-3 for gold-doped copper crystals. Drastic reductions

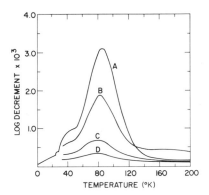

FIG. 13-3.   Effect of gold doping on the Bordoni peak for cross-rolled single crystals of copper. Curve A: 99.999% pure Cu. Curves B, C, and D: with additions of 0.065, 0.25, and 0.50 at. % Au, respectively. Measurements in longitudinal vibration at about 40 kHz. (From Caswell, 1958.)

in peak heights are also reported by Niblett and Wilks (1957) for copper doped with 0.003% B and 0.03% P. In the case of aluminum, it is reported (Sack, 1962) that the peak for the zone refined material is 15 times greater than that for 99.996% Al!

Neutron irradiation of the prestrained metal produces a reduction in the height of the peak, as observed by Niblett and Wilks (1957) and Thompson and Holmes (1959). The amount of irradiation required to produce a substantial reduction in the peak height, however, corresponds to an integrated flux of the order of 10^{18} n cm^{-2}. This flux is several orders of magnitude greater than the radiation needed to eliminate the non-relaxation damping of a pure metal, or the modulus defect due to dislocations (Section 12.2). In other words, the Bordoni effect is much more resistant to radiation than are other dislocation effects.

The relatively high melting point fcc metals like Cu, Ag, and Au show no substantial change in the height of the Bordoni peak as a result of

---

[†] In nickel there is another peak (peak Y) at lower temperatures which is associated almost entirely with stage III and is not understood.

prolonged aging at room temperature. Rather, it is necessary to take such samples up into the recrystallization range (150–250°C) to eliminate the peak completely. An example of the annealing behavior of copper is shown in Fig. 13-4, taken from Niblett and Wilks (1957). More detailed annealing experiments on copper (Niblett and Wilks, 1960) have shown that there is a range of annealing temperatures in which the peak increases in height before it finally decreases, and that this range depends on the grain size of the material. Similar observations were made at lower temperatures for aluminum by Völkl et al. (1965). In spite of several studies of annealing behavior, it is surprising that no one has undertaken to relate the damping behavior to the recrystallization process directly with the aid of microstructural examination.

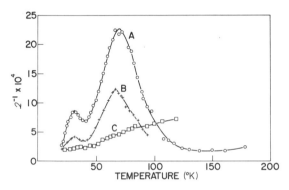

Fig. 13-4. Effect of annealing treatments on the Bordoni peak of pure copper. A: after straining 8.4%; B: after 1 hr at 180°C; C: after 1 hr at 350°C. Measurements in flexural vibration at 1.1 kHz. (From Niblett and Wilks, 1957.)

Although most experimenters deformed their samples at room temperature, there have been studies on Cu, Au, and Al (Bruner and Mecs, 1963; Okuda, 1963a; Routbort and Sack, 1967) in which the deformation was carried out at 4°K. Annealing was then carried out stepwise up to and above room temperature. For Cu and Au, the height of the peak was found to decrease for anneals up to ~200°K; it then increased again above room temperature. There were also changes in the shape and position of the peak which will be discussed later. The fact that the peak is found to be fully developed immediately after deformation at 4°K has been widely regarded as strong evidence that migration of defects to the dislocations is not required for the Bordoni effect. The reason for this view is that the major annealing of point defects in metals deformed at low temperatures takes place at temperatures above the Bordoni peak.

B. The Peak Position

Unlike the peak height, the peak temperature (for a given frequency) is relatively insensitive to the previous history of the sample. This relative insensitivity of the peak position to the previous treatment and purity of the material is probably the most remarkable single feature of the Bordoni peak, which has led to the belief that the peak reflects some fundamental property of dislocations. There is, however, some dependence of peak position on structural factors. Increased amounts of deformation, for example, move the peak to higher temperatures by a few degrees (Caswell, 1958; Bordoni *et al.*, 1960; Sack, 1962) while annealing, which serves to lower the peak height, also reduces the temperature several degrees (Niblett and Wilks, 1957; see e.g., Fig. 13-4). Impurities also produce a lowering of the peak temperature (Caswell, 1958; Paré, 1961; Sack, 1962).

In view of these factors which cause shifts in the peak position, it becomes rather difficult to obtain a precise activation energy by the usual plot of logarithm of frequency versus the reciprocal of the peak temperature for a wide range of samples. Several workers have plotted all available data in this way, but the scatter obtained is rather high. Bordoni *et al.* (1959) have used one specimen of copper and covered a wide range of frequency, to obtain an activation energy of 0.122 eV and a frequency factor v_0 (or τ_0^{-1}) of 4×10^{11} sec^{-1}. Their data are shown in Fig. 13-5. Unfortunately, the purity of the sample is not very high. Accordingly, Niblett (1961) has gathered all available data on 99.999% pure copper from various sources, covering a wide frequency range. The data show appreciable scatter, but a best value of 0.14 eV and $v_0 = 4 \times 10^{12}$ sec^{-1} is obtained. Other papers report values for the activation energy in copper

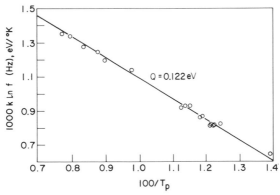

FIG. 13-5. Variation of reciprocal peak temperature with vibration frequency for the Bordoni peak in a sample of impure copper. (From Bordoni *et al.*, 1959.)

in the range 0.1–0.15 eV. The value of ν_0 is an important quantity to the theory, since it appears to be distinctly lower than values obtained for point-defect relaxation processes, and therefore leads to the conclusion that dislocations must be responsible.[†] For fcc metals other than copper, Bordoni *et al.* (1960) also report low ν_0 values, in the range 10^{10}–10^{12} sec^{-1}.

C. THE PEAK SHAPE

The main Bordoni internal friction peak is usually several times broader than that corresponding to a single relaxation time (i.e., to a standard anelastic solid). In addition, there is the subsidiary peak at lower temperatures, first reported for copper by Niblett and Wilks (see Fig. 13-1) and often referred to as the Niblett–Wilks peak. The subsidiary peak has since been observed in Au by Okuda (1963) and by Alers and Thompson (1961), as well as in Pt and Pd by Bordoni *et al.* (1960). It is therefore apparent that the subsidiary peak is an inherent part of the relaxation phenomenon, at least for several of the fcc metals. The fact that the subsidiary peak decreases approximately proportionally to the main peak during annealing (see, e.g., Fig. 13-4) also suggests the close relationship between the two peaks.

Because of the overlap with the main peak and the relatively small size of the subsidiary peak, its activation energy is not easily obtained with reasonable reliability. Nevertheless, values $\sim$0.04–0.05 eV are reported (Bordoni *et al.*, 1959; Alers and Thompson, 1961), with a frequency factor ν_0 similar to that for the main peak.

A remarkable aspect of the subsidiary peak appears when one deforms a sample at 4°K, as in the work of Okuda (1963a) and of Bruner and Mecs (1963). In such a case, the Niblett–Wilks peak appears with almost the same magnitude as the main peak. After annealing near room temperature, however, it decreases to the point where it resembles the case of a room-temperature deformed sample.

The shape of the main Bordoni peak is also sensitive to deformation and annealing. In the very early stages of deformation the peak is usually very broad, particularly on the high-temperature side. It then sharpens up and becomes better defined with increasing deformation (see, e.g., Fig. 13-1). This is a surprising result, since the internal dislocation structure of a crystal is known to become more complex as deformation

---

[†] We will see in Section 14.1 that typical dislocation oscillation frequencies are in the range 10^9–10^{10} sec^{-1}.

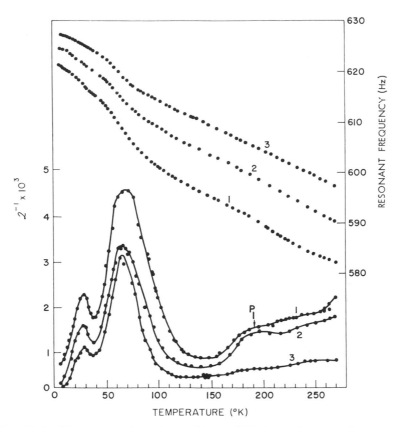

FIG. 13-6. Temperature dependence of internal friction and resonant frequency for deformed polycrystalline copper immediately after deformation by 2.5% (curve 1) and after recovery anneals (curve 2: after 3 hr at room temperature and curve 3: after 3 days anneal at 65°C). (From Mecs and Nowick, 1965.)

proceeds. Annealing in the recovery range also tends to sharpen the peak, since the high-temperature side anneals more rapidly than the rest of the peak. This point is demonstrated, for example, in Fig. 13-6, which also shows that the subsidiary peak is very sensitive to low-temperature recovery.[†] There is no doubt that the small shifts in peak position with deformation and annealing (reported above) are due, in fact, to these changes in the relative magnitudes of the components of the various relaxations which together comprise the broad Bordoni relaxation.

Probably the most detailed study of the structure of the Bordoni peak

[†] The peak near 200°K labeled P_1 is one of the Hasiguti-type peaks, which will be discussed in Section 13.3.

is that by Thompson and Holmes (1959), who made use of the better resolving power of the dynamic modulus as compared to the internal friction (see Sections 3.4 and 3.5) to study the relaxation in lightly cold-worked 99.999% copper. They conclude, from the steplike structure of the modulus versus temperature curve, that there are at least four, and perhaps as many as seven, discrete relaxations which constitute the Bordoni effect. Other workers have not examined the peak structure in such detail, but have preferred instead to assume a continuous relaxation spectrum, in the manner discussed in Chapter 4 (Caswell, 1958; Bordoni et al., 1959; Paré, 1961; Niblett, 1961). In terms of the lognormal distribution, values of about 5.0 are obtained for the distribution parameter β associated with the main peak. Attempts have been made to determine whether this broad distribution of relaxation times is primarily one in τ_0 or in Q. This involves a determination of the peak width (and therefore of β) as a function of temperature (see Section 4.8). The first such attempt was that of Bordoni et al. (1959) who concluded that the shape of the peak is independent of temperature and, therefore, that the distribution is in τ_0 only. [†] (In this analysis they use the Fuoss–Kirkwood distribution.) From a theoretical viewpoint, it is difficult to explain a distribution of this width ($\beta \sim 5$) in $\ln \tau_0$ only. Such a result implies a distribution of τ_0 over a range of about four decades, all for a single activation energy.

An entirely different result is claimed by Niblett (1961) who concludes that the peak width is a strong enough function of temperature that it can be explained by a distribution in the activation energy alone. In doing this analysis Niblett deals with the high-temperature side of the peak in order to avoid the uncertainties related to the subsidiary peak. In spite of this, the experimental scatter among the data is rather large. Nevertheless, in contrast to Bordoni's conclusion, it appears that the distribution cannot be in τ_0 alone.

D. SUMMARY OF BORDONI PEAK CHARACTERISTICS

In order to characterize the Bordoni peak, it is desirable to gather together the most well-defined features from the information given in this section. It now appears that these defining characteristics are most reasonably listed as follows:

(1) The peak occurs in single crystals as well as polycrystals.

[†] A similar claim is made by Routbort and Sack (1967) for the main Bordoni peak in the case of Al.

(2) The peak is amplitude independent in the usual range of strain amplitudes and is much broader than a single relaxation time.

(3) It is not observed in fully annealed materials, but is developed by cold-working.

(4) Deformation at a high rate of work hardening (stage II of the stress–strain curve) leads to rapid development of the peak. Easy glide (stage I) deformation gives rise to only a small peak.

(5) Impurities reduce the peak height substantially.

(6) The frequency factor ν_0 associated with the relaxation time is of the order of 10^{10}–10^{12} sec^{-1}.

(7) In addition to the main peak, a smaller but closely related subsidiary peak is present at lower temperatures.

(8) Although annealing in the recovery range produces some changes in the structure of the peak, the complete elimination of the peak seems to require recrystallization.

(9) The peak is relatively resistant to irradiation; to produce a substantial decrease requires a high dose.

13.2 Theories of the Bordoni Relaxation

The large relaxation strength of the Bordoni relaxation, its dependence on cold-work, its elimination by annealing, and its relatively low frequency factor ν_0, are all suggestive of a dislocation mechanism. The possibility that point defects, either alone or in close proximity to dislocations, are required for the effect tends to be ruled out on the grounds of (1) the resistance of the peak to annealing in the recovery range, (2) the fact that moderate irradiation does not increase the peak, and (3) the observation of a peak immediately after 4°K deformation. Accordingly, an explanation for the Bordoni effect has generally been sought under the assumption that the mechanism is due to dislocations alone. But what type of dislocation is required, what environment must it be in, and what characteristic of the dislocation controls the relaxation time? These are the questions that have been difficult to answer.

In 1954, the fact that a peak had been found, where the internal friction was independent of amplitude and the peak position relatively insensitive to treatments, was indeed an important discovery, considering the complexity of the dislocation effects which were then known. For this reason the Bordoni relaxation attracted considerable theoretical attention beginning in 1955. In this section some of the theories advanced for this phenomenon will be briefly reviewed.

The first theory, proposed by Mason (1955b, c), suggested that the relaxation originates in the displacement of a segment of dislocation line, located between two pinning points, from one Peierls well to the next. On this basis the activation energy would be proportional to the distance between pinning points. Mason's theory has been criticized on the grounds that the distance between pinning points must be very sensitive to such structural factors as the degree of cold work or the impurity of the sample, while the activation energy is not. This difficulty was overcome by the theory of Seeger and co-workers which will now be discussed in some detail.

A. Theory of Seeger and Co-workers

In this theory a distinction is made between dislocations which run parallel to one of the close-packed directions of the crystals (i.e., along a Peierls valley) and those which do not. The latter type may be regarded as having a high density of kinks built in along its length, while the former type would only have kinks generated through thermal fluctuations. Seeger (1955, 1956) assumes that kinks present on a dislocation line move with relative ease even at temperatures near the Bordoni relaxation. Dislocations with a large number of built-in kinks therefore have no difficulty in bowing out under the influence of an applied stress. In fact, if the built-in kinks overlap each other, such a dislocation can be described by the flexible string model (see Section 12.2). The dislocation which lies along a Peierls valley, on the other hand, is limited in its motion. It is this type of dislocation to which Seeger attributes the Bordoni relaxation. The rate limiting step in the relaxation process is taken to be the formation of a pair of kinks of opposite sign (often called a "double kink") as in Fig. 12-9, separated by at least a critical distance d_{cr}. For a separation closer than d_{cr} it is assumed that the pair will rapidly come together and be annihilated, while for distances greater than d_{cr} the applied stress will drive the two kinks apart, thus producing a displacement of the entire dislocation segment by one interatomic distance. The process of generation of such a double kink fulfills the requirements of an activated relaxation process. In his first treatment, Seeger (1955) took the activation energy Q to be given by

$$Q = 2W_k \qquad (13.2\text{-}1)$$

where W_k is the energy of formation of a single kink, which is related to the Peierls stress by Eq. (12.2-3). In a later treatment (Seeger, 1956) it was recognized that Q must depend on d_{cr}, which in turn is a function of the applied stress. Specifically, by equating the work done by the applied stress in bowing out the dislocation segment to the interaction energy between the kinks, Seeger obtained a relation of the form $d_{cr} = A \ln(B/\sigma)$. From this, he found the following expression for the activation energy:

$$Q = W_k[1 + \tfrac{1}{4} \ln(16\sigma_p/\pi\sigma)] \qquad (13.2\text{-}2)$$

A second refinement, made by Donth (1957) and Seeger et al. (1957) recognizes that ordinary rate theory as applied to point defects (Section 7.3) is not applicable to dislocation lines. The reason for this statement is that the saddle-point configuration in double-kink formation involves a length which is large compared to atomic dimensions and to the coherency length of thermal fluctuations. Donth's more refined treatment gives a complex expression for the effective activation energy Q, which is given in graphical form. Here again Q is a function of the applied stress. In addition, the theory predicts that the relaxation strength is also a function of stress. Lothe (1960a, b) has presented a critique of this theory and a modified version in which he concludes that Eq. (13.2-1) for the activation energy is still rather nearly correct, provided that σ/σ_p is not too large.

By comparing the results of their theoretical calculations with experimental Q values for the Bordoni effect, Seeger et al. (1957) obtain values for σ_p/G (where G is the shear modulus) ranging from 3 to 10×10^{-4}. [If Eq. (13.2-1) is used, the results are not too different.] Unfortunately, there are no other experiments which yield independent estimates of the Peierls stress σ_p, but these values are consistent with theoretical estimates.

Although the Seeger theory predicts essentially standard-solid behavior for the Bordoni relaxation, an explanation is also offered for the existence of a subsidiary peak at a lower temperature than the main Bordoni peak. Seeger points out that in the fcc lattice there are two types of dislocations which may lie along a $\langle 110 \rangle$ close packed direction, namely those for which the Burgers vector is parallel to the dislocation line (a pure screw type) and those for which the Burgers vector lies at $\pm 60°$ to the direction of the dislocation line. These two types of dislocations should have different values for W_k, and therefore for the activation energy for relaxation.

While the Seeger theory presents a reasonable qualitative picture, it cannot be regarded as successful on a quantitative basis for the following reasons:

(1) The theory predicts a stress dependence of the activation energy, and therefore of the peak position, which was not observed experimentally (Paré, 1961).

(2) The fact that both the main Bordoni peak and the subsidiary peak are much broader than a single relaxation time is not predicted by the theory. In particular, there is no explanation given for the extreme sensitivity of the high-temperature side of the peak to various treatments (e.g., deformation, annealing, and irradiation).

(3) The observation by Mecs and Nowick (1965), that about half the modulus defect which anneals at room temperature is related to the Bordoni relaxation, seems inconsistent with Seeger's idea that the only dislocations which participate in the process are those parallel to Peierls valleys. Rather, it suggests that a large fraction of the dislocation network contributes to the Bordoni effect.

Because of these difficulties, there have been a number of modifications of the Seeger theory. These modifications are designed to retain the essential feature of the original theory, but yet to explain the experiments in greater detail, as well as to correct some theoretical oversimplifications.

B. REFINEMENTS OF THE SEEGER THEORY

Paré (1961) has been critical of the Seeger theory on the grounds that it fails to consider the probability of a backward jump once a critical kink pair is formed. He shows that actually recombination of the kink pair is more probable than further separation of the pair. The effect is to introduce a factor $\exp(-|\Delta W|/kT)$ in the expression for the relaxation strength, where $|\Delta W|$ is the magnitude of the energy difference between the doubly kinked and the straight dislocation segment. The relaxation strength will then be very small unless $|\Delta W|$ is near zero. The quantity ΔW is given by

$$\Delta W = 2W_{\mathrm{k}} - \sigma abl \qquad (13.2\text{-}3)$$

where σ is the local stress, and σabl is then the work done by the stress in moving the loop l into the deformed position [Eq. (12.3-3)]. For $|\Delta W|$ to be small it is required that $2W_{\mathrm{k}} \simeq \sigma abl$, a condition which is not attainable with the usual small external applied stresses for reasonable values of l. Instead, Paré postulates that an *internal stress* σ_{i} is required in order to make the magnitude of dislocation relaxation strength appreciable. He also shows that once the stress σ_{i} required to make $\Delta W = 0$ is exceeded, the loop bows out to a shape approximating the arc of a circle, but modified by the Peierls potential so that the outermost portion runs for some distance in one of the Peierls valleys. Under these conditions, Paré shows that the energy change resulting when this outermost portion is advanced to an adjacent valley is small, in most cases. Thus, the condition for the occurrence of an appreciable contribution to the dislocation relaxation by a loop of length l is that it be subject to an internal stress given by

$$\sigma_i abl \geq 2W_k \qquad (13.2\text{-}4)$$

The role of internal stress as described above can be pictured with the aid of Fig. 13-7. This diagram shows how the energy of a dislocation is

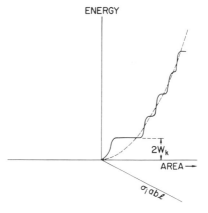

FIG. 13-7.   Diagram of energy versus the area swept out by a bowing dislocation segment. The dashed (parabolic) curve corresponds to the dislocation string model, while the solid curve shows the stepwise energy increase when double kink generation takes place over Peierls potential barriers in the absence of stress. The presence of internal stress σ_i contributes an additional linear energy term, $\sigma_i abl$, which tilts this energy diagram.

increased stepwise as it bows out through a series of double-kink generations. The presence of internal (or external) stress serves to tilt the diagram so as to lower the energy of the dislocation when bowed out in the favorable direction. Each step in the series of dislocation displacements is separated from the previous one by an energy $2W_k$. Lothe and Hirth (1959) then argue that the energy barrier is also $\sim 2W_k$. Nevertheless, since the internal stress required to satisfy Eq. (13.2-4) is an appreciable fraction (~ 0.01–0.3) of the Peierls stress, σ_p, the value of σ_i must be expected to enter into the exact expression for the activation energy.

The presence of internal stress, as postulated by Paré, has the following consequences:

(1) The fact that the small measuring stress σ is now superimposed on a larger internal stress σ_i means that the influence of σ on the activation energy and on the relaxation strength is considerably reduced since the total stress, $\sigma_i + \sigma$, may be replaced by σ_i to a good approximation.

(2) The inevitable presence of a distribution in σ_i leads to a distribution in the activation energy, from Eq. (13.2-2), and therefore to a broadening of the relaxation. The high-temperature side of the peak corresponds to dislocations under low σ_i.

(3) Because of the presence of internal stress, not only can dislocations which lie along the Peierls valley participate in the relaxation process, but also those with built-in kinks. The internal stress serves to sweep such kinks out to the ends of the dislocation loop thus leaving a segment in the center which, in fact, does lie parallel to the Peierls valley.

The reader will note that these three predicted consequences of the presence of internal stress provide, respectively, answers to the three problems with the original Seeger theory that are listed in part A of the present section. Paré's modification of Seeger's theory seems, therefore, to provide a reasonable overall picture of the Bordoni relaxation. Strong support for the Seeger–Paré model comes from the observation of non-linear effects in the vicinity of the Bordoni peak by Alefeld et al. (1968). These effects are observed either by the use of a very high stress amplitude σ_0, or by the application of a static bias stress in addition to the oscillatory stress. A most striking result is that when these stresses were applied, the Bordoni peak could be observed in slightly cold-worked samples, for which there was no appreciable peak in the ordinary low-amplitude internal friction experiment. In this experiment, the high applied stress apparently takes the place of Paré's internal stress.

The Seeger–Paré theory has been further amplified by several authors. Alefeld (1967) pointed out that there is configurational entropy ΔS as well as an energy difference associated with a double kink and proposed that Eq. (13.2-4) be modified to state that significant bowing of a dislocation can only occur if

$$\sigma_i abl \gtrsim 2W_k - T\,\Delta S \qquad (13.2\text{-}5)$$

Accordingly, at sufficiently high temperatures the entropy term alone will be sufficient to favor the presence of a large number of double kinks on the dislocation.

The other modifications have been concerned with the fact that, in addition to double-kink generation, the kinetics of the relaxation process are affected by kink migration and kink–kink interactions. Such questions have been dealt with by Lothe (1960b) and by Brailsford (1965). The most thorough treatment of this topic is due to Seeger and Schiller (1962, 1966). They note that neglecting the time for kink motion relative to the time for kink generation in the original theory cannot be correct. Rather, it is necessary to treat the separation of kinks as a diffusion process in a force field. In this way, they find that the relaxation time for relaxation is given by

$$\tau = \tau_g + \tau_d \tag{13.2-6}$$

where τ_g, the time for generation, is a thermally activated quantity, proportional to $\exp(2W_k/kT)$. On the other hand τ_d, the kink diffusion time, is itself composed of two parts: τ_w, related to kink–kink interactions and τ_p due to kink–phonon interactions, neither of which is thermally activated. In this theory the presence of the term τ_d is believed to result in the broadening of the peak on the high temperature side (see Problem 13-1). The theory is inherently nonlinear, so that the results cannot be expressed as simply the superpositions of single relaxation times, but the extent of the nonlinearity has not yet been calculated in a form capable of comparison with experiment. The experiments of König et al. (1964) on α-particle irradiation of deformed copper have been interpreted in terms of Eq. (13.2-6).

C. ALTERNATIVE THEORIES

Other theories have been suggested which still regard the Bordoni relaxation as a basic property of dislocations, but not in terms of double kink generation as the dominant process.

The theory of Brailsford (1961, 1962) rejects the calculations which show that the kink width is substantial (50–100 atom distances), and instead makes the *ad hoc* assumption that kinks are abrupt (widths of a few atom distances). A consequence of this assumption is that the activation energy for kink motion is no longer negligible, and in fact Brailsford assumes that kink motion is the rate limiting step in the Bordoni relaxation process. Accordingly, it follows that geometrical kinks, on dislocations which do *not* lie along the Peierls valley, are required for the effect. The relaxation time depends on the loop length l and is given by

$$\tau = l^2/\pi^2 D \tag{13.2-7}$$

where D is the one-dimensional diffusion coefficient for kink migration. The relaxation strength is also dependent on l, varying, in fact, as l^3. Brailsford attributes the breadth of the peak to a distribution in loop lengths, taken according to the probability function

$$P(l) \, dl = \exp(-l/l_0) \, dl/l_0 \tag{13.2-8}$$

where l_0 is the mean loop length. A distribution in relaxation times is therefore predicted, but as a distribution entirely in τ_0, with a constant activation energy equal to that for motion of an abrupt kink. The reason for the existence of two peaks can be attributed to the existence of two dissimilar kinds of kink ("acute" and "obtuse") which move with different activation energies.

Interesting as this theory is, there are some rather serious objections that can be raised against it. First, as already mentioned, the data do not seem to favor a distribution entirely in τ_0. Second, using the best τ_0 values ($\sim 10^{-10}$–10^{-11} sec) leads to a calculation of an unreasonably small value for the mean loop length l_0. More important is the question of the fundamental assumption on which the theory is built. Although calculations of kink widths are undoubtedly crude, there is no calculation presently available to support the suggestion of abrupt kinks. Finally, the question arises that if kink motion is rate controlling at the Bordoni peak, what process remains to produce the modulus defect which occurs below the Bordoni peak, in fact, at 4°K and below (Alers and Zimmerman, 1965)? Brailsford (1965) attributes such behavior to dislocations on which kinks are present at a high enough density that they overlap. The concept of the Seeger–Paré theory, that dislocation motion below the Bordoni peak is due to the motion of geometrical kinks, while that at and above the peak is due to both generation and motion, however, seems to provide a more satisfactory explanation.

Other theories do not consider kink motion at all but turn to other aspects of dislocation structure. Thus, Feltham (1966) attributes the Bordoni relaxation to intersectional jogs on dislocation lines. Gilman (1963), on the other hand, focuses attention on the properties of edge dislocation dipoles. Such dipoles consist of two parallel edge dislocations of opposite sign lying on parallel glide planes and separated by a small distance h. The interactions of the two edge dislocations leads to two equivalent stable configurations, with an activated flip–flop motion between them. Relaxation can then be produced by preferential motion between the two positions under stress, which takes place by a step-by-step migration of the cross-over point between the two configurations. The relative stability of the Bordoni peak to annealing is attributed to the fact that such dislocation dipoles are quite stable, in that it is necessary to have dislocation climb in order to eliminate them.

One objection to Gilman's theory is that the Bordoni peak is very small in the easy glide (stage I) range of the stress–strain curve in spite of the fact that an appreciable density of dipoles is present. The dipoles that are visible in the electron microscope, however, correspond to large values of h, while the theory requires values smaller than the visibility limit. Some workers (e.g., Wilsdorf, 1963) have even expressed doubt that dipoles of the small separations required for Gilman's theory are present following plastic deformation. Finally, Beshers (1970) showed that the activation energy for dipole flipping is too high to account for the Bordoni relaxation.

It is interesting that most of the theories presented here give little or no consideration to the question of whether or not the dislocations are extended, i.e., split into partials. In this connection, the fact that the peak appears to be largest for metals of high stacking-fault energy suggests that splitting into extended dislocations is not an essential feature of the mechanism, and in fact that such splitting probably acts to hinder the basic process which gives rise to the Bordoni relaxation.

13.3 Other Low-Temperature Peaks in fcc Metals

The Bordoni peak and its low temperature subsidiary are not the only ones which appear when a fcc metal is deformed. A set of three peaks has also been observed for the noble metals in the range of temperature between room temperature and the Bordoni peaks. These peaks were first reported in the Japanese literature by Hasiguti and his co-workers (for a bibliography, see Hasiguti *et al.*, 1962), and some of them have been seen subsequently by others. We will refer to these peaks as the "Hasiguti peaks."

The most extensive investigations have been made by Baxter and Wilks (1962) and Koiwa and Hasiguti (1963) on copper, and by Okuda and Hasiguti (1963) on both copper and gold. It was found that samples deformed at room temperature and quickly cooled down show two peaks, called P_1 and P_3, which occur at about 145 and 240°K, respectively, for a frequency of 1 Hz. These peaks anneal out after the specimen is allowed to stand for some time at room temperature. During this room temperature anneal P_1 first grows, then it decays. Deformation at liquid nitrogen temperature, on the other hand, results in what appears to be a very pronounced peak P_2 near 185°K which after annealing goes into P_1 and P_3. Figure 13-8 shows this behavior for a sample of gold deformed near 80°K. It is not clear that P_2 is a true peak since the sample is annealing rapidly as the peak is being traced out.[†]

[†] It may also be the same as P_1, but initially located at a higher peak temperature.

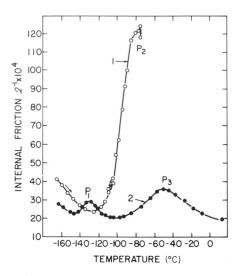

FIG. 13-8. The internal friction of a specimen of gold deformed 16.4% in torsion at about −170°C. Curve 1 was taken immediately after deformation, and curve 2 after an anneal of 32 min at 20°C. Measurements in torsion at 4 Hz. (From Okuda and Hasiguti, 1963.)

The best investigated peak is P_1 which has been reported also by Niblett and Wilks (1957), Thompson and Holmes (1959), Bruner (1960), and Paré (1961). The peak width of P_1 is somewhat larger than a Debye peak but not nearly as large as that of the Bordoni peak. When the data for copper of these various investigators, covering five decades in fre-

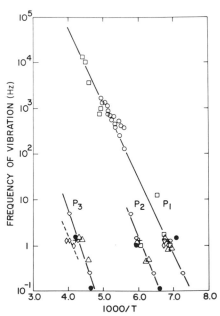

FIG. 13-9.   The Arrhenius relation between frequency and peak temperature for the Hasiguti peaks in copper, obtained by combining the data of many workers. (From Koiwa and Hasiguti, 1963.)

quency, are plotted together they give a very good Arrhenius plot. Figure 13-9 shows all the available data for the Hasiguti peaks in copper. For P_1, the activation energy is 0.32 eV and the frequency factor is 10^{12} sec^{-1}. It is remarkable that such a variety of data from different laboratories and on samples that differ in cold work and purity fit a single plot as well as do the data for P_1. (This plot, in fact, shows less scatter than the corresponding composite plot for the Bordoni peak.) This result suggests that the peak may originate in a simple mechanism. The peak heights are not so reproducible, however, and show an increase with increasing cold work with a tendency toward saturation. They also depend on pretreatments in a complex manner that is not well understood (Koiwa and Hasiguti, 1963). For the peak P_3 in copper, the activation energy is 0.43 eV and the frequency factor 10^{10} sec^{-1}. On the other hand, the activation energies for the processes of decay of these peaks upon annealing are higher, being $\sim$0.6 and $\sim$1 eV for P_1 and P_3, respectively. It is precisely because of these higher activation energies for annealing that the peaks are stable enough to be traced out without appreciable decay.

The low value for the frequency factors, 10^{10}–10^{12} sec^{-1}, and the relatively high relaxation strength[†] suggest a dislocation mechanism rather than one involving purely point defect relaxation. Other facts suggest, however, that point defects must be involved along with the dislocations. These are (a) the initial rise of P_1 upon aging; (b) the ease of annealing out of the peaks by comparison to the Bordoni peaks; and (c) the drastic reduction of P_1 immediately after a small amount of additional cold work (Koiwa and Hasiguti, 1963). Item (a) suggests that point defects, generated within the crystal by the deformation process, migrate to the dislocations during aging, and thereby create the configuration necessary to the relaxation process. The effect of annealing at relatively low temperatures, item (b), implies a decrease in the number of point defects at the dislocations, which may take place by means of coagulation or annihilation along the dislocation lines. Finally, item (c) suggests that a small additional deformation after aging pulls the dislocations away from the point defects with which they interact.

While the general concepts just reviewed are widely accepted, there is a considerable range of ideas about the detailed mechanisms of the peaks. Bruner (1960), for example, suggested a mechanism whereby a point

---

[†] To account for such large relaxation strengths in terms of a point defect relaxation requires either an unreasonably high defect concentration or an unusually large value for the quantity $|\delta\lambda|$ (see Section 8.4D).

defect is trapped in a plane adjacent to the slip plane of an extended dislocation. Such a configuration has two positions of equilibrium for the dislocation, viz., where the point defect lies just above one or the other of the partial dislocations. Internal friction can then arise from a thermally activated flip-flop motion between the two stable positions. Although Bruner actually suggested this mechanism for the Bordoni relaxation, others (Niblett and Wilks, 1960) have pointed out that it is in fact more suited to the Hasiguti peaks. Another suggested mechanism is that of Okuda and Hasiguti (1963), according to which the relaxation is attributed to the breaking away of a dislocation line segment from a defect acting as a pinning point, followed by a repinning as the defect jumps into the dislocation line again. The dislocation line considered is one which lies along a close-packed direction, and the breakaway is assumed to take place by thermal activation. Each of the three peaks (P_1, P_2, and P_3) is then attributed to pinning by a different point defect. A somewhat different idea, advanced by Schiller (1964), examines the potential curve in which the configuration of a defect plus a dislocation can move and the modification of this potential curve by an applied stress. In these models, it is *not* required that the point defect involved should possess a lower symmetry than the crystal and thus be capable of relaxation in the absence of the dislocation.

Still another mechanism for these peaks is that suggested by Hasiguti (1963). According to this mechanism, the built-in kinks present in a dislocation line which is not parallel to the Peierls potential diffuse easily unless held up by point defects. The internal friction peak is then attributed to the thermally activated unpinning of a kink from an appropriate point defect. This model applies only when dislocation movement is principally through kink migration, i.e., when the Peierls potential is large. In cases in which the Peierls potential is relatively small, Hasiguti (1965) has proposed a "trapped loop" model in which the dislocation takes a zig-zag form so as to accommodate pinning by point defects. Motion again takes place by thermal unpinning. Still other models are due to Koiwa and Hasiguti (1965) and Feltham (1966).

The number of detailed theories advanced for the Hasiguti peaks is remarkably large, Hasiguti himself (with co-workers) having contributed as many as five different models. Although most of these various models give results that are generally consistent with the facts, it has not been possible to distinguish definitively among them. In such a situation, it is better to return to experimental considerations and, in particular, to see if the same peak (or related peaks) can be produced by different methods.

Interestingly enough, Keefer and Vitt (1967) have found two peaks in *electron irradiated* copper which fall very near the temperatures of the Hasiguti P_1 and P_3 peaks. The larger and better defined peak is that at 240°K for $\sim$1 Hz. In view of the fact that electron irradiation is expected to produce only point defects, Keefer and Vitt have examined the possibility that this peak is due to point defects alone. Estimates of the concentration of point defects produced by the irradiation in comparison to the peak height make this possibility remote, however. In addition, it is found that prior irradiation or cold working followed by a recovery anneal suppresses the development of the 240°K peak on subsequent irradiation. These results strongly suggest that dislocations (which become fully pinned by these prior treatments) as well as point defects are required for the relaxation effect. Based on previous studies of dislocation pinning by means of modulus measurements, they further conclude that the point defects involved are interstitials. This same interpretation may then be attributed to the P_3 peak in cold-worked material, but it is not yet fully clear that the two peaks are the same, even though they do fall at very nearly the same temperature. Neuman (1966), on the other hand, finds a large peak in the range 240°–260°K in gold wires quenched from above 800°C. It is unlikely that this peak is due to interstitials. The peak is attributed to the motion of dislocations which are pinned by quenched-in vacancy clusters.

We now turn to other peaks found in cold-worked fcc metals, but not identified as Hasiguti peaks. Völkl and Schilling (1963) report several peaks for copper deformed at 20°K. For the peak which they find at 255°K at 3 Hz, they obtain an activation energy $\sim$0.7 eV and $\tau_0 = 10^{-15 \pm 1}$ sec, which is strikingly different from the values $Q \sim 0.4$ eV and $\tau_0 \sim 10^{-10}$ sec reported by Hasiguti for the P_3 peak. Völkl and Schilling attribute this peak to the split interstitial defect (see Section 11.2). On the other hand, Walz (1964) finds this same peak in deformed single crystals of copper and observes that the peak height is nearly independent of orientation, in contradiction to the strong anisotropy expected for a tetragonal defect. He, therefore, favors the mechanism which involves the split interstitial located near a dislocation [based on the model of Schiller (1964)]. The peak observed by Seeger and Wagner in deformed nickel (at $\sim$60°C and with $Q = 0.87$ eV) also shows no appreciable anisotropy (Section 11.2). It is very likely the same peak as that observed by Völkl and by Walz in Cu, the higher temperature being simply due to the fact that corresponding activation energies can be expected to scale roughly as the melting points of the two metals.

There remains the problem of sorting out these various peaks. As things now stand, there are several peaks found in Cu and Au near 250°K: Following deformation, there is the P_3 Hasiguti peak observed by several workers, as well as the peak reported by Völkl and Schilling and by Walz; following electron irradiation, there is the peak of Keefer and Vitt; after quenching there is the peak of Neuman. In addition, König *et al.* (1964) find a peak in this region at 70 Hz in α-particle irradiated Cu. (The temperature for 1 Hz would be distinctly lower, however.) Probably some of these peaks are the same, although they have not been identified as such. In particular, there is reason to wonder whether Völkl and Schilling and Walz in fact observed the same peak as Hasiguti's P_3 since all of them are produced by low-temperature deformation. Here the alleged large differences in Q and τ_0 among the different workers need to be resolved. In any case, it is not likely that *all* of the peaks in the vicinity of 250°K are the same, in view of differences in peak temperature and in the conditions of formation (e.g., irradiation and quenching as against cold working). Nevertheless, it is interesting to note that a mechanism of relaxation involving interstitials or vacancy clusters in the vicinity of dislocations has been invoked in almost every case. While such models often appear plausible, it is first necessary to characterize better the various relaxation phenomena and the conditions for generating them before real theoretical progress can be expected.

13.4   Relaxation Peaks in bcc and hcp Metals

In view of the fact that the Bordoni relaxation has been interpreted in terms of the fundamental properties of isolated dislocation lines, it follows that the same relaxation phenomenon should exist for materials other than the fcc metals. Accordingly, the most important objective in the study of dislocation relaxations in crystal structures other than the fcc metals has been to seek relaxations which are the analogs of the Bordoni peaks. The problem of identifying such analogs of the Bordoni relaxation has, however, been an elusive one, as we shall see. The present section deals with the body-centered cubic (bcc) and hexagonal close-packed (hcp) metals, while the next section deals with results on ionic and covalent crystals.

A. THE BCC METALS

The most complete information on relaxations in deformed bcc metals is available for the transition metals Ta, Nb, W, and Mo. A low-temperature relaxation peak was first reported for Nb by Bruner (1960), Chambers and Schultz (1960), and Bordoni *et al.* (1961), while De Batist (1960) investigated a similar peak in Mo. The most extensive study of these transition metals was carried out by Chambers and Schultz (1961, 1962). [For a detailed review, see Chambers (1966).] When these metals are deformed, they show two relatively broad internal friction peaks (called the α and β peaks by Chambers and Schultz) each, in turn, apparently made up of a number of component peaks. At 1 Hz the α peak occurs near 100°K and the β peak near 220°K. Average values for the activation energies and frequency factors of the peaks in Nb, Ta, and Mo are listed in Table 13-1. The peaks are absent for annealed metals studied at the usual low-strain amplitudes. They may be observed in annealed metals, however, by driving the samples to large strain amplitudes, i.e., outside the anelastic range.

TABLE 13-1

RELAXATION PARAMETERS FOR DEFORMED
BCC TRANSITION METALS

Metal	Peak	ν_0 (sec^{-1})	Q (eV)
Nb	α	$10^{12.8}$	0.25
	β	$10^{12.5}$	0.47
Ta	α	10^{12}	0.25
	β	10^{12}	0.40
Mo	α	$10^{12.7}$	0.18
	β	$10^{11.2}$	0.46

Upon annealing at temperatures as low as one-quarter of the recrystallization temperature, these peaks are observed to decrease monotonically. In addition, there is a very substantial decrease in the peak temperature during aging. An example of the changes in the α peak of Mo during aging is given in Fig. 13-10, where the peak temperature falls from 122° to 70°K. This behavior differs from that of the Bordoni peak in fcc metals, where (a) in some ranges the peak is observed to grow upon annealing; (b) the major decrease of the peak height occurs near the recrystallization temperature; and (c) the peak temperature decreases, but only slightly, as the peak height decreases.

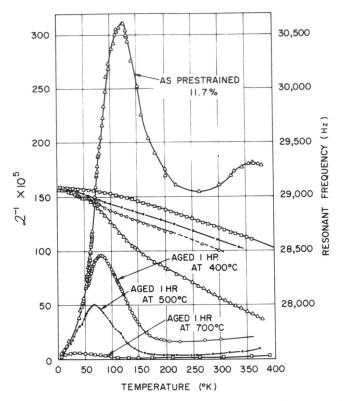

FIG. 13-10. Temperature dependence of internal friction and resonant frequency for polycrystalline molybdenum prestrained 11.7% at 23°C and following various iso-chronal anneals. (From Chambers and Schultz, 1962.)

Recent experiments by Stanley and Szkopiak (1967a) show that both a small α peak and a substantial set of β peaks can be observed following neutron irradiation of Nb. From the fact that large β peaks appear upon irradiation, as well as the detailed behavior as a function of dose, annealing, and dislocation density, these authors conclude that the β peaks are due to point defect complexes and do not involve dislocations.

For bcc iron, the experimental situation is not so well established as for the bcc metals already discussed. Bruner (1960) failed to find a peak below room temperature for deformed samples. In contrast, Takita and Sakamoto (1970) have recently reported a peak at 50°K (for 100 kHz) which may be of the Bordoni type. Other peaks of uncertain origin have been reported at higher temperatures by Swartz (1962) and Hasiguti et al. (1962).

There are two suggestions concerning the peaks in the bcc metals which have been given wide attention. The first is that the α peak corresponds to the Niblett-Wilks peak and the β peak to the Bordoni peak of the fcc's; the second is that the α peak (with its substructure) constitutes the Bordoni relaxation, while the β peak is related to the Hasiguti peaks of the fcc metals. In either case a problem arises because the annealing characteristics of the peaks in the bcc metals are so different from those of the Bordoni relaxation. Chambers (1966) emphasizes that there is no evidence for the growth of the β peak following deformation; rather, this peak seems to be fully formed upon deformation and only decays with aging.[†] This behavior is quite different from the Hasiguti peaks, or any other phenomenon which requires the migration of point defects to newly formed dislocations. Further, the effect of an additional low-temperature deformation is to enhance the β peak, rather than to decrease it as in the case of the Hasiguti P_1 peak. Chambers then favors associating the β peak with the Bordoni relaxation. In order to account for the differences in behavior of the bcc peaks and the Bordoni peak, Chambers and Schultz have emphasized that stronger impurity–dislocation interaction exists in the bcc than in the fcc metals. They believe that the decrease in the bcc peaks upon aging at relatively low temperatures may be attributed to strong pinning of dislocations by interstitial impurities or by self-interstitial defects. In fact, they have shown that the purer the sample, the higher the annealing temperature required to produce a given decrease in peak height.

In contrast to the ideas of Chambers and Schultz, Amateau *et al.* (1969) have concluded that the α peak is the true Bordoni peak in the bcc metals.[‡] Their work was carried out on single crystals of Nb and Nb–Mo alloys. It shows that the α peak height increases in proportion to the square of the work-hardening stress, and therefore, to the dislocation density. In particular, deformation in easy glide (stage I) produces only a small α peak and major growth of the peak occurs during stage II of the stress–strain curve, in a manner very similar to the fcc Bordoni peaks. In a later paper, however (Gibala *et al.*, 1970), this same group of workers focuses attention on their experimental result that the frequency

[†] On the other hand, Stanley and Szkopiak (1967b) report that the β peak develops after annealing at 70°C. Whether this difference is due to the higher interstitial impurity content of the material used by these authors remains to be established.

[‡] This conclusion is, of course, consistent with Stanley and Szkopiak's claim, already mentioned, that the β peak cannot be due to dislocations.

factor ν_0 in the Arrhenius expression *decreases* with increasing purity. They argue that this single result is incompatible with double-kink generation since, the larger the loop length between impurity pinning points the more places at which kink pairs can be nucleated and, therefore, the *higher* ν_0 should be. Instead they propose that the α peak may be due to dislocations breaking away from pinning points, i.e., a model involving both dislocations and point defects. Nevertheless, they find the similarity of the α peak to the fcc Bordoni peak too strong to ignore, and therefore raise the question of whether a thermally activated breakaway mechanism might also be valid for the fcc case as well!

It is not yet clear as to how much emphasis to place on the dependence of ν_0 on purity, especially since it is often difficult in practice to separate a change in ν_0 from a change in Q. Nevertheless, it now appears that, if any peak in the bcc metals is the Bordoni peak, it is the α peak.

B. The hcp Metals

For hcp metals, one would expect a closer similarity to the fcc's because of the similar close-packed structure, as well as the absence of the unusually strong impurity-dislocation interactions present in the bcc metals. Although a number of preliminary observations were reported earlier, the most extensive study, involving both polycrystals and single crystals, was reported recently by Tsui and Sack (1967) for magnesium. The major peak in deformed Mg is an extremely broad peak covering the range from about 40° to 280°K at 40 kHz. [†] The dislocation origin of this peak is well established because of the existence of only one primary set of slip planes, viz. the basal plane. Figure 13-11 shows the strong orientation dependence of the peak, where θ is the angle between the crystal axis and the hexagonal axis. Such single-crystal investigations show that only dislocations in the basal, or (0001), plane contribute to the peak, which is observable only if the vibrational stress has a component resolved in that plane. Comparison with electron micrographs also shows that the highest peaks occur when most dislocations form networks and tangles. In this respect the results resemble the fcc metals. On the other hand, in the fcc case, the component peaks are well defined; further, the annealing characteristics in the fcc and hcp cases are somewhat different.

[†] These authors also observe a low temperature peak near 20°K, but it is present only for polycrystals, and its origin is not established.

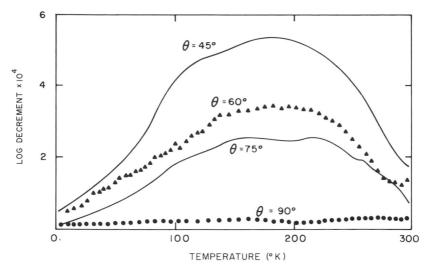

FIG. 13-11.   Internal friction of single crystals of magnesium of different orientations, after 0.5% compression. (From Tsui and Sack, 1967.)

In summary, the results on Mg are disappointing in view of the lack of sharpness of the component peaks and the inability to relate the results clearly to the fcc Bordoni peaks. On the other hand, due to the single slip plane, studies of the orientation dependence give more definitive results in the hcp than in the fcc case.

13.5   Peaks in Ionic and Covalent Crystals

The first study of deformation produced peaks in nonmetallic crystals was carried out on MgO by Chang (1961), who found a peak near 0°C at 27 MHz with an activation energy given as 0.15 eV. The peak increases with increasing deformation. Fitting the results to the theory of Seeger *et al.* (Section 13.2), he obtained $\sigma_p/G \sim 10^{-5}$, which is much smaller than the Peierls stress in the fcc metals.

Gibbons and Chirba (1962) and also Taylor (1962) found peaks in deformed LiF, one near 70°K and another (very broad peak) near 160°K at $\sim$50 kHz. They find that x-irradiation and room-temperature aging eliminates the peaks. Koss and Gordon (1966) have examined a number of different LiF samples including some of relatively high purity. Whereas they find the same two peaks for the less pure LiF, the low temperature peak is absent or nearly absent for the high purity material.

The effect of x-irradiation at low temperature is also compared with that at room temperature. They conclude that the low-temperature peak, at least, cannot be identified with the Bordoni peak in the fcc metals.

Ikushima and Suzuki (1963) have examined deformed LiF, KCl, MgO, and PbS and obtained a variety of low-temperature peaks, most of which are not too well defined. Nevertheless, they apply Seeger's theory to obtain $\sigma_p/G \sim 10^{-4}$. They point out, however, that dislocation theory predicts much higher values for the Peierls stress in ionic crystals. Accordingly, they consider the possibility that these low-temperature peaks are due to the motion of geometrical kinks which face a barrier due to the presence of jogs. They also conclude that if the Seeger mechanism of kink generation gives rise to peaks in these ionic materials, such peaks would appear at much higher temperatures. In all, there is not much evidence to support the idea that any of the peaks which have been observed in ionic crystals are of the Bordoni type.

In the case of covalent crystals, notably Si and Ge, a number of low-temperature peaks have been found which are apparently related to the dislocation content. Mecs and Nowick (1966) reported a peak near 150°–200°K for 2000 Hz in the case of crystals for which the surface had been damaged by cutting and polishing. The peak temperature was lower for $\langle 100 \rangle$ than for $\langle 111 \rangle$ oriented crystals. Similar peaks were observed by Zuckerwar and Pechhold (1968) in Ge, and by Hermann (1968) in InSb and GaAs as well as Ge. The latter author found somewhat different results when the samples were ground in D_2O instead of H_2O, and was therefore led to consider that the peaks might be due to a point defect-dislocation mechanism in which hydrogen is the point defect. Peaks in Si and Ge were also reported by Khiznichenko et al. (1967) at somewhat lower temperatures. These peaks increase with deformation (e.g., bending at 1000°C) and decrease with annealing in the manner expected for relaxations originating in dislocations. In view of the anticipated high Peierls barrier in covalent crystals, the latter authors suggest that Brailsford's abrupt kink model rather than Seeger's kink generation model may be applicable here. The characteristics of the observed peaks are not yet well enough established, however, to support this or any other well-defined model.

Higher-temperature peaks have also been found in deformed covalent crystals by Southgate and Mendelson (1965). These authors found a peak in Si which had been deformed by bending at 900°C. The peak is seen against a strongly rising background near 800°C for a frequency of 500 Hz. An apparently similar peak was also observed for deformed

InSb crystals. These authors attribute the peak to the bowing out of dislocations interacting with point defects that may diffuse with the dislocation (see Section 13.6) rather than to a mechanism which reflects the behavior of dislocation kinks.

In summary, there are quite a number of peaks found in deformed nonmetallic crystals. As far as the search for an analogy to the Bordoni relaxation, however, studies of these materials have so far not proved to be particularly illuminating.

13.6   The Snoek–Köster (Cold Work) Relaxation in bcc Metals

In this section we return to the case of cold worked transition metals to discuss their relaxation behavior in a more elevated temperature range than that considered in Section 13.4. The principal reason for discussing this relaxation separately is that its defining characteristics are much clearer than that of the low-temperature relaxations. Accordingly, the theory of this phenomenon has been carried to a higher state of refinement than that for the low temperature peaks.

It was first reported by Snoek (1941) that cold worked iron containing nitrogen or carbon exhibited an internal friction peak near 200°C (for a frequency of 0.2 Hz). The peak could be observed reproducibly on heating and cooling only after a short anneal at 350°C, a treatment which was found to eliminate the normal Snoek peak due to interstitial impurities. These observations were later verified and extended by Kê (1948b) and particularly by Köster et al. (1954). An example of the peak, taken from the work of Petarra and Beshers (1967), is shown in Fig. 13-12. Various authors have referred to this peak either as the "cold-work" peak or as the Köster peak. The former name is rather unsatisfactory since there are several other peaks (e.g., the Bordoni and Hasiguti peaks) which are also produced by cold working. In this book we shall refer to this relaxation process as the Snoek–Köster (or S–K) relaxation. We thus include the name of the original discoverer, and also avoid possible confusion between this phenomena and that known as the Köster effect (i.e., the recovery of internal friction following cold-work, Section 14.2).

Though most studies of the S–K relaxation have been pursued on iron alloys containing carbon and/or nitrogen, it appears possible that the peak observed by Gibala (1967) in hydrogen-charged iron may provide another example of the relaxation. There is also evidence that the relaxation occurs

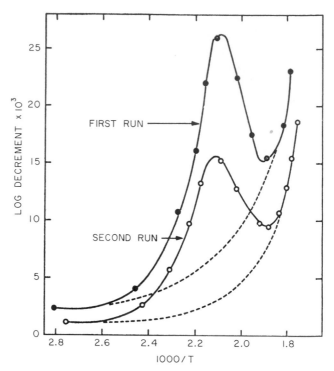

Fig. 13-12.   The Snoek–Köster peak in vacuum melted iron containing 0.016 wt %
nitrogen, deformed by 30% reduction in area. Measurements in torsional vibration at
~1 Hz. (From Petarra and Beshers, 1967.)

in other appropriately treated bcc transitional metals. The clearest
example is provided by the work of Boone and Wert (1963) on Nb–N
alloys.

A. EXPERIMENTAL ASPECTS

The S–K relaxation is a characteristic of deformed and aged bcc
metals containing interstitial impurities. The deformation is usually
carried out at room temperature in amounts of 5–50% reduction of area,
i.e., deformations which substantially raise the dislocation density. In
order to measure the S–K peak, such deformed specimens are necessarily
subjected to an aging treatment, which consists at least of the thermal
excursion required to trace out the peak. The fact that this minimal
treatment causes substantial aging is evident from the drastic reduction
it produces in the Snoek peak, which completely disappears in iron-

based specimens and is greatly reduced in Nb–N alloys. In the case of Fe–N alloys, the S–K peak is fully developed by the first heating excursion, and thereafter decreases in size on further aging. For Fe–C alloys, the S–K peak is also seen on first heating, but then continues to increase slowly by ~50% during the first few hours aging at 240°C before starting to decline (Kamber et al., 1961; Barrand and Leak, 1964). An effect similar to this was also noted by Boone and Wert in Nb–N alloys containing residual oxygen.

For a given deformation, it was reported by Köster et al. that the height of the S–K peak at first rises linearly with increasing solute content (as monitored by the height of the Snoek peak), and then rather abruptly levels off to a saturation value which is higher the larger the extent of the prior deformation. This behavior, which is illustrated by Fig. 13-13,

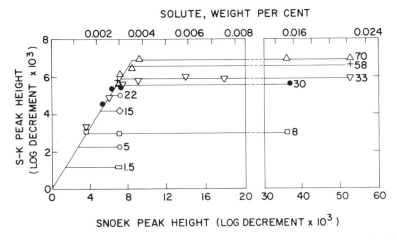

FIG. 13-13. Relation between the height of the Snoek peak in freshly quenched iron specimens and the height of the S–K peak developed at 200°C following the percentage reductions in area indicated on the curves. (From Köster et al., 1954.)

was observed in a technically pure iron in which carbon was thought to be the dominant interstitial impurity. It is noteworthy that the initial (presaturation) portion of the curves of Fig. 13-13 indicates that a direct and almost one-to-one (actually 2 : 3) proportionality exists between the initial height of the Snoek peak and the height of the subsequent S–K peak. While this finding had a considerable influence on the explanation of the S–K peak advanced by Köster et al., subsequent work has failed to substantiate the generality of this result. For example, though Boone and Wert (1963) found an analogous saturation effect in Nb–N alloys, examination of their data in terms of the ratio of the height of the S–K peak to the corresponding loss in height of the Snoek peak shows that the contribution made by one nitrogen atom to the strength of the S–K peak is about ten times as large as its contribution to the strength of the Snoek peak. Sugeno *et al.* (1963) have reported a similarly large ratio (a factor of eight) from work on very dilute Fe–N alloys. More information for Fe–N alloys is available from the work of Petarra and Beshers (1967), who obtained results of the type shown in Fig. 13-14. These data confirm

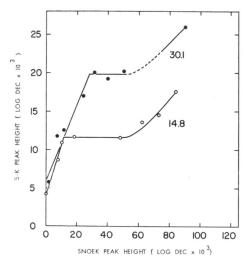

Fig. 13-14.   Relation between the height of the Snoek peak in nitrided high-purity iron and the height of the S–K peak observed after the indicated percentage reductions in area. Note that these curves do not pass through the origin. (From Petarra and Beshers, 1967.)

the existence of the saturation plateau given by Köster *et al.*, but show in addition that at higher solute contents the height of the S–K peak shows a further increase. (This effect is thought to be related to the introduction of more dislocations by the onset of general precipitation of nitride particles within the grains.) The results of Fig. 13-14 are of particular interest in the presaturation range. Though the slope of the curves in this region is comparable with that obtained by Köster *et al.* (Fig. 13-13), the data of Petarra and Beshers reveal (as indicated by the positive intercept in Fig. 13-14) a "residual" S–K peak in deformed specimens which have been hydrogen-purified to the point where the Snoek peak is no longer detectable. Due to the presence of the residual peak, the ratio of the S–K and Snoek peak heights is not a constant, but becomes larger the smaller the Snoek peak, which is consistent with the high ratio observed by Sugeno *et al.* in the very dilute alloys. The presence of the residual peak is not interpreted to mean that the S–K peak occurs in the absence of nitrogen, but rather that the Snoek peak fails to reveal an entrapped residue of nitrogen which however does contribute to the S–K peak after deformation and aging.

With regard to the kinetics of the relaxation, the first point of note is that the peak temperature T_p shows considerable structure sensitivity. The peak temperature at first increases linearly with increasing solute concentration, and then levels off in a complementary manner to the saturation of the peak height. The dependence of T_p on solute content is very marked in the Nb–N alloys, where T_p (measured at $\sim$1 Hz) shifts from about 380 to 520°C. As can be seen from Fig. 13-15, the magnitude of the change in Fe–N samples is smaller, covering a range of about 30°C. It will also be noted that increasing amounts of deformation

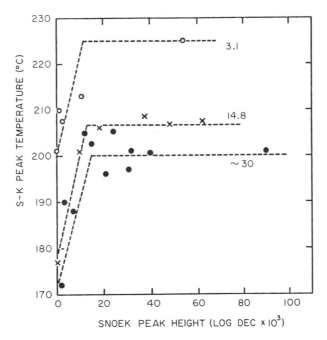

FIG. 13-15. Variation of the temperature of the S–K peak with the height of the Snoek peak in nitrided samples of vacuum-melted iron. The number labeling each curve is the percentage reduction in area. Measurements in torsional vibration at about 1 Hz. (From Petarra and Beshers, 1967.)

produce a downward shift in the curves of Fig. 13-15. Petarra and Beshers have also obtained evidence that T_p is lowered by the presence of substitutional impurities. The structure sensitivity of T_p implies that either or both the frequency factor τ_0^{-1} and activation energy Q are structure sensitive quantities, but it has not been clearly established how much variation occurs in each of the quantities. Reported activation energies for the S–K relaxation in iron-based alloys have been compiled by Ino and Sugeno (1967). Most values fall in the range 1.3–1.6 eV, with 1.4 eV being typical. Petarra and Beshers' (1967) results, which are not included above, indicate that with increasing solute content τ_0^{-1} increases from 10^{14} to 10^{18} sec^{-1} and Q increases from 1.3 to 1.65 eV. Boone and Wert (1963) report $\tau_0^{-1} = 10^{14}$ sec^{-1} and $Q = 2.1$ eV for the fully developed S–K peak in a Nb–0.066 wt % N alloy.

It is at least clear that the activation energy for the S–K relaxation is considerably higher than that for the free lattice migration of interstitial atoms, i.e., the activation energy of the Snoek relaxation. (Values of Q for the Snoek relaxation in Fe–C, Fe–N, and Nb–N alloys, are 0.84, 0.80, and 1.52 eV, respectively.) There is also general agreement that the relaxation exhibits a distribution of relaxation times, and that the peaks are commonly about twice as broad as would be predicted on the basis of a single relaxation time.

A most intriguing aspect of the S–K relaxation is the possibility that the relaxation may be specific to only certain species of the group of solute elements capable of producing a Snoek relaxation. The strongest evidence for this has been summarized by Petarra and Beshers (1967) who, from their own data and consideration of the results of others, conclude that carbon (unlike nitrogen) does not contribute to the S–K relaxation and indeed retards its formation by interfering with the behavior of nitrogen. Boone and Wert (1963) have also commented on the apparently minor effect of oxygen on the S–K relaxation in niobium. The clarification of these apparent differences in behavior of different interstitial solutes is aided by direct electron microscopic observations of Rudee and Huggins (1966). These authors observe grain boundary precipitation in Fe–C alloys at temperatures below the S–K peak, but no precipitation in Fe–N alloys. In addition there were no visible precipitates at dislocations in either alloy.

To close this summary of experimental results, it should be mentioned that martensitic steels exhibit an internal friction peak of very similar characteristics to the S–K peak shown by the ferritic alloys. The overall similarity of these relaxations with respect to such factors as peak height, peak temperature, activation energy, and annealing behavior has been demonstrated by several investigators including Gladman and Pickering (1966), McGrath and Rawlings (1966), and Ward and Capus (1963). It seems highly probable therefore that any acceptable explanation of the S–K relaxation in deformed iron must also serve as a basis for understanding the relaxation in martensite.

B. THEORIES OF THE RELAXATION

It should first be noted that the theories which have been proposed for the S–K relaxation differ among themselves in two main respects. First, different investigators have made different suggestions for the particular atomistic configuration which must be achieved for the appearance of the relaxation. These differences largely reflect the fact that the strain-aged condition cannot be given a simple and unique description. Second, there has been ambiguity over the origin of the anelastic strain which accompanies the stress-induced internal rearrangement. The first proposal we shall describe is that due to Köster et al. (1954), who assumed it was sufficient to consider a structure consisting of a dislocation line pinned along its core by a row of interstitial atoms.[†] It was argued that application of a shear stress at low temperatures would not cause the dislocation to move because the interstitial atoms bound to it are immobile, while at high temperatures (i.e., well above the peak temperature), the dislocation and bound impurities would move together in phase with the stress and again cause no damping. In the temperature range of the peak, the damping was associated with the lag of the impurity atoms behind the dislocation. It appears that in this early proposal, Köster et al. were of the opinion that the origin of the anelastic strain was the change in orientation of the interstitial atoms as they were dragged to neighboring sites, by analogy to the reorientation process involved in the Snoek relaxation. On this basis they could account for the nearly one-to-one proportionality observed in their experiments between the Snoek and S–K peak heights in the presaturation range (Fig. 13-13). Also, the saturation effect could be explained as being due to the filling of all available dislocation sites with interstitial atoms. Based on this explanation, a rough estimate of the dislocation density turns out to have a reasonable order of magnitude. For example, approximately 10^{-5} atom fraction of solute atoms are required to produce saturation in a specimen

---

[†] An attempt to generalize this picture in terms of a more diffuse atmosphere has been made by Beshers (1958).

deformed 20%. With the assumption that this value corresponds to the fraction of available sites at the dislocation core, the required dislocation density is approximately 10^{11} cm^{-2}. A figure of this magnitude is in satisfactory agreement with the dislocation densities that are estimated from observations of the initial rate of strain aging (see Section 9.3). On the other hand, the explanation of the saturation effect given by Köster et al. runs into difficulties in other respects. First, the assumption of a one-to-one correspondence between changes in the height of the Snoek peak and the height of the S–K peak does not appear to be generally valid. Second, the structure-sensitivity of the relaxation time is not easily explained, particularly where large changes in τ_0^{-1} appear to be involved.

Schoeck (1963) has pointed out that these difficulties appear to arise from a misidentification of the source of the anelastic strain. Whereas Köster et al. assumed the strain to arise from the reorientation of bound interstitial atoms and neglected the strain produced by the motion of the dislocation line, Schoeck has taken the opposite, and seemingly more plausible, viewpoint that the anelastic strain is due only to the motion of dislocation segments which bow out (until stopped by line tension) at a rate controlled by the migration rate of the bound solute atoms. Simple considerations involving the bowing of dislocation segments (Section 12.2) yield the following estimate for the relaxation strength

$$\Delta = \beta \Lambda l^2 \tag{13.6-1}$$

where β is a geometrical parameter having a value between 0.01 and 0.1, Λ is the length of pinned dislocation line/cm^3 and l is the average segment length between immobile locking points such as dislocation intersections and precipitate particles. The behavior of the S–K peak on aging may be interpreted in terms of this relation. For example, in iron alloys, where it is known from electron microscopy that precipitation occurs at dislocations quite early in the aging sequence, l (and hence Δ) can be expected to show considerable sensitivity to aging. On the other hand, in systems (e.g., Nb–N) where the peaks are relatively insensitive to aging, it may be inferred that there is a much smaller tendency for precipitation to occur at dislocations.

For a dilute concentration of interstitials, the expression derived by Schoeck for the relaxation time is

$$\tau = \alpha k T C_d l^2 / G b^3 D \tag{13.6-2}$$

where α is a constant of order unity, b is the magnitude of the Burgers vector, G is the shear modulus, and C_d and D are, respectively, the concentration at the dislocation and the diffusion coefficient of the bound interstitial atoms. It is to be noted that τ depends on both C_d and l. Variations in these quantities can thus be used in a qualitative way to explain the structure sensitivity of T_p. As yet, searching quantitative tests of Eqs. (13.6-1) and (13.6-2) have not been performed. However, a start in this direction has been made by Barrand and Leak (1964), Gibala (1967), and particularly by Ino and Sugeno (1967). Among other experiments, these latter workers have examined the anisotropy of the S–K relaxation strength in iron single crystals, and found it to be much smaller than that for the Snoek peak. This behavior is interpreted as favoring dislocation motion as the origin of the anelastic strain, rather than defect reorientation. Another factor which can be cited in support of Schoeck's theory is the explanation offered for the magnitude of the relaxation activation energy which appears implicitly in Eq. (13.6-2) through the diffusion coefficient D. In the unstrained lattice, there are three distinguishable sets of sites of equal energy but different orientation (x, y, or z) that may be occupied by an interstitial atom. However, the large distortions near the core of a dislocation produce an appreciable shifting and splitting of these levels with a preferential occupancy of low-energy sites. Successive neighboring sites of different orientation will then have, alternately, favorable and unfavorable interactions with the dislocation stress field. Accordingly, an interstitial atom in a favorable site on the dislocation will have an activation energy Q which is larger than the Snoek activation energy Q_0 by an amount of approximately its binding energy E_B to the dislocation. Thus Schoeck and Mondino (1963) propose that

$$Q \simeq Q_0 + E_B \qquad (13.6-3)$$

Support for this explanation is obtained from the fact that the difference between the S–K and Snoek activation energies yields an estimate of E_B which is in reasonable agreement with other independent estimates of this quantity (Cochardt et al., 1955; Thomas and Leak, 1955c; Kamber et al., 1961; Petarra and Beshers, 1967).

Though it appears probable that the essential mechanism of the S–K relaxation is contained in Schoeck's model of the diffusion controlled bowing of pinned dislocation segments, the overall complexity of the strain aged structure has led to several other suggestions for the relaxation mechanism. For example, Hermant (1966) has proposed a mechanism involving stacking faults, while Boone and Wert (1963) have suggested the stress-induced reorientation of large clusters of solute atoms formed by segregation to dislocations. Mura *et al.* (1961) have put forward a model involving the diffusion-controlled change of shape of a precipitate particle in the neighborhood of oscillating dislocations. Both of these models involving large clusters or precipitates are rendered doubtful by the failure of Rudee and Huggins (1966) to observe microscopically any evidence for precipitation along dislocations.

PROBLEM

13-1. What form does a Debye peak take as a function of temperature if $\tau = \tau_1 + \tau_2$, where τ_1 obeys the Arrhenius equation and τ_2 is independent of T? Apply your result to Eq. (13.2-6) by showing qualitatively the predicted shape of the Bordoni peak.

General References

BORDONI, P. G. (1960). *Nuovo Cimento Suppl.* 1 **17**, 43.
BURDETT, C. F., and QUEEN, T. J. (1970). *Met. Rev.* No. 143 ,47. [*In* Metals and Materials **4** (May 1970).]
CHAMBERS, R. H. (1966). "Physical Acoustics" (W. P. Mason, ed.), Vol. 3A, Chapter 4. Academic Press, New York.
NIBLETT, D. H. (1966). "Physical Acoustics" (W. P. Mason, ed.), Vol. 3A, Chapter 3. Academic Press, New York.
NIBLETT, D. H., and WILKS, J. (1960). *Advan. Phys.* **9**, 1.

Chapter 14 / Further Dislocation Effects

In addition to the relaxation phenomena attributable to dislocations, which were described in the last chapter, dislocations can produce internal friction in two other important ways. One of these, as discussed in Section 14.1, leads to internal friction by a mechanism which may be either of a relaxation or a resonance absorption type. The other loss mechanism is of a hysteretic nature which strictly falls outside the scope of this book. However, since both effects form an important part of the internal friction literature, both will be discussed in the present chapter.

Read (1940, 1941) was probably the first to recognize that the damping of pure metals near room temperature was due in large part to a dislocation mechanism. As shown in Fig. 14-1, the damping of high-purity annealed (or lightly worked) metals increases and becomes strongly *amplitude dependent* above strain amplitudes of the order of 10^{-7}–10^{-6}. Such a nonlinear effect cannot be accounted for in terms of an anelastic mechanism. Read pointed out, however, that it was possible to understand such behavior in terms of a hysteresis due to microplastic yielding (dislocation motion) under the applied stress. Qualitative support for this idea is not hard to find. For example, in metals which have been strengthened by heavy cold working or by alloying, the damping may not become amplitude dependent until the strain amplitude exceeds 10^{-5}–10^{-4}. Such observations make it attractive to regard each damping curve of Fig. 14-1 as composed of two parts, as in Fig. 14-2, the first part marked ϕ_i being *independent* of amplitude, and the second part ϕ_h being *dependent* on amplitude. As we shall see, such a division has some basis in theory, although as Trott and Birnbaum (1970) have emphasized, the amplitude independence of ϕ_i breaks down with the onset of the dislocation breakaway process that leads to the appearance of ϕ_h. [†]

The first two sections deal with the theory and experiments related to ϕ_i, while the last two sections cover the same ground for ϕ_h.

[†] In the literature, it has become customary to identify the amplitude dependent damping with the subscript h for "hysteresis." It is best not to overemphasize this point, however, since we later point out that there may even be a hysteresis contribution to ϕ_i.

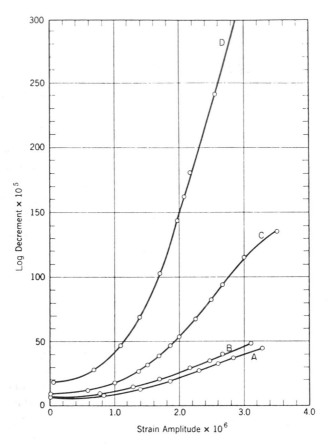

FIG. 14-1.   Internal friction as a function of strain amplitude for an undeformed
copper crystal (curve A) and after application of stresses of 60, 120, and 150 psi, respectively (curves B, C, and D). Measurements in longitudinal vibration at about 30 kHz.
(From Read, 1941.)

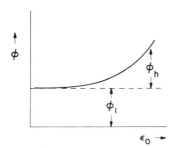

FIG. 14-2.   Schematic diagram of internal friction
versus strain amplitude, showing the components
ϕ_i and ϕ_h.

14.1 The Vibrating-String Model and Dislocation Resonance

This model, first suggested by Koehler (1952) and later developed further by Granato and Lücke (1956), has served as the basis for the interpretation of ϕ_i by a number of authors.

Consider a dislocation loop of length l pinned firmly at its ends and executing forced vibration (like a vibrating string) under an applied alternating stress, as in Fig. 12-10. If a mechanism for damping exists, energy will be dissipated. In addition, there will be a modulus defect of the type already calculated (see Section 12.2). Because a dislocation has an effective mass per unit length m_l, one obtains an equation of motion in the displacement $u(y, t)$ similar to that of a resonant mechanical system, namely,

$$m_l \ddot{u} + B\dot{u} - \gamma(\partial^2 u/\partial y^2) = \sigma b = \sigma_0 b e^{i\omega t} \qquad (14.1-1)$$

with boundary conditions $u(0, t) = u(l, t) = 0$. Here y is the coordinate which measures distance along the line, and $\sigma = \sigma_0 e^{i\omega t}$ is the applied periodic resolved shear stress. The first term in Eq. (14.1-1) is the inertial term, the second is the damping term with B as the appropriate damping constant, and the third term is the restoring force per unit length with γ the effective line tension of the dislocation (see Section 12.1). The right-hand side of Eq. (14.1-1) is the external force per unit length, as a consequence of Eq. (12.2-1). The quantity m_l is given by dislocation theory as approximately

$$m_l \sim \varrho b^2 \qquad (14.1-2)$$

where ϱ is the density of the material and b is the magnitude of the Burgers vector.

If the angular frequency ω of stress variation is not too high, one may simplify this calculation by taking the dislocation loop shape to be the same as under a static stress.[†] This shape is $u = A\sigma(ly - y^2)$, where $A = b/2\gamma$. Under periodic conditions,

$$u(y, t) = A\sigma_0(ly - y^2)e^{i\omega t} \qquad (14.1-3)$$

where, due to the damping term, the quantity A is now, in general, complex and is given by

$$A = A_1 - iA_2 \qquad (14.1-4)$$

[†] Granato and Lücke performed a more exact calculation, taking into account the change of shape at high frequencies, but obtained essentially the same answer.

to allow for the phase lag of the displacement behind the applied stress. Substituting Eqs. (14.1-3) and (14.1-4) into (14.1-1) and integrating from $y = 0$ to $y = l$, we obtain

$$-\omega^2 m_l(Al^3/6) + i\omega B(Al^3/6) + 2\gamma Al = bl$$

or

$$A = (b/2\gamma)[1 + i\omega\tau - (\omega^2/\omega_0^2)]^{-1} \qquad (14.1\text{-}5)$$

where

$$\omega_0^2 = 12\gamma/m_l l^2 \qquad (14.1\text{-}6)$$

and

$$\tau = Bl^2/12\gamma \qquad (14.1\text{-}7)$$

Clearly, for a small damping constant, $\omega_0/2\pi$ plays the role of a resonant frequency, at which $|A|$ attains its maximum value limited only by the damping constant. Substituting Eqs. (14.1-2) and (12.1-1) and reasonable numbers for the physical constants, we obtain $\omega_0/2\pi \sim 10^9$ for $l \sim 10^{-4}$ cm. This is higher than the usual range of frequencies employed experimentally, and therefore the assumption of quasi-static conditions [Eq. (14.1-3)] is essentially justified.

In order to obtain the internal friction and modulus defect we proceed as follows. First we assume that the material contains N_v dislocation segments per unit volume in one set of slip planes and all of the same length. (This amounts to assuming a Dirac δ function distribution in the loop lengths.) Then the shear strain on the slip plane ε_d due to dislocations is [see Eq. (12.2-6)]

$$\varepsilon_d = N_v b\, \delta s$$

Here δs is the area swept out by the bowing dislocation segment, and is equal to $\bar{u}l$, where the mean displacement $\bar{u}$ is given by

$$\bar{u} = (1/l) \int_0^l u\, dy = (1/6)A\sigma_0 l^2 e^{i\omega t}$$

from Eq. (14.1-3). Further, as in Eq. (12.2-9), we have

$$N_v l = \Lambda$$

where Λ is the dislocation density. Combining these results gives for the compliance due to dislocations:

$$J_d = \varepsilon_d/\sigma = (1/6)\Lambda l^2 b A \qquad (14.1\text{-}8)$$

Following the usual notation for relaxation processes, we denote by J_U the compliance of the perfect crystal, by J_1 the compliance of the actual crystal in phase with the applied stress, and by J_2 the 90° out-of-phase compliance. Since A is complex, it is clear that J_d will contribute to both J_1 and J_2 as follows:

$$(J_d)_1 = J_1 - J_U = (1/6)\Lambda l^2 b A_1 \tag{14.1-9}$$

$$(J_d)_2 = J_2 = (1/6)\Lambda l^2 b A_2 \tag{14.1-10}$$

Substituting for A_1 and A_2 from Eq. (14.1-5), we obtain

$$\frac{J_1 - J_U}{J_U} = \frac{\Lambda l^2 b^2}{12\gamma J_U} \frac{1 - (\omega^2/\omega_0^2)}{[1 - (\omega^2/\omega_0^2)]^2 + \omega^2\tau^2} \tag{14.1-11}$$

$$\tan\phi \simeq \frac{J_2}{J_U} = \frac{\Lambda l^2 b^2}{12\gamma J_U} \frac{\omega\tau}{[1 - (\omega^2/\omega_0^2)]^2 + \omega^2\tau^2} \tag{14.1-12}$$

where in the last equation we assume that the total dislocation contribution is small, so that $(J_1 - J_U)/J_U \ll 1$. Both of the above expressions take on simpler asymptotic forms at low frequencies (where both ω^2/ω_0^2 and $\omega^2\tau^2 \ll 1$), namely,

$$(J_1 - J_U)/J_U \simeq (1/6)\Lambda l^2 \tag{14.1-13}$$

$$\tan\phi \simeq \Lambda B l^4 \omega/36 G b^2 \tag{14.1-14}$$

where we have also substituted Eqs. (14.1-2), (14.1-7), and (12.1-1) and taken $G^{-1} = J$. Equation (14.1-13), for the modulus defect due to dislocations, is the same as (12.2-9), while Eq. (14.1-14) shows that the low-frequency internal friction is proportional to the frequency, the dislocation density, the damping constant B and the fourth power of the loop length.

Examination of Eqs. (14.1-11) and (14.1-12) shows that this dislocation string model corresponds closely to the mechanical model discussed in Appendix C. Turning to the high-frequency behavior, it is clear from Eqs. (14.1-11) and (14.1-12) that much depends on the relative magnitudes of the terms $\omega\tau$ and ω/ω_0. If the damping constant is small, such that $\tau \ll 1/\omega_0$, resonance-type behavior occurs in which J_1 varies rapidly in the vicinity of the frequency ω_0, while $\tan\phi$ goes through a steep maximum at $\omega = \omega_0$. On the other hand, if $\tau \gg 1/\omega_0$, $\tan\phi$ takes on the form of a Debye peak with maximum at $\omega\tau = 1$. The transition between these two ranges is shown in Fig. 14-3, where $\tan\phi$ on a

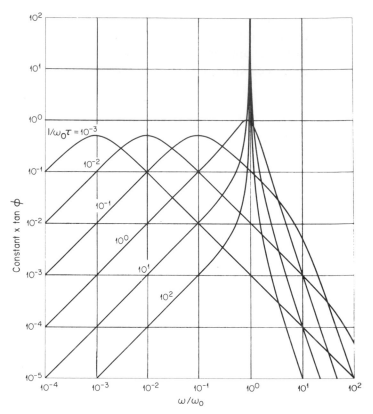

FIG. 14-3.   Calculated frequency dependence of internal friction for the dislocation string model, for different values of the parameter $1/\omega_0\tau$. The constant multiplying $\tan\phi$ is equal to $\Lambda l^2 b^2/24\gamma J_U$.

relative scale is plotted versus ω/ω_0 with $1/\omega_0$ as a parameter. The figure shows that for $1/\omega_0\tau \gg 1$, resonance-type behavior is observed, while for $1/\omega_0\tau \ll 1$ relaxation-type behavior (or "overdamped resonance") is obtained.

As already mentioned, the above derivation is oversimplified in two ways: (1) It considers only the stress and strain resolved onto the slip plane, and therefore calculates the compliances J_1 and J_2 for this plane only. (2) It considers only a δ-function distribution in loop lengths. Granato and Lücke (1956) concern themselves with improving the calculation with respect to these two points. They find, however, that the above result is not changed in any substantial way. It is shown that to generalize item (1) requires the introduction of an orientation factor which multiplies expressions (14.1-11) and (14.1-12). On the other hand, the generalization of item (2) leads to the replacement of l by an effective loop length l_e in these equations. This effective length is always larger than the average loop length, since the internal friction varies as the fourth power of the loop length and is therefore more sensitive to large l values. [†]

The most important predictions of the vibrating string model are as follows:

(a) At low frequency (e.g., kilohertz range) the internal friction is proportional to Λl^4 and to the frequency ω.

(b) At sufficiently high frequencies, there exists a peak in tan ϕ versus ω, with resonance or relaxation-type behavior depending upon the magnitude of the damping constant B.

Before closing this section, it should be noted that the vibrating-string model assumes that the pinning points at the dislocation lines are static, i.e., that they cannot diffuse. Clearly, this assumption can only be valid at relatively low temperatures. In a bowed out dislocation, the pinning defects will be subjected to forces directed both parallel and perpendicular to the dislocation line. At moderate temperatures, the pinning points should be able to diffuse along the dislocation line in response to the parallel force, and thereby to alter the (initially) random distribution of loop lengths. Yamafuji and Bauer (1965) have pointed out that this effect will give rise to a time dependence of the internal friction ϕ_i once the stress σ exceeds a critical value σ_c. Further, they show how the time constant of this process can be analyzed so as to yield the dislocation pipe diffusion coefficient of the pinning species. [‡] Lücke and Schlipf (1968), on the other hand, consider a more general case in which migration of pinning points both parallel and perpendicular to the dislocation line is permitted.

14.2 Experimental Observations concerning ϕ_i

There are two types of sample which have primarily been used to study the amplitude independent dislocation damping ϕ_i. The first is the *high-purity sample* in a well-annealed condition. The fact that internal friction

---

[†] In addition, however, introducing a distribution of loop lengths results in relaxation-type peaks which are broader than a simple Debye peak.

[‡] Such time-dependent effects have subsequently been observed by Oren and Bauer (1967) for dilute copper alloys in the range 200–350°C.

increases rapidly with increasing purity shows that impurities in small amounts produce dislocation pinning and thereby reduce the damping. High concentration alloys, such as α-brass, show extremely low damping near room temperature, implying that the pinning is essentially complete. In a high purity sample an important tool in the study of the dislocation damping results from the ability to eliminate this damping, as well as the associated modulus defect, through irradiation. This technique has been used extensively by Thompson and Holmes (1956, 1957) and others to study internal friction in high purity copper. Figure 14-4 shows an example taken from their work which will be discussed later in some detail.

The second type of sample often used in the study of dislocation damping is the *freshly cold-worked sample*. In such a sample a high damping is observed immediately after cold working, which then decreases with time. Correspondingly, the modulus increases with time. This type

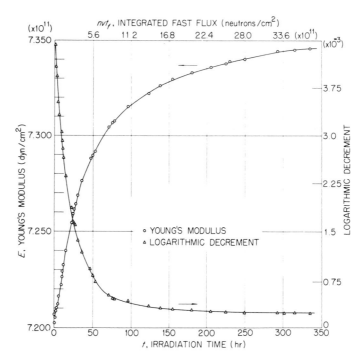

FIG. 14-4.   Effect of fast neutron irradiation on Young's modulus and internal friction of an annealed high purity copper crystal. Neutron flux is 3×10^6 cm^{-2} sec^{-1}. Measurements in longitudinal vibration at 12 kHz. (From Thompson and Holmes, 1956.)

of unstable damping was first studied in some detail by Köster and co-workers (Köster, 1940b, 1940–1941; Köster and Stolte, 1954) and has been called the "Köster effect." Figure 14-5 shows an example for the case of deformed nickel. Although the Köster damping is unstable in time, we will see that there is every reason to believe that it is the same dislocation phenomenon that occurs in well-annealed high-purity samples.

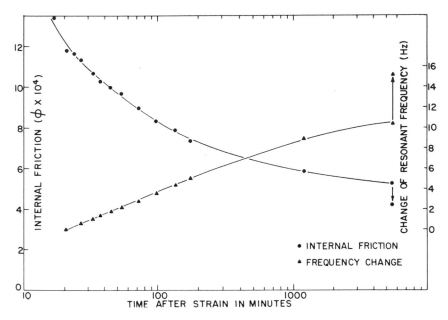

FIG. 14-5. Room temperature recovery of the internal friction and resonant frequency of a bar of commercially pure nickel following 10% plastic deformation. Measurements in flexural vibration at about 2 kHz. The vertical arrows point to final values obtained after annealing at an elevated temperature.

In both of the above cases, measurements are usually made at low amplitudes, in the range where $\phi = \phi_i$. It is therefore appropriate to compare the results with the predictions of the vibrating string model of Section 14.1. The most striking predictions of the model relate to the frequency dependence. First, there is the prediction of an internal friction peak at sufficiently high frequencies. Evidence for the existence of such a peak in copper was first given by Alers and Thompson (1961) and by Stern and Granato (1962), as illustrated in Fig. 14-6. The low frequency at which the peak occurs relative to a value $\omega_0/2\pi \sim 10^9$ sec^{-1} indicates that the dislocations are overdamped, corresponding to the case of low

$1/\omega_0\tau$ (high damping coefficient B) in Fig. 14-3. The fact that irradiation with γ rays decreases the height of the peak and moves it to higher frequencies is consistent with the string model,[†] since irradiation is expected to generate pinning points and thereby to shorten l.

Alers and Thompson made an independent determination of the dislocation density Λ by etch pit counting. In this way, they were able to determine the damping constant B from the internal friction data (see Problem 14-1). Over the temperature range investigated (20°–280°K), their data indicate that B is directly proportional to T. The temperature dependence of B was also investigated for copper by Suzuki et al. (1964). As indicated in Table 14-1 the room temperature value of B obtained

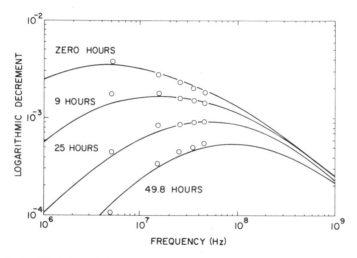

FIG. 14-6.   Variation of internal friction with frequency for high purity copper, after different times of irradiation in a cobalt gamma source (flux: $1.7 \times 10^{11}\gamma$ sec^{-1} cm^{-2}). (From Stern and Granato, 1962.)

by these workers was only one-tenth the Alers and Thompson value, and from data at two other temperatures, the temperature dependence down to 77°K appears less marked. In addition to their observations on metals, Suzuki et al. also obtained room temperature values of B for LiF and KCl. Their value for LiF entered in Table 14-1 is in fair accord with the data of Mitchell (1965), who extended the measurements down to 20°K and found B to be essentially temperature independent. The work on LiF is of particular interest because a separate room temperature

[†] Note from Eq. (14.1-7) that $\tau \propto l^2$, so that the peak frequency goes as $1/l^2$.

TABLE 14-1

COMPARISON OF DIFFERENT EXPERIMENTAL VALUES
FOR THE DAMPING CONSTANT B AT 300°K[a]

	Internal friction	"Direct" measurement
Cu	8[b]	
	0.8[c]	
LiF	13[c]	7[f]
	4[d]	
Al	0.5[e]	

[a] B is given in cgs units $\times 10^4$.
[b] Alers and Thompson (1961).
[c] Suzuki et al. (1964).
[d] Mitchell (1965).
[e] Hikata et al. (1970).
[f] Johnston and Gilman (1959).

measurement of the damping constant B has been made in a relatively direct way by Johnston and Gilman (1959) from the velocity of dislocations under a known stress, as observed by etch pit techniques. As shown in Table 14-1 there is good agreement between the two methods of measurement.

In the attenuation studies mentioned above, one source of uncertainty in the determination of B lies in the measurement of the dislocation density. Hikata et al. (1970) have developed a technique for obtaining B which avoids this problem and is claimed to give more reliable values. The procedure involves measuring the frequency dependence of the incremental increase in attenuation which is brought about by the application of a bias stress. (This stress serves to unpin some of the dislocations and increase the average loop length.) Data obtained by this technique on aluminum over the range 10°–250°K are shown in Fig. 14-7, and the extrapolated value for 300°K is entered in Table 14-1. In contrast to the results of Alers and Thompson, a flattening off in the temperature dependence of B at low temperatures is quite evident from these results.

Theories of the damping constant B have been proposed by a number of workers. Eshelby's (1949) theory, which considers radiation and thermoelastic damping effects, was followed by Leibfried's (1950) treat-

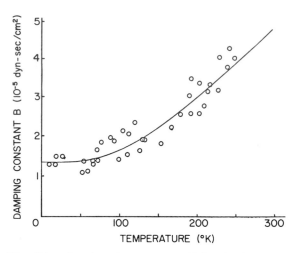

Fig. 14-7.   The dislocation damping parameter B for aluminum, as measured over a range of temperature by Hikata *et al.* (1970).

ment of the scattering of thermal waves (phonons) by the elastic strain field of a moving dislocation. Leibfried's theory predicts that at temperatures well above the Debye temperature B should vary linearly with T, since the density of phonons is then proportional to T. An alternative theory developed by Mason (1960, 1964) is based on a concept of "phonon viscosity," in which a dislocation is pictured as moving in a viscous phonon gas. Mason's theory leads to a relatively small temperature dependence of B and appears to fit quite well the data which are presently available for LiF. On the other hand, the most extensive data are available for the metals Cu and Al, and here Leibfried's theory appears to apply much better. Hikata *et al.* have pointed out that Mason's theory is unable to account for the magnitude as well as the temperature dependence of their data (Fig. 14-7). These workers find they can quantitatively account for their results by combining Leibfried's theory with an additional temperature independent contribution to B, which is of electronic origin. Very recently, a unified theory which includes the various anharmonic (i.e., nonelectronic) contributions to the dislocation damping constant has been given by Brailsford (1972).

   In summary, while it cannot be said that theory and experiment concerning the damping constant B are in universal accord, most workers seem to accept that dislocation–phonon interactions provide the most important source of dissipation at normal temperatures.

   Turning now to the frequency dependence of the internal friction in the lower (e.g., kilohertz) frequency range, the vibrating string model predicts $\phi_i = \omega l^4$ [Eq. (14.1-14)]. Although there have been reports of this type of frequency dependence in the low megahertz range (Hikata and Truell, 1957; Granato and Lücke, 1956; Heiple and Birnbaum, 1967), there seems to be widespread evidence that, for metals in the kilohertz range, direct proportionality to the frequency is not observed. This statement seems to apply both to undeformed pure metals and to the Köster damping following deformation. The first work on the frequency dependence was that of Nowick (1950) who studied the internal friction of relatively pure copper crystals at the fundamental and second harmonic frequencies. In spite of considerable scatter in the frequency dependence (which was due to an inhomogeneous dislocation distribution), the data indicated frequency independence rather than proportionality to the frequency. Although Hiki (1958) has claimed to observe direct proportionality between damping and frequency, both Takahashi (1956) and Bordoni et al. (1959) find very little frequency dependence of ϕ_i for copper. For the Köster-type damping in Al, Holwech (1960) reports independence of frequency in the megahertz range.

Even more striking is the observation by Weinig and Machlin (1956) and more recently by Routbort and Sack (1966) that even at 1 Hz the values of ϕ_i are of the same order as in the kilohertz range, again indicating essential frequency independence. (Clearly, if the megahertz damping were proportional to ω over the entire frequency range, the corresponding values at 1 Hz would be completely negligible.) As a result of all these experiments there is good reason to doubt that the predictions of the string model with respect to frequency dependence are fulfilled over the entire frequency range. Routbort and Sack further claim that the low-frequency damping is nearly independent of frequency and also differs in its behavior under irradiation from that expected from the string model. Accordingly, they propose that there are two different components which make up ϕ_i, one of which is nearly frequency independent. The origin of this latter component is not yet understood. A possible explanation is that there is an additional source of dislocation damping which originates in a hysteresis mechanism and is therefore frequency independent. One suggested mechanism for a hysteretic contribution to ϕ_i is that of Weertman and Salkovitz (1955), which has been criticized by Granato and Lücke as being inapplicable at very low strain amplitudes. Another suggestion has been made recently by Mason and Wehr (1970) according to which the energy loss is produced by the nonlinear motion of dislocation kinks across Peierls-type barriers.

In spite of these difficulties with the frequency dependence, the prediction of the string model that ϕ_i is proportional to the fourth power of the loop length has received striking verification in the kilohertz frequency range. In the first case, Thompson and Holmes (1956) used neutron irradiation of high purity copper to study quantitatively the effect of dislocation pinning on both the damping and the modulus (i.e., the resonant frequency). An example of their data was already given in Fig. 14-4. Other investigations were carried out at about the same time using electron irradiation (Dieckamp and Sosin, 1956) and gamma irradiation (Thompson and Holmes, 1957). It is reasonable to expect that the irradiation produces no change in the dislocation density or position, but merely generates point defects which diffuse to the dislocation lines and shorten the loop lengths. Since the total number of pinning points generated is reasonably taken as proportional to the total flux, the mean loop length l should vary with time t as

$$l \propto (1 + \zeta R t)^{-1} \qquad (14.2\text{-}1)$$

where ζ is a constant which depends on dislocation density, and R is the dose rate. The power to which the modulus defect or the damping depends on the loop length can then be determined from the form of the time dependence. Qualitatively, one can see that the damping in Fig. 14-4

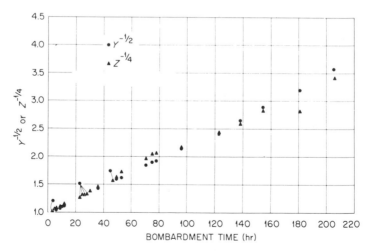

FIG. 14-8. Analysis of the data of Fig. 14-4. The quantity $y(t)$ is obtained from modulus measurements and is equal to $(1 + \zeta R t)^{-2}$, while $z(t)$ is obtained from internal friction measurements and equals $(1 + \zeta R t)^{-4}$, in terms of the theory of Section 14.1 and Eq. (14.2-1). (From Thompson and Paré, 1960.)

approaches a saturation value faster than the modulus. A quantitative analysis of data of the type shown in Fig. 14-4 along these lines is given in Fig. 14-8. The agreement between the two curves as well as their linear variation with time is consistent with an l^2 loop length dependence for the modulus defect and an l^4 dependence for the internal friction.

In a similar way Bray and Nowick (unpublished) have used the annealing of the Köster effect, following deformation, as an indication of

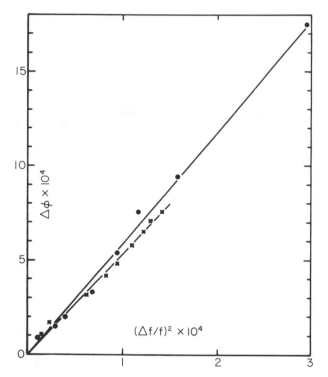

FIG. 14-9. A plot of the change in internal friction versus the square of the fractional change in resonant frequency during annealing of the Köster effect following deformation, for two samples of polycrystalline copper.

the loop length dependence of the damping. Assuming that the annealing of this effect occurs by diffusion of point defects (generated by the deformation) to the dislocations, and therefore involves only a change in loop length with time, Eqs. (14.1-13) and (14.1-14) then predict that $\phi(t)$ should be proportional to $[\delta J(t)/J]^2$. Figure 14-9 shows a verification of this prediction for the case of deformed copper. For NaCl crystals following deformation, Gordon and Nowick (1956) have shown by irradiation techniques that the modulus defect obeys an l^2 dependence, but the internal friction was not studied. Granato *et al.* (1958) have analyzed the annealing of the Köster effect in a number of materials in terms of pinning of dislocations by diffusion of point defects and again obtain results consistent with the l^4 loop length dependence for the damping.

These results, involving both the pinning of dislocations in high purity copper, and the annealing of the Köster effect, seem to follow the predictions of the string model quite closely. Nevertheless, there are other experiments, in addition to those dealing with the frequency dependence, which leave the situation somewhat uncertain. Thus, further studies of irradiation pinning using reactor irradiation (see Thompson and Paré, 1966) show that, in fact, the parameters $y^{-1/2}$ and $z^{-1/4}$ which are obtained, respectively, from the modulus change and the damping, do not always coincide as in Fig. 14-8 and are not always linear in dose. These deviations can be explained by assuming that two or more types of dislocations, with different pinning parameters, are present. Other effects, involving defect clustering and time delays in the pinning process, however, have led these authors to raise some doubts as to the quantitative validity of the studies of loop length dependence. Probably the most serious problem, however, is the failure to obtain the predicted frequency dependence of the internal friction in the kilohertz frequency range, as discussed earlier. If there is a hysteretic contribution to ϕ_i, it is not yet clear whether this damping may also vary as l^4, or whether it is simply not pinned out during irradiation or Köster annealing. In any case, present indications are that we do not really understand the mechanism of low-frequency (kilohertz and below) damping of pure metals in the vicinity of room temperature, in spite of the considerable efforts that have been made.

Despite these difficulties, modulus and damping measurements have constituted a very important tool in the study of radiation damage. This follows from the fact that extremely small concentrations of defects can be detected by these techniques in terms of the pinning effects they produce at dislocations (see Problem 14-2). Accordingly, different stages of defect migration can be detected and the appropriate activation energies for migration obtained by means of these measurements. Since this subject is well outside the scope of this book, we will not discuss it here. For the interested reader, detailed references in the study of radiation damage in metals are given in reviews by Holmes and Thompson (1964) and by Thompson and Paré (1966). Among the more recent papers on the subject are those of Keefer *et al.* (1965, 1966) and Thompson *et al.* (1967). In the field of ionic crystals an interesting study of the effects of x-irradiation and illumination with light on dislocations in NaCl crystals was made by Bauer and Gordon (1962).

It is important to note that in most of these studies, the modulus defect has been used more widely than the internal friction. The interpretation of the modulus defect is, in fact, on safer ground than that of the internal friction. The modulus defect is, essentially, a zero-order effect, since it may be calculated based on the (nearly correct) assumption that the dislocation motion is in phase with the applied stress (see Section 12.2); the l^2 dependence of the modulus defect, therefore, seems beyond question. On the other hand, the internal friction is a first-order effect since it depends on the presence of a phase lag, and, in particular, on the assumed form for the damping force on a moving dislocation. It is just this term that causes the theory to predict that internal friction is proportional to ω at low frequencies, a prediction that we have already seen is not generally confirmed.

14.3   Theory of the Amplitude-Dependent Damping ϕ_h

It was mentioned at the beginning of this chapter that early attention was given to the idea that the amplitude dependent damping ϕ_h originated from a hysteresis phenomenon involving dislocation motion. A mechanism for this effect (Koehler, 1952), which has attracted wide attention, involves dislocations breaking away from pinning points distributed along their length. The theory of this phenomenon was developed further by Granato and Lücke (1956). The ideas involved can be explained by reference to Fig. 14-10. In part (a) of this figure, the sequence a–f shows the behavior under stress of a single dislocation segment, which initially is pinned along its length by a number of point defects. Under an increasing shear stress, the segment first bows reversibly into a series of loops between the pinning points ($a \rightarrow b \rightarrow c$). This range of stresses corresponds to that considered in the vibrating string model, Section 14.1. The bowed loops exert a net force on the pinning points, tending to overcome the binding force, which has a certain maximum value F_{max}. Consider the force F_P exerted by the loops l_1 and l_2 on the pinning point P in Fig. 14-10a. Evaluating the angles θ_1 and θ_2 (assumed small) from the simplified (quasi-static) shape given by Eq. (14.1-3), and taking the components of the line tension, we find

$$F_P = \sigma b(l_1 + l_2)/2 \qquad (14.3\text{-}1)$$

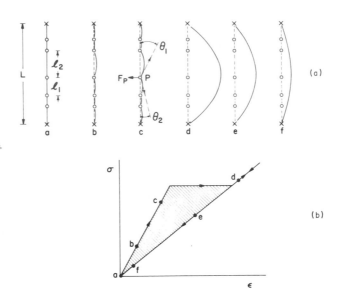

FIG. 14-10.   (a) The sequence *a–f* illustrates schematically the breakaway of a dislocation segment from a number of pinning points during a loading cycle. (b) The corresponding stress–strain curve and hysteresis loop. The lettered points match the sequence
a–f in (a).

This result can also be obtained by multiplying σb, the force per unit
length acting on the dislocation, by the length $(l_1 + l_2)/2$ associated with
the pinning point P. It is apparent from Eq. (14.3-1) that F_P increases
with the applied stress σ, and will exceed $F_{\max}$ first at that particular
pinning point for which the sum of the adjacent loop lengths, $l_i + l_{i+1}$
has the largest value anywhere along the segment. We may call this
greatest length the "breakaway length" of the segment, and denote it
by l'. At the critical value of stress which causes breakaway from the
pinning point contained in the length l', the whole segment is catastroph-
ically torn away from the row of pinning points $(c \rightarrow d)$. Following
this catastrophic process, a further increase in stress merely causes further
bowing of the whole segment L and the material consequently responds
with a lower effective modulus which, on unloading, governs the response
down to zero stress $(d \rightarrow e \rightarrow f)$. In the above description, the maximum
applied stress is presumed to be not great enough to cause the segment
to act as a Frank–Read source. It will be seen from Fig. 14-10b that, as
a result of breakaway, a sample containing only a single dislocation segment would exhibit a closed hysteresis loop each half cycle of vibration.
The energy dissipated per unit volume in one complete cycle ΔW is

given by twice the shaded area in Fig. 14-10b. The strain amplitude-dependence of the damping of such a sample is shown schematically in Fig. 14-11. It can be seen that ϕ_h is zero until breakaway occurs and then jumps discontinuously to a finite (and maximum) value. The damping decreases at higher amplitudes since ΔW remains constant while the strain energy density W continues to increase as the square of the elastic component of the strain. Such amplitude dependence bears no resemblance to the form of ϕ_h as shown, e.g., in Fig. 14-1. To convert the behavior of ϕ_h shown in Fig. 14-11 to that of Fig. 14-1, it is necessary to introduce the additional factor that in a real material, containing a multitude of segments, the breakaway length l' should exhibit a distribution of values. Since a distribution in l' leads to a distribution in the stress

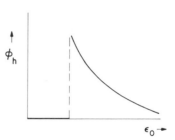

FIG. 14-11. The variation of ϕ_h with strain amplitude for a sample containing only the single dislocation segment of Fig. 14-10.

necessary for various segments to break away, the following physical picture emerges of what happens during an excursion to some intermediate value of stress. As the stress rises, an increasing number of pinned segments break loose, the fraction letting go in each increment of stress being determined by the form of the distribution. Those which already have broken loose bow out as complete segments, while those for which the breakaway stress has not yet been exceeded bow out in a series of small loops. The ascending portion of the stress–strain curve is now continuously curved. On unloading, the numbers of pinned and unpinned segments remain constant at the values attained at the extremity of the excursion, and the descending limb of the stress–strain curve is again linear. Granato and Lücke have performed the calculation of ϕ_h using this model and Koehler's original assumption that the pinning points are distributed at random along the dislocation line. This assumption leads to the following exponential distribution of loop lengths:

$$N(l)\,dl = (A/l_0{}^2)\exp(-l/l_0)\,dl \qquad (14.3\text{-}2)$$

where $N(l)\,dl$ is the number of loops per cubic centimeter having a length between l and $l + dl$, l_0 is the average loop length, and Λ is the dislocation density. Using Eq. (14.3-2), Granato and Lücke determined the distribution function $N(l')\,dl'$ for the breakaway length l', and arrived at the following result[†] for ϕ_h of a single crystal subject to a homogeneous tensile strain of amplitude ε_0

$$\phi_h = (C_1/\varepsilon_0)\exp(-C_2/\varepsilon_0) \qquad (14.3-3)$$

where

$$C_2 = Ka\delta/l_0 \qquad \text{and} \qquad C_1 = (\Omega\Delta_0/\pi^2)(\Lambda L^3/l_0)C_2$$

Also, the amplitude-dependent modulus defect $\Delta E/E$ was found to be proportional to, and approximately equal in magnitude to, $\pi\phi_h$. The symbols used above have the following meanings: In the lumped parameter C_2, K is a factor depending on the anisotropy of the elastic constants and the orientation of the sample with respect to the applied stress, δ is the size factor of the pinning solute atoms with respect to the solvent, and a is the lattice parameter of the crystal. Of the remaining quantities appearing in the lumped parameter C_1, Ω is an orientation factor involved in summing the contributions from dislocations in each of the slip systems, and $\Delta_0 \equiv 4(1 - \chi)/\pi^2$, where χ is Poisson's ratio.

From inspection of Eq. (14.3-3), it will be seen that $\log(\varepsilon_0\phi_h)$ should vary linearly with the reciprocal strain amplitude ε_0^{-1}. The slope of such a "Granato–Lücke" plot is predicted to vary inversely with the loop length while the intercept at $\varepsilon_0^{-1} = 0$ is sensitive to the combination of terms $\Lambda L^3/l_0^2$. We shall see how these results compare with experimental observations in the following section.

The theory as outlined above is actually applicable only near $0°K$ since it does not take into account the effect of thermal fluctuations on the breakaway process. Actually, for a reasonable interaction energy (~ 0.1 eV) between the pinning defect and the dislocation, it appears that thermal breakaway should be more important than mechanical breakaway at room temperature. The problem of thermal breakaway, and its effect on the damping phenomenon has been dealt with by Friedel (1963), by Teutonico et al. (1964), and by Lücke et al. (1968). This problem is

---

[†] Because of the assumptions and mathematical simplifications made in its derivation, this result can be expected to apply best for the beginning of breakaway and when there are a relatively large number of loops per network length. A mathematically less restrictive treatment, yielding numerical results only, has been described by Trott and Birnbaum (1970).

quite complex, but these authors give some indication that the dependence of decrement on strain amplitude might be similar to that given by the tero-temperature theory. However, the parameters appearing in the zheory must then be reinterpreted.

14.4 Experimental Studies of Amplitude-Dependent Damping

One of the most important experiments in attempting to establish the origin of ϕ_h is to measure the frequency dependence of this loss. If the mechanism is of a hysteretic type in which time effects are completely negligible, ϕ_h should exhibit no frequency dependence. Such investigations should ideally be performed on one sample subject to the same distribution of strain at all frequencies, for otherwise a nonuniform dislocation distribution in the sample can affect the results. However, the usual procedure has been to obtain different frequencies by using two or more harmonics of a resonant bar. From measurements on copper single crystals, Nowick (1950) concluded that the amplitude dependent loss was frequency independent. Similar conclusions were also obtained for copper by Marx (quoted by Granato and Lücke, 1956) and by Hiki (1958) for samples of lead. It therefore seems reasonable to accept ϕ_h as being frequency independent, and hence of a hysteretic origin. [†]

In contrast to its insensitivity to frequency, ϕ_h has been found to be dependent (usually markedly so) on a number of other experimental variables, notably the degree of cold work, alloying additions, exposure to radiation, and the temperature of testing. An extensive review and discussion of results available up to 1956 have been given by Granato and Lücke (1956). Further work is included in the reviews of Niblett and Wilks (1960) and Burdett and Queen (1970b).

An analysis of Read's data of Fig. 14-1, in terms of the Granato–Lücke theory, is presented in Fig. 14-12. These plots are in accord with the predicted linear variation of $\log(\varepsilon_0 \phi_h)$ with ε_0^{-1}, though deviations do occur at small strain amplitudes. A notable feature of the data shown in Fig. 14-12 is that increasing small amounts of cold work serve only to increase the intercept of the lines at $\varepsilon_0^{-1} = 0$, without appreciably altering their slope. The interpretation of this effect in terms of Eq. (14.3-3) is that while the intercept shifts primarily due to an increase in the dislocation density Λ, enough impurity exists in the material to maintain

---

[†] It should be mentioned that not all investigations have agreed on this point (Read, 1940; and Kamentsky, 1956).

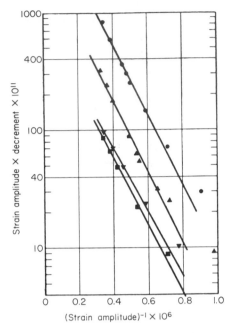

FIG. 14-12. Granato–Lücke plots of the data of Fig. 14-1. (From Granato and Lücke, 1956.)

a constant value of l_0, and therefore of C_2. Such good Granato–Lücke plots were not found by Beshers (1959), for copper of somewhat higher purity, but the addition of gold as an impurity (in amounts up to 0.13%) did produce linear plots. It is clear that the breakaway model cannot apply to pure metals which contain virtually no pinning points, but whether this factor accounts entirely for the difference between the results of Read and Beshers is uncertain. For example, Caswell (1958) has reported finding curved Granato–Lücke plots both for pure copper and for copper with up to 0.5% gold.

In contrast to the effect of cold work, the addition of impurities serves to change the slope of the Granato–Lücke plot in a manner consistent with the idea that impurities act as pinning points and decrease the mean loop length l_0. This effect has been discussed by Granato and Lücke (1956) using the data of Weertman and Salkovitz (1955) for samples of lead doped with bismuth, tin, or cadmium. For a given doping level (lead with 0.058% tin), Weertman and Salkovitz also give data on how ϕ_h changes with temperature. These data are consistent with the idea of Cottrell pinning, for which the concentration of pinning points on the dislocations would be expected to vary as $\exp(-g_b/kT)$ where g_b is the binding free energy between a dislocation and a solute atom [see Eq.

(12.3-2)]. The experimental data for tin in lead yield $g_b = 0.1$ eV. More detailed work along these lines has been performed by Chambers and Smoluchowski (1960) using aluminum crystals, which data obey the Granato–Lücke analysis very closely. More recently, Hinton and Rider (1966) have performed a new investigation of Pb–Sn and Pb–In alloys. They found a considerable measure of agreement between the experiments and the Granato–Lücke theory, particularly with regard to the strong concentration dependence of the internal friction.

In addition to solute atoms acting as pinning points, evidence has been obtained that other point defects (in particular vacancies or vacancy clusters) can pin dislocations. For example, Roswell and Nowick (1957) found that the amplitude-dependent damping in gold could be suppressed by quenching treatments. Along the same lines, Barnes et al. (1958) found suppression of ϕ_h in copper subject either to quenching, or irradiation by either γ rays or neutrons. Pinning appears to be the only reasonable explanation for these effects, since such treatments are not likely to change the dislocation density by an appreciable amount.

In conclusion, there appears to be little doubt that dislocation breakaway is the fundamental phenomenon in the amplitude-dependent damping of metals. Deviations between experiment and the Granato–Lücke theory probably do not reflect a basically wrong approach, but rather an oversimplification of the factors involved. For example, we have not emphasized here that a real crystal will contain dislocations of many different characters, ranging from pure edge to pure screw. This will clearly affect the strength of the solute pinning, as indeed will the state of dissociation of the dislocation. While modifications of this nature have been considered [e.g., by Swartz and Weertman (1961) and, particularly, by Rogers (1962)], experimentalists on the whole have tended to compare their results only against the original Granato–Lücke formulas.

PROBLEMS

14-1. Show from the equations of Section 14.1 how it is possible to obtain the ratio B/Λ from measurements of overdamped resonance of dislocations. Thus, the value of the damping constant B can be obtained if an independent measurement of the dislocation density, Λ, is available.

14-2. Assume that a crystal has a dislocation density $\Lambda \sim 10^7$ cm^{-2} and loop length $l \sim 10^{-4}$ cm. Show that if 10^{10} point defects per cm^3 are present and these migrate to the dislocation to act as pinning points, there will be a substantial reduction in the internal friction and modulus defect. Since 10^{10} defects per cm^3 represents a mole fraction $\sim 10^{-13}$, it is clear that this technique is one of the most sensitive ones available for the detection of point defects produced, for example, by irradiation.

14-3. Verify Eq. (14.3-1).

General References

Lücke, K., and Granato, A. (1957). *In* "Dislocations and Mechanical Properties of Crystals" (J. C. Fisher *et al.*, eds.), p. 425. Wiley, New York.

Niblett, D. H., and Wilks, J. (1960). *Advan. Phys.* **9**, 1.

Granato, A. (1968). *In* "Dislocation Dynamics" (A. R. Rosenfield *et al.*, eds.). McGraw-Hill, New York.

Chapter **15** | Boundary Relaxation Processes and Internal Friction at High Temperatures

This chapter is chiefly concerned with the anelasticity associated with grain boundaries in metals and alloys. Experiments in this area have usually been performed on polycrystalline aggregates of a more or less random nature, which therefore contain a wide distribution of boundary types and orientations. There are, however, two examples where specific types of boundaries have been of interest. These are the twin boundaries and low-angle subboundaries discussed in Sections 15.5 and 15.6.

The prediction of a grain boundary relaxation phenomenon was made by Zener, based on a variety of early evidences that viscous sliding could occur between two adjacent crystals. A direct manifestation of this behavior is provided by the gradual offset produced in a scratch mark made across the boundary (see Section 15.3). In Zener's picture the shear stress which initially acts across a boundary is gradually reduced through viscous slip while the grain corners sustain more and more of the total shearing force. Figure 15-1 shows schematically how this process

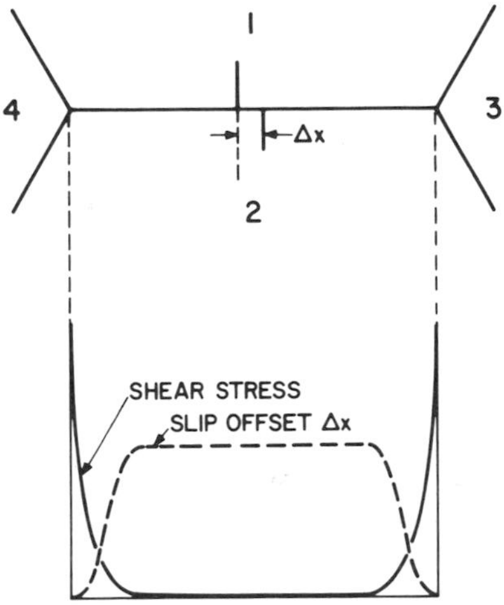

FIG. 15-1. Relaxation of an initially uniform shear stress distribution by grain-boundary sliding.

occurs. Grain 1 slides over grain 2 under the influence of the applied shear stress to build up opposing stresses at the ends of the boundaries and into grains 3 and 4. This relaxation process comes to a halt when the shear stress has dropped to zero across most of the length of the boundary. At low stress levels, the distortion at the edges is purely elastic. Upon removal of the applied stress, this distortion subjects the boundary to a reverse shear stress and produces the elastic aftereffect. When recovery is complete, the distortions at the edges of the grain boundary are eliminated and the specimen has returned to its original condition. The similarity between this behavior and that of the three-parameter Maxwell-type model (Fig. 3-7) indicates that an idealized sample containing a collection of identical boundaries would correspond to the standard anelastic solid. In the following section, some of the quantitative features of this model will be examined.

15.1   Formal Theory of Relaxation by Grain-Boundary Sliding

Consider for simplicity an aggregate of regular polyhedral grains, all of the same size and possessing boundaries of linear dimension d (which may be taken as a convenient measure of the grain size). It is easily appreciated that for the viscous sliding model, the relaxation strength Δ is independent of the grain size d, provided that d is small compared with the dimensions of the sample. Perhaps the simplest way of seeing this is to recognize that for the same level of applied stress (and hence unrelaxed strain ε_U) the ratio $\Delta x/d$ in Fig. 15-1 is independent of d, i.e., a condition of geometric similarity applies. Since $\Delta x/d$ is proportional to the anelastic strain ε^{an}, it follows directly that $\Delta = \bar{\varepsilon}^{an}/\varepsilon_U$ is independent of d.

Zener (1941) has calculated the relaxation strength in tension for a regular network of polyhedra under the simplifying assumptions that each grain may be represented as an elastically isotropic sphere. He compares the strain energy under uniform stress with that under conditions of zero shearing stress across the boundary but for the same average stress in the sample. In this way he obtains

$$E_R/E_U = \tfrac{1}{2}(7 + 5\chi)/(7 + \chi - 5\chi^2) \qquad (15.1\text{-}1)$$

where χ is Poisson's ratio. The equivalent formula for the shear modulus (see Problem 15-1) has been given by Kê (1947a):

$$G_R/G_U = \tfrac{2}{5}(7 + 5\chi)/(7 - 4\chi) \qquad (15.1\text{-}2)$$

For the typical value $\chi = \frac{1}{3}$, Eq. (15.1-2) gives $G_R/G_U = 0.61$, or $\Delta_G = 0.64$. This is a very large relaxation strength compared to most of the effects discussed in earlier chapters. It is important to note that these results are based on the assumption that grain boundary sliding can occur entirely across the boundary, thereby relieving shear stress across the boundary completely (except near the corner regions). If the sliding were stopped by obstructions spaced at distances small compared to d, the relaxation strength would be much smaller.

We shall consider now the kinetics of the relaxation, based on the assignment of an effective viscosity coefficient η to the grain boundary. By analogy with the model of Fig. 3-7, both the decay of the shear stress across the boundary, and the growth of the offset or slip distance Δx, will be simple exponential functions of time. For constant applied stress, the corresponding relaxation equation for Δx is thus

$$d(\Delta x)/dt = -(\Delta x - \overline{\Delta x})/\tau_\sigma \qquad (15.1\text{-}3)$$

where $\overline{\Delta x}$ is the final (equilibrium) slip distance for constant stress and τ_σ is the relaxation time. On setting Δx equal to zero, we obtain the initial slip velocity

$$v(0) = \overline{\Delta x}/\tau_\sigma \qquad (15.1\text{-}4)$$

For a boundary of width b under an initially uniform shear stress σ, $v(0)$ may also be written

$$v(0) = \sigma b/\eta \qquad (15.1\text{-}5)$$

From Eqs. (15.1-4) and (15.1-5), we obtain

$$\tau_\sigma = \eta \, \overline{\Delta x}/\sigma b \qquad (15.1\text{-}6)$$

Since, to reduce the shear stress at the boundary to zero, the local anelastic strain at the boundary $\Delta x/d$ must relieve the elastic strain, we have further that

$$\overline{\Delta x}/d = \sigma/G_U \qquad (15.1\text{-}7)$$

Hence, by combining Eqs. (15.1-6) and (15.1-7), we obtain

$$\tau_\sigma = \eta d/b G_U \qquad (15.1\text{-}8)$$

Alternatively, by combining Eqs. (15.1-4) and (15.1-7), we have

$$\tau_\sigma = \sigma d/G_U v(0) \qquad (15.1\text{-}9)$$

The model thus predicts that the relaxation time τ should vary directly as the linear grain dimension d. We shall see how this compares with experimental results in the following section.

15.2 Experimental Studies of the Grain-Boundary Relaxation

After some early exploratory work on polycrystalline zinc (Barnes and Zener, 1940) and brass (Zener et al., 1942) a firm experimental foundation for the viscous slip model was established by the work of Kê. By the use of quasistatic and low-frequency (torsion pendulum) internal friction measurements, Kê was able to observe the complete grain boundary relaxation at conveniently low temperatures (200–300°C). He also made the fortunate choice of the metal aluminum for which consistent and relatively simple results are obtained. Because of the importance of Kê's early work on "pure" (i.e., 99.99%) Al, we will review his results in some detail before considering other work on nominally pure metals.

A. Kê's Work on "Pure" Aluminum

In his two basic papers (Kê, 1947a,b), Kê arrived at the following results.

1. An internal friction peak is present in polycrystalline aluminum at about 300°C for a frequency of 1 Hz. The same phenomenon manifests itself in other relaxation experiments, viz., creep, stress relaxation, and a modulus defect. This peak is evidently associated with grain boundaries, since it is absent for "single crystals" (i.e., when the grain size is several times the diameter of the sample). Figure 15-2 illustrates this point.

2. The relaxation strength is in very good accord with Eq. (15.1-2). Specifically, $G_R/G_U = 0.67$ is obtained experimentally while, using $\chi = 0.35$, the formula gives $G_R/G_U = 0.64$.

3. The peak height, and by inference the relaxation strength, is found to be independent of the grain diameter, d (so long as d is less than the specimen diameter), in agreement with the viscous slip model. These results are shown in Fig. 15-3. (Since the specimen diameter is 0.084 cm, it is in fact surprising that the theory should apply for d values of 0.04 and 0.07 cm, where it certainly cannot be claimed that the grain size is small compared to the specimen diameter.)

4. The relaxation time τ is proportional to the grain diameter d, again, as predicted by the viscous slip model. Kê showed that grain growth is

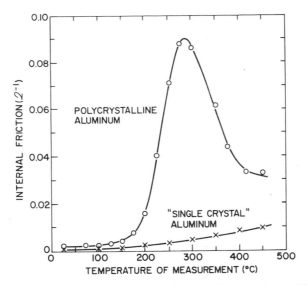

FIG. 15-2. The grain-boundary peak in polycrystalline aluminum. Measurements in torsional vibration at 0.8 Hz. (From Kê, 1947a.)

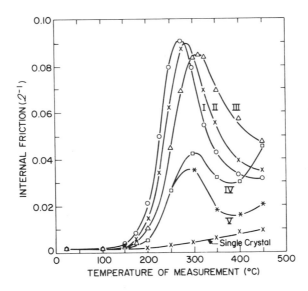

FIG. 15-3. Effect of grain size on the grain boundary peak of aluminum wire 0.084 cm in diameter. The average grain diameter is 0.02, 0.04, and 0.07 cm for curves I, II, and III, respectively. For curves IV and V, the grain diameter exceeded the wire diameter. (From Kê, 1947b.)

accompanied by displacement of the peak to higher temperatures, and that a plot of internal friction versus the parameter $\omega d \exp(Q/RT)$ causes data for different grain sizes and frequencies to fall onto one curve.

5. The activation energy associated with this relaxation process is 1.48 eV. This is very close to the activation energy for self diffusion in Al. The calculated value of τ_0 is 10^{-14} sec (for $d = 0.03$ cm).

6. The peak is almost three times broader than for the standard anelastic solid. It is in fact broad enough that the approximate inter-relations between the various response functions are found to apply extremely well (see Fig. 4-2).

7. From the extrapolated value of τ and an assumed value for the grain boundary thickness of 4Å, Kê showed that the effective viscosity of the grain boundary at the melting point agreed with the viscosity of liquid Al at the melting point.

From these results, particularly items 1–4 which relate directly to the formal theory, Kê concluded that the viscous slip model represents a satisfactory description of grain-boundary relaxation in aluminum. Further, the fact that he found similar peaks in other polycrystalline materials indicated that the phenomenon was a general one.

B. Subsequent Work on Nominally Pure Metals

Most of the work on nominally pure metals subsequent to Kê's experiments on Al has shown that there is considerably more complexity to the grain-boundary relaxation than Kê's work had indicated. The noble metals (Cu, Ag, Au) in particular, generally show grain-boundary peaks which are lower in height and more spread out than those for aluminum. Typically $\mathcal{Q}_{max}^{-1} \sim 0.02$–$0.05$ as compared with 0.08 for Al. In addition, Mash and Hall (1953) working with gold found the relaxation produced a double peak for the highest purity material after annealing at 830°C though not for the less pure (99.98%) material. The two activation energies of 1.50 and 2.52 eV were obtained for the lower- and higher-temperature peaks, respectively. Only the lower temperature peak appeared for the less pure gold and in the work of Köster et al. (1956). A similar double peak was observed for nickel by Datsko and Pavlov (1963), but not by Cordea and Spretnak (1966).

More recently, the occurrence of double peaks was studied in greater detail by De Morton and Leak (1966) and by Williams and Leak (1967). In these papers, the existence of high-temperature peaks was demonstrated for Cu, Al, Au, and Cu–Au alloys. That these peaks also originate in grain boundaries is shown by their absence for single crystals. Williams and Leak made the significant observation that the high-temperature peak (near 700°C for Cu at 1 Hz) is first observed when some grain boundaries extend completely across the specimen, and that this peak is fully developed for a "bamboo"-type structure. Belous et al. (1967) and Roberts and Barrand (1968a) have made this same observation for the high-temperature peak in Ni. Williams and Leak report the very surprising values of $Q = 4.6$ eV and $\tau_0 \sim 10^{-21}$ sec for the high-temperature peak in Cu. They further observed an intermediate peak in Cu near 550°C (but not in Al) for a restricted range of grain sizes. This intermediate peak seemed to correlate with the presence of annealing twins, and it was therefore suggested that the migration of small steps along the surface of the twins gives rise to the peak. The absence of such a peak in Al where annealing twins do not occur tends to support this suggestion. Roberts and Barrand (1968a), however, report an intermediate peak for Ni (which also has a high stacking fault energy) and instead attribute it to boundaries which contain impurity atoms.

As for items 3 and 4 under Kê's results, concerning the effects of varying the grain size, there have been significant differences among different workers. With regard to the dependence of τ on d, Starr et al. (1953) report that $\tau \propto d^{1.80}$ for Al and its dilute alloys, clearly not in accord with Kê's results. Leak (1961) also reported $\tau \propto d^2$ for pure iron. Later data of Kê (1949a) on Al shows that $\tau \propto d$ is not obeyed when samples given different amounts of cold work, followed by identical recrystallization anneals, are compared. (The older experiments involved the same amount of cold work and different anneals.) Clearly, the situation is more complex than Kê's earlier work had indicated. One complication which may enter into these experiments is that the mean activation energy may also shift slightly with treatments that are intended to produce only differences in grain size. Turning to the effect of grain size on the magnitude of the relaxation, Köster et al. (1955) reported that the height of the peak in copper increases with decreasing grain size. However, they also found that the peak for larger grain size was broader than for the smaller grain size, leaving an ambiguity concerning the relaxation strength Δ. (In passing, it should be mentioned that small amounts of deformation reduced the peak height until, for a deformation of about 10%, the peak could not be identified. It was suggested that cold working roughens the boundaries and thereby impedes the sliding motion.)

More definitive information was obtained in a careful study of the grain-boundary peak in 99.999% copper by Peters et al. (1964). These authors

fitted the grain-boundary peaks to the lognormal distribution and obtained values of the distribution parameter β. They found a very wide
peak ($\beta = 5.85$ at 280°C) as compared to $\beta = 3.47$ (at 328°C) for Al.
Further, β is found to depend on grain size in the manner shown in

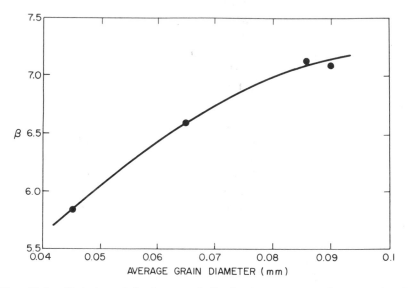

Fig. 15-4.   Variation of the lognormal distribution parameter β with grain size,
for the grain-boundary relaxation in copper of 99.999% purity. (From Peters *et al.*,
1964.)

Fig. 15-4. Although the peak heights vary for different grain sizes, by
using the lognormal distribution analysis they obtain the relaxation
strength and find it to be independent of grain size, with a value of
$\Delta_{\mathrm{G}} = 0.14$. This value corresponds to $G_{\mathrm{R}}/G_{\mathrm{U}} = 0.88$ which is substantially higher than the value 0.61 predicted from Eq. (15.1-2). Perhaps the
discrepancy is due to the fact that copper is strongly elastically anisotropic
(in contrast to Al). Nevertheless, the fact that Δ is independent of d
substantiates Kê's earlier result (item 3) although here the peak height
itself varies with grain size. Peters *et al.* also find that β increases with
increasing temperature, suggesting that the wide distribution of τ values
is due, at least in part, to a distribution in activation energies (see Section
4.8). They point out that although the distribution of grain sizes is often
found to be a lognormal distribution, the β values for the grain size distribution are relatively small (less than unity); therefore the distribution
in d can only account for a small part of the width of the grain-boundary

peak. Cordea and Spretnak (1966) applied the lognormal-distribution analysis to Ni and Al as well as to Cu. They found an interesting correlation between the grain-boundary relaxation strength Δ_G and the stacking fault energy γ for four pure metals, as illustrated in Fig. 15-5. Roberts and Barrand (1968b) place greater significance on the correlation of Δ_G with the width of the extended dislocation d_0 which varies inversely with the stacking fault energy, according to the relation

$$d_0 = Ga^2/24\pi\gamma \qquad (15.2\text{-}1)$$

They also claim that the activation energy seems to correlate with γ, and use both of these correlations as the basis for their model of grain boundary relaxation (see Section 15.4).

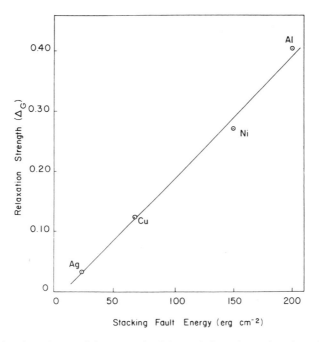

FIG. 15-5. Correlation of the strength of the grain boundary relaxation with stacking fault energy, for four fcc metals. (From Cordea and Spretnak, 1966.)

Table 15-1 provides a summary of the data on the kinetic aspects of the grain boundary relaxation peak for some nominally pure materials, in particular the activation energies Q and the τ_0 values reported for the process. Since not all activation energy values are determined with the

TABLE 15-1

GRAIN-BOUNDARY RELAXATION DATA FOR SOME NOMINALLY PURE METALS

Metal	Purity (%)	T_p (°C)[a]	τ_0 (sec)	Q_{gb} (eV)	Q_{sd} (eV)	Reference
Al	99.99	280	10^{-14}	1.48	1.48	Kê (1947a,b)
	99.98	315	10^{-14}	1.50		Cordea and Spretnak (1966)
	99.999	295	10^{-15}	1.65		Williams and Leak (1967)
Cu	OFHC	300	10^{-14}	1.43	2.04	Weining and Machlin (1957)
	99.999	235	10^{-17}	1.63		Peters et al. (1964)
	99.999	215	$10^{-14.5}$	1.37		Cordea and Spretnak (1966)
	99.999	250	10^{-16}	1.56		Williams and Leak (1967)
Fe	"Puron"	490	10^{-25}	3.7	2.45	Kê (1948b)
	99.99	530	10^{-13}	2.0		Leak (1961)
	"Pro-Analysis"	500	10^{-17}	2.5		De Batist (1969)
Sn	99.99	20	10^{-15}	0.83	$1.01(\perp)^b$ $1.11(\|)$	Rotherham et al. (1951)

[a] Peak temperature at 1 Hz and for a grain size of 0.10 mm.
[b] Values of Q_{sd} for Sn are given for diffusion both perpendicular and parallel to the tetragonal axis of the crystal.

same care,[†] values of peak temperature T_p are also given for comparison. In the absence of a coincidence, it may reasonably be assumed that peaks obtained by different observers at essentially the same location are equivalent. In this regard, there is a striking shift between OFHC and spectrographically pure (99.999%) Cu. For comparison, the activation energies for self-diffusion Q_{sd} in the pure metal are also given. It may be seen that often Q_{sd} is distinctly greater than Q. (Similar results to the data for Cu are also available for Ag and Au. Here, the activation energies are not as reliably determined as that for Cu; however, there is no doubt that they are much less than Q_{sd}.) This comparison clearly refutes a correlation between Q and Q_{sd} which was suggested by Kê (1948) at a time when comparatively few data for both activation energies were available. We will see later, however, that the situation is different for the case of solid solutions.

One intriguing fact brought out by Table 15-1 is that the magnitude of τ_0 is typically in the same range as that for point defect relaxations. According to the slip model which leads to Eq. (15.1-8), however, τ_0 for the grain boundary relaxation involves the grain size d. There is, therefore, no reason why such a similarity should be regarded as more than a coincidence. The problem is compounded by the fact that an estimate of τ_0, based on the simplest assumption of a homogeneous boundary process (see Problem 15-2), gives a result which is several orders of magnitude larger than the experimental values. At present, therefore, it can only be stated that the magnitude of τ_0 is not understood, and provides an important area in which future work may shed light on the atomistics of the relaxation mechanism.

C. EFFECTS OF GRAIN–BOUNDARY PRECIPITATES

The fact that particles of a second phase may precipitate preferentially at grain boundaries and impede or block grain-boundary relaxation is indicated in a number of investigations. For example, Kê (1949a) showed that the grain-boundary peak for commercial aluminum is much smaller than for high purity aluminum. He also showed that the peak is absent in iron containing 0.07 wt % C. In the case of copper, heating in oxygen

---

[†] Often the frequency is changed by a factor of two or three, the peak is rerun, and Q is obtained from the small shift of the low-temperature side of the peak. If there is any change in background, in height, or in peak shape itself between the two runs, such a method may give a value for Q which is quite unreliable. For example, Kê's values of Q and τ_0 for Fe are undoubtedly incorrect in view of the later work.

evidently produces oxide precipitation at grain boundaries, as shown
by the disappearance of the grain boundary peak (Kê, 1949a; Pearson
and Rotherham, 1956). Peters *et al.* (1964) showed a similar behavior
for Cu + 2 % Co.

In terms of the viscous slip model (Section 15.1), the formation of
precipitate particles in the boundaries means that the average slip is
proportional to $l = n^{-1/2}$ (where n is the number of particles per unit
area in the boundary) rather than to d, the grain diameter. Since precipitation rapidly brings l to values $\ll d$, the relaxation strength must be
correspondingly reduced greatly.

One example of a precipitating system, Bi in Cu, studied by Kê (1949b)
is anomalous in that a new peak is developed at lower temperatures as Bi
precipitates out (original peak above 450°C for 1000 Hz, the new peak
at ~300°C). No explanation for this peak has been given, nor is there a
similar effect reported thus far for any other precipitating system.

D. EFFECT OF SOLUTES

Turning now to substitutional solutes (i.e., solid solution alloys) we
encounter some highly significant experiments. The pioneering work in
this field was carried out by Pearson and Rotherham (1956) who dissolved
a number of higher-valency solutes in copper and silver. They found
that for solute content near 1%, the original grain boundary peak for the
pure metal (which we will call the "PM peak") is suppressed, and a new
solid solution peak (the "SS peak") then appears at higher temperatures.
The SS peak, which generally appears between 420–500°C for a frequency
of 1 Hz is shown to be a true grain boundary peak, in that it vanishes for
very coarse grained materials. At appropriate small solute concentrations
both the PM peak and SS peaks are obtained. This result led Pearson and
Rotherham to conclude that the PM peak does not move but is gradually
suppressed as the SS peak builds up. The SS peak is better defined, i.e.,
sharper, than the PM peak though it is still much broader than the
standard anelastic solid. The activation energies for the SS peak in a large
number of copper and silver solutions falls in the range between 1.7 and
2.2 eV, i.e., near values characteristic of self-diffusion and of solute bulk
diffusion for these alloys. The τ_0 values, on the other hand, fall in the
same range as those in Table 15-1, typically 10^{-14}–10^{-16} sec.

The findings of Pearson were substantiated and enlarged by Weinig
and Machlin (1957a) who added impurities to copper in smaller steps
(from ~0.03 to 1 at. %) and could therefore more clearly see the PM

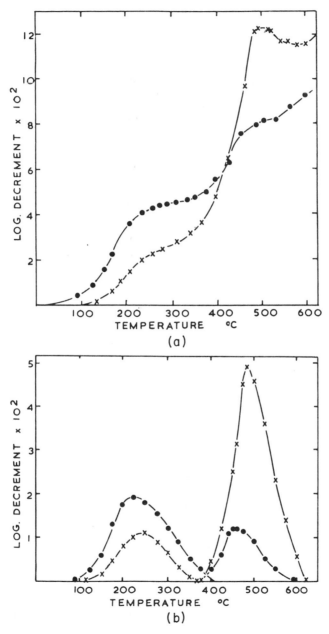

FIG. 15-6. Effect of alloy content on the PM and SS grain boundary peaks in annealed copper containing 0.1 wt % Ni (○) and 0.5 wt % Ni (×). (a) original data; (b) after subtraction of the background. Measurements in torsional vibration at 0.2 Hz. (From Roberts and Barrand, 1968.)

peak diminish as the SS peak formed. An example of such behavior is shown in Fig. 15-6. The composition at which the cross-over occurs was shown to be dependent on solute; e.g., it occurred much earlier for Si than for Ni. Weinig and Machlin also report values for the activation energies in the intermediate state in which both peaks were present and claimed to find strange behavior, viz., an increasing activation energy for the PM peak as it falls in height, and very high activation energies for the SS peak as it first forms. The fact that the peak temperatures do not change in a corresponding way indicates that perhaps the anomalous activation energies for the partially formed peaks should not be taken too seriously (see footnote on p. 445). It was shown, however, that the fully formed SS peaks have activation energies near those for self-diffusion, in agreement with Pearson's work. In more recent work, Barrand (1966) has obtained a PM and a SS peak in Fe–Cr alloys, where the SS peak again showed an activation energy close to that for self diffusion.

Interstitial solutes, on the other hand, do not give rise to a separate solid–solution peak. As shown by Miles and Leak (1961) who studied dilute Fe–C and Fe–N alloys, the effect of the solute is to move the peak temperature to slightly higher values and to produce changes in the peak height. Apparently, the activation energy becomes higher due to solute addition. In none of these cases, however, is there evidence for the development of a second peak as occurs for substitutional solutes.

E. RELATION OF GRAIN-BOUNDARY RELAXATION TO DIFFUSION

As already mentioned, Kê (1948) proposed at an early stage of the study of the grain-boundary relaxation that the activation energy for relaxation was the same as that for volume self-diffusion (Q_{sd}). Subsequent results on the pure metals (see Table 15-1) do not support this suggestion consistently. In fact, Leak (1962) has noted that the activation energy for the PM peak is more nearly in agreement with that for grain-boundary diffusion (which is $\sim$0.5–0.6 of Q_{sd}). On the other hand, for the SS peak, activation energies are consistently found to be close to those for volume diffusion of either the solute or solvent. If these results are not coincidental, but due to the fact that the grain-boundary relaxation is volume-diffusion limited in the case of solid solutions, one must expect that quenching will enhance the relaxation rate. This point was looked for by Nowick and Li (1961) in the alloys Ag–30 at. % Zn and Cu–15 at. % Al, both of which also show a Zener relaxation. It was demonstrated that quenching from 400°C increases the rate of the grain-boundary relaxation about in the same ratio as that of the Zener relaxation. The simplest interpretation for this result is that quenched-in lattice vacancies enhance the diffusion rate and therefore the rate of relaxation of any process which is controlled by volume diffusion. It was pointed out, however, that an alternate interpretation, according to which defects are quenched into the grain boundary itself, is also a possibility. Nevertheless, at present it seems most reasonable to regard that these experiments support the idea that the SS grain-boundary peak is rate limited by volume diffusion.

It is noteworthy that the SS peak is characterized by two features: (a) an activation energy approximately equal to or a little higher than that for volume diffusion, and (b) a relatively good peak definition and peak height $Q_m^{-1} \sim 0.08$–0.12. Since Kê's observations on "pure" (99.99%) Al show a peak with both these characteristics, it is intriguing to consider the possibility that Kê's work was all on a SS peak and not on the PM peak! The small solubility of most solutes in Al suggests strong solute–grain boundary interactions so that it might well be that a very low level of certain impurities is sufficient to suppress the PM peak completely. Roberts and Barrand (1968b), on the other hand, claim that the higher activation energy in Al is an intrinsic property related to its high stacking fault energy.

15.3 Studies of the Macroscopic Sliding of Boundaries

If the grain-boundary relaxation is due to shearing of one grain across another, such shearing movement should also be directly observable as a macroscopic displacement across the boundary in bicrystals or in polycrystals. There have been several experiments which demonstrate that this indeed occurs. The scale of displacements in such experiments is much larger than is typical in internal friction experiments (~ 10 Å), since movements must be at least 100 Å, and often as high as 10^4 Å, to be barely detectable. In view of several excellent reviews of this subject (McLean, 1957; Stevens, 1966; Bell and Langdon, 1969) we will present here just a brief survey of the topic.

There are different reports concerning the start of the sliding process upon application of stress. Some authors report the occurrence of an incubation period, while others observe an initial "instantaneous" shear. The sliding rate generally decreases with time; this increased resistance of the boundary to shearing is termed "slide hardening." The dependence of the shear rate on stress is usually not linear as in viscous behavior but more often obeys a power law or even an exponential function.

Metallographic observations on bicrystals deformed in tension, with the boundary at 45° to the tensile axis, shows that sliding involves a wide zone of deformation around the boundary itself (Rhines *et al.*, 1956). But in such samples, extensive sliding is not possible without deformation in the crystals to relieve the bending moment produced by sliding. On the other hand, with geometries designed for pure shear, the zone of shear was found to be undetectably small. Also, evidence for grain boundary migration as well as sliding is often obtained since fiducial lines are found to become curved or split into short straight segments during sliding.

Comparison of bicrystal measurements with internal friction results shows that, while the temperature dependences (i.e., the activation energies) are roughly similar, absolute rates of sliding are as much as 10^5–10^8 times faster in internal friction than in the macroscopic measurements. In fact, Harper (1961) has shown that even when shear displacements of a copper bicrystal are only 400 Å the initial sliding rate is 10^5 times slower than in a typical internal friction experiment (where maximum displacements are only about an order of magnitude smaller). It is clear, therefore, that the two types of experiments involve phenomena on different scales, i.e., the macroscopic experiments principally observe the deformation that occurs after the anelastic phenomenon is over. It may well be that plastic deformation within the crystal is generally involved in the macroscopic experiments, even when such deformation is not visible metallographically.

Now that transmission electron microscopy and field ion microscopy have begun to be used widely to observe directly the structure of grain boundaries, it is anticipated that major progress in identifying boundary sliding mechanisms will come from the use of such techniques.

15.4   Mechanism of the Grain-Boundary Relaxation

Despite the fact that experimental work on the grain-boundary relaxation dates back to 1947, a satisfactory quantitative atomistic theory of the phenomenon has not yet emerged. In fact, we will see that even the qualitative concepts are still in doubt.

Perhaps the earliest attempt at an atomistic theory was that of Kê (1948, 1949) who designed his idea to explain the agreement which he had found between the activation energy for lattice self-diffusion Q_{sd} and that for grain-boundary relaxation Q for the three metals he had investigated. It was proposed that the grain boundary was made up of local disordered groups containing fewer atoms than a similar volume of crystal, and that the rate-controlling step of the sliding process involved the movement of a pair of atoms in such a group. This concept is similar to that employed in a model of diffusion in a liquid, and it is difficult to see how this proposal would accomplish the objective of making Q equal to Q_{sd}. However, as noted in Section 15.2B, later work has shown that such equality is not generally observed, at least for pure metals.

Mott (1948) advanced another idea for sliding in terms of his island model of a large angle grain boundary (Section 12.4). He suggested that the elementary act of sliding accompanies the disordering or melting of a group of atoms in an island of good fit. The free energy to do this is $nL[1 - (T/T_m)]$ where n is the number of atoms involved, L the latent heat of fusion per atom, and T_m the melting temperature. In this way, he could explain Kê's observation that the extrapolated effective viscosity of the grain boundary at T_m was equal to that of the liquid at the same temperature. The predicted activation energy is given by $Q = nL$. To explain Kê's data for Al, it was necessary to set $n \simeq 14$. In terms of this model, the value of n should depend greatly on the crystallography of the particular boundary. Moreover, the similarity between Q and Q_{sd} for the SS peak in alloys must be regarded as coincidental, which is hard to accept.

The fact that a grain boundary may be regarded as composed of a collection of dislocations has led to models for grain-boundary relaxation based on the behavior of individual dislocations. In the mechanism of Nowick (1952b), based on a model of Read and Shockley for small-angle boundaries, vacancies are generated at, and migrate between, edge-type dislocations in the boundary. Since the process involves generation and migration of vacancies, the activation energy is predicted to be close to that of lattice self diffusion. More recently, Roberts and Barrand (1968b) have proposed a very qualitative model involving climb and glide of individual dislocations in the boundary. This model, which is based largely on the experimental correlation of relaxation strength and activation energy with dislocation width d_0 [see Eq. (15.2-1)], introduces many *ad hoc* assumptions, and is hard to accept without further development. The trouble with all models based on individual dislocations is that they ignore the strong interaction among dislocations which constitute boundaries. Such an approach cannot be realistic, and therefore, a more phenomenological approach may be more useful until more is known about the behavior of dislocations in boundaries under stress.

In terms of the experimental evidence presented in the previous section, it appears that the major observation to be accounted for is the occurrence of two peaks, the PM and SS peaks (Section 15.2D), with the latter peak having a larger activation energy which is close to that for lattice diffusion. The abrupt appearance of a second (SS) peak at a new location and the simultaneous disappearance of the first (PM) peak with addition of solute, suggests a change in the dominant mechanism from one of lower activation energy to one controlled by diffusion. It is reasonable, therefore, to regard that a two-step process is involved; if these steps are in series, the slower one must be the rate-controlling process. A stimulating suggestion has been made by Machlin and Weinig (unpublished). They point out that a grain boundary is not ideally plane, but must contain ledges, as has now been shown directly by field-ion microscopy (Brandon *et al.*, 1964). These ledges must then block grain-boundary sliding and limit the extent of stress relaxation to distances of the order of the interledge spacing. On this basis, τ would not be proportional to the grain diameter d and the relaxation strength would be quite small. To obtain the full relaxation requires that the slip be able to pass across the ledges. This can be accomplished if local migration (i.e., smoothing) is possible at the ledge. If the two steps (slip and migration) take place in series, the rate-controlling step is the slower one. For high purity metals, it is well known that migration takes place easily with an activation energy Q_m much less than Q_{sd}. Therefore, it is reasonable to assume that sliding between ledges is the rate-controlling step in pure metals, with an activation energy Q_s in the range $Q_m < Q_s < Q_{sd}$.[†] As indicated in Fig. 15-7, the situation $Q_s > Q_m$ depicted for the region of the PM peak can be expected to reverse on alloying, since the dragging effect of the preferential solute distribution established around the boundary causes Q_m to increase to the vicinity of Q_{sd}. Under these conditions, then, local boundary migration controlled by solute dragging would become the rate-limiting step for the SS peak.[‡] In support of this, Weinig and Machlin (1957b) have studied grain growth of the same copper alloys as those used for anelastic studies, and found

---

[†] Despite the previously noted suggestions by Kê and Mott, the elementary process involved in sliding cannot be regarded as established. However, it may be significant that the required magnitude for Q_s (i.e., $Q_m < Q_s < Q_{sd}$) places it in the range associated with grain boundary diffusion, typically taken as $0.5\,Q_{sd}$.

[‡] The extreme sensitivity of the rate of grain-boundary migration to the presence of impurities is well known (see, e.g., Aust and Rutter, 1963), especially in aluminum, where the activation energy for boundary migration increases rapidly as one goes from ultrapure (99.9999%) to slightly less pure material. These data support the suggestion made earlier, p. 449, that the grain-boundary peak reported in Al (see Table 15-1) may, in fact, be the SS peak.

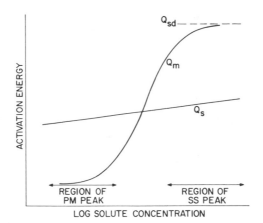

FIG. 15-7. Possible dependence of the activation energies for grain boundary sliding (Q_s) and migration (Q_m) on solute content. With this scheme, the PM relaxation is governed by Q_s and the SS relaxation by $Q_m \simeq Q_{sd}$.

the same activation energy ($\sim$2.3 eV) for both the grain growth and the SS peak. The presence of both the PM and SS peaks at intermediate solute concentrations may be interpreted in terms of the differing abilities of boundaries of different orientations to absorb solute atoms.

While the above description provides a reasonable working hypothesis, clearly more work is required, of both experimental and theoretical nature, before it can be stated that the phenomenon of grain-boundary relaxation is well understood. For example, one suggestion which deserves further investigation is that relaxation may occur by a mechanism which solely involves the migration of the boundary, in the manner of a membrane which bows out under an applied pressure (see, e.g., Leak, 1961; Miles and Leak, 1961). It should be noted first that such a model does not involve a relaxation of the shear stress distribution around the boundary, and therefore may only serve to augment, rather than supplant, Zener's slip model. So far, a pure migration model has not been developed quantitatively; indeed, it has not been pointed out specifically why stress should be expected to induce boundary migration, with the appearance of an attendant anelastic strain. One reason that such a coupling may exist, however, is the elastic anisotropy generally exhibited by the component grains. Relaxation may then occur through boundary migration which enlarges those grains which happen to be oriented for a high compliance under the applied stress, at the expense of neighboring grains oriented for lower compliance.

15.5 Twin-Boundary Relaxation

When a diffusionless transformation occurs from a cubic to a tetragonal structure, heavy twinning is necessary in order to avoid high residual stresses in the material. Such twinned structures have been observed in a Mn–12% Cu alloy by Worrell (1948), and further examples are now known in other alloy systems (e.g., In–Tl and Au–Cd). An internal friction maximum located near 0°C (frequency, 700 Hz) was observed by Worrell for the twinned Mn–Cu alloy. Zener (1948, p. 159) has suggested that relaxation by the stress-induced movement of twin boundaries may explain this observation. Inasmuch as crystallographic coherency exists across a twin interface, the mechanism of relaxation cannot involve interfacial sliding. The tetragonality of the twinned structure suggests, however, that the application of shear stress will induce movements of the boundaries *normal* to themselves, in such a way as to enlarge the twin in which the direction of tetragonality is favorable to the applied stress, at the expense of that in which it is unfavorable.

Following Worrell's original work, further measurements were made for the Mn–Cu alloy by Siefert and Worrell (1951), but the internal friction was still not studied as a function of frequency. Thus, it is not as yet clearly established that the observations correspond to a true relaxation process, nor is an activation energy known for this material. DeMorton (1969) has made a more detailed study of indium–thallium alloys (18–25 at. % Tl), and observed a thermally activated relaxation peak below the transformation temperature. This peak appears to have a relatively high activation energy ($\sim$1.3 eV) and also exhibits a peak height which increases significantly with the strain amplitude. While an explanation involving solute ordering and the stress-induced motion of twin boundaries was suggested, it appears that much further work may be required before the complex behavior observed experimentally is satisfactorily understood.

15.6 The High-Temperature Background

At relatively high temperatures, the damping-temperature curve of most materials rises continuously to very large values of internal friction. This phenomenon, which has become known as the "high-temperature background," is manifest by polycrystalline metals as an upturn in the internal friction on the high-temperature side of the grain boundary peak, as shown in Fig. 15-8. The magnitude of the high-temperature back-

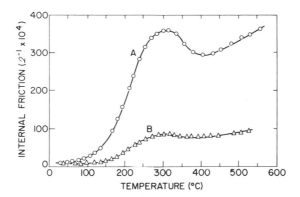

FIG. 15-8. Grain boundary peaks in 99.999% Cu, superimposed on a monotonically increasing high-temperature background. Curves A and B are for fine and coarse-grained samples, respectively. Measurements in torsional vibration at approximately 5 Hz. (From Peters *et al.*, 1964.)

ground (for some chosen reference temperature and vibration frequency) is highly structure-sensitive. In general, the background is much smaller in single crystals than in polycrystals, and is smaller in coarse grained polycrystals (showing small grain boundary peaks) than in fine grained samples (exhibiting larger grain boundary peaks, cf. Fig. 15-8). The background is greatly enhanced in deformed and partially recovered or polygonized samples (Kê and Zener, 1950; Kê, 1950; Friedel *et al.*, 1955), and is reduced by annealing treatments at successively higher temperatures. It is often found that the high-temperature background damping, tan ϕ_B, can be fitted quite well by an expression of the type

$$\tan \phi_B = A \exp(-C/kT) \tag{15.6-1}$$

where A and C are empirical parameters whose values are found from the intercept and slope of a semilogarithmic plot of tan ϕ_B versus $1/T$. An example of such a plot is shown in Fig. 15-9 for an aluminum single crystal (Chambers, 1957). The amplitude dependence of tan ϕ_B has not been investigated in great detail, but tan ϕ_B is usually considered to be sensibly amplitude-independent up to strains of $\sim 10^{-5}$. In the few cases where measurements have been pursued almost to the melting point (e.g., Friedel *et al.*, 1955) tan ϕ_B continues to increase rather steadily. In no case has tan ϕ_B been ultimately found to decrease. Thus, while the amplitude independence (insofar as this exists) shows that high-temperature background damping exhibits linear behavior, the absence of a detectable relaxation peak leaves unanswered the question of whether

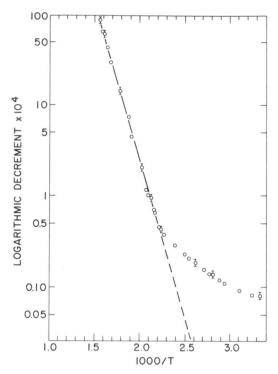

FIG. 15-9.   The high temperature background of an aluminum single crystal, showing conformity to Eq. (15.6-1). The plain circles represent data taken on heating; circles with vertical bars indicate data on cooling. (From Chambers, 1957.)

anelasticity or linear viscoelasticity is involved.[†] Speculation as to the anelastic and/or viscoelastic nature of the mechanisms producing the high-temperature background is of course answerable experimentally through the use of quasi-static experiments (cf. Chapter 1). Unfortunately, there is almost no work of this type to categorize the nature of the background. Kê (1950) and Kê and Zener (1950) have, however, studied the background in heavily deformed (95% reduction in area) aluminum recovered at various temperatures, using both internal friction and strain relaxation measurements. A specimen recovered at 250°C and subjected to strain relaxation measurements at 200°C (Fig. 15-10) exhibited after four hours a total strain which was nine times as large as the initial elastic strain, and still showed no sign of approaching an equilibrium

[†] To account for the form of the high-temperature background in purely anelastic terms would require a broad spectrum of relaxation times which increases monotonically and without a detectable limit with increasing values of τ.

value. Despite this exceptionally large value of the creep strain, nearly complete recovery was found upon removing the stress and observing the aftereffect. Such recovery indicates that in this case an anelastic mechanism is responsible for the creep behavior and the corresponding internal friction. From a number of creep tests conducted at various temperatures the activation energy governing the creep process was found to be 1.35 eV. Using this value, Kê and Zener deduced from their creep data [and a relation similar to Eq. (4.4-3)] that if it were possible to make internal friction measurements above 250°C on the specimen of Fig. 15-10, without causing further recovery, tan ϕ_B would approximately obey Eq. (15.6-1) with tan ϕ_B reaching a value of 0.7 at 450°C. To explain the very large magnitude of the anelasticity encountered in this study, Kê and Zener suggested the existence of a *coupled* relaxation behavior. The nature of the relaxation was conjectured to involve shear stress relaxation across "viscous" slip bands, in a manner akin to the grain boundary relaxation. Considered individually, each slip band is expected to have a relaxation time proportional to its length. The shortest slip bands therefore relax first. However, as the longer slip bands continue to relax, additional stress can be thrown upon the shorter bands. The short bands will thus be forced to continue to relax while the longer ones are undergoing relaxation. As time goes on, progressively longer and longer slip bands undergo relaxation, so that the resultant relaxation spectrum shows a cumulatively increasing magnitude up to the longest τ value in the observed region of the spectrum. It should be noted that,

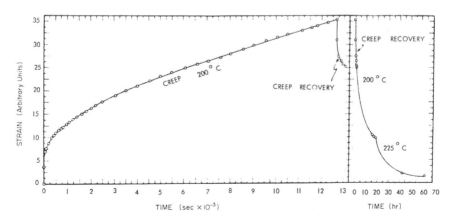

FIG. 15-10. Creep and creep recovery (elastic aftereffect) at 200°C in aluminum deformed 95% R of A and annealed at 250°C for 2 hr. Note that the sample was eventually raised to 225°C to hasten recovery. (From Kê and Zener, 1950.)

in this concept, the *individual slip bands* are highly coupled and no one-to-one correspondence exists between slip bands and τ values. This is no contradiction, however, to the notion that the relaxational normal modes are decoupled, giving rise to the individual relaxation times which constitute the spectrum, as described in Section 5.2.

It will be noted that the activation energy obtained by Kê and Zener is close to that for self-diffusion in aluminum. Such a correspondence has not always been reported. Pearson and Rotherham (1956), investigating the background internal friction in several (well-annealed) polycrystalline copper alloys, obtained activation energies which are distinctly smaller than those for diffusion. Pearson and Rotherham take the view that the high-temperature background in their experiments is not of an anelastic nature, and cite various somewhat indirect observations to support their view. They propose that the buildup of stress at the grain edges due to the grain boundary relaxation produces local irrecoverable (plastic) creep of a linear and thermally activated type, such that the specimen exhibits a plastic creep strain ε_p under constant stress σ at a rate given by

$$\dot{\varepsilon}_p = F\sigma \exp(-Q_B/kT) \qquad (15.6\text{-}2)$$

where F is a constant and Q_B is the activation energy of the creep process. This implies that the material behaves as a Maxwell solid, Section 3.2; the corresponding background internal friction would then be given by

$$\tan \phi_B = (J_U/\omega)F \exp(-Q_B/kT) \qquad (15.6\text{-}3)$$

The similarity between Eqs. (15.6-1) and (15.6-3) should be noted.

As emphasized by Schoeck *et al.* (1964), the internal friction given by Eq. (15.6-3) has the characteristic that the activation energy Q_B derived from the slope of the plot of $\log \tan \phi_B$ versus $1/T$ should be identical with the activation energy derived from the $1/T$ shift between curves measured at different frequencies. On the other hand, if the background were an anelastic phenomenon exhibiting a broad spectrum of relaxation times, the quantity C in Eq. (15.6-1) will be less than the activation energy derived from measurements at different frequencies, by an amount depending on the width of the spectrum involved (e.g., see Section 4.8). [†] The necessary measurements were not performed by Pearson and Rotherham, but such a check has been made for aluminum

---

[†] In this case the quantity C has no fundamental significance, a point which appears to have been missed by a number of writers.

by Schoeck *et al.* Since, at least for temperatures up to 300°C, the quantity C is generally only about one-half the activation energy derived from measurements at different frequencies, it can be concluded that in this case the background is of a predominantly anelastic character. Furthermore, since the true activation energy controlling the background is found to be equal to that for self-diffusion, these authors concluded that a broad spectrum of diffusion-controlled relaxations (involving dislocation motion) is responsible for the background.

A significant study of aluminum and aluminum alloys was performed by Friedel *et al.* (1955). These workers proposed two mechanisms for a diffusion-controlled dislocation relaxation. The first of these involves the bowing (by glide) of a dislocation segment which is pinned at its ends and is surrounded by an atmosphere of impurity atoms. For stresses below the level necessary to tear the dislocation from its atmosphere, this model produces a diffusion-controlled relaxation since the rate at which the glide strain develops is controlled by the diffusion rate of the impurities.[†] For a sample containing N_v dislocations per unit volume, of mean segment length l, the relaxation strength is given by the approximate relation [cf. Eq. (12.2-9)]

$$\Delta_M = N_v l^3 / 18 \qquad (15.6\text{-}4)$$

For a recrystallized specimen containing a random (Frank) network $N_v l^3 \simeq 1$, so that Eq. (15.6-4) leads to a relaxation strength of roughly 0.05. However, much larger relaxation strengths can be obtained from polygonized samples. For example, in a sample which has polygonized into blocks of size L and which contains dislocations spaced a distance h apart on the dislocation walls

$$N_v l^3 \simeq L/h \qquad (15.6\text{-}5)$$

In the work of Friedel *et al.*, it was estimated from x-ray measurements that $L \simeq 50h$, so that Δ_M becomes as large as 2.5. The temperature at which relaxation occurs was estimated to be about 450°C for the frequency employed ($1/15$ sec^{-1}). The applicability of this model of course involves the questionable assumption that the binding energy of an impurity to a dislocation is strong enough to maintain the atmosphere at such high temperatures.

[†] The basic similarity of this model and that of Schoeck (1963) to explain the Snoek–Köster (cold-work) peak, Section 13.6, should be noted.

A further augmentation of the modulus defect can occur if climb as well as glide of the bowing dislocation are considered. This mechanism was discussed by Friedel *et al.*, and also considered by Weertman (1957). The total modulus defect obtainable by combined climb and glide is

$$\Delta_M \simeq N_v l^3/6 \tag{15.6-6}$$

Equation (15.6-6) combined with Eq. (15.6-5), accounts quite well for the magnitude of the total modulus defect observed by Friedel *et al.* in both recrystallized and polygonized Al specimens. The location of the relaxation peak due to climb was calculated to be about 600°C (again for a frequency of 1/15 sec^{-1}).

Both the diffusion-controlled glide and climb mechanisms discussed above represent examples of relaxation processes which can be thought of as producing broad internal friction peaks. This, however, will only be true so long as the material is capable of sustaining a relaxed condition. If, in an overlapping temperature range, the material begins to creep plastically by a thermally activated process [cf. Eq. (15.6-2)], it will lose its anelastic character and take on the behavior of a viscoelastic solid. The background internal friction will then continue to increase at high temperatures, without the appearance of a resolvable internal friction peak. One mechanism by which a solid containing dislocations becomes endowed with viscous behavior at high temperatures is Nabarro–Herring creep (cf. Section 12.4) as has been discussed by Friedel (1961) and Escaig (1962). As given in Eq. (12.4-4), this mechanism produces a creep rate under constant stress of the type shown in Eq. (15.6-2), where the constant F is given by

$$F = \alpha D_0 b^3/L^2 kT \tag{15.6-7}$$

The quantity Q_B is now identified with the activation energy for self-diffusion, while D_0 is the corresponding preexponential constant [Eq. (7.5-10)]. The length L in Eq. (15.6-7) is the mean spacing between the dislocation walls which emit or absorb vacancies, and can be taken as the grain size in an annealed polycrystal or as the subgrain size in a polygonized single crystal. For an undeformed single crystal containing only a random network of average spacing L, Friedel (1961) has shown that the factor L^2 in Eq. (15.6-7) should be multiplied by $\ln(L/b)$, where b is the interatomic spacing. The internal friction due to Nabarro–Herring creep is most easily calculated assuming the frequency is low enough to produce quasi-static loading (such that at each instant of time the vacancy concentration gradient is in equilibrium with the applied stress). Under these conditions, the damping is simply given by inserting Eq. (15.6-7) into Eq. (15.6-3). When the frequency of vibration is too great for the assumption of quasi-static loading (e.g., in the kilohertz frequency range), both Friedel and Escaig predict a change in the internal friction behavior due to Nabarro–Herring creep. It is thought that the activation energy should then decrease to a value $\Delta h_v + \frac{1}{2} \Delta h^*$ (where Δh_v and Δh^* are the formation and motion energies of a vacancy), and that $\tan \phi_B$ should vary with frequency not as $1/f$ but as $1/f^{1/2}$. Behavior of this type does not yet appear to have been observed.

In summary, it is clear that the phenomenon generally referred to simply as "the high-temperature background" can best be thought of as the composite result of several mechanisms, all of which, however, are dependent on the high-temperature behavior of dislocations. While in some investigations the high-temperature background simply interferes with the observation of other relaxation processes, it seems very probable that a more active interest in this phenomenon could give further insight into high-temperature dislocation behavior, in much the same way that studies of the Bordoni peak and high-frequency attenuation measurements have given information about the behavior of dislocations at low temperatures.

PROBLEMS

15-1. Show from Eq. (6.2-12) for an isotropic medium that in the absence of a hydrostatic relaxation ($\Delta_K = 0$),

$$\Delta_G = 3(G_U/E_U) \Delta_E$$

Show that this result may also be written as

$$\Delta_G = 3 \Delta_E/2(1 + \chi)$$

where χ is Poisson's ratio. Use this last equation to derive Eq. (15.1-2) from Eq. (15.1-1).

15-2. Verify from Section 15.1 that for constant stress the relaxation rate for grain boundary sliding is given by

$$\tau^{-1} = G_U v(0)/\sigma d$$

Let $v(0) = XY$, where X is the number of rate-controlling jumps per second and Y is the boundary slip per jump. If each elementary jump produces a slip δ_1 over an area A_1, verify that $Y = \delta_1(A_1/A_{gb})$, where A_{gb} is the area of the grain boundary considered. Next, show that

$$X = (n/A_{gb})w_0\{\exp(-\Delta h^* + T\,\Delta s^*)/kT\}\sinh(A_d\,\delta^*\sigma'/kT)$$

where n_a is the density of active sites at which jumps can occur, A_d is the effective area of the defect, δ^* is the displacement during activation, and σ' is the local stress at an active site. Replace the hyperbolic term by its argument, and show that

$$\tau_0^{-1} = (n_aG_U/dkT)(\sigma'/\sigma)(A_d\,\delta^*A_1\,\delta_1)w_0\exp(\Delta s^*/k)$$

Assuming a homogeneous process of atomic dimensions (say $a/2$ where a is the lattice parameter) show further that this result reduces to

$$\tau_0^{-1} \simeq a^4w_0\exp(\Delta s^*/k)/8dkT$$

Calculate τ_0 for the conditions $a = 3.5$ Å, $w_0\exp(\Delta s^*/k) = 10^{14}$, $T = 600°K$, and $d = 0.03$ cm. Compare the result with Table 15-1 and state your conclusion.

15-3. Derive Eq. (15.6-3), using Eq. (15.6-2).

15-4. Show that a model of grain-boundary relaxation involving migration predicts a relaxation strength independent of grain size d and a relaxation time $\tau \propto d$, just as did the grain boundary sliding model. (Consider that the migrating boundaries are held fixed at the ends, so that they bow out, similarly to a dislocation loop.) It therefore follows that the dependence of Δ and τ on d cannot be used to distinguish between sliding and migration models.

General References

McLean, D. (1957). "Grain Boundaries in Metals." Oxford Univ. Press, London and New York.

Mason, W. P. (1958). "Physical Acoustics and the Properties of Solids," Chap. 9. Van Nostrand-Reinhold, Princeton, New Jersey.

Niblett, D. H., and Wilks, J. (1960). *Advan. Phys.* **9**, 1.

Van Bueren, H. G. (1961). "Imperfections in Crystals," Chap. 17. North-Holland Publ., Amsterdam.

Chapter 16 / Relaxations Associated with Phase Transformations

A substance or mixture may, at an appropriate temperature, undergo a change from one phase (or mixture of phases) to another. Such a phase transformation may involve a change in crystal structure, or a change in the state of order in a crystal. Examples of a change of order include order–disorder transformations (atomic order), ferromagnetic transformations (magnetic order), and ferroelectric transformations (dipolar order).

The condition for equilibrium of a thermodynamic system at constant temperature T and pressure P is the existence of a minimum in the Gibbs free energy per unit volume g. At a phase transition g will always be continuous, but its derivatives show discontinuities. The internal state of a material close to a phase transition may be described in terms of one or more internal (order) variables. For simplicity, we will deal here with only a single internal variable ξ. There are two kinds of phase transitions which occur most commonly, depending upon the behavior of the equilibrium value of ξ as a function of temperature. A transition of the first kind (also called "first order") is one in which the order variable (and consequently the enthalpy, volume, and crystal structure) undergo a discontinuous change. Figure 16-1a shows the behavior of the order variable ξ and the enthalpy per unit volume h as a function of temperature for such a transition. Examples include most allotropic transformations, eutectoid transformations, and some order–disorder reactions. A transition of the second kind (also called a *lambda transition* or critical-point phenomenon) is one in which the order, the enthalpy and the volume change continuously, but the temperature derivatives of these quantities show singularities. The corresponding curves for ξ, h, and the specific heat c_p are shown in Fig. 16-1b. Here the rate of change of ξ becomes catastrophic at the transition temperature, but ξ remains continuous, and therefore h behaves similarly. The specific heat, which is dh/dT, shows the well-known cusplike peak which has led to the name "lambda point" for such a transition. Examples include ferroelectric,

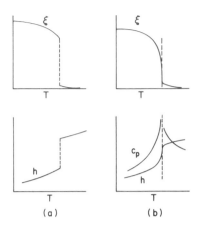

FIG. 16-1. Behavior of the order variable ξ and the enthalpy h for phase transformations of first kind (a) and second kind (b). Note the λ point variation of c_p near the temperature of a transformation of the second kind.

ferromagnetic, antiferromagnetic, and superconducting transitions, as well as many of the order–disorder transformations in molecular crystals and alloys.

Two basic types of phenomena will be considered in this chapter. The first case (Sections 16.1, 16.2) involves a crystal which undergoes a lambda-type transition. Large anelastic effects have been found near the critical temperature for the transition, due to stress-induced changes in the order variables. These effects bear a close resemblance to point-defect relaxations, but the anelastic behavior is quite unorthodox owing to the rapid change in thermodynamic parameters in the vicinity of the critical temperature. The second case (Section 16.3) involves a system consisting of a two-phase mixture which forms by means of a first-order transformation or, in any case, by a mechanism of nucleation and growth. Here again, stress can have an influence in changing the state of the material. In some cases, however, the phenomena observed in such systems appear to be accounted for by interfacial relaxation of the type described in Chapter 15.

16.1 Theory of Relaxation near a Lambda Transition

A lambda-type phase transition is describable in terms of an order parameter which changes rapidly (but not discontinuously) with increasing temperature, at a critical temperature T_c (see Fig. 16-1b). The theory of such "critical phenomena" has been very actively studied in recent years, and is still in a rapidly developing stage. Rather than become involved in the more intricate aspects of the theory, we will review here in some detail a relatively simple approach due to Landau which includes the effect of stress. [This theory was given initially by Landau and Khalatnikov (1954) and then in a modified form in a paper by Yakovlev and Velichkina (1957). The present approach is similar to the latter paper.] One advantage of this theory is that it introduces a single internal variable to describe the dynamical behavior of materials near critical points, and as such, represents a simple extension of the theory already presented in Chapter 5. A second advantage of the theory is that it successfully describes the qualitative aspects of dynamical behavior near critical points. On the other hand, we will see that the Landau theory is too oversimplified and ad hoc in its approach to represent the ultimate in a quantitative approach. The directions that have been taken in more refined theories will then be briefly reviewed in Part B of this section.

A. Landau Theory

This theory uses the thermodynamic approach of Section 5.3 with a single internal variable ξ, except that an additional higher term is added in the free energy expansion. Similarly to Eq. (5.3-3) we write the Gibbs function per unit volume in the differential form

$$dg = -\varepsilon \, d\sigma - s \, dT - A \, d\xi \qquad (16.1\text{-}1)$$

where s is the entropy per unit volume and A is the affinity. To obtain a second-kind phase transformation, requires more than the parabolic form, Eq. (5.3-10), for the g function. Rather, we take $g(\sigma, \xi, T)$ in the form

$$g(\sigma, \xi, T) = g(0, 0, T) - \tfrac{1}{2}J_U\sigma^2 - \varkappa\sigma\xi - \alpha\sigma\,\varDelta T + \tfrac{1}{2}\beta\xi^2 + \tfrac{1}{4}\gamma\xi^4 \quad (16.1\text{-}2)$$

Landau has shown that the last two terms meet the requirements for a phase transition of the second kind, provided that $\gamma > 0$ and that

$$\beta = a(T - T_c) \qquad (16.1\text{-}3)$$

with $a > 0$. We shall see shortly why these conditions are sufficient. From Eqs. (16.1-1) and (16.1-2), we obtain

$$\varepsilon = -(\partial g/\partial\sigma)_{\xi,T} = J_U\sigma + \varkappa\xi + \alpha\,\varDelta T \qquad (16.1\text{-}4)$$

$$A = -(\partial g/\partial\xi)_{\sigma,T} = \varkappa\sigma - \beta\xi - \gamma\xi^3 \qquad (16.1\text{-}5)$$

The condition for equilibrium at a given stress is $A = 0$, or

$$\beta\bar{\xi} + \gamma\bar{\xi}^3 = \varkappa\sigma \tag{16.1-6}$$

where $\bar{\xi}$ is the equilibrium value of ξ. In particular, for $\sigma = 0$, we designate $\bar{\xi} = \xi_0$ and obtain, from Eqs. (16.1-3) and (16.1-6),

$$\xi_0[\gamma\xi_0^2 - a(T_c - T)] = 0 \tag{16.1-7}$$

It is easy to show that the solution which minimizes g is

$$\xi_0 = \begin{cases} [a(T_c - T)/\gamma]^{1/2}, & T < T_c \\ 0, & T > T_c \end{cases} \tag{16.1-8}$$

This meets the requirement for a phase change of the second kind, since the internal order parameter ξ_0 has a finite value (representing spontaneous order) below T_c, and goes continuously to zero at T_c. It is readily shown that this behavior at zero stress corresponds to the Bragg–Williams theory[†] of the order–disorder phenomenon (e.g., see Problem 16-1).

We now consider the effect of applying a finite stress when $T < T_c$. Equation (16.1-6) yields

$$\beta(\bar{\xi} - \xi_0) + \gamma(\bar{\xi}^3 - \xi_0^3) = \varkappa\sigma \tag{16.1-9}$$

Taking σ to be small, it follows that $\bar{\xi} - \xi_0 \ll \xi_0$, and so $\bar{\xi}^3 - \xi_0^3 \simeq 3\xi_0^2(\bar{\xi} - \xi_0)$. With the aid of Eq. (16.1-8), we then obtain

$$\bar{\xi} - \xi_0 = \varkappa\sigma/2a(T_c - T) \tag{16.1-10}$$

Since, from (16.1-4), the isothermal equilibrium anelastic strain is $\varkappa(\bar{\xi} - \xi_0)$, the relaxation magnitude δJ is then given by

$$\delta J = \varkappa^2/2a(T_c - T), \qquad T < T_c \tag{16.1-11}$$

For the range above T_c, $\xi_0 = 0$ and the $\bar{\xi}^3$ term may be neglected. Accordingly, we obtain

$$\delta J = \varkappa^2/a(T - T_c), \qquad T > T_c \tag{16.1-12}$$

The striking result is that $\delta J \to \infty$, and therefore $J_R \to \infty$, as $T \to T_c$ both from below and from above T_c. The reason for this result is that close to T_c the influence of stress on the shift in $\bar{\xi}$ becomes very large,

---

[†] See, e.g., Fowler and Guggenheim (1949).

as shown for example by Eq. (16.1-10). Equation (16.1-12) is the mechanical analogy of the Curie–Weiss law for the paramagnetic susceptibility of a ferromagnetic material above the Curie temperature.

The kinetics of the relaxation process are readily obtained in a manner analogous to Section 5.3. Specifically, we assume that the time derivative of ξ is proportional to A, so that

$$\dot{\xi} = LA \qquad (16.1\text{-}13)$$

where L varies so slowly near T_c that it can be taken as a constant. In the range below T_c, utilizing Eqs. (16.1-5) and (16.1-6) and the assumption that $\xi - \bar{\xi} \ll \bar{\xi} \simeq \xi_0$, and recalling that $\gamma \xi_0{}^2 = -\beta$, we obtain

$$A \simeq 2\beta(\xi - \bar{\xi}) \qquad (16.1\text{-}14)$$

Combining (16.1-13) and (16.1-14)

$$\dot{\xi} = 2\beta L(\xi - \bar{\xi}) \equiv -\tau^{-1}(\xi - \bar{\xi}) \qquad (16.1\text{-}15)$$

which gives, for the relaxation rate τ^{-1}

$$\tau^{-1} = 2aL(T_c - T), \qquad T < T_c \qquad (16.1\text{-}16)$$

where Eq. (16.1-3) has been introduced. Similarly, above T_c,

$$\tau^{-1} = aL(T - T_c), \qquad T > T_c \qquad (16.1\text{-}17)$$

Thus, the relaxation time becomes infinite near $T = T_c$. The fact that both the relaxation strength and relaxation time become appreciable only in the vicinity of T_c, and vary rapidly with temperature near T_c, gives this type of relaxation process a character very different from those with which we have dealt earlier.

One interesting aspect of the present process is the creep behavior near T_c. Since this is a single relaxation process (i.e., a standard anelastic solid) the creep function must take the exponential form

$$J(t) = \delta J[1 - \exp(-t/\tau)] \qquad (16.1\text{-}18)$$

with δJ and τ as given in Eqs. (16.1-11), (16.1-12), (16.1-16), and (16.1-17). On the other hand, very close to T_c, τ^{-1} is small, so that the exponential can be expanded as $\exp(-t/\tau) \simeq 1 - (t/\tau)$, to obtain

$$J(t) \simeq (\delta J/\tau)t = (\varkappa^2 L)t \qquad (16.1\text{-}19)$$

In the last step we substitute either (16.1-11) and (16.1-16) or (16.1-12) and (16.1-17). Equation (16.1-19) expresses the remarkable result that near to T_c the material, though anelastic, undergoes simple *viscous creep*. This comes about from the combination of a relaxation strength and a relaxation time, both of which become infinite together. The viscous-like behavior of materials near a phase transformation is well known (see, e.g., Perrier and de Mandrot, 1922, 1924). The creep function further away from T_c is simply obtained by substituting Eqs. (16.1-11) and (16.1-16) or (16.1-12) and (16.1-17) into Eq. (16.1-18).

Turning now to the dynamical response functions, we may use the forms for the standard anelastic solid [Eqs. (3.4-2), (3.4-3), and (3.4-7)] and substitute δJ and τ^{-1} as calculated above. It then appears that the internal friction should go through a finite maximum at $T = T_c$ given by

$$\tan \phi(T_c) = \delta J / J_U \omega \tau = \varkappa^2 L / J_U \omega \qquad (16.1\text{-}20)$$

while the real part of the compliance difference, $J_1 - J_U$, becomes zero at $T = T_c$, since it varies as $\delta J / \omega^2 \tau^2$.

Actually, this approach for obtaining the dynamical response functions is not correct for the conditions of the usual experiment. The thermodynamic approach used in this section made use of the Gibbs function g, and therefore corresponds to the case in which σ, T, and ξ are the appropriate independent variables. This was necessary for a correct calculation of the equilibrium condition (16.1-8), i.e., at zero stress and constant temperature. The quantities δJ and τ^{-1} calculated using the Gibbs function are the values of the relaxation magnitude and relaxation rate at *constant stress and temperature*. These are clearly the correct quantities to calculate the creep function, since creep takes place at constant σ and T. On the other hand, dynamical experiments are usually conducted at frequencies high enough that the process is *adiabatic* rather than isothermal. (In fact, in the present field of study, ultrasonic pulse measurements in the megahertz range are commonly employed.) Ordinarily, the difference between the adiabatic and isothermal quantities are negligible [see Eq. (5.4-6)]. In the vicinity of a phase transition, however, corrections for the difference between adiabatic and isothermal quantities may be quite significant. In the case of the relaxation rate, we may use Eq. (5.4-12) with $\chi = -a\xi_0$ (see Problem 16-2) together with Eq. (16.1-8), to obtain

$$\tau_{\sigma,s}^{-1} = \tau_{\sigma,T}^{-1}[1 + (Ta^2/c_\sigma \gamma)], \qquad T < T_c \qquad (16.1\text{-}21)$$

It should be noted that the quantity c_σ is defined [Eq. (5.3-7)] as the specific heat per unit volume at constant σ and ξ, i.e., it is the *unrelaxed* specific heat, and not the relaxed quantity $c_{R,\sigma}$ [Eq. (5.4-13)] which shows the lambda point behavior. Since the bracketed quantity in Eq. (16.1-21) remains finite close to T_c, it is clear that $\tau_{\sigma,s}^{-1}$, like $\tau_{\sigma,T}^{-1}$, is proportional to $T_c - T$. For $T > T_c$, $\chi = 0$ so that

$$\tau_{\sigma,s}^{-1} = \tau_{\sigma,T}^{-1}, \qquad T > T_c \qquad (16.1\text{-}22)$$

In an analogous way one may correct δJ of Eq. (16.1-11), which is really δJ_T, to the adiabatic value δJ_s, using Eq. (5.4-9) and $\chi = a\xi_0$. It is clear that, since $\xi_0(T_c) = 0$, the correction term goes to zero as $T \to T_c$. Thus δJ_s, as well as δJ_T, becomes infinite near the critical point. It is clear then that the adiabatic as well as the isothermal quantities τ_σ and δJ become infinite as $T \to T_c$.

In view of the anomalous temperature dependence of τ and δJ near T_c, under adiabatic conditions, we may well expect to obtain a maximum value for $\tan \phi$ as given by Eq. (16.1-20) at $T = T_c$, with a corresponding ω^{-1} dependence. At the same time, J_1 must go to J_U near T_c. In actual experimental situations, however, these results are not obtained. Rather, it is found quite generally that $\tan \phi$ varies *proportionally* to the frequency (or attenuation $\mathscr{A} \propto \omega^2$), while J_1 tends toward a sharp maximum and is independent of frequency. An example showing attenuation curves for $NaNO_3$ near its critical temperature is shown in Fig. 16-2. Such results can only be explained if the condition $\omega\tau \ll 1$ obtains over the entire temperature range of the observations. Theoretically, this means that $aL \mid T - T_c \mid \gg \omega$ except for temperatures extremely close to T_c. Under these conditions, in the vicinity of T_c, $\tan \phi$ is given by

$$\tan \phi \simeq [\Delta/(1 + \Delta)]\omega\tau_\sigma = (\delta J/J_R)\omega\tau_\sigma = (\delta M/M_U)\omega\tau_\sigma \qquad (16.1\text{-}23)$$

where, for high-frequency measurements, all quantities will be taken as adiabatic values. In view of the condition $\omega\tau_\sigma \ll 1$, the compliance takes the simple form

$$J_1(T) \simeq J_R \simeq J_U + \delta J \qquad (16.1\text{-}24)$$

and is independent of the frequency. Since $\delta J \to \infty$ for $T \to T_c$, a plot of J_1 versus T should take the form of a cusp turning sharply upward at $T = T_c$, or a plot of M_1 versus T as a downward cusp at $T = T_c$.

Equation (16.1-23) may be further examined for the temperature

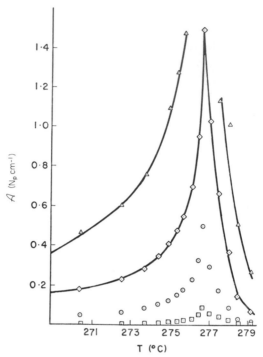

FIG. 16-2. Dependence of attenuation in a crystal of NaNO$_3$ on temperature and frequency ($\square$, 5; $\odot$, 15; $\diamond$, 25; $\triangle$, 35 MHz). Longitudinal acoustic waves are propagated along the trigonal axis. (From Craft and Slutsky, 1968.)

dependence of tan ϕ. Quite close to T_c, it is clear that tan ϕ varies with T in the same way as τ_σ, i.e., as $|T - T_c|^{-1}$. Further away, however, where $\varDelta \ll 1$, we anticipate that tan $\phi \propto \delta J \tau_\sigma$ or tan $\phi \propto (T - T_c)^{-2}$. These considerations are equally valid above or below T_c. This variation of tan ϕ with temperature is in striking contrast to the usual standard anelastic solid with thermally activated relaxation rate, for which $\omega\tau \gg 1$ on the low temperature side of the loss peak and $\omega\tau \ll 1$ on the other side. In the present case, due to the unusual thermodynamic relations, $\omega\tau \ll 1$ on *both* sides of the peak. Further, the peak occurs at $T = T_c$ regardless of the frequency. This failure of the damping peak to shift with changing frequency has sometimes been regarded as an indication that the phenomenon is not an anelastic relaxation process. We see, however, that such a presumption is incorrect.

As for the dependence of the compliance on temperature near the critical point, there are actually two types of curves that are commonly observed, as illustrated in Fig. 16-3. In the first case (curve *a*), the compliance shows an inflection type behavior, while in the second (curve *b*) it shows the predicted cusp. These results are readily understood. Since the order parameter ξ_0 changes rapidly near T_c, it is reasonable to expect that essentially all physical properties (e.g., density, lattice parameter, and elastic constants) will reflect this order–disorder behavior. The inflection-type behavior shown in Fig. 16-3a may, therefore, be regarded as a direct dependence of the compliance S_{11} of $NaNO_3$ on the degree of order ξ_0. It is, therefore, not a relaxation anomaly, and no internal friction should accompany this behavior. On the other hand, a modulus or compliance which undergoes relaxation will show a cusp as in Fig. 16-3b and also, a peak in the internal friction. (In this field of study the moduli are usually obtained from the velocity of ultrasonic

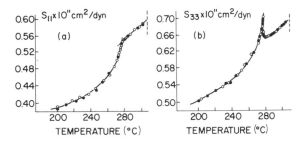

FIG. 16-3. Elastic compliance constants S_{11} and S_{33} as a function of temperature near the critical point of $NaNO_3$. (From Kornfel'd and Chubinov, 1958.)

waves; the sharp downward cusp in the velocity near T_c is then termed the "velocity anomaly.") The criterion for a modulus to show relaxation is simply [from Eqs. (16.1-11) and (16.1-12)] that $\varkappa \equiv \partial\varepsilon/\partial\xi \neq 0$, where ε is the appropriate strain. When the transformation occurs with no change in crystal structure (as, e.g., the cubic → cubic transformation in NH_4Cl or trigonal → trigonal in $NaNO_3$) it follows that only moduli of type I may undergo relaxation. Thus for NH_4Cl, only the bulk modulus $(C_{11} + 2C_{12})/3$ shows relaxation, and not the two shear moduli. Since C_{11} can be written as

$$C_{11} = \tfrac{1}{3}(C_{11} + 2C_{12}) + \tfrac{2}{3}(C_{11} - C_{12}) \qquad (16.1\text{-}25),$$

this elastic constant shows relaxation behavior only by virtue of the first component in Eq. (16.1-25). It is noteworthy that, for NH_4Cl, propagation of pure shear waves show neither attenuation peaks nor cusps in the sound velocity versus temperature (Garland and Jones, 1963).

B. Other Theories

As already mentioned, the Landau theory has the advantage of simplicity and of predicting qualitatively, and sometimes semiquantitatively, the form of the dynamic anomalies associated with critical phenomena. Because of its success, a number of papers have attempted to improve upon the Landau theory by introducing additional internal variables. Thus, for example, Tanaka *et al.* (1962) and Kikuchi (1960) have modified the theory by introducing short-range order parameters as well as long-range order, in the same way as Bethe's approximation improves on the Bragg–Williams theory of order–disorder phenomena.

There are, however, several fundamental objections to the Landau theory which are not rectified by such modifications. First, it is known that a free energy expansion, as given by Eq. (16.1-2) does not give a good description of static phenomena near critical points (Kadanoff *et al.*, 1967). (See, e.g., Problem 16-1.) This is due to the failure to consider fluctuations in the order parameter which take place near T_c. Fluctuations are relatively unimportant at temperatures relatively far from T_c, specifically, for $\eta \gg \eta_c$ where $\eta \equiv | T - T_c |/T_c$ is the reduced temperature, and η_c is a critical value characteristic of each substance. When long-range ordering forces operate, η_c becomes small. In ferroelectrics, for example, where long-range Coulomb forces are involved, $\eta_c \sim 10^{-4}$ (Kadanoff *et al.*, 1967) and the Landau theory then becomes a reasonable description. In NH_4Cl, on the other hand, the forces are short range, so that one actually has no reason to expect the Landau theory to work well. The second major objection to the theory is the purely ad hoc assumption involved in Eq. (16.1-13), that L is essentially constant near T_c.

The major theoretical developments in the past few years involve the so-called fluctuation theories based on the idea that ultrasonic waves will be perturbed or scattered by fluctuations in the order parameter through the agency of an appropriate coupling mechanism (e.g., a spin–phonon coupling in the case of ferromagnetic or antiferromagnetic materials). Various fluctuation theories have been reviewed by Garland (1970) and will not be dealt with here, especially since these theories are still in a state of development and evaluation. Further, in contrast to the Landau theory, the effect described is not a relaxation phenomenon. These fluctuation theories generally predict that the attenuation $\mathscr{A}$ will take the form

$$\mathscr{A} \propto \omega^2 (T - T_c)^{-\theta} \tag{16.1-26}$$

when T is close to T_c, where θ is called the *critical exponent*. Further discussion of the values of θ will be given under the specific types of transformations in the next section.

16.2 Examples of Relaxation near a Lambda Transition

Examples of such phase transformations include ferromagnetism, ferro-electricity, and antiferromagnetism, as well as other order–disorder transformations not involving magnetic spins or electric dipoles. Cases, such as ferromagnetism and ferroelectricity, in which ordered antiphase domains are present, offer additional complications due to the fact that an applied stress may move domain boundaries in addition to changing the local degree of order of the system (see Chapter 18). In these cases, however, application of an external field (magnetic or electric) of suitable magnitude may eliminate the problem by essentially converting the structure to a single domain.

A. FERROELECTRIC TRANSITIONS

A ferroelectric transition involves the ordering of electric dipoles. Above T_c these are disordered and the crystal shows paraelectric behavior. Below T_c the crystal develops a spontaneous electric moment, due to alignment of the dipoles within macroregions called domains. The appropriate internal variable is the electric polarization, which may be coupled to the strain linearly (piezoelectric coupling) or quadratically (electrostrictive coupling). The low-temperature ferroelectric phase is always piezoelectric, but the high-temperature paraelectric phase may or may not be piezoelectric. Crystals, such as Rochelle salt and KDP, which are piezoelectric in both phases, always have linear (piezoelectric) coupling; in these cases, the Landau theory can be most directly applied. The original application of the Landau theory to ferroelectrics was by Yakovlev and Velichkina (1957). Recently, Geguzina and Krivoglas (1968) have presented a more refined theory which considers the long-range dipole–dipole interaction between variations in polarization at different points in the crystal. This theory, which is applicable only to ferroelectric crystals which are piezoelectric in the paraelectric phase, predicts strong directional dependences for the attenuation and the velocity anomaly. For crystals which are nonpiezoelectric in the para-electric region, Levanyuk *et al.* (1969) have developed a fluctuation type theory involving interaction of ultrasonic waves with thermal fluctuations in the polarization. The coupling is via electrostriction; the strain is therefore proportional to the square of the polarization. Such effects are only observable very close to T_c and do not show strong directionality.

An additional external variable in the study of relaxation in ferroelectrics is the electric field. Geguzina and Timan (1968) have considered the effect of applying an electric field F along the polar axis. They use the Landau approach, and find that the relaxation time τ decreases as F increases and, in particular, that $\tau \propto F^{-2/3}$ at T_c. It is, therefore, expected that both the velocity anomaly and the attenuation will be reduced as the field is increased.

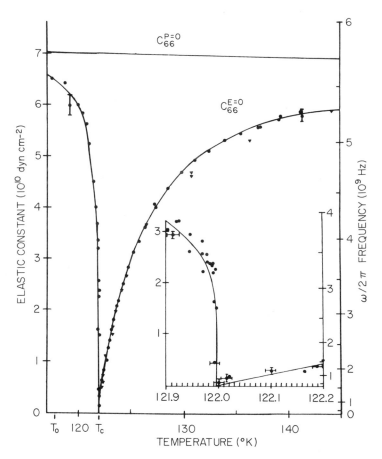

FIG. 16-4.   Elastic constant C_{66} of KDP in the vicinity of its critical temperature. C_{66}^p, the constant at constant polarization, is the unrelaxed value, obtained from piezoelectric resonance data; C_{66}^E, the constant at zero field is essentially the relaxed value. Circles are points from Brillouin shifts; triangles are from ultrasonic measurements. (From Brody and Cummins, 1968.)

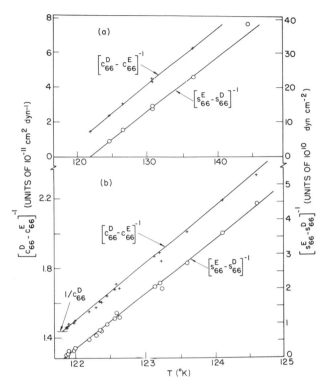

FIG. 16-5.   Verification of the mechanical Curie–Weiss law for KDP, showing the temperature variation of both δC_{66}^{-1} and δS_{66}^{-1}. Data in (a) cover a wide temperature interval, and in (b) an interval much closer to T_c. The corresponding lines in (a) and (b) are drawn with the same slopes. (From Garland and Novotny, 1969.)

Turning now to specific ferroelectrics, we first consider the crystal potassium dihydrogen phosphate, or KDP, which is a uniaxial ferroelectric for which $T_c = 122°K$. (For the crystal containing deuterium in place of hydrogen, called KD*P, T_c increases to $222°K$.) The structure is tetragonal ($\bar{4}2m$) in the paraelectric phase such that the strain ε_6 couples piezoelectrically to P_3, the polarization along the z axis (which is the internal variable that spontaneously orders at T_c). Therefore, a relaxation anomaly occurs in the elastic constant C_{66} or [see Eq. (6.4-23)] in the sound velocity, $v_{[100]}^{[010]}$ as shown in Fig. 16-4, which includes both ultrasonic measurements and the much higher-frequency Brillouin-shift data.[†] It is noteworthy that C_{66} goes essentially to zero at T_c, in agree-

---

[†] Brillouin scattering is the scattering of light by the lattice vibrations (phonons) in a solid.

ment with Eq. (16.1-24) and the prediction of the Landau theory that $\delta J \to \infty$ as $T \to T_c$. More specifically, the mechanical Curie–Weiss law for the paraelectric region, Eq. (16.1-12), has been verified, as shown in Fig. 16-5. Attenuation data have also been obtained over a range of frequencies, as illustrated in Fig. 16-6 for the deuterated material KD*P. These data show that $\mathscr{A} \propto \omega^2$. The availability of data for both attenuation (i.e., internal friction) and velocity (i.e., M_R) as a function of temperature means that $\tau_\sigma(T)$ is readily obtained with the aid of Eq. (16.1-23). The dependence of τ_σ on T for KDP above T_c is shown in Fig. 16-7; clearly Eq. (16.1-17) is strikingly verified. The fact that $\tau_\sigma \sim 10^{-11}$ sec shows again that the approximation $\omega\tau_\sigma \ll 1$ is a good one at megahertz frequencies (or even in the range of 10^9 Hz when measuring Brillouin scattering). Similarly the data of Fig. 16-6 have been analyzed to show that $\tau_\sigma \propto 1/|T - T_c|$ both above and below T_c. It is interesting, however, that the τ values for KD*P are an order of magnitude smaller than for KDP. This result is not unreasonable in view of the expectation that proton tunneling constitutes the rate determining process in this material. Finally, the data of Fig. 16-6 have been used to calculate the kinetic parameter L of Eq. (16.1-13), which is indeed found to vary slowly in the vicinity of T_c. Considering all of these results, it may be said that

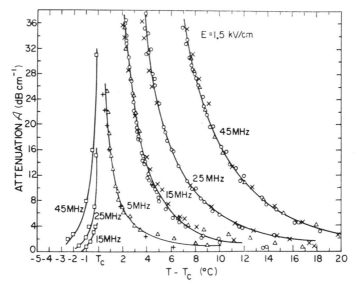

FIG. 16-6.   Attenuation versus temperature at several frequencies for the deuterated compound KD*P (i.e., KD_2PO_4). An electric field of 1.5 kV/cm is applied to align ferroelectric domains below T_c. (From Litov and Uehling, 1968.)

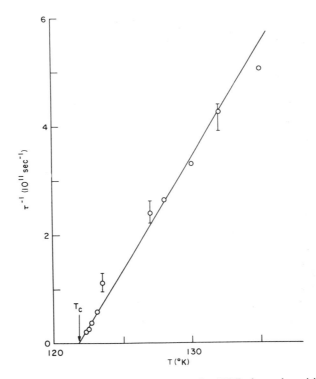

FIG. 16-7. Dependence of τ_σ^{-1} on temperature for KDP above the critical temperature. (From Garland and Novotny, 1969.)

this ferroelectric material shows behavior near the critical point which is in excellent agreement with the simple Landau theory of Section 16.1.

Another crystal which is also piezoelectric above T_c is Rochelle salt. One school of Soviet workers (Yakovlev and Velichkina, 1957; Shustin *et al.*, 1961; Baranskii *et al.*, 1963) has given considerable attention to this material which, in fact, shows two transformations, an upper one at 24°C and a lower one at -18°C. Sharp attenuation peaks are observed near both transformations, but most of the work deals with the upper transformation. Relaxation anomalies occur only for certain selected moduli.

The crystal triglycine sulfate (TGS) is a uniaxial ferroelectric which is monoclinic both above and below $T_c = 49$°C, and is nonpiezoelectric in the paraelectric phase. Its anelastic behavior has been studied by O'Brien and Litovitz (1964). By working with a single crystal, these authors showed that an absorption peak near T_c was obtained for a longitudinal wave perpendicular to the ferroelectric axis, while the absorption was negligible for longitudinal waves along this axis. As in other studies, an ω^2 dependence of the attenuation was demonstrated. The authors analyzed their results below T_c in terms of the Landau theory, but because the crystal is nonpiezoelectric above T_c they considered an entirely different (scattering) mechanism for the attenuation in that range. More recent work by Minaeva *et al.* (1969) shows that the fluctuation contribution to the attenuation occurs closer to T_c and is far less directionally dependent than the relaxation contribution. The attenuation below T_c, due to relaxation, was shown to vary as

$$\mathscr{A} \propto \omega^2/(T_c - T) \qquad\qquad (16.2\text{-}1)$$

Another group of ferroelectric crystals are the displacive-type ferroelectrics, of which $BaTiO_3$, $SrTiO_3$, and $KTaO_3$ are well-known examples. Anomalies in the elastic properties of these materials are associated with interaction between the ultrasonic wave and a "soft" transverse optic vibrational mode of the lattice, for which $\omega \to 0$ at zero wave vector as $T \to T_c$. This phenomenon then falls into the category of phonon–phonon interactions (Sections 17.6 and 17.7) rather than of stress-induced order–disorder transitions (see, e.g., Lefkowitz and Hazony, 1968).

B. FERROMAGNETIC AND ANTIFERROMAGNETIC TRANSITIONS

For ferromagnetic and antiferromagnetic phase changes, the coupling of strain to the appropriate internal variable ξ, which measures spin order, is usually magnetostrictive in nature. A thermodynamic theory analogous to the Landau theory has been considered [see, e.g., Belov *et al.* (1960)] in which the term $\varkappa\sigma\xi$ of Eq. (16.1-2) is replaced by a term $\gamma\sigma^2\xi$ where γ is a magnetostrictive constant. On the other hand, in the case of magnetic transitions, large fluctuations in magnetic order occur near a Curie point or a Néel point, so that the most recent descriptions of ultrasonic anomalies in the vicinity of these critical points is given by fluctuation-type theories. The theory must involve, as internal variables, the spins on all the sites rather than a single long-range order parameter as in the simple thermodynamic (Landau) theory. The basic concept is that an ultrasonic wave will be perturbed by thermal fluctuations of the local spins if there is a suitable coupling mechanism. This coupling is usually magnetostrictive in nature, relating strain to the square of the order parameter. When the coupling is via volume magnetostriction, only longitudinal velocities will show anomalies and not shear velocities.

A major objective of such a theory is to calculate the critical exponent θ in the expression (16.1-26). The quantity θ reflects how the ultrasonic wave couples to the spin system, and depends on such factors as the range of exchange interactions and whether the exchange interaction is strongly anisotropic or essentially isotropic. Most theoretical predictions are for the paramagnetic range, and give, typically, values of θ between 1 and 2 for antiferromagnets and somewhat higher values for ferromagnets. [See the review by Lüthi *et al.* (1970).]

Internal friction and elastic constant measurements have provided a particularly convenient tool for the detection and study of antiferromagnetic transitions. Probably the most widely studied material of this type is metallic chromium for which anomalous behavior was observed at kilohertz frequencies near 37°C by Fine *et al.* in 1951. Since that work, there have been various studies of the phenomenon (e.g., Pursey, 1957, 1958; Bolef and De Klerk, 1963; Klein, 1964). The detailed single-crystal modulus measurements of Bolef and De Klerk show that the anomaly takes the form of a strong cusp for C_{11} or for the bulk modulus, but is small and apparently of the inflection type for the shear constants. This behavior is very similar to the case of NH_4Cl, as already mentioned on p. 471.

In addition to the 37°C anomaly, there is still another anomaly near -150°C, first found by Fine *et al.* and studied in further detail by Bolef and De Klerk. This transformation, which is believed to involve two different antiferromagnetic states, gives rise to cusplike anomalies in the shear constants as well as in the compressibility. The situation here is clearly more complex.

Among the rare earth metals, ultrasonic anomalies near antiferromagnetic transitions have been observed for terbium, dysprosium, and holmium (Lüthi *et. al.*, 1970). The cusplike velocity anomalies for these three metals are shown in Fig. 16-8. It should be noted that the magnitude of the anomaly is only a few percent of the total velocity. Attenuation maxima were also observed and found to obey Eq. (16.1-26), both with respect to the ω^2 dependence and the temperature dependence. However, the attenuation maxima appeared at a slightly higher temperature T_n, than the cusp as shown, e.g., in the inset to Fig. 16-8 for the case of Ho. The critical exponent θ obtained from the attenuation data was found to be 1.24, 1.37, and 1.0, for Tb, Dy, and Ho, respectively. In the case of Tb and Ho, the attenuation is due to a volume magnetostrictive coupling, so that there are no anomalies in the elastic shear constants of these hexagonal crystals. On the other hand, Dy also shows a small attenuation anomaly for shear waves propagated along the

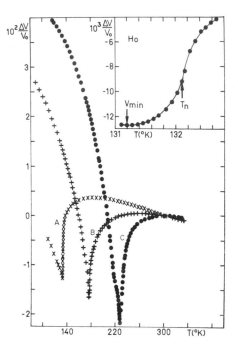

FIG. 16-8. Dependence of the change in longitudinal sound velocity along the hexagonal axis on temperature for three antiferromagnetic rare earth metals: A, holmium; B, dysprosium; C, terbium. The inset is an expanded plot showing the temperature, T_n, at which the attenuation peak occurs for Ho. (From Lüthi *et al.*, 1970.)

hexagonal axis. In this case, the coupling is believed to be of a linear magnetostrictive (single ion) type.

Among insulating crystals, $RbMnF_3$, a cubic antiferromagnetic crystal of the perovskite structure, has been studied recently. Golding (1968) observed the ultrasonic attenuation and velocity in this crystal over a range of frequencies near its Néel temperature T_c of 83°K. A value of the critical exponent of $\theta = 0.32$ is reported. Lüthi *et al.* (1970) show, however, that there are really two regions, one very close to T_c for which $\theta = 0.3$ and another, further away, for which $\theta = 0.7$. In any case, such low values of θ are not in agreement with any of the existing fluctuation-type theories. Melcher and Bolef (1969) studied the elastic constants of this material and found no anomalies in the shear constants, suggesting that spin–phonon coupling is via volume magnetostriction.

The crystal MnF_2 is different from $RbMnF_3$ in that it is a tetragonal crystal and a uniaxial antiferromagnet, with $T_c = 67°K$. A study by Neighbours and Moss (1968) shows that here too anomalies occur only in longitudinal and not in shear wave attenuation along principal crystal axes. Also, in common with $RbMnF_3$, θ is very low, being equal to 0.18 in the temperature range just below T_c and 0.40 above T_c.

Other antiferromagnetic materials of interest are the oxides MnO, CoO, and NiO. The internal friction and modulus of CoO was studied at an early date by Street and Lewis (1951) and by Fine (1952a). Antiferromagnetic ordering converts this material from a cubic (NaCl) structure above T_c to tetragonal below. Noting the absence of amplitude dependence near T_c, Fine rejected the suggestion of Street and Lewis that stress-induced domain boundary movement was involved, and instead proposed that the mechanism was a stress-induced change in the degree of antiferromagnetic order. Recently this material was studied by Ikushima (1969) and by Evans and Daniel (1968). In contrast to the usual behavior, the attenuation was found to vary linearly with frequency.

In addition to the above mentioned antiferromagnets, there have been several studies of internal friction and modulus changes of ferromagnetic materials near their Curie temperatures. Belov *et al.* (1960) have summarized their internal friction and modulus measurements on a number of ferromagnetic alloys containing Fe, Ni, Cr, and Co. A magnetic field

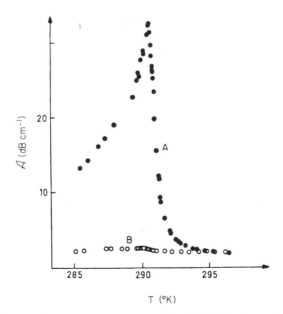

FIG. 16-9. Attenuation versus temperature for (50 MHz) ultrasonic waves in Gd along the *c* axis. A, longitudinal waves; B, transverse waves. (From Lüthi and Pollina, 1968.)

sufficient to produce saturation, i.e., a single domain, was often applied in order to eliminate the complexities of stress-induced domain wall movements mentioned earlier. Sharp internal friction peaks are consistently observed near the Curie points. Of particular interest is the recent work of Golding and Barmatz (1969) who made observations on high purity Ni close enough to T_c that the condition $\omega\tau < 1$ breaks down. Accordingly dispersion (i.e., frequency dependence) of the sound velocity is obtained.

The ferromagnetic rare earth metal gadolinium ($T_c = 290°K$) has been studied in some detail by Lüthi and Pollina (1968). They find a large anomalous attenuation for a longitudinal wave parallel to the hexagonal c axis, while transverse waves show almost no effect (see Fig. 16-9). These results again point to volume magnetostriction as the source of the spin–phonon coupling. For the critical exponent, a value $\theta = 1.2$ is obtained, which is in good agreement with the fluctuation theory of Laramore and Kadanoff (1969), which utilizes the concept of mode–mode coupling (Kadanoff and Swift, 1968).

C. OTHER ORDER–DISORDER PHENOMENA

In addition to crystals which order to produce a spontaneous electric polarization or an alignment of spins, there are many other examples of crystals which undergo a phase transition involving a random arrangement on certain atomic sites above a critical temperature T_c, and an ordered arrangement below T_c. Probably the most studied transition, from the viewpoint of anelasticity (primarily by Garland and co-workers), is that in the crystal NH_4Cl. This material has essentially the CsCl structure with the tetrahedral NH_4^+ ion replacing the Cs^+. The stable orientation of the NH_4^+ ion is one in which the hydrogen atoms point toward the nearest Cl^- ions. Accordingly, there are two possible orientations for the NH_4^+ tetrahedra. Above T_c ($= 242°K$) the NH_4^+ tetrahedra are randomly oriented. Below T_c more NH_4^+ ions are in one orientation than in the other; a state of long-range order then exists. The interaction between neighboring NH_4^+ ions is of an octapole–octapole type, and is therefore of a very short range. Accordingly, the Landau theory (with ξ as the long-range order parameter) should not be obeyed too well. Nevertheless, that theory does provide a semiquantitative picture of the ultrasonic velocity and attenuation behavior near the critical point. Thus, the attenuation is proportional to ω^2 and rises to a sharp maximum at T_c, as shown in Fig. 16-10 which is a plot of $\omega^2/\mathscr{A}$ as a function of

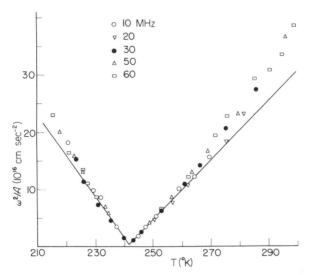

FIG. 16-10. Plot of $\omega^2/\mathscr{A}$ versus temperature for NH_4Cl near the critical point. Data cover the range from 10 to 60 MHz. (From Garland and Yarnell, 1966.)

temperature and includes data over a factor of six in frequency. The linear behavior on both sides of T_c shows that $\tau_\sigma^{-1} \propto | T - T_c |$. The existence of a steeper slope below T_c is also predicted, at least qualitatively, by Eqs. (16.1-16) and (16.1-17). Finally, the departure from linearity (approaching a quadratic dependence) at temperatures farther from T_c was also predicted in the discussion following Eq. (16.1-24).

There are two aspects to the anelastic behavior of NH_4Cl which are not in agreement with the Landau theory. First, as in the case of many other transformations (e.g., those in antiferromagnets), δJ does not go to infinity and therefore M_R to zero as $T \rightarrow T_c$. On the other hand, the bulk modulus $(C_{11} + 2C_{12})/3$ does show a sharp downward cusp of the type predicted by the theory, in which it falls to about 0.6 of the normal value (Garland and Jones, 1963). Second, there is evidence for a small discontinuity in the moduli close to T_c and the existence of small hysteresis effects. This behavior is suggestive of a *first-order* transformation, rather than the lambda-type transition on which the Landau theory is based. Garland and Renard (1966a), using the "compressible Ising model," in fact show theoretically that the NH_4Cl structure should become unstable in the immediate vicinity of T_c. This instability disappears at elevated pressures (Garland and Renard, 1966b). Another advantage of the high pressure measurements is that they make it possible to obtain elastic constants *at constant volume*, which are essentially the unrelaxed constants.

Other crystals which resemble NH_4Cl are NH_4Br and $NaNO_3$. In the case of NH_4Br, there are the same ordered and disordered phases as for NH_4Cl, but in addition there are other ordered phases, viz., an ordered tetragonal phase at low pressures and an additional high-pressure ordered phase (Garland and Young, 1968). The existence of these phases serves to make the anelastic behavior more complex. The crystal $NaNO_3$ shows an order–disorder transformation at 276°C involving two possible orientations of the NO_3^- ion. This crystal is trigonal both above and below the transition and, therefore, as already noted on p. 471, only moduli of type I show anomalies. Elastic compliance data, measured in the kilohertz range have been shown in Fig. 16-3, while attenuation peaks for longitudinal ultrasonic waves (5–35 MHz) along the c axis of the crystal, are shown in Fig. 16-2. Such data give rise to a plot similar to Fig. 16-10 for NH_4Cl (Craft and Slutsky, 1968). There is no evidence for a first-order transition in the case of $NaNO_3$, so that its behavior, in fact, appears to be simpler than that of NH_4Cl.

In alloy systems, probably the best known order–disorder transformation of the lambda-type is that in β brass (CuZn). Early work on this alloy has been primarily by resonant-bar methods in the frequency range $\sim 10^4$ Hz (Artman, 1952; Köster, 1940a). In view of the fact that $\tan \phi \propto \omega$ for these phenomena, it would be worthwhile to study this alloy using pulse (megahertz range) methods.

D. MARTENSITIC TRANSFORMATIONS

Recently the alloy TiNi has been studied in the vicinity of its martensitic (i.e., diffusionless or shear-type) transformation (Bradley, 1965; Spinner and Rozner, 1966; Pace and Saunders, 1970). Sharp attenuation peaks and anomalous behavior of the elastic constants are observed, which are indicative of a relaxation process whose relaxation time is strongly temperature dependent. It thus appears that this type of transformation may also show the behavior already described for order–disorder transformations. The nature of the internal variable involved is not completely clear, although Pace and Saunders suggest an unstable phonon mode.

16.3 Relaxation in Two-Phase Mixtures

When a transformation of the first kind (or of first order) occurs at a given temperature T_0, two phases will be present simultaneously at temperatures close to T_0. In such a case one may also expect to obtain stress-induced changes in the degree of transformation near T_0, giving rise to internal friction and anomalous modulus effects. Krivoglas (1960, 1961) has developed a theory for the effect of stress on a two-phase mixture, both for the case of a one component and a two component system. He deals with an isotropic material and assumes that only relaxation of the bulk modulus K takes place due to the ability of a hydrostatic stress to disturb the state of equilibrium. The result is essentially standard-solid behavior, with the relaxation time related to the time for the phase transformation to occur. For the two-component system, for example, a compositional difference is involved, and the relaxation time, which is controlled by diffusion, is given by

$$\tau_\sigma = r_0{}^2/3Dx_2 \qquad (16.3\text{-}1)$$

where r_0 is the radius of the second phase particle (assumed spherical), x_2 is the volume fraction of the second phase, and D is the appropriate diffusion coefficient. For a one-component system, on the other hand, τ_σ varies inversely as the linear growth rate of a second-phase particle.

Because of the nature of a first-order transformation, namely, the occurrence of a discontinuity in structure (and therefore in all properties) near T_0, the transformation usually occurs by a mechanism of nucleation and growth. As a consequence of this, first-order solid-state transformations characteristically show hysteresis effects in the variation of properties with T. Therefore, a quantitative study of the temperature and frequency dependence of the internal friction and elastic modulus near T_0, as carried out for lambda transitions, is not readily possible here.

However, several examples of one-component first-order transformations have been studied by anelastic methods, particularly the allotropic transformations in iron (Garbyer and Kovalev, 1959), cobalt (Köster, 1948; Postnikov, 1957) and zirconium (Bratina and Winegard, 1950). About the most definitive statement that one can make about such investigations is that they all show a high damping near T_0.

In contrast to such at-temperature measurements, in which the structure itself changes with changing T, greater opportunities exist in the case of systems of two (or more) components which undergo a first-order transformation. In such cases, because the transformation is diffusion controlled, it is usually possible to quench in the high temperature phase and then to allow the transformation to take place under controlled conditions at a lower temperature. Most notable examples are systems which are single phase at high temperature and precipitate a second phase at a lower temperature. The advantage of this approach is that the two phase system can be metastabilized into a particular structural condition, and its anelastic properties then studied at relatively low temperatures.

A. CASE OF TRANSITIONAL PRECIPITATES

It is not uncommon for supersaturated solid solutions to exhibit a precipitation sequence of the form

| homogeneous solid solution | → | depleted matrix containing solute clusters (or G.P. zones)[†] | → | depleted matrix + coherent transitional ppt. | → | depleted matrix + final (equilibrium) ppt. |

As reviewed in detail by Hardy and Heal (1954), such a sequence is found in the alloys Al–4 wt % Cu and Al–20 wt % Ag, both of which have been the subject of internal friction studies. The more clearly defined situation occurs for the Al–Cu alloy (Berry and Nowick, 1958), which will be discussed first.

In the solution-treated and quenched condition, Al–4 wt % Cu exhibits a Zener peak (cf. Section 10.2). The location of this peak is stable (at 175°C for 1 Hz) once excess vacancies introduced by quenching have been removed (as can be accomplished by a short anneal at 200°C). This treatment also produces re-solution (reversion) of any previously formed solute clusters, called G.P. [1] zones, so that the peak height observed on first cooling from 200°C is representative of the alloy with all the copper in solution. The internal friction behavior of specimen subsequently aged for increasing periods of time near 200°C is shown in Fig. 16-11. For the first three hours or so, the only change is a decline of the Zener peak (at 170°C), indicating a depletion of the matrix. The structural change associated with this stage of aging is the formation of zones on the {100} planes of the matrix. These have a different and more elaborate structure than G.P. [1], and are designated as G.P. [2] zones. On further aging, the G.P. [2] structure is gradually replaced by the transitional precipitate θ', which is present in maximum quantity after a total of about 150 hr. This new phase, which has essentially the composition $CuAl_2$ and the fluorite structure, precipitates in platelike form on the {100} planes of the matrix, with which it forms a coherent interface.

[†] The term G.P. zones refers to Guinier–Preston zones, named after their discoverers.

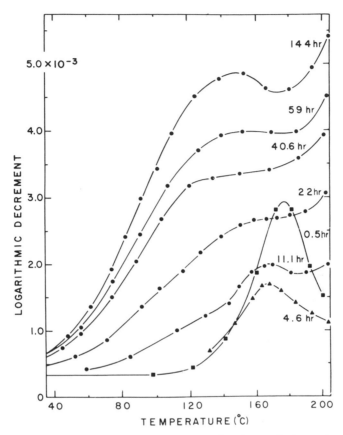

FIG. 16-11.   Internal friction of a solution-treated and quenched sample of Al–4%
Cu, after aging for various periods at 203°C. Measurements in torsional vibration at 0.5
Hz (except for the 0.5 hr curve, which refers to 1.3 Hz). (From Berry and Nowick,
1958.)

As can be seen from Fig. 16-11, the appearance and growth of the θ'
phase produce marked changes in the internal friction behavior. The
changes can be resolved into (a) the appearance and growth of a broad
peak located below the Zener peak, (b) an enhancement of the smoothly
rising high-temperature background internal friction, and (c) a further
decline of the Zener peak, which can be estimated to have fallen to a
negligible value by the time θ' precipitation is complete. The second
peak is not fully resolved from the rising high-temperature background,
but does eventually produce a clear maximum in the curve after 144 hr
aging. By comparing the kinetics of θ' precipitation with the growth
kinetics of the second peak, as is done in Fig. 16-12, it becomes clear that

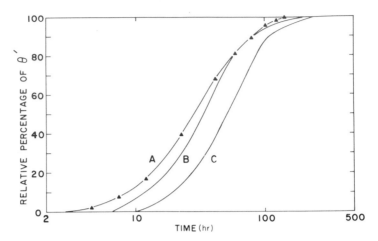

FIG. 16-12.   Comparison of results on the kinetics of θ' precipitation in Al–4% Cu. A, from the internal friction data of Fig. 16-11; B, from the dilatometric measurements of Lankes and Wassermann (1950); C, from the x-ray measurements of Guinier (1952). Curve A refers to an aging temperature of 203°C, B and C to 200°C.

the magnitude of the second peak is at least roughly proportional to the amount of θ' present. Further experiments have shown that prolonged aging treatments at higher temperatures produce a decline of the second peak. Such treatments cause the transitional precipitate θ' to transform, with loss of coherency, to the final equilibrium precipitate ($CuAl_2$), which has a complex tetragonal structure. Since the second peak is completely absent in specimens containing only the final θ phase, it is clear that the peak is linked exclusively to the presence of θ', and can therefore be designated as the θ' peak. By contrast, the increase in the high temperature background which accompanies θ' precipitation is not removed by the transformation $\theta' \to \theta$; rather this transformation causes the background to increase somewhat further.

The following additional experimental information is available concerning the θ' peak:

(a) The peak grows with nearly constant shape, to a height which is approximately independent of crystal orientation.

(b) The temperature of the peak shifts upward by about 30°C in the course of growth and overaging.

(c) In the fully formed condition, the activation energy of the peak is 0.95 ± 0.05 eV and $\tau_0 = 10^{-12.5 \pm 0.8}$ sec.

(d) The width of the peak is about three times larger than that for a process having only a single relaxation time.

As already mentioned, the second example of a peak due to a transitional precipitate occurs in the Al–Ag alloy. This peak was first observed by Damask and Nowick (1955) in Al–20 wt % Ag. After solution treatment and quenching, this alloy exhibited a relaxation whose rate decreases markedly with aging time at or slightly above room temperature. A short anneal at 155°C produced a temporarily stable peak at about 140°C (for 0.25 Hz). With continued aging between 155° and 232°C, the peak first migrated to slightly higher temperatures while increasing in height, then returned to lower temperatures and decreased in height. After aging to above 200°C, the peak position remained constant while the height decreased very slowly. At this point, the peak is characterized by an activation energy of 1.09 ± 0.02 eV and a τ_0 value of $10^{-13.2}$ sec. Comparison of the internal friction behavior with the known stages of precipitation led the authors to conclude that the peak is first due to the presence of spherical clusters of Ag and later to the platelike transition γ' precipitate. This point constitutes a major puzzle for the Al–Ag system, since it is rather surprising, on this basis, that there are not more dramatic changes in the peak at the point in the aging process where γ' starts to form. In contrast the Al–Cu system showed a unique connection between the transitional θ' precipitate and the damping peak. The existence of a relaxation associated with intermediate stages of precipitation in Al–Ag alloys was recently confirmed simultaneously by Miner *et al.* (1969) and by Schoeck and Bisogni (1969) both of whom studied a wide range of compositions. They each showed that the peak height is proportional to the concentration of Ag in the alloy.

In attempting to deduce the origin of these peaks, the first question to be considered is whether the peak is due to a mechanism in the precipitate phase alone, independently of the matrix phase (e.g., a Zener relaxation). Various factors, such as the lack of strong anisotropy in the relaxation strength, the large width of the peak, and the relatively high values of τ_0, are not in accord with such a suggestion. The alternative is then that anelasticity arises as a result of the relationship between the matrix and the transitional precipitate. It is not likely that the observed relaxation is a *hydrostatic* stress-induced transformation in accordance with the Krivoglas theory, in view of the fact that observations have been made using torsional deformation on single crystals. [†] Damask and Nowick (1955)

[†] This does not eliminate the possibility of some microscopic hydrostatic stresses, because of the presence of two phases, but it is doubtful that such stress components are large enough to account for the relaxation.

have proposed instead the occurrence of a stress-induced change in particle shape. They suggest that this could come about as a consequence of the interaction of the applied stress with the internal stress in the vicinity of a precipitate particle. In this way, there can be a change in the local equilibrium under stress leading to a limited re-solution in some areas of the precipitate and further precipitation in others. The rate limiting process is then atom migration around the matrix–precipitate interface which accounts for the activation energy being lower than that for solute diffusion. In the case of Al–Ag, at least, subsequent direct observations by transmission electron microscopy (Nicholson and Nutting, 1961) has shown no evidence for the presence of long range shear strain fields about the transitional γ' particles. Instead, therefore, Schoek and Bisogni (1969) propose that the peak is caused by the movement of the partial dislocations surrounding the precipitates. This suggestion is more in line with electron microscopic observations on Al–Ag alloys. The activation energy is then attributed to the diffusion of Ag atoms in the domain wall, i.e., the dragging along of regions of Ag enrichment in the dislocation stacking fault. Miner *et al.* (1969) on the other hand, propose a mechanism involving ledge motion along the edges of precipitate particles, again based on some electron microscopic observations. Clearly, enough work has not yet been done on either the Al–Cu or the Al–Ag alloys to distinguish among these diverse suggestions.

Still another example of anelasticity in a precipitating system is that observed by Entwistle in Duralumin. In this case, the evidence indicates that clusters are involved, and that the relaxation effect is due to atom groupings within the individual clusters. The effect appears, therefore, to fall more nearly into the area of point defect phenomena. Accordingly, it was discussed earlier, in Section 11.6E.

B. Case of Discontinuous Precipitation

In contrast to the very low levels of internal friction with which we have just been concerned, we turn now to the extremely high internal friction which can be exhibited by an alloy as a result of large scale discontinuous precipitation. Discontinuous precipitation is characterized by a preferential precipitation beginning at grain boundaries, and spreading into the grains with the decomposition of the supersaturated matrix occurring at an advancing interface. Precipitation of this type occurs in the alloy Al–39 wt % Zn, studied by Nowick (1951a). The precipitation (of essentially pure zinc) which is complete in a few hours at 150°C, produces a progressive and substantial increase in the monotonically rising internal friction curve measured between room temperature and the aging temperature. The anelastic nature of the mechanism producing this internal friction was ascertained from the strain recovery observed in quasi-static experiments. Prolonged aging at somewhat higher temperatures coarsens the microstructure and depresses or shifts the internal friction curves somewhat; at even higher temperatures a reduction in internal friction is obtained by partial re-solution of the precipitate. This fact complicates attempts to determine the internal friction at high temperatures. To circumvent this difficulty, creep measurements were performed at 200°C on a specimen stabilized at this temperature by prior aging. Using the approximate relation given by Eq. (4.4-3), and the measured activation energy of 1.0 eV, the creep data were converted to an internal friction curve for the range above 200°C. As shown in Fig. 16-13, the curve obtained in this way rises smoothly to extremely high values of internal friction without the appearance of a relaxation peak. It was pointed out that this result is most readily explained by the existence of

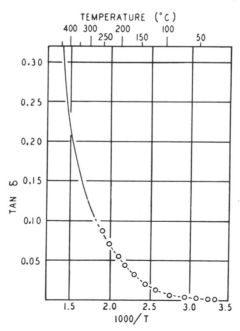

FIG. 16-13.   Anelastic behavior of an Al–39 wt % Zn alloy aged 15 days at 250°C to produce discontinuous precipitation. Data points represent internal friction measurements. The full line shows the extension of this data, as derived from creep measurements made at 200°C. (From Nowick, 1951a).

coupled relaxations, of the sort previously discussed in Section 15.6. From metallographic observation of the structure of the aged alloy, such a behavior can be understood in terms of a mechanism of shear stress relaxation across the network of interfaces formed between the matrix and the precipitated phase. This mechanism then suggests that the phenomenon described is closely related to the interface relaxations of the type discussed in Chapter 15.

PROBLEMS

16-1. Obtain the additional specific heat Δc_p due to the variation of ξ_0 with temperature in the Landau theory. Show that this specific heat has a linear temperature dependence up to T_c and drops abruptly to zero above T_c. (This result is the same as for the Bragg–Williams theory of the order–disorder transformation.) Note that this variation is far more gradual than experimentally obtained "lambda point" behavior of Δc_p.

16-2. Compare Eq. (16.1-5) with Eq. (5.3-9) noting that in the former case β is an explicit function of T. Show that the quantity $\chi = (\partial A / \partial T)_{\sigma, \xi}$ which appears in Eq. (5.3-9) is now equal to $-a \xi_0$, to the first order (i.e., linear) approximation.

16-3. Obtain Eq. (16.1-17) for the relaxation time above T_c.

16-4. Show that the quantity $\delta M / M_U$ which appears in Eq. (16.1-23) not only remains finite at $T = T_c$, but that it varies with temperature as $(T - T_1)^{-1}$, where T_1 is a temperature lower than T_c.

General References

GARLAND, C. W. (1970). *In* "Physical Acoustics" (W. P. Mason, ed.), Vol. 7. Academic Press, New York.
LÜTHI, B., MORAN, T. J., and POLLINA, R. J. (1970). *J. Phys. Chem. Solids* **31**, 1741.

Chapter 17 / Thermoelastic Relaxation and the Interaction of Acoustic Waves with Lattice Vibrations

In this chapter we will consider two types of thermal relaxation phenomena. The first, which is a strictly classical effect, was quantitatively understood at an early date largely through the work of Zener. The basis for this source of anelasticity is the ability of an applied stress to change the temperature of a specimen relative to its surroundings, or of one part of a specimen relative to another. The heat flow which then occurs in order to equalize the temperature difference gives rise to energy dissipation and to anelastic behavior. The treatment of this phenomenon, which requires only classical thermodynamics and the Fourier law of heat flow, is given in Sections 17.1–17.5.

The second phenomenon is one which has been studied much more recently with the advent of high-frequency techniques. It requires a quantum picture of thermal vibrations, in which these vibrations are regarded as a system of elastic waves with energy quanta known as "phonons." In thermal equilibrium the number of phonons of each frequency is given by the well-known Planck distribution law. An incoming ultrasonic wave (which may itself be regarded as a beam of phonons) interacts with the thermal phonons and upsets their state of thermal equilibrium (an effect which some authors therefore refer to as a "phonon–phonon interaction"). The irreversible processes which then occur provide a mechanism for the attenuation of the ultrasonic wave, as discussed in Sections 17.6 and 17.7.

Phonon phenomena are usually well separated from classical thermoelastic effects because the time constant for relaxation of the phonon distribution is very short and generally much smaller than that for thermal conduction. This is just another way of saying that temperature can be defined locally even when a sample is not in a state of thermal equilibrium. On the other hand, the classical and phonon phenomena are interrelated in that both are direct manifestations of the anharmonic behavior of a crystal lattice.

17.1 Thermoelastic Coupling as a Source of Anelasticity

As the name suggests, the thermoelastic coupling refers to the inter-relation between the conjugate pair of variables stress and strain and the conjugate pair temperature and entropy. (Either variable from each pair may be chosen as the independent one.) This coupling is a source of anelastic behavior, since restoration of a stress-induced difference in the thermal equilibrium of a sample produces strain (via a thermal expansion or contraction) at a rate limited by thermal diffusion. To develop the theory of thermoelastic relaxation, we shall proceed in this section to parallel the approach of Chapter 5, regarding the entropy per unit volume s as the internal variable analogous to ξ in Section 5.1.

The most familiar example of thermoelastic coupling is the phenom-enon of thermal expansion. Choosing σ and T as the independent vari-ables, and employing the equation for the differential of the Gibbs free energy per unit volume

$$dg = -s \, dT - \varepsilon \, d\sigma \qquad (17.1\text{-}1)$$

we obtain the cross relationship

$$(\partial s/\partial \sigma)_T = (\partial \varepsilon/\partial T)_\sigma \equiv \alpha_\varepsilon \qquad (17.1\text{-}2)$$

where $(\partial \varepsilon/\partial T)_\sigma$ defines an appropriate expansion coefficient α_ε. (For example, if ε is a uniaxial strain, α_ε is the coefficient of linear expansion in the direction α. On the other hand, if ε is a volumetric strain, α_ε is the volumetric expansion coefficient.) Equation (17.1-2) clearly shows that provided $\alpha_\varepsilon \neq 0$, the application of stress will produce a change in s under isothermal conditions. In addition to this cross-coupling between the nonconjugate variables s and σ, there is of course the direct relation between the conjugate variables temperature and entropy:

$$(\partial s/\partial T)_\sigma = c_\sigma/T \qquad (17.1\text{-}3)$$

where c_σ is the specific heat per unit volume at constant σ. An alternative though less familiar manifestation of thermoelastic coupling is the "thermoelastic effect," i.e., the temperature change from a reference value T_0 induced by application of a stress under adiabatic (and therefore isentropic) conditions. In this case we have

$$(\partial T/\partial \sigma)_s = -(\partial s/\partial \sigma)_T/(\partial s/\partial T)_\sigma = -\alpha_\varepsilon T_0/c_\sigma \qquad (17.1\text{-}4)$$

where the last equality is obtained by the use of Eqs. (17.1-2) and (17.1-3).

To appreciate the order of magnitude of the temperature change induced by stress, the reader is referred to Problem 17-1.

It should be noted that because the expansion produced by temperature does not change the symmetry of a crystal, it follows that thermoelastic coupling can only occur if the strain ε is at least partially of type I, as defined in Chapter 6 (cf. Problem 17-2). Thus, for example, in a crystal of symmetry which is orthorhombic or higher, a pure shear stress cannot change the entropy, since thermal expansion does not give rise to shear strain in such materials.

A simple example of relaxation resulting from the thermoelastic coupling is that of a rod, originally in equilibrium with its surroundings at T_0, which is suddenly subjected to a uniaxial tension σ. If the linear expansion coefficient α is positive, as is commonly the case, Eq. (17.1-4) shows that the rod will first cool to a temperature T given by $T - T_0 = -\alpha T_0 \sigma / c_\sigma$. As time proceeds, heat flow from the surroundings will restore the temperature of the rod back to T_0, and the accompanying thermal expansion will constitute an anelastic strain. If the rod is highly conductive and the rate of heat transfer to the rod is not too great, the temperature of the rod may be regarded as uniform during warm-up. This very simple example then represents a homogeneous relaxation process. Clearly, the unrelaxed compliance J_U is the isentropic compliance $(\partial \varepsilon / \partial \sigma)_s$, while the relaxed compliance J_R is the isothermal compliance $(\partial \varepsilon / \partial \sigma)_T$. Since $\delta J = \bar{\varepsilon}^{an} / \sigma$ and $\bar{\varepsilon}^{an} = \alpha (T_0 - T) |_s$, it follows immediately that

$$\delta J = \alpha^2 T_0 / c_\sigma \tag{17.1-5}$$

in agreement with Eq. (5.4-6).

We shall now adopt the internal variable approach to show that the differential stress–strain equation obtained for this example is that of the standard anelastic solid. In the approach used by Zener, T is chosen as the independent variable, and the strain $\varepsilon(\sigma, T)$ as given by a linear expansion about the reference state $\sigma = \varepsilon = 0$; $T = T_0$ has the form

$$\varepsilon(\sigma, T) = (\partial \varepsilon / \partial \sigma)_T \sigma + (\partial \varepsilon / \partial T)_\sigma \, \Delta T$$
$$= J_R \sigma + \alpha \, \Delta T \tag{17.1-6}$$

where $\Delta T = T - T_0$. Equation (17.1-6) differs from the approach taken in Chapter 5 of writing ε in the form [cf. Eq. (5.1-1)]:

$$\varepsilon(\sigma, \xi) = J_U \sigma + \varkappa \xi \tag{17.1-7}$$

where ξ is the independent internal variable and $\varkappa = (\partial \varepsilon / \partial \xi)_\sigma$. To maintain the practice of working with an equation of this form, it is only necessary to adopt s instead of T as the independent variable. With this choice, the temperature difference ΔT assumes the significance of a driving force for equilibrium which vanishes only when the internal variable s has the value $\bar{s}$, the equilibrium value for stress σ and temperature T_0. (In fact, $-\Delta T$ is equivalent to the affinity in Chapter 5.) With the adoption of σ and s as the independent variables, the appropriate state function is the enthalpy h. For, in differential form [cf. Eq. (5.4-1)]

$$dh = -\varepsilon \, d\sigma + T \, ds \qquad (17.1\text{-}8)$$

and thus

$$(\partial \varepsilon / \partial s)_\sigma = -(\partial T / \partial \sigma)_s = \alpha T_0 / c_\sigma \qquad (17.1\text{-}9)$$

where the last equality makes use of Eq. (17.1-4). Thus, Eq. (17.1-7) becomes

$$\varepsilon = J_U \sigma + (\alpha T_0 / c_\sigma) \, \Delta s \qquad (17.1\text{-}10)$$

where $\Delta s = s - s_0$ and s_0 is the entropy per unit volume in the equilibrium reference state. Following the procedure of Chapter 5, we now perform a first-order expansion on the remaining dependent variable T in terms of the independent variables s and σ to obtain

$$\Delta T = (T_0 / c_\sigma)(\Delta s - \alpha \sigma) \qquad (17.1\text{-}11)$$

where use has been made of Eqs. (17.1-3) and (17.1-4) to express the partial derivatives in explicit form. Since $\Delta T = 0$ when equilibrium is established under the stress σ, the equilibrium value $\overline{\Delta s}$ is given by

$$\overline{\Delta s} = \alpha \sigma \qquad (17.1\text{-}12)$$

which provides the analog to Eq. (5.1-2). Inserting Eq. (17.1-12) into (17.1-11), we obtain

$$-\Delta T = -(T_0 / c_\sigma)(\Delta s - \overline{\Delta s}) \qquad (17.1\text{-}13)$$

In Section 5.3, the proportionality constant between the time derivative of the internal variable and the affinity was introduced formally in terms of an Onsager coefficient L [cf. Eq. (5.3-13) for the case of a single internal variable]. In the present case we may directly utilize the law of heat flow to assert that the rate $\dot{q}$ at which heat is transferred from the surroundings to the specimen is proportional to $-\Delta T$ through a heat transfer coefficient μ. Thus, to first order,

$$\dot{q} = T_0 \, d(\Delta s)/dt = -\mu \, \Delta T \qquad (17.1\text{-}14)$$

from which it can be seen that in this case $L = \mu/T_0$. Combining Eqs. (17.1-13) and (17.1-14) gives the kinetic equation

$$d(\Delta s)/dt = -(\Delta s - \overline{\Delta s})/\tau_\sigma \qquad (17.1\text{-}15)$$

where

$$\tau_\sigma \equiv c_\sigma/\mu \qquad (17.1\text{-}16)$$

Equations (17.1-10), (17.1-12), and (17.1-15) are the direct analogs of Eqs. (5.1-1)–(5.1-3), and again it is readily shown that elimination of the internal variable leads to the differential equation of the standard anelastic solid. It should be emphasized that this simple result applies only to the extreme case where the relaxation is homogeneous, which as noted earlier is obtained in the limit where heat transfer within the rod occurs much faster than between the rod and its surroundings. Examples taken for the opposite limit have been considered, and show a much more complicated behavior represented by a distribution of relaxation times of slowly diminishing strength (Zener, 1948, p. 81). We shall encounter another example of this type in Section 17.5. First, however, we shall pursue in the next two sections some examples of inhomogeneous thermal relaxation where the behavior turns out to be very close to that of a standard anelastic solid.

17.2 Thermal Relaxation under Inhomogeneous Deformation

A homogeneous material subject to a homogeneous stress, as considered in the example of the previous section, can undergo thermal relaxation only by heat exchange with its surroundings. If the deformation is inhomogeneous, however, temperature gradients are generated within the sample which lead to relaxation by internal heat flow or "thermal currents" (Zener, 1937, 1938a, 1948). The treatment of this problem contains the same basic steps outlined in the previous section, but now all the variables must be taken as both functions of time t and position x, y, z within the sample. If for simplicity we denote the strain $\varepsilon(x, y, z, t)$ by ε, and so on for the other variables, Eqs. (17.1-10) and (17.1-12) may be retained without change.

The third basic equation needed to set up the problem is one which expresses the fact that relaxation of the internal variable s occurs by conduction of heat within the sample. Accordingly, we take the differential equation for heat flow, and transform it into an equation involving s. Assuming that the thermal conductivity K_{th} is a scalar (as is the case for cubic crystals) the heat flow equation[†] is

$$dq/dt = K_{\mathrm{th}}\, \nabla^2 T \qquad\qquad (17.2\text{-}1)$$

where the heat q refers to unit volume. Using Eq. (17.1-13) and the conversion $dq/dt = T\, d(\varDelta s)/dt$, Eq. (17.2-1) becomes

$$d(\varDelta s)/dt = D_{\mathrm{th}}\, \nabla^2(\varDelta s - \overline{\varDelta s}) \qquad\qquad (17.2\text{-}2)$$

where D_{th} is the *thermal diffusivity* K_{th}/c_σ.

To separate spatial from time dependences in the variables ε, σ, and s, we follow the method employed by Zener (1938). Each variable is expanded in the form

$$\varepsilon = \sum \varepsilon_n(t)U_n(x, y, z) \qquad\qquad (17.2\text{-}3)$$

$$\sigma = \sum \sigma_n(t)U_n(x, y, z) \qquad\qquad (17.2\text{-}4)$$

$$\varDelta s = \sum \varDelta s_n(t)U_n(x, y, z) \qquad\qquad (17.2\text{-}5)$$

where ε_n, σ_n, and $\varDelta s_n$ are functions of time only, and the position functions U_n are the complete set of orthonormal eigenfunctions obtained as solutions of the equation[‡]

$$\nabla^2 U + \zeta U = 0 \qquad\qquad (17.2\text{-}6)$$

The eigenvalues ζ_n of the parameter ζ are determined by the choice of the boundary conditions in a specific case. The eigenfunctions U_n are, by definition, orthonormal if

$$\int U_k U_l \, dV = \delta_{kl} \qquad\qquad (17.2\text{-}7)$$

[†] For crystals of lower than cubic symmetry the equation is

$$dq/dt = \mathrm{div}(\mathbf{K}_{\mathrm{th}} \cdot \boldsymbol{\nabla} T)$$

where $\mathbf{K}_{\mathrm{th}}$ is now a second rank symmetric tensor. See, e.g., Nye (1957), Chapter 11.

[‡] When K_{th} is a tensor, the eigenfunctions are those which satisfy the equation $\mathrm{div}(\mathbf{K}_{\mathrm{th}} \cdot \boldsymbol{\nabla} U) + \eta U = 0$, subject to the desired boundary conditions.

where the integration is performed over the volume of the sample and δ is the Kronecker delta ($\delta_{kl} = 1$ if $k = l$; $\delta_{kl} = 0$ if $k \neq l$). On substituting Eqs. (17.2-3), (17.2-4), and (17.2-5) into Eq. (17.1-10), multiplying by U_n and integrating over the volume in the manner of Eq. (17.2-7), we obtain

$$\varepsilon_n(t) = J_{\mathrm{U}}\sigma_n(t) + (\alpha T_0/c_\sigma)\,\Delta s_n(t) \qquad (17.2\text{-}8)$$

which is independent of the spatial coordinates. Similar manipulation of Eq. (17.1-12) gives

$$\overline{\Delta s_n(t)} = \alpha\sigma_n(t) \qquad (17.2\text{-}9)$$

Finally, substitution of Eq. (17.2-5) into Eq. (17.2-2) yields, with the use of Eq. (17.2-6) and the condition of orthonormality,

$$d(\Delta s_n)/dt = -(\Delta s_n - \overline{\Delta s_n})/\tau_n \qquad (17.2\text{-}10)$$

where

$$\tau_n^{-1} \equiv D_{\mathrm{th}}\zeta_n \qquad (17.2\text{-}11)$$

It can be seen from Eqs. (17.2-8)–(17.2-10) that each set of variables ε_n, σ_n leads to the equation of the standard anelastic solid, with a δJ given by Eq. (17.1-5) and a particular relaxation time τ_n. The complete relaxation behavior can therefore be represented by a discrete spectrum of relaxation times. To obtain the relative magnitude of each line in the spectrum, we may proceed to calculate the overall internal friction of the sample in terms of the energy dissipated per cycle ΔW_n by each component. For each line in the spectrum we have, with the assumption of small damping [see Eq. (1.5-19)],

$$\frac{\Delta W_n}{2\pi W_n} = \frac{\delta J}{J_{\mathrm{U}}}\frac{\omega\tau_n}{1 + \omega^2\tau_n^2} \qquad (17.2\text{-}12)$$

On the other hand, the total internal friction is given by

$$\tan\phi = \Delta W/2\pi W = (1/2\pi)\sum f_n(\Delta W_n/W_n)$$

$$= \frac{\delta J}{J_{\mathrm{U}}}\sum f_n\frac{\omega\tau_n}{1 + \omega^2\tau_n^2} \qquad (17.2\text{-}13)$$

where we have defined weighting factors f_n by

$$f_n \equiv W_n/W \qquad (17.2\text{-}14)$$

It is clear from the above definition that the weighting factors f_n satisfy the condition $\sum f_n = 1$, and hence that $\{f_n, \tau_n\}$ constitute the distribution function of the discrete spectrum. To put f_n in a form suitable for evaluation, we write the strain energies W_n and W as functions of the corresponding peak strains ε_{n0} and $\varepsilon_0(x, y, z)$

$$f_n = \frac{\int (\varepsilon_{n0} U_n)^2 \, dV}{\int \varepsilon_0^2 \, dV} = \frac{\varepsilon_{n0}^2}{\int \varepsilon_0^2 \, dV} \qquad (17.2\text{-}15)$$

To eliminate ε_{n0} from Eq. (17.2-15) we express Eq. (17.2-3) in the form

$$\varepsilon_0 = \sum \varepsilon_{m0} U_m \qquad (17.2\text{-}16)$$

On multiplying both sides of Eq. (17.2-16) by U_n and integrating over the volume, we obtain

$$\varepsilon_{n0} = \int \varepsilon_0 U_n \, dV \qquad (17.2\text{-}17)$$

which upon insertion in Eq. (17.2-15) gives the final result

$$f_n = [\int \varepsilon_0 U_n \, dV]^2 / \int \varepsilon_0^2 \, dV \qquad (17.2\text{-}18)$$

Equation (17.2-18) may be used to find f_n when $\varepsilon_0(x, y, z)$ and the eigenfunctions U_n have been obtained for a particular case. An example is given in the following section.

17.3   Transverse Thermal Currents

An important case of thermal relaxation under inhomogeneous stress occurs in the transverse vibration of a reed or thin beam. Here the uniaxial strain produced by bending varies virtually linearly with the distance from the neutral axis. In general, therefore, an alternating temperature gradient exists between the opposite faces of a vibrating reed. Relaxation can thus occur by heat flow from the hotter (compressed) layers to the cooler (extended) layers of the sample. This is the situation which Zener termed "relaxation by the flow of transverse thermal currents." If we assume a state of essentially simple bending so that strain is a function only of the transverse distance x from the neutral axis ($x = 0$), then the desired eigenfunctions U_j are those which satisfy the ordinary differential equation

$$(d^2 U / dx^2) + \zeta U = 0 \qquad (17.3\text{-}1)$$

subject to the boundary condition

$$dU/dx = 0 \qquad \text{at} \quad x = \pm a/2 \qquad (17.3\text{-}2)$$

where a is the thickness of the beam. The boundary condition of Eq. (17.3-2) is imposed to represent the situation where no heat is exchanged between the specimen and its surroundings.

The orthonormal eigenfunctions and eigenvalues which satisfy Eqs. (17.3-1) and (17.3-2) are

$$U_n = (2/a)^{1/2} \sin[(2n + 1)(\pi x/a)] \qquad (17.3\text{-}3)$$

and

$$\zeta_n = [(2n + 1)\pi/a]^2, \qquad n = 0, 1, 2, \ldots \qquad (17.3\text{-}4)$$

The fact that these are solutions of Eq. (17.3-1) satisfying Eq. (17.3-2) may be checked by substitution; the orthonormality of the eigenfunctions may be verified by the use of Eq. (17.2-7). Taking ε_0 to be proportional to x, and substitution of Eq. (17.3-3) into Eq. (17.2-18) gives, after evaluation of the integrals

$$f_n = 96/\pi^4(2n + 1)^4 \qquad (17.3\text{-}5)$$

Further, combining Eq. (17.3-4) with Eq. (17.2-11) leads to

$$\tau_n^{-1} = (2n + 1)^2\pi^2 D_{\text{th}}/a^2 \qquad (17.3\text{-}6)$$

The complete expression for the transverse thermal current damping of a reed is thus finally obtained by substituting Eqs. (17.3-5) and (17.3-6) into Eq. (17.2-13) together with the expression $E_U\alpha^2 T_0/c_\sigma$ for the relaxation strength $\delta J/J_U = \Delta_E$. However, it can be seen from Eq. (17.3-5) by evaluating the first few weighting factors f_n ($f_0 = 0.986$, $f_1 = 0.012$, and $f_2 = 0.0016$) that very little error is made by retaining only the first term of the summation, with the result that for practical purposes we may write the thermoelastic internal friction in the simple form

$$\tan \phi \simeq (E_U\alpha^2 T_0/c_\sigma)[\omega\tau/(1 + \omega^2\tau^2)] \qquad (17.3\text{-}7)$$

where

$$\tau = a^2/\pi^2 D_{\text{th}} \qquad (17.3\text{-}8)$$

The above expressions were derived for a reed or beam of rectangular cross section whose thickness is a. For a specimen of circular cross section, such as a wire or rod, Zener (1938a) has shown that Eq. (17.3-7) remains an excellent approximation for the internal friction. However, the expression for the relaxation time is changed to

$$\tau = d^2/13.55 D_{th} \qquad (17.3-9)$$

where d is the diameter of the sample.

Zener (1948) has tabulated the room-temperature values of Δ_E and D_{th} for several metals. For aluminum (a metal of high thermal expansivity and diffusivity), $\Delta_E = 0.0046$, and $D_{th} = 0.88$ cm² sec⁻¹. A reed of aluminum 1-mm thick would exhibit a transverse thermal current peak at about 140 Hz. On the other hand, for tantalum (a metal of low thermal expansivity and diffusivity), the values are $\Delta_E = 0.0003$ and $D_{th} = 0.22$ cm² sec⁻¹. The peak in a 1 mm thick sample of tantalum would appear at roughly 35 Hz. It should be noted that the study of such peaks can only be accomplished by varying ω, since D_{th} (and hence τ) for thermal diffusion does not show the strong (exponential) temperature dependence associated with atomic diffusion.

The first experiments against which Zener's theory of transverse thermal currents could be checked were actually performed before the development of the theory (Bennewitz and Rötger, 1936). These investigators had measured the internal friction of various wire samples in transverse vibration and observed peaks at frequencies which were later shown to be consistent with Eq. (17.3-9) (Zener *et al.*, 1938). A later investigation by Bennewitz and Rötger (1938) on the alloy German silver gave for the most part good agreement between theory and experiment in terms of the location, shape, and height of the peak. Later experiments on α-brass by Berry (1955a) confirmed the theory with even higher precision. The excellent agreement obtained between theory and experiment in this case is shown in Fig. 17-1. From the location of the peak, it is possible to determine the thermal diffusivity D_{th} with considerable precision. This provides an interesting area of application which so far does not appear to have been exploited to any extent. Recently, however, Berry has observed the transverse thermal current peak in a Pd–20 at. % Si alloy produced by splat cooling (i.e., high-speed quenching from the liquid state). There is good evidence that such a treatment produces a glassy rather than a crystalline structure. Interestingly, and in support of this view, it was found that the thermal diffusivity was only 0.05 cm² sec⁻¹, a value about one-fifth the value of comparable crystalline alloys.

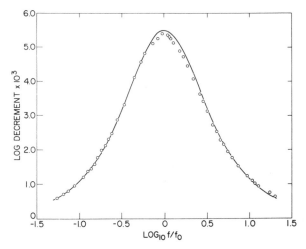

FIG. 17-1. A precise verification of the theory of damping by transverse thermal currents. The measurements were performed on reeds of α-brass; actual frequencies f are divided by the frequency of peak damping f_0. The curve is calculated from the theory with no adjustable parameters. (From Berry, 1955a.)

In closing, it should be noted that the example of relaxation by thermal diffusion across the thickness of a flexed reed bears a close analogy to the Gorsky relaxation considered in Section 11.2. In that case, however, the relaxation is produced by *atomic* diffusion over the thickness of the sample, and consequently may be revealed either by measurements as a function of temperature or frequency.

17.4 Longitudinal Thermal Currents

The propagation of a longitudinal wave through a solid provides another situation in which the thermoelastic effect leads to energy dissipation by the flow of internal currents. If the frequency and velocity of the wave are f and v, respectively, the stress varies sinusoidally with distance in the sample with a wavelength λ given by

$$\lambda = v/f \qquad\qquad (17.4\text{-}1)$$

The problem of calculating the internal friction due to thermal diffusion between the hotter (compressed) and cooler (extended) parts of the solid is analogous to the transverse thermal current problem of the previous section. In the present case the results are even simpler, owing to the sinusoidal variation of stress with distance. This means that all terms beyond the first can be dropped from Eqs. (17.3-3) and (17.3-4), and the behavior is precisely that of a standard anelastic solid. To obtain the relaxation time τ we need observe only that the positions of maximum extension and compression are separated by a distance of $\lambda/2$. Replacing the distance a by $\lambda/2$ in Eq. (17.3-8) gives

$$\tau = \lambda^2/(2\pi)^2 D_{th} \qquad (17.4\text{-}2)$$

In contrast to the usual situation where τ is independent of ω ($= 2\pi f$), comparison of Eqs. (17.4-1) and (17.4-2) shows that we have encountered in this case an example of a relaxation where τ varies as ω^{-2}. As a result, and in contrast to the normal case, it is the low-frequency tail of this relaxation which corresponds to essentially unrelaxed (adiabatic) conditions. This is because λ becomes so large at low frequencies that no appreciable heat flow can occur in one cycle. Combining Eqs. (17.4-1) and (17.4-2), the product $\omega\tau$ is found to be

$$\omega\tau = v\lambda/2\pi D_{th} \qquad (17.4\text{-}3)$$

The critical wavelength λ' for maximum damping (i.e., when $\omega\tau = 1$) is

$$\lambda' = 2\pi D_{th}/v \qquad (17.4\text{-}4)$$

and the corresponding relaxation time τ' is

$$\tau' = D_{th}/v^2 \qquad (17.4\text{-}5)$$

As typical of metals, we may insert $D_{th} = 0.3$ cm^2 sec^{-1} and $v = 10^5$ cm sec^{-1} into Eq. (17.4-5) to obtain $\tau' \simeq 3 \times 10^{-11}$ sec. To achieve peak damping would therefore require an extremely high frequency ($\sim 5 \times 10^9$ Hz) for metals, and even higher frequencies for crystals of lower thermal diffusivity.[†] Consequently, this loss is usually negligibly small in comparison with other losses, even at frequencies as high as 100 MHz. However, results providing one exception to this statement have been quoted by Lücke (1956) in a paper dealing with the theory of this effect in cubic and hexagonal crystals. Lücke has pointed out that, for the case

[†] At sufficiently high frequencies, however, the assumption of local thermodynamic equilibrium implicit in this classical thermoelastic treatment will no longer be valid. Breakdown occurs when the period of oscillation becomes as short as the phonon relaxation time given by Eq. (17.6-11), and relaxation of the phonon distribution must then be considered.

of high frequency wave propagation, the modulus and expansion coefficient to be used in the calculation of the relaxation strength no longer have their normal values. The reason for this is that, at frequencies so high that the wavelength λ is small compared to the transverse dimensions of the sample, the normal Poisson contraction is inhibited. In this limit, the thermoelastic relaxation strength for an isotropic material is approximately six times larger than its value at low frequencies (see Problem 17-3).

17.5   Intercrystalline Thermal Currents

In the previous two sections, we considered examples of thermal relaxation originating from the application of an inhomogeneous stress to a homogeneous sample. We turn now to the thermal relaxation behavior exhibited when a stress is applied to an inhomogeneous polycrystalline aggregate. For a noncubic crystal, the linear coefficient of thermal expansion α is a function of orientation; therefore, under a uniaxial homogeneous stress, the temperature will vary from grain to grain [see Eq. (17.1-4)]. As a consequence, relaxation can occur by the flow of intercrystalline thermal currents. In a cubic crystal, on the other hand, α is independent of orientation. Nevertheless, as Zener has pointed out, this relaxation will occur in cubic materials if the component crystals are elastically anisotropic, for then a given macroscopic stress will produce a different strain in different grains. The constraints requiring that lateral strains at grain interfaces be the same, then lead to the occurrence of fluctuations in the dilatational stress, and therefore in temperature, from grain to grain. Since the strain energy associated with these dilatational fluctuations accounts for only some fraction R of the total strain energy, the relaxation strength Δ_i associated with the intercrystalline loss can be written

$$\Delta_i = R\,\Delta_K = R(3\alpha)^2 TK_U/c_\sigma \qquad (17.5\text{-}1)$$

where K is the bulk modulus and the term 3α represents the volumetric expansion coefficient. The magnitude of the coefficient R depends on the elastic anisotropy of the crystal, as expressed, e.g., in terms of the ratio of the two shear compliances S_{44} and $2(S_{11} - S_{12})$ (see Section 6.2), and also on the degree of preferred orientation of the aggregate. For an isotropic material [$S_{44} = 2(S_{11} - S_{12})$], $R = 0$, and the intercrystalline relaxation vanishes. The low elastic anisotropy of aluminum (also of tungsten) should therefore result in a very small intercrystalline damping loss, a result which has received some support experimentally (Randall and Zener, 1940).

Zener (1948) argues that the factor R may be calculated crudely as the relative mean square deviation of an appropriate elastic constant, e.g., using the compliance E^{-1},

$$R = \overline{(E^{-1} - \overline{E^{-1}})^2}/(\overline{E^{-1}})^2 \qquad (17.5\text{-}2)$$

Values calculated by Zener for various materials are listed in Table 17-1. These values should be more nearly correct relatively to each other than as absolute values. For example, thus far, detailed experimental observations on damping due to intercrystalline thermal currents are available only for α-brass (Randall *et al.*, 1939; Entwistle, 1948). The strength of the relaxation, as estimated from the data of Fig. 17-2, is about an order of magnitude smaller than that calculated from Eq. (17.5-1) with R obtained from Table 17-1.

TABLE 17-1

ESTIMATES OF THE ANISOTROPY FACTOR R FOR SOME CUBIC METALS[a]

Metal	$R \times 10^3$	Metal	$R \times 10^3$
Ag	63	K	150
Al	2.4	Na	160
Au	67	Pb	100
Cu	71	W	0
Fe	40	α-brass	91

[a] From Zener (1948).

Unfortunately, there has been no attempt at a systematic study of this loss mechanism for crystals of lower-than-cubic symmetry, where the factor R could be calculated primarily from the anisotropy of the thermal expansion coefficient.

Turning now to kinetic considerations, it can be seen from Fig. 17-2 that the internal friction varies as a function of frequency f and grain size d through a dimensionless composite variable of the form fd^2/D_{th}. The similarity of this quantity to the ratio f/f_0 used in Fig. 17-1 should be noted. It is clear that in the present case the peak is not symmetrical,

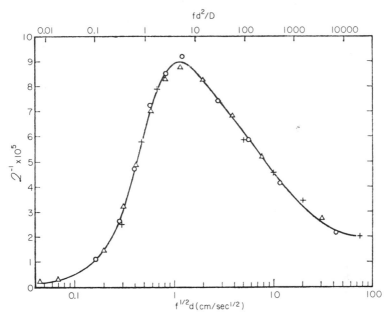

Fig. 17-2.   Internal friction peak associated with intercrystalline thermal currents in α-brass; ($\triangle$) 6000; ($\bigcirc$) 12,000; ($+$) 36,000 Hz. (From Randall *et al.*, 1939.)

and is considerably broader than a Debye peak on the high frequency side. Clearly, the distribution of relaxation times $\{f_n; \tau_n\}$ needed to account for this result must converge much more slowly than Eqs. (17.3-5) and (17.3-6) for the transverse thermal current case. Zener (1948) has emphasized that a rapid decrease of f_n is to be expected only in cases where stress does not induce discontinuous changes (with respect to distance) in the internal variable. In contrast, the intercrystalline relaxation is due precisely to the presence of boundaries across which the stress changes abruptly, and for this case the terms f_n converge much more slowly. Zener has shown that in the high-frequency (adiabatic) limit, the intercrystalline thermal current damping will approach zero as $\omega^{-1/2}$, rather than with the ω^{-1} variation of the standard solid. This can be easily appreciated from the fact that at high frequencies, where the energy dissipation is confined to the vicinity of the boundaries, the magnitude of the internal friction must vary as d^{-1}. (Note that the energy dissipated per unit volume is proportional to d^2, while the stored energy per unit volume is proportional to d^3.) Now, since the internal friction is a unique function of fd^2/D_{th}, the proportionality between $\tan \phi$ and d^{-1} implies that at this limit $\tan \phi \propto \omega^{-1/2}$. On the other hand, in the isothermal limit at low frequencies, the normal linear dependence on ω is preserved. Both types of limiting frequency behavior are verified by the data of Fig. 17-2. Finally, the position of the maximum accords well with Zener's (1940) estimate that the dominant relaxation time τ_1 should be given approximately by

$$\tau_1 = d^2/3\pi^2 D_{\text{th}} \qquad (17.5\text{-}3)$$

which corresponds to

$$f_0 d^2/D_{\text{th}} = 3\pi/2 \qquad (17.5\text{-}4)$$

for the frequency of maximum damping f_0. It may be observed from Eq. (17.5-4) that for rather fine-grained metals ($d \simeq 10^{-3}$ cm) the intercrystalline loss is important in the megahertz frequency range. Exploration of this loss by pulse experiments at these high frequencies would have the disadvantage that the dissipation losses caused by the relaxation would be accompanied by scattering losses of the type discussed by Bhatia (1967, p. 278).

17.6   Interaction of Ultrasonic Waves with Lattice Vibrations: Theory

We now turn to high frequency phenomena involving ultrasonic waves and the way in which they interact with the lattice vibrations of the crystal. The present section will be concerned with the theoretical formulation, while the next section will cover the experimental observations.

A. BACKGROUND

We shall present here a brief review of those features of the theory of lattice vibrations or "thermal phonons" which will serve as background for the material to follow.[†] The reader who wishes to read further on the subject should consult a textbook such as Kittel (1966) or Ziman's (1960) treatise.

Because a crystal is not an elastic continuum, but rather is made up of a discrete atomic lattice, ultrasonic waves of all frequencies cannot be propagated through the crystal. Further, *dispersion* will occur, i.e., the velocity v of a wave having a given polarization and direction is not independent of frequency. An ultrasonic wave may be described by a

[†] It will be assumed, however, that the reader is familiar with the Debye theory.

wave vector **q** whose magnitude is $q = 2\pi/\lambda$ (where λ is the wavelength) and whose direction is the direction of wave propagation. The relation between q and the angular frequency ω is then

$$\omega = vq \tag{17.6-1}$$

Thus, a plot of ω versus q, for waves of a given polarization and propagation direction gives a straight line in the absence of dispersion or departs from linearity as evidence of dispersion. Examples of such dispersion curves for metallic sodium are shown in Fig. 17-3.

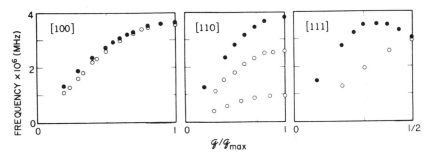

FIG. 17-3. Dispersion curves for Na metal for ultrasonic waves propagated in the three principal crystallographic directions at 90°K, as determined by inelastic scattering of neutrons: (●) Longitudinal; (○) transverse. (From Woods *et al.*, 1962.)

Note that the curves (called "branches") for longitudinal and transverse waves are different, and that there are two transverse waves for ⟨110⟩ propagation corresponding to different directions of polarization (see Section 6.4). In crystals with more than one atom per primitive cell of the lattice there are additional longitudinal and transverse branches for which atoms in the same cell are vibrating against each other. These are the so-called *optical branches*.

From the viewpoint of quantum theory, each vibrational mode of the lattice is a simple harmonic oscillator which may gain or lose energy in units of $\hbar\omega$ ($\hbar \equiv h/2\pi$, where h is Planck's constant). In a manner analogous to the description of an electromagnetic wave as a beam of photons, elastic waves may be represented as quasi-particles called *phonons* having energy $\hbar\omega$ and momentum $\hbar\mathbf{q}$. In thermal equilibrium, the number of phonons present in mode m of frequency ω_m is given by the Planck distribution law

$$N_m = [\exp(\hbar\omega_m/kT) - 1]^{-1} \tag{17.6-2}$$

It can be shown that *elastic scattering* of phonons by a crystal (as in Bragg diffraction) takes place according to the relation

$$\mathbf{q} \rightarrow \mathbf{q}' + \mathbf{G} \qquad (17.6\text{-}3)$$

where $\mathbf{q}$ is the initial and $\mathbf{q}'$ is the final wave vector, while $\mathbf{G}$ is a reciprocal lattice vector of the crystal. This is the form which the law of conservation of momentum takes in a crystal. It states that so long as the momenta of the initial and final phonons differ by $\hbar\mathbf{G}$ the scattering process is an elastic one. On the other hand, a process of *inelastic scattering* by another phonon of wave vector $\mathbf{k}$ within a crystal is described by

$$\mathbf{q} + \mathbf{k} \rightarrow \mathbf{q}' + \mathbf{G} \qquad (17.6\text{-}4)$$

This equation describes a three-phonon interaction process. The case for which $\mathbf{G} = 0$ is called a *normal process* and Eq. (17.6-4) then simply represents the conservation of momentum of the interacting phonons. The case for which $\mathbf{G} \neq 0$ is called an *umklapp process* (from the German *umklappen*, to flip over).

Such phonon–phonon interactions among thermal phonons provide the dominant mechanism for the thermal resistivity (i.e., reciprocal of thermal conductivity) of insulators. In this case, only the umklapp processes contribute. As we shall see ahead, phonon–phonon interactions may also occur between the impressed ultrasonic phonons and the thermal phonons.

The scattering of one phonon by another is a consequence of *anharmonicity*, i.e., the dependence of elastic constants on strain. For, if the crystal showed purely harmonic behavior, two elastic waves acting simultaneously would not change each other, but would simply obey a superposition principle. Only if the strain produced by the first wave changes the velocity of the second can there be interaction effects. Anharmonicity is best described in terms of the *third-order elastic constants* defined by the following expression for the potential energy per unit volume of a strained crystal

$$U = U_0 + \tfrac{1}{2} \sum_{i,j=1}^{6} C_{ij}\varepsilon_i\varepsilon_j + \tfrac{1}{6} \sum_{i,j,k=1}^{6} C_{ijk}\varepsilon_i\varepsilon_j\varepsilon_k + \cdots \qquad (17.6\text{-}5)$$

Here U_0 is the potential energy in the absence of strains, the C_{ij} are the ordinary (second-order) characteristic elastic constants (assuming standard orientation of the crystal, see Section 6.2) and the C_{ijk} are known as the third-order elastic constants. Like the second-order constants, the number of third-order constants is considerably reduced for crystals of high symmetry. Thus, for a cubic crystal, there exist only six independent third-order constants, namely,

$$C_{111} = C_{222} = C_{333}, \qquad C_{144} = C_{255} = C_{366}$$
$$C_{112} = C_{223} = C_{133} = C_{122} = C_{233} = C_{113}$$
$$C_{155} = C_{244} = C_{344} = C_{166} = C_{266} = C_{355} \qquad (17.6\text{-}6)$$
$$C_{123} \quad \text{and} \quad C_{456}$$

all others being zero. The third-order elastic constants may be determined from measurements of the various sound velocities as functions of static stress.

As a consequence of anharmonic effects, the frequencies of the various lattice vibrational modes are changed by strain. Another form for expressing anharmonicity is through these frequency changes, as follows,

$$(\Delta\omega/\omega)_m = -\gamma_m{}^j \varepsilon_j \qquad (17.6\text{-}7)$$

where $(\Delta\omega/\omega)_m$ is the fractional change in frequency for mode m and $\gamma_m{}^j$ is called the *Grüneisen number* for that mode. Clearly, these Grüneisen numbers are related to the third-order elastic constants. It is often convenient to make the rather unrealistic assumption that the mode frequencies are functions of dilatational strain only and that all modes have the same γ. In this case γ, called the *Grüneisen constant*, can be expressed in terms of the Debye temperature Θ_D in the well-known Debye approximation (where $\Theta_D = \hbar\omega_D/k$ in which ω_D is the Debye cutoff frequency and k is Boltzmann's constant). This relation is

$$\gamma = -d(\ln \omega_D)/d(\ln V) = -d(\ln \Theta_D)/d(\ln V) \qquad (17.6\text{-}8)$$

It can then be shown thermodynamically that γ is given by

$$\gamma = 3\alpha K/c_v \qquad (17.6\text{-}9)$$

where α is the linear thermal expansion coefficient, K the isothermal bulk modulus, and c_v the specific heat per unit volume at constant volume. Typical values of γ are in the range 1.2–2.5. This approach, which attempts to describe all anharmonic behavior in terms of a single constant is clearly oversimplified but often useful.

B. Phonon Relaxation (Akhieser Effect)

The idea of an anelastic relaxation process due to thermal phonons was first suggested by Akhieser (1939). He pointed out that an ultrasonic wave passing through a crystal would change the frequencies of the phonon modes and consequently disturb the equilibrium (Planck) distribution of the thermal phonons. The relaxation nature of the process can be seen by considering what happens when a uniform strain is abruptly applied to the specimen. Immediately after application of the strain the various modes will have changed frequencies [in accordance with Eq. (17.6-7)], but the occupation of these modes will be that which was previously in equilibrium [given by Eq. (17.6-2) with the original frequencies]. As time proceeds interaction among the thermal phonons must redistribute the populations to the new state of equilibrium. Such behavior is typical of an anelastic relaxation process. The theory was developed in a simple form by Bömmel and Dransfeld (1960), and in a more detailed form by Woodruff and Ehrenreich (1961), and by Mason and Bateman (1964a). The treatment of Woodruff and Ehrenreich is the most rigorous one, but it gives expressions for the attenuation that are too complicated and contain too many unknowns to allow direct comparison with experiment. Other authors have made simplifications so that the theory would be more tractable; it is these simplified approaches that we will consider here.

Consider a branch of the phonon dispersion curve (see, e.g., Fig. 17-3) given by defining both the polarization and propagation directions, and let us assume that all phonons belonging to the same branch have the same Grüneisen number $\gamma_k{}^j$, where the index k refers to the branch. Since, from Eq. (17.6-7), all frequencies in branch k are changed by the same fractional amount, this means that the form of the distribution given by Eq. (17.6-2) is unchanged, provided that we assign a change in temperature to the branch. This change in temperature ΔT_k is clearly given by

$$(\Delta T/T)_k = (\Delta \omega/\omega)_k = -\gamma_k{}^j \varepsilon_j \qquad (17.6\text{-}10)$$

Since $\gamma_k{}^j$ can be negative, some branches may have $\Delta T > 0$ and others $\Delta T < 0$ for a given strain. The relaxation of the phonon distribution toward equilibrium may then be described, in a formal way, as a *heat flow between branches* in a homogeneously strained matrix.

The resulting expression for the internal friction or for the attenuation is precisely that of the standard anelastic solid. The relaxation time τ is the time for establishment of equilibrium among phonons of different branches. A useful expression for τ is that which relates it to the thermal conductivity K_{th}. Except at very low temperatures, the lattice vibrations may be regarded as a phonon gas, and treated by the kinetic theory of gases, which gives

$$K_{th} = \tfrac{1}{3}c_v v l = \tfrac{1}{3}c_v v^2 \tau_{th} \qquad (17.6\text{-}11)$$

where l is the phonon mean free path, $\tau_{th} = l/v$ is the thermal relaxation time, and v is usually taken as the Debye-averaged sound velocity:

$$3/v^3 = (2/v_t{}^3) + (1/v_l{}^3) \qquad (17.6\text{-}12)$$

v_t being the transverse and v_l the longitudinal phonon velocity.[†] At temperatures above the Debye temperature l, and therefore τ_{th}, varies as $1/T$. Typically, in this range, $\tau_{th} \sim 10^{-12}$ sec, so that $\omega\tau_{th} \ll 1$ for any reasonably attainable frequencies. Further, such values of τ_{th} are much less than the relaxation time for macroscopic flow [see Eq. (17.4-2)]. At very low temperatures $(T \ll \Theta_D)$ the quantity τ_{th} appearing in (17.6-11) is no longer directly correlated with the desired phonon relaxation time. This follows because thermal resistivity unlike the relaxation process, is determined only by umklapp processes, the probability of which decreases very rapidly [as $\exp(-\text{constant}/kT)$] at low temperatures.

Turning now to the magnitude of the phonon relaxation process, Bömmel and Dransfeld (1960) and also Woodruff and Ehrenreich (1961) express the relaxation magnitude in terms of a mean square average Grüneisen constant $\overline{\gamma^2}$. For example, for longitudinal waves they obtain

$$\delta C_{11} = c_v T \overline{\gamma^2} \qquad (17.6\text{-}13)$$

Such a result is to be expected, since the relaxation depends on the magnitude of the anharmonicity of the crystal but not on its sign; therefore, it is anticipated that some type of mean square Grüneisen constant should appear. In Eq. (17.6-13), however, $\overline{\gamma^2}$ serves as a semiempirical constant; it is not the same as the square of the ordinary Grüneisen constant given by Eq. (17.6-8). This approximation, even when $\overline{\gamma^2}$ is taken as an empirical parameter, turns out to be too much of a simplification, however. A more complete expression for the elastic constant C_{jj} (e.g., the longitudinal constant C_{11} or the shear constant C_{44}) takes the

---

[†] Equation (17.6-12) actually applies to an isotropic solid. For crystals there are methods available for determining a suitable average velocity (Alers, 1965).

form of a summation over branches:

$$\delta C_{jj} = T \sum_k c_{v_k} (\gamma_k{}^j)^2 \tag{17.6-14}$$

where c_{v_k} is the specific heat per unit volume associated with the kth branch. Actually Eq. (17.6-14) applies to the case of shear waves for which there is no volume change and therefore no average temperature change during the passage of the waves. For longitudinal waves, where there is a temperature change, the phonon distribution relaxes toward a modified average temperature. This results in the need to subtract a thermoelastic term, $\gamma^2 c_v T$, representing the difference between the adiabatic and isothermal constants (see Problem 17-5). Equation (17.6-14) is not equivalent to (17.6-13) since the various branches of the phonon spectrum are excited in different temperature ranges (i.e., they may be assigned different Debye temperatures). Thus Eq. (17.6-13) cannot strictly apply unless $\overline{\gamma^2}$ is allowed to be temperature dependent.

The attenuation itself is obtained in terms of δC_{jj} and τ_{th}, using Eqs. (1.6-7) and (1.6-8) and the fact that we are dealing with a standard anelastic solid, as follows:

$$\mathscr{A} = \frac{\delta C_{jj}}{2\varrho v^3} \frac{\omega^2 \tau_{\text{th}}}{1 + \omega^2 \tau_{\text{th}}^2} \simeq \frac{\delta C_{jj}}{2\varrho v^3} \omega^2 \tau_{\text{th}} \tag{17.6-15}$$

since $\omega \tau_{\text{th}} \ll 1$.

Mason and Bateman (1964) have attempted to carry the theory further in two ways: (1) They converted Eq. (17.6-14) into a formula involving the thermal energy per unit volume u_k, associated with the kth branch, and then further simplified the expression using the Debye theory. (2) They calculated the coefficients $\gamma_k{}^j$ from the third-order elastic constants. Their approach has given very good agreement between theory and experiment for the case of the Akhieser effect in Si and Ge. It was recently pointed out (Barrett and Holland, 1970) however, that step (1) above is theoretically not justified and that the good agreement between theory and experiment obtained by Mason and Bateman is fortuitous. There is, however, as yet no alternative reliable way to obtain the quantities c_{v_k}. Mason and Bateman's second step, of calculating the Grüneisen numbers from third-order elastic constants, is certainly a useful contribution. Unfortunately, however, the complete set of these constants is only available for a limited number of materials. In other cases (see, e.g., Keck and Sladek, 1970) the $\gamma_k{}^j$ were obtained by fitting of thermal expansion data.

In summary, while the qualitative principles behind the Akhieser effect seem to be well understood, reliable quantitative expressions which can be compared directly to experimental data are still lacking.

C. PHONON–PHONON COLLISIONS (LANDAU–RUMER EFFECT)

Although the above theory of phonon relaxation leads to anelastic behavior corresponding to a standard anelastic solid, the calculation actually breaks down when $\omega\tau \gtrsim 1$ so that, in fact, it only applies to the range of small $\omega\tau$. The difficulty comes about from the original assumption that phonon relaxation takes place within a region of homogeneous stress. This assumption can only be valid when the mean free path l over which phonons travel between collisions is small compared to the wavelength λ of the acoustic wave. In this way the phonons can adjust to the applied stress in a region over which the stress is homogeneous. Since $l = v\tau_{th}$ and $\lambda/2\pi = v/\omega$, the condition $l \ll \lambda$ implies that $\omega\tau_{th} \ll 1$.

In the region where $\omega\tau_{th} > 1$ it is best to use an entirely different approach. (This region generally occurs at very high frequencies or, more conveniently, at very low temperatures.) Under these circumstances it becomes advantageous to treat the acoustic wave as a beam of phonons with well-defined energy and momentum. The attenuation is then regarded as caused by phonon–phonon collision processes in which energy and momentum are conserved. This approach was originally suggested by Landau and Rumer (1937), who took the potential energy of the lattice out to third-order terms in the strains [as in Eq. (17.6-5)]. This means that they were limiting themselves to "three phonon processes" in which an incoming phonon plus one thermal phonon collide to generate a third phonon. Conservation of energy and momentum means that

$$\omega_1 + \omega_2 = \omega_3, \qquad \mathbf{q}_1 + \mathbf{q}_2 = \mathbf{q}_3 \qquad (17.6\text{-}16)$$

The right-hand equation is the same as Eq. (17.6-4), but with $\mathbf{G} = 0$, since umklapp processes are highly unlikely when one phonon is in the low frequency ($<10^{10}$ Hz) range. It turns out from these conservation equations that scattering only occurs for thermal waves having velocities $v_{th} \geq v_{us}$, the velocity of the ultrasonic wave. This condition strongly restricts the collisions of longitudinal ultrasonic waves, because the longitudinal branch always has a higher velocity than the transverse branches (e.g., see Fig. 17-3). Also, in the longitudinal branch, high-frequency thermal phonons have a lower velocity (due to the bending over of the dispersion curves). The above condition on the velocities therefore implies that a longitudinal ultrasonic wave can only interact with longitudinal thermal phonons of relatively low frequency. Transverse ultrasonic waves, on the other hand, may interact with both longitudinal and transverse thermal phonons. For the attenuation of such transverse waves, Landau and Rumer obtained the expression

$$\mathcal{A}_t = (\pi k^4 / 80 \varrho \hbar^3 v_l{}^6) \gamma_t{}^2 [1 - (v_t/v_l)^2] \omega T^4, \qquad \text{for} \quad \omega \tau_{\text{th}} \gg 1 \qquad (17.6\text{-}17)$$

Here ϱ is the density, v_l and v_t are as in Eq. (17.6-12), and γ_t involves the ratio of an appropriate third-order elastic constant to a second-order constant. This result corresponds to an internal friction which is *independent* of ω, thus showing that the behavior no longer corresponds to a conventional anelastic relaxation process.

For longitudinal waves, Landau and Rumer predict a negligible attenuation $\mathcal{A}_l$ for the reasons given above. Since it is experimentally observed that the longitudinal attenuation is of the same order as the transverse attenuation, various authors have sought to improve on the Landau–Rumer approach. Pomeranchuk (1941) and others considered higher-order, i.e., four-phonon, processes while Herring (1954) introduced the effects of elastic anisotropy. Both approaches yield additional contributions to $\mathcal{A}_l$, but still not enough to account for observed losses. More recently (Simons, 1963; Nava *et al.*, 1964; Maris, 1964) the idea was developed that a longitudinal ultrasonic wave could interact with longitudinal thermal phonons in a three phonon process if the mean lifetime of the thermal phonons is sufficiently short. In that case, the Heisenberg uncertainty principle gives $\delta\omega \sim \tau_{\text{th}}^{-1}$, for the uncertainty in the frequency of the thermal phonon. It then turns out that the probability for occurrence of the condition $v_{\text{th}} \geq v_{\text{us}}$ is no longer negligible, and so three phonon interactions may take place. The expression obtained for $\mathcal{A}_l$ is similar to Eq. (17.6-17), but without the bracketed term and with a different anharmonic constant γ_l.

17.7   Interaction of Ultrasonic Waves with Lattice Vibrations: Experiments

The observation of ultrasonic attenuation due to phonon processes has been confined to insulators since in good conductors, electronic effects (see Chapter 19) completely dominate the observations. Experimental work has been carried out primarily on quartz, Al_2O_3, and

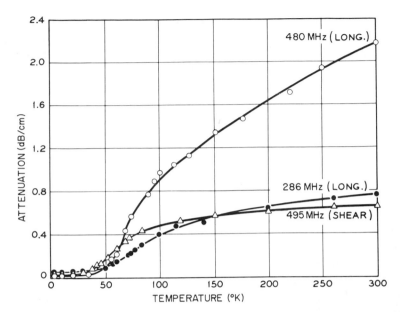

FIG. 17-4. Attenuation of longitudinal and shear waves propagated along a ⟨100⟩ axis in pure silicon. (From Mason and Bateman, 1964a.)

pure Ge and Si crystals. Figure 17-4 shows the attenuation of both longitudinal and shear waves in pure silicon. These curves are typical of data on phonon effects. First, at very low temperatures (below 20°K) the attenuation is small and independent of temperature. This residual attenuation is regarded as a background value, determined by scattering from surfaces and crystal imperfections; it is usually subtracted from the attenuation measured at higher temperatures. Next, above 50°K there is a rapid increase of attenuation with increasing temperature, and finally above 100°K a slower increase. Since dislocations and electronic defects are small in number in these pure crystals, the only source to which this attenuation can reasonably be ascribed is to processes involving thermal phonons. Figure 17-4 brings out several additional features of interest. In the highest temperature range (near room temperature) it shows a frequency dependence very nearly as ω^2, in accord with phonon relaxation theory in the range $\omega\tau \ll 1$. At lower temperatures there is a slower dependence on ω; e.g., at 100°K, $\mathscr{A}$ varies as $\sim\omega^{1.5}$. This change in power law may be attributed to approaching the condition $\omega\tau \sim 1$ where the phonon relaxation theory should break down. The steep temperature dependence at lower temperatures is suggestive of the strong temperature dependence given by the phonon–phonon collision theory, as, e.g., in Eq. (17.6-17). Another feature of this figure is the comparison of longitudinal and shear wave attenuations for the same frequency and direction, showing a much smaller effect for the shear wave at the higher temperatures.

Further verification of the ω^2 dependence in the case of Ge at room temperature is given in Fig. 17-5 which shows data on the variation of attenuation with frequency, from a variety of sources, on a log–log plot. Below 10 MHz, $\mathscr{A}$ varies as ω^{-1}; this was explained by Miller (1963) as a diffraction effect and can be ignored for present purposes. For frequencies >30 MHz, $\mathscr{A}$ varies very nearly as ω^2.

An interesting example of phonon relaxation occurs in ferroelectrics which have the perovskite structure (e.g., $KTaO_3$ and $SrTiO_3$). In such materials it is well established that the ferroelectric transition is related to the instability of a long wavelength transverse optical (TO) mode. Specifically, it is found that the lowest-frequency TO phonon branch near zero wave vector is strongly temperature dependent, with its frequency approaching zero near the ferroelectric Curie temperature. Since

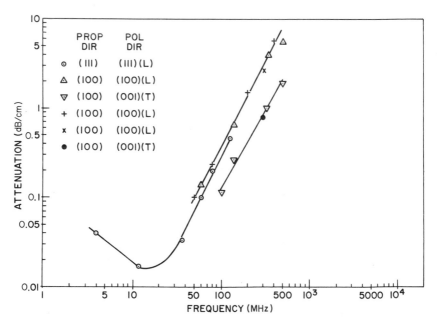

FIG. 17-5. Compilation of data of various authors on ultrasonic attenuation in germanium as a function of frequency. Prop Dir refers to the direction of propagation, Pol Dir to the polarization direction and whether the wave is longitudinal (L) or transverse (T). (From Pomerantz, 1965b.)

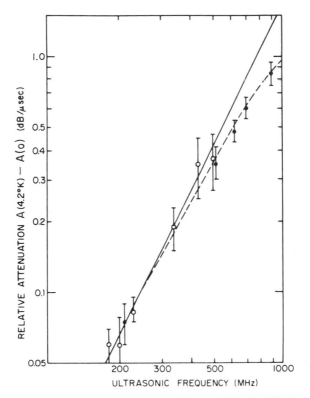

FIG. 17-6. The relative longitudinal attenuation at 4.2°K in KTaO₃ as a function of ultrasonic frequency. Solid curve is $\propto \omega^2$, dashed curve is $\propto \omega^2\tau/(1 + \omega^2\tau^2)$ with $\tau = 1.3 \times 10^{-10}$ sec. (From Barrett, 1970.)

the frequency is related to a restoring force, this TO branch is commonly referred to as the "soft" mode. In most materials, where the important thermal phonons are in the acoustic branches, the condition $\omega\tau \ll 1$ required for the phonon relaxation (Akhieser) mechanism will not be satisfied at low temperatures, as already mentioned. However when a soft optical mode is present, the relaxation times tend to be much smaller than for acoustic modes; the Akhieser description is thus applicable down to much lower temperatures. The behavior of such materials has been reviewed by Barrett (1970). The major anomalous behavior is for longitudinal ultrasonic waves, where the attenuation is very high and shows rapid temperature dependence with a peak at low temperatures. Figure 17-6 shows the frequency dependence of the attenuation for the case of KTaO₃, as measured at 4°K (after subtracting off a background value). It is clear that the frequency dependence of $\mathscr{A}$ obeys Eq. (17.6-15), except that the value of τ ($= 1.3 \times 10^{-10}$ sec) is an order of magnitude smaller than the acoustic-mode relaxation time derived from thermal conductivity at this temperature. These results show that the attenuation cannot be attributed to interactions with acoustic phonons, but they are consistent with the concept of Akhieser-type interactions with the soft optic mode.

Experimental evidence in the Landau–Rumer range for which $\omega\tau_{th} \gg 1$ is given by Pomerantz (1965a) at 9 GHz for a number of different crystals and for various propagation directions and polarizations. Pomerantz generally obtains straight lines in the log–log plots of $\mathscr{A}$ versus T, thus indicating that $\mathscr{A} \propto T^n$, with n values scattering about a mean value of 4. Figure 17-7 taken from his work shows the attenuation of longitudinal waves in various crystals with the slope corresponding roughly

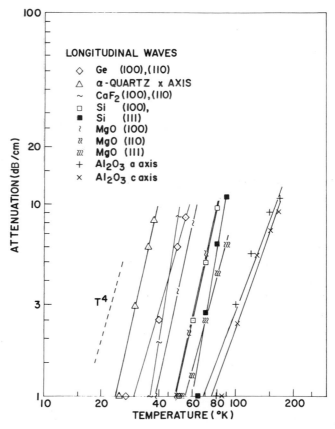

FIG. 17-7.   Attenuation of longitudinal 9 GHz ultrasonic waves in various materials as a function of temperature. (From Pomerantz, 1965a.)

to the T^4 law predicted from three-phonon theories [as in Eq. (17.6-17)]. Pomerantz also compares his results more quantitatively with expressions derived from such theories and obtains good agreement in some, but not all, cases. He also finds an empirical rule, that at 9 GHz $\mathscr{A} = 3$ dB/cm when $T/\Theta_D \sim 0.1$ (where Θ_D is the Debye temperature). This agrees with expectations from the Debye theory that the number of thermally

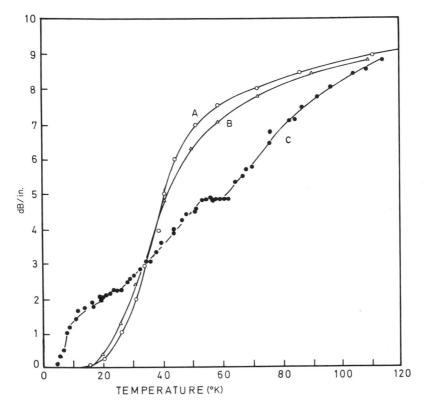

Fig. 17-8.   Effect of neutron irradiation on the ultrasonic attenuation of an X-cut quartz crystal at 1000 MHz. A, before irradiation; B, after irradiation at 10^{18} n cm^{-2}; C, after irradiation at 3×10^{19} n cm^{-2}. (From Bömmel and Dransfeld, 1960.)

excited phonons is a function of temperature through the ratio T/Θ_D. The predicted frequency dependence $\mathscr{A} \propto \omega$ was also verified for MgO and Al_2O_3. More recently, McBride et al. (1969) report that $\mathscr{A} \propto T^9$ for longitudinal waves in pure Al_2O_3 and is independent of frequency, for temperatures in the range 40–60°K. A key point in their theoretical considerations of collisions of the ultrasonic wave with transverse thermal phonons is the necessity to allow for the frequency dependence of the thermal phonon lifetime.

A striking way to see the distinction between the Akhieser ($\omega\tau_{th} \ll 1$) region and the Landau-Rumer ($\omega\tau_{th} \gg 1$) region is through the effects of radiation damage on the attenuation curve, as shown in Fig. 17-8. Since the lifetime τ_{th} of thermal phonons is decreased by collisions with point defects, $\mathscr{A}$ is decreased by irradiation in the Akhieser range where $\mathscr{A} \propto \omega^2\tau_{th}$. In the Landau–Rumer region, on the other hand, the reduction of τ_{th} increases the uncertainty of the phonon energy. In this way more thermal phonons can interact with the applied ultrasonic phonons, so that the attenuation increases.

PROBLEMS

17-1. Show that a tensile stress of 1000 psi applied adiabatically to a bar of copper at room temperature produces a cooling of approximately 0.01°C.

17-2. Consider a noncubic crystal in which a type I stress σ_j is linked to a nonconjugate type I strain ε_i through the compliance constant S_{ij} (e.g., S_{13} in tetragonal crystals). Show that the magnitude of the thermoelastic relaxation is given by

$$\delta S_{ij} = T\alpha_i\alpha_j/c_\sigma$$

Compare this result with Eq. (17.1-5).

17-3. Prove the following relations for the effective Young's modulus E' and linear expansion coefficient α' of an isotropic material which is not allowed to change its lateral dimensions:

$$E'/E = C_{11}/E = (1 - \chi)/(1 - 2\chi)(1 + \chi)$$
$$\alpha'/\alpha = (C_{11} + 2C_{12})/C_{11} = (1 + \chi)/(1 - \chi)$$

where χ is Poisson's ratio. Hence show that if $\chi = \frac{1}{3}$, such a constraint raises the thermoelastic relaxation strength by a factor of six.

17-4. Show that the thermoelastic relaxation strength of a cubic crystal under hydrostatic pressure is $(c_p - c_v)/c_v$, where c_p and c_v denote the specific heat at constant pressure and constant volume, respectively.

17-5. Show that the difference between the adiabatic and isothermal elastic constant C_{11} of a cubic crystal is given by

$$C_{11}^{s} - C_{11}^{T} \simeq \gamma^{2}c_{v}T$$

where γ is the ordinary Grüneisen constant.

Hint: Derive a result similar to Eq. (5.4-6) but without lateral contraction so that α' (Problem 17-3) replaces α. Also use the Grüneisen relation, Eq. (17.6-9), and the fact that the ratios c_{p}/c_{v} and C_{11}^{s}/C_{11}^{T} are $\simeq 1$.

General References

BEYER, R. T. (1969). "Physical Ultrasonics," Chap. 8. Academic Press, New York.

BHATIA, A. B. (1967). "Ultrasonic Absorption," Chaps. 11 and 12. Oxford Univ. Press, London and New York.

KLEMENS, P. G. (1965). In "Physical Acoustics" (W. P. Mason, ed.), Vol. 3B. Academic Press, New York.

TRUELL, R., ELBAUM, C., and CHICK, B. B. (1969). "Ultrasonic Methods in Solid State Physics," Chap. 3, Part VI. Academic Press, New York.

ZENER, C. (1948). "Elasticity and Anelasticity of Metals." Univ. of Chicago Press, Chicago, Illinois.

Chapter 18 / Magnetoelastic Relaxations and Hysteresis Damping of Ferromagnetic Materials

In this chapter we shall discuss the mechanisms of internal friction that are unique to ferromagnetic materials. For the most part we shall be concerned with relaxation processes. However, Section 18.4 consists of a short account of the magnetomechanical hysteresis effects which frequently dominate the loss behavior of these materials. The relaxation phenomena divide into categories associated with (a) eddy currents and (b) directional ordering. Eddy current relaxations may occur on both a macroscopic and microscopic scale and these aspects are treated separately in Sections 18.2 and 18.3. The macroscopic behavior can be discussed without reference to the domain structure of the material. However, this is not the case for the remaining topics of the chapter, and accordingly we shall start with a brief review of the domain theory of ferromagnetism. Readers who desire additional information to that given in Section 18.1 should consult any of a number of well-known texts, some of which are referenced at the end of the chapter.

18.1 Background Review

The spontaneous magnetization developed by a ferromagnetic material below the Curie point is accompanied by a division of the material into an aggregate of domains. Each domain is a volume element magnetized to the saturation intensity $I_s(T)$ in a particular direction, which by definition is different from the magnetization direction in adjacent domains. A sample which in conventional terms is said to be "demagnetized" is thus not actually devoid of magnetization, but rather possesses a domain configuration for which the vector sum of the domain moments is zero. Correspondingly, the progressive "magnetization" of a sample does not involve a change in the saturation magnetization $I_s(T)$, but rather a progressive change in the domain pattern so as to produce a net moment.

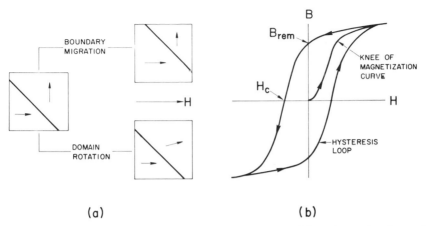

FIG. 18-1. Schematic illustration of (a) the processes of boundary migration and domain rotation, (b) the magnetization curve and hysteresis loop of a ferromagnetic material. The slope of the foot of the magnetization curve corresponds to the initial permeability μ_0.

Magnetization can proceed by two conceptually distinct local processes, namely, boundary migration and domain rotation. These processes are illustrated schematically in Fig. 18-1. In contrast to the structure-insensitive magnetic properties (such as the saturation intensity I_s), an understanding of all structure-sensitive properties must be sought in terms of the behavior of domains. The primary structure-sensitive properties are those concerned with the dependence of the net magnetization **I** (or magnetic induction **B**) on the conjugate variable **H** (the magnetic field). As illustrated in Fig. 18-1 the dominant properties in this category consist of (a) the magnetization curve, which is nonlinear and generally sigmoidal in shape; (b) the hysteresis loop; and (c) various specific quantities such as the initial permeability μ_0, the remanence B_{rem}, and the coercive force H_c.

In general, domain boundary migration is the dominant process in magnetization at low fields while domain rotation takes over above the knee of the magnetization curve. The tendency for the domain magnetization vectors to remain initially in their original directions is a result of *magnetocrystalline anisotropy*, i.e., a variation in the energy of magnetization with crystallographic direction. The energetically preferred direction of magnetization is known simply as the "easy axis" of magnetization and is invariably an axis of major symmetry in the crystal (e.g., $\langle 100 \rangle$ in bcc Fe, $\langle 111 \rangle$ in fcc Ni). In materials with $\langle 100 \rangle$ as the easy axis, the magnetization vectors of neighboring domains may differ in orientation by 90° or 180°. Accordingly the boundaries (or domain walls) are said to be of a 90° or 180° type. For other directions of the easy axis, the relationships of adjacent domains are more complex.

As shown first by the well-known Barkhausen experiment, a smooth change in the applied field produces a change in magnetization that exhibits a fine spectrum of small irreversible jumps (Barkhausen jumps). These jumps correspond to local instabilities in the rearrangement of the domain structure, and provide the microscopic basis for the phenomenon of ferromagnetic hysteresis. A major cause of such local irreversibilities is the presence of internal stresses in the material. The fact that stress interacts with the local domain configuration is of central importance to the present chapter, and provides one manifestation of a magnetoelastic coupling (i.e., a general interrelation between the magnetic and mechanical states of the material). A converse manifestation of this coupling is the phenomenon of magnetostriction, which refers to the dimensional changes which accompany the appearance of the spontaneous magnetization. The component of strain which appears along the direction of the domain magnetization vector is generally denoted by λ_s; its actual value varies with the material considered both in magnitude and sign. For example, the magnetostriction of nickel is negative and relatively large ($\lambda_s \sim -30 \times 10^{-6}$).

The magnetoelastic coupling is responsible for both anelastic relaxation effects and hysteretic internal friction in ferromagnetic materials. The reason for this duality is that, as for an applied magnetic field, a quasi-static applied stress can induce both reversible and irreversible changes in the configuration of the domains. Changes in the configuration which occur linearly and reversibly under a quasi-static stress lead, as we shall see, to the appearance of anelastic behavior under dynamic conditions of stressing. The anelasticity may in this case be said to arise from a magnetoelastic relaxation. On the other hand, a smoothly increasing quasi-static stress can produce, between intervals of reversible motion, sudden irreversible jumps in the local domain configuration. These irreversible jumps (which are analogous to the Barkhausen jumps manifest under an applied magnetic field) are the source of the nonlinear magnetomechanical hysteresis damping. Though this type of internal friction is strictly outside the scope of the book, it is often in practice the dominant source of internal friction in ferromagnetic materials, and in any event provides a background on which the relaxation effects are superposed. For these reasons, it is dealt with briefly in Section 18.4.

It is interesting to note from the above the analogy that exists between the effects of stress on domain walls and on dislocations. In both cases the anelastic effects arise from linear damped motions, whereas the non-linear hysteretic effects are associated with "breakaway" phenomena. The anelastic effects may be discussed separately by restricting attention to vanishingly small stress amplitudes, where the hysteretic effects disappear. The first anelastic effects we shall discuss are those associated with the flow of eddy currents.

18.2 Macroeddy Currents

A stress-induced change in the *net* intensity of magnetization of an electrically conductive sample produces a transient flow of induced eddy currents which retards the approach to equilibrium and leads to relaxation behavior. These eddy currents flow in a path related to the geometry and size of the sample, and are referred to as macroeddy currents, to distinguish them from the microeddy currents which accompany local changes in the domain configuration. To develop a treatment of eddy current relaxation behavior (whether in macro- or microscopic terms), some idealization of the behavior of a ferromagnetic material is necessary. We shall assume that a stress σ or incremental change in the magnetic field **H** will produce, if applied quasi-statically, a thermodynamically reversible change in the magnetic induction of the sample **B**.

As a simple and practical example with which to illustrate the principles involved, consider a long thin rod lying along the z axis and axially magnetized to some intermediate magnetic induction **B**. (For this geometry we may discard the x and y components and write B for the magnitude along the z axis.) Consider now the sudden application of a uniaxial stress σ along the axis of the rod. Immediately, the intensity of magnetization I suffers a stress-induced change [†] and a circumferential eddy current is induced in the sample. The magnitude and direction of the magnetic field produced by the eddy current are such as to prevent a discontinuous change in B. As time proceeds and the eddy current field collapses, B relaxes toward the equilibrium value appropriate to the stress σ. Accordingly, B is the appropriate internal variable with which to describe the relaxation. Furthermore, it should be evident that the unrelaxed modulus E_U can now be written as E_B

[†] The instantaneous change $(\Delta I)_U$ in I is only a small fraction $(1/\mu_r)$ of the change $(\Delta I)_R$ obtained when relaxation is complete. (See Problem 18-1.)

(the modulus at constant B) while the relaxed modulus E_R corresponds to E_H (the modulus for sufficiently slow loading that an eddy current field is not induced). From the strain equation analogous to Eq. (5.1-1),

$$\varepsilon = E_U^{-1}\sigma + (\partial\varepsilon/\partial B)_\sigma \, \Delta B \qquad (18.2\text{-}1)$$

we see that

$$\delta E^{-1} = E_R^{-1} - E_U^{-1} = (\partial\varepsilon/\partial B)_\sigma(\overline{\Delta B}/\sigma) \qquad (18.2\text{-}2)$$

where

$$\overline{\Delta B} \equiv \bar{B}(\sigma) - \bar{B}(0) \qquad (18.2\text{-}3)$$

and the barred quantities refer to equilibrium values. Since it is also clear that

$$\overline{\Delta B} = (\partial B/\partial\sigma)_H \sigma \qquad (18.2\text{-}4)$$

we obtain, from Eqs. (18.2-2) and (18.2-4)

$$\delta E^{-1} = (\partial\varepsilon/\partial B)_\sigma(\partial B/\partial\sigma)_H \qquad (18.2\text{-}5)$$

It should be noted that both partial derivatives in Eq. (18.2-5) depend on the intensity of magnetization of the sample. While it is easily appreciated that each derivative must tend to zero with the approach to saturation, the same is also true but perhaps less obvious for the approach to the demagnetized state. This result can be obtained from the fact that σ and ε are components of a tensor while B is the component of an axial vector; it follows for the most common crystal symmetries that both derivatives in Eq. (18.2-5) vanish in the vicinity of the demagnetized condition, $B = 0$.

It is now our purpose to show that the rate at which B relaxes toward its new equilibrium value is governed by a diffusion equation which is obtained from Maxwell's equations. Neglecting the displacement current, elimination of the electric field from Maxwell's equations by the use of Ohm's law leads to the equation

$$\partial \mathbf{B}/\partial t = -(1/\varkappa_{el}) \text{ curl curl } \mathbf{H} \qquad (18.2\text{-}6)$$

where $\varkappa_{el}$ is the electrical conductivity in mksa units. For the example of the axially magnetized rod, where transverse components of the field and flux are neglected, Eq. (18.2-6) simplifies to

$$\frac{\partial(\Delta B)}{\partial t} = \frac{1}{\varkappa_{el}}\left(\frac{\partial^2}{\partial x^2} + \frac{\partial^2}{\partial y^2}\right)\Delta H \qquad (18.2\text{-}7)$$

where $\varDelta H$ is the field produced by the eddy currents. To express Eq. (18.2-7) solely in terms of B, we write B as a function of H and σ to obtain

$$\varDelta B = (\partial B/\partial H)_\sigma \varDelta H + (\partial B/\partial \sigma)_H \sigma \qquad (18.2\text{-}8)$$

The derivative $(\partial B/\partial H)_\sigma$ represents the quantity known as the reversible permeability of the material. In mksa units this quantity (whose actual value depends strongly on the state of magnetization of the sample) will be denoted by $\mu^* \mu_r$, where μ^* is the permeability of free space in the mksa system and μ_r is the dimensionless reversible permeability of practical interest. Equation (18.2-8) can thus be written

$$\varDelta B = \mu^* \mu_r \varDelta H + \overline{\varDelta B} \qquad (18.2\text{-}9)$$

where the derivative $(\partial B/\partial \sigma)_H$ has been eliminated by the use of Eq. (18.2-4). Combining Eqs. (18.2-7) and (18.2-9) by the elimination of $\varDelta H$, we obtain the diffusion equation

$$\frac{\partial(\varDelta B)}{\partial t} = D_m \left(\frac{\partial}{\partial x^2} + \frac{\partial}{\partial y^2} \right)(\varDelta B - \overline{\varDelta B}) \qquad (18.2\text{-}10)$$

where the flux diffusion coefficient D_m is given by

$$D_m \equiv 1/\mu^* \mu_r \varkappa_{el} \qquad (18.2\text{-}11)$$

The similarity between Eqs. (18.2-1), (18.2-4), and (18.2-10) and Eqs. (17.1-10), (17.1-12), and (17.2-2) for the case of inhomogeneous thermal relaxation should be noted. We may therefore again utilize the method of solution employed in Chapter 17, namely expansion of the variables ε, σ, and B into a complete set of orthonormal eigenfunctions subject to appropriate boundary conditions. (In the present example the boundary conditions are $\varDelta H = 0$ at the surface of the specimen.) As shown in Chapter 17, the response then becomes expressible in terms of a discrete spectrum of relaxation times, and in particular, the internal friction is given by

$$\tan \phi = \varDelta_E \sum_{j=1}^{\infty} f_j [\omega \tau_j / (1 + \omega^2 \tau_j^2)] \qquad (18.2\text{-}12)$$

Zener (1938) has evaluated the constants in Eq. (18.2-12) for the cases of an axially magnetized circular rod in either flexural or longitudinal vibration, and also for a reed of rectangular cross section in flexural vibration. The results can be expressed by rewriting Eq. (18.2-12) in the form

$$\tan \phi = \Delta_E\, g(\theta) \qquad (18.2\text{-}13)$$

where θ is the dimensionless parameter given by

$$\theta \equiv \omega a^2 / D_m \qquad (18.2\text{-}14)$$

and a is either the radius of the circular rod or the full thickness of the reed. For each of the cases mentioned above, the result of Zener's calculations for the function $g(\theta)$ is shown graphically in Fig. 18-2. As a

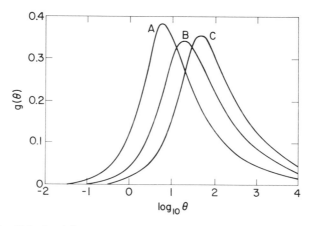

FIG. 18-2.   Calculated form of the internal friction peaks for the macroeddy current relaxation in axially magnetized specimens. A: rod in longitudinal vibration; B: rod in transverse vibration; C: reed in transverse vibration. The parameter $\theta \equiv \omega a^2 / D_m$ where a is the radius of the rod or the full thickness of the reed. [Adapted with correction from Zener (1938b).]

consequence of the summation appearing in Eq. (18.2-12), the peaks tail off more slowly on the high-frequency side than on the low-frequency side. Zener has also given analytic expressions for the asymptotic forms of the curves in Fig. 18-2. In the low-frequency limit the internal friction is given by

$$\tan \phi \propto \theta \propto \omega \qquad (18.2\text{-}15)$$

while in the high-frequency limit

$$\tan \phi \propto \theta^{-1/2} \propto \omega^{-1/2} \qquad (18.2\text{-}16)$$

As discussed by Becker and Döring (1939) and Bozorth (1951), the relations (18.2-15) and (18.2-16) are understandable from the viewpoint of considering directly the energy loss per cycle due to the eddy current dissipation. At low frequencies, where the flux density is essentially uniform over the cross section at any instant of time, the energy dissipated per cycle by the eddy currents rises linearly with frequency. At high frequencies, however, the magnetic skin effect confines the changes in **B** to a thin layer near the surface and the energy loss per cycle then takes the same frequency dependence ($\omega^{-1/2}$) as is shown by the skin depth (see also p. 507).

We turn now to consider the magnitude of the relaxation strength $\varDelta_E$ in Eq. (18.2-12). To this end we first introduce the reciprocity relationship

$$(\partial \varepsilon / \partial H)_\sigma = (\partial B / \partial \sigma)_H \qquad (18.2\text{-}17)$$

where mksa units are again employed. With the substitution of Eq. (18.2-17) into (18.2-5) we obtain

$$\delta E^{-1} = (\partial \varepsilon / \partial B)_\sigma (\partial \varepsilon / \partial H)_\sigma \qquad (18.2\text{-}18)$$

Hence, using the relationship

$$(\partial \varepsilon / \partial B)_\sigma = (\partial \varepsilon / \partial H)_\sigma / (\partial B / \partial H)_\sigma \qquad (18.2\text{-}19)$$

we obtain the alternative forms

$$\varDelta_E = \delta E^{-1} / E_U^{-1} = \mu^* \mu_r E_U (\partial \varepsilon / \partial B)_\sigma^2 = (E_U / \mu^* \mu_r)(\partial \varepsilon / \partial H)_\sigma^2$$
$$= (E_U / \mu^* \mu_r)(\partial B / \partial \sigma)_H^2 \qquad (18.2\text{-}20)$$

Despite the fact that the theory of the macroeddy current relaxation has been available for many years, it appears that an example of this peak has only recently been observed experimentally. In earlier investigations (Köster, 1943; Cooke, 1936; Brown, 1936), the specimens employed had dimensions such that a considerable disparity ($f \gg f_0$) existed between the actual vibration frequencies f and the estimated peak location f_0. Later, Ochsenfeld (1955) studied the separation of magnetic losses over a range of frequencies below f_0, using thin reed samples excited into a series of free–free flexural modes. Measurements over a wide range of frequencies, including the peak frequency f_0, have now been made by Berry and Pritchet, in as yet unpublished work. Their measurements on pure nickel are shown in Fig. 18-3. All the data points represent extrapolations to zero vibration amplitude, so as to eliminate nonlinear hys-

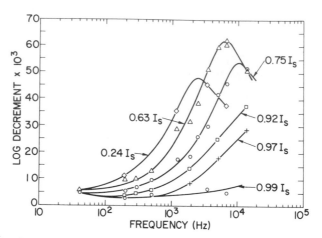

FIG. 18-3.   Internal friction peaks produced by the macroeddy current relaxation in a reed of pure nickel 0.060 in. thick, magnetized to the levels shown. (Unpublished data of Berry and Pritchet.)

teretic losses. The data show that, with increasing magnetization, the strength of the relaxation peak passes through a maximum, while the peak frequency f_0 increases steadily. The existence of a maximum value for the relaxation strength is to be expected from the remarks made below Eq. (18.2-5). The shift in f_0 toward higher frequencies, on the other hand, is due to the increase in D_m which accompanies the decrease in μ_r produced by magnetization [cf. Eq. (18.2-11)]. The strength of the macroeddy current peak is an interesting parameter from a number of viewpoints. For example, it is evident from Eq. (18.2-20) that if Δ_E and μ_r are known for a given magnetization I, the value of the parameter $(\partial B/\partial\sigma)_H$ may be calculated. Actually a more descriptive related quantity is $[\partial(I/I_S)/\partial\varepsilon]_H$, which expresses the change in the fractional magnetization I/I_S per unit applied strain. The maximum value of this latter derivative for the nickel sample of Fig. 18-3 is 0.4. It should be remembered that this value refers to the equilibrium change brought about by the reversible (nonhysteretic) component of the stress-induced change in the domain configuration. A related second quantity of interest is the saturation magnetostrictive strain λ_r which accompanies the reversible component of magnetization. From Eq. (18.2-20) and the definition

$$\lambda_r = \int_0^\infty (\partial\varepsilon/\partial H)_\sigma \, dH \qquad (18.2\text{-}21)$$

it follows that λ_r can be estimated from the variation of Δ_E and μ_r with magnetization. For the nickel specimen of Fig. 18-3, λ_r has been found to be 14×10^{-6}, or approximately 0.4 of the total saturation magnetostriction λ_s.

A final noteworthy aspect of the macroeddy relaxation is the contribution its relaxation strength Δ_E makes to the total "ΔE-effect" of the material. [The "ΔE-effect" is the name traditionally given to the dependence of the modulus E on the magnetization I; see, e.g., Bozorth (1951).] At high frequencies ($f \gg f_0$), Δ_E does not contribute to the measured ΔE and under these circumstances $E(I)$ has a lowest value for the demagnetized state and its highest value E_U for the saturated state. At low frequencies ($f < f_0$) on the other hand, the Δ_E of the macroeddy current relaxation is included in the observed ΔE, and this can lead to the appearance of a maximum in the curve of ΔE versus I. It is this behavior which leads to the *minimum* which has sometimes been reported in the curve of resonant frequency versus magnetization I or applied field H (see, e.g., Ochsenfeld, 1955).

18.3 Microeddy Currents

In the previous section the domain structure of a ferromagnetic material was neglected and the quantities **B** and **H** were treated as macrovariables. As noted earlier, this approach does not give a complete account of the magnetoelastic relaxation behavior, since it ignores the fact that while some stress-induced domain movements may cancel each other as far as the net magnetization and macroscopic relaxation of a sample are concerned, the microeddy current losses associated with each of these local movements do not cancel, but add together to give an additional source of relaxation damping. The microscopic contribution may be seen most clearly in demagnetized samples, where the macroscopic contribution vanishes. The existence of both macro- and microeddy current damping contributions originating from the magnetoelastic coupling may be likened to the macro- and microthermal current damping originating from the thermoelastic coupling. In both cases the calculated macroscopic relaxation is that of a structureless continuum having the same bulk properties as the sample considered. The additional microscopic losses (microeddy currents or intercrystalline thermal currents) reflect the existence of a domain or grain structure in actual samples.

As for the case of intercrystalline thermal current damping (Section 17.5) there is no complete treatment of the relaxation associated with the flow of microeddy currents. It can be expected, however, that the internal friction will follow a relationship formally similar to Eq. (18.2-12), and show a limiting low- and high-frequency dependence of the type given by Eqs. (18.2-15) and (18.2-16). Similarly, the location of the microeddy current peak can be expected in the vicinity of the condition

$$\omega_p \simeq D_m/l^2 \tag{18.3-1}$$

where l is the average linear domain size. For domain sizes of about 10^{-3} cm, it is apparent that the microeddy current peak is a megahertz frequency phenomenon, in contrast to the much lower frequencies usually characteristic of the macroeddy current peak. As a consequence, it can be expected that the low-frequency behavior $\phi \propto \omega$ should persist in this case well into the kilocycle frequency range. Within this range, Becker and Döring (1939) and McColl[†] have calculated the damping associated with the microeddy current loss for various idealized domain models. The results are quite similar and can be expressed as

$$\tan \phi = A\varkappa_{el}I_s^2l^2E_U\omega/\sigma_i^2 \tag{18.3-2}$$

where I_s is the saturation magnetization of the material and σ_i is the amplitude of the internal stress. The value of the dimensionless constant A is in the range 1–3 according to Becker and Döring, and 2–6 according to McColl.

Equation (18.3-2) appears to be in reasonable accord with the experiments of Williams and Bozorth (1941) on the material 68 Permalloy (Fe–68% Ni). Further details of this work have been given by Bozorth (1951, p. 709). Some of the data, taken on demagnetized specimens to exclude macroeddy current damping, are shown in Fig. 18-4. In the cold-worked condition, the internal friction is relatively low and barely sensitive to the frequency of vibration. All magnetic contributions to the internal friction are probably essentially suppressed in this sample, since the high internal stresses introduced by cold-working act to lock the domains in a fixed configuration. In the annealed sample, the zero frequency intercept is larger, which can be accounted for by the appearance of a component of frequency-independent magnetomechanical damping (see Section 18.4). Subtracting out the intercept internal friction from the data leaves a component of internal friction which is proportional to the frequency up to 50 kHz. Assuming this component corresponds

---

[†] Unpublished work quoted by Bozorth (1951, p. 706).

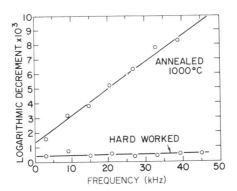

FIG. 18-4. Frequency dependence of the internal friction in demganetized 68 Permalloy. In the annealed specimen the component of damping which is directly proportional to the frequency is attributed to anelastic damping by the flow of microeddy currents. (From Bozorth, 1951.)

to the low-frequency tail of the microeddy current peak, the slope of the experimental line may be set equal to $\pi\phi/\omega$ as given by Eq. (18.3-2). All the quantities in this equation are readily known except for σ_i and l. A value of σ_i may however be estimated from the initial permeability of the sample μ_0 by assuming that μ_0 is controlled primarily by the movement of domains against internal stresses rather than the magneto-crystalline anisotropy forces. It has been shown (see, e.g., Bozorth, 1951, p. 882) that in this case

$$\mu_0 \simeq (8\pi/9)(I_s^2/\lambda_s\sigma_i) \qquad (18.3\text{-}3)$$

where λ_s is the saturation magnetostriction of the sample. Combining Eqs. (18.3-2) and (18.3-3) to eliminate σ_i, Williams and Bozorth obtained the not unreasonable value of approximately 10^{-3} cm for the domain size l.

In later work, Bozorth et al. (1951) carried measurements of the frequency dependence of the damping and dynamic modulus of pure nickel to 150 kHz, while Levy and Truell (1951) and Johnson and Rogers (1952) obtained megahertz data by the pulse method. These measurements have been collated and discussed by Mason (1951, 1953) and are shown in Fig. 18-5. Taken together, the two sets of internal friction data indicate a peak at about the highest frequency (150 kHz) reached by Bozorth et al. Taking this as the frequency of the microeddy current peak, Mason has calculated a value of 0.05 cm for the average domain size, which is compatible with the range of domain sizes (0.02–

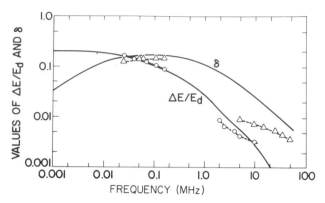

FIG. 18-5.   The microeddy current peak in pure nickel, as compiled from the damping and modulus data ($\triangle$ and $\bigcirc$, respectively) of several workers. The solid curves
show the results of Mason's calculations. (From Mason, 1953.)

0.2 cm) directly observed in nickel by the Bitter pattern technique. To
take account of the existence of a distribution of domain sizes, Mason
has attempted to fit the data of Fig. 18-5 with the aid of an empirical
spectrum of relaxation times. The solid lines of Fig. 18-5 indicate the
fair degree of fit obtained. In the computation of these curves, Mason
included a small high-frequency contribution due to relaxation by domain
rotation, rather than wall motion. The available experimental data are
not sufficient to show clearly whether this refinement is justified or not.
It should also be mentioned that for the purpose of these calculations it
was assumed that the observed modulus difference between the saturated
and demagnetized conditions at frequency ω, namely, $[(E_s - E_d)/E_d]_\omega$,
written simply as $\Delta E/E_d$ in the ordinate of Fig. 18-5, can be taken as a
reasonable measure of the anelastic quantity $[E_U - E(\omega)]/E_R$. In other
words, it was assumed that the stress level of the measurements was
sufficiently small that irreversible changes in the domain configuration
did not contribute appreciably to E_d or to the logarithmic decrement δ.

18.4   Magnetomechanical Hysteresis Damping

In the two previous sections, the quasi-static application of a stress
to a ferromagnetic material was taken to produce proportional and
reversible changes in the domain configuration. In that case, the stress–
strain loop at zero frequency is a straight line whose slope corresponds
to the relaxed modulus M_R. The absence of energy dissipation is shown
by the fact that zero area is enclosed by the stress–strain loop. As pointed

out at the beginning of this chapter, real ferromagnetic materials do not behave in this way except in the limit of a vanishingly small applied stress. The irregular internal stress pattern built into a ferromagnetic material either by magnetostriction alone, or augmented by the presence of a dislocation network or precipitates, causes the large-scale movement of domains to occur partly by a series of irreversible jumps. For this reason, at stresses well below those for conventional plastic deformation, the cyclic stress–strain loop of a ferromagnetic material exhibits a magnetomechanical hysteresis behavior. The similarity of this behavior to the hysteresis exhibited in a magnetization loop can be seen most clearly by plotting, as in Fig. 18-6, just the nonelastic or magnetostrictively produced component ε_λ of the strain against stress σ, rather than the total strain $\varepsilon = (\varepsilon_{el} + \varepsilon_\lambda)$ against σ. By analogy with magnetic terminology, the magnetomechanical hysteresis loop can be described in terms of such quantities as the saturation and remanent strains, and a magnetomechanical coercive force. It should be apparent that $(\varepsilon_\lambda)_{sat}$ is intimately related to the saturation magnetostriction λ_s. Just as the area of the I–H loop represents ΔW_H, the energy dissipated per unit volume per cycle by irreversible domain movements induced by an applied magnetic field, the area of the magnetomechanical ε–σ loop represents ΔW_σ, the net work expended per unit volume per cycle by the applied stress. In

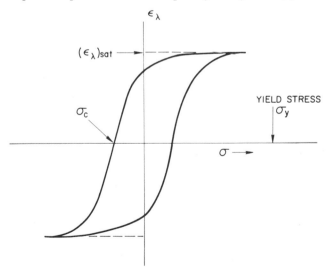

FIG. 18-6.   Illustration of the hysteresis between stress and the magnetostrictive strain component ε_λ, for excursions below the yield stress σ_y. The loop shown is for a material with a small magnetomechanical coercive force σ_c, so that a stress below σ_y produces saturation of ε_λ.

terms of ΔW_σ, the magnetomechanical damping ϕ_h can be written

$$\phi_h = \Delta W_\sigma / 2\pi W \tag{18.4-1}$$

where W is the maximum strain energy density, $\sigma_0^2/2M$ or $M\varepsilon_0^2/2$. It is emphasized that ϕ_h has an essentially frequency-independent hysteretic origin, and is not produced by a relaxation process.

At *low* values of H or σ, there appears to be a close analogy between the way the susceptibility $\chi \equiv I/H$ and ΔW_H vary with H, and the way $J = M^{-1} \equiv \varepsilon_0/\sigma_0$ and ΔW_σ vary with σ_0. It is well known in ferromagnetism [see, e.g., Bozorth (1951)] that at low fields many materials obey the "Rayleigh relations"

$$\chi = \chi_0 + \alpha H \tag{18.4-2}$$

$$\Delta W_H = \tfrac{4}{3}\alpha H^3 \tag{18.4-3}$$

where χ_0 is the initial susceptibility and α is a magnetic hysteresis coefficient. Analogous expressions for the mechanical case are

$$M^{-1} = M_0^{-1} + \beta\sigma_0 \tag{18.4-4}$$

$$\Delta W_\sigma = \tfrac{4}{3}\beta\sigma_0^3 \tag{18.4-5}$$

where β is a mechanical hysteresis coefficient. Substitution of the foregoing relationships for W and ΔW_σ into Eq. (18.4-1) leads to the expressions

$$\phi_h = (4/3\pi)\beta M\sigma_0 = (4/3\pi)\beta M^2\varepsilon_0 \tag{18.4-6}$$

According to Eq. (18.4-6), ϕ should vary linearly with the vibration amplitude, a behavior which is in fact commonly observed at low stress levels. The amplitude dependence of both the internal friction and the dynamic modulus was studied by Förster and Köster (1937a) for a series of iron–nickel alloys. By eliminating β from Eqs. (18.4-4) and (18.4-6), we obtain the equation

$$(1/M)(dM/d\varepsilon_0) = -(3\pi/4)(d\phi_h/d\varepsilon_0) \tag{18.4-7}$$

which was shown by Kornetski (1938) to be in good accord with the results of Förster and Köster. Kornetski (1943) has also given estimates of the magnitude of ϕ_h. Based on a calculation of the change of remanent magnetization with stress via the movement of 90° domain boundaries against internal stresses, Kornetski derived the expression

$$\phi_h \simeq (243/128\pi)(\alpha|\lambda_s|^3 E^2\varepsilon_0/I_s^3) \tag{18.4-8}$$

Cochardt (1959) has found satisfactory agreement between this expression and the very large magnetomechanical damping exhibited by the specially developed cobalt-base alloy Nivco 10. It should be noted from Eq. (18.4-8) that much of the observed structure sensitivity and temperature dependence of ϕ_h can be attributed to its dependence on the magnetic hysteresis coefficient α. Bibliographies on work in this area have been given in the reviews of Bozorth (1951), Cochardt (1959), and Kneller (1962). Equation (18.4-8) also indicates that ϕ_h should depend markedly on the saturation magnetostriction λ_s. This is borne out by Förster and Köster's measurements on the iron–nickel alloys. Here, λ_s varies strongly with composition and the internal friction passes through a well-defined minimum at the approximate composition Ni–20% Fe, where λ_s passes through zero.

At higher vibration amplitudes than those discussed so far, the proportionality between ϕ_h and σ_0 as given by Eq. (18.4-6) must be expected to break down for the reason that ΔW_σ then no longer obeys Eq. (18.4-5). Indeed, if the material is strong enough and the magnetomechanical coercive force is small enough to realize saturation of the magnetomechanical hysteresis loop (as shown in Fig. 18-6), ΔW_σ reaches a saturation value and becomes independent of σ. At this point Eq. (18.4-1) shows that ϕ_h should have a maximum value and should subsequently decrease as the inverse square of the vibration amplitude. The appearance of such a maximum has been observed by a number of workers in a variety of materials (e.g., Boulanger, 1949; Sumner and Entwistle, 1959). An example is shown in Fig. 18-7. The predicted inverse square decrease is not however generally well obeyed. For the case of two iron alloys, Smith and Burchak (1968) have shown that the more linear decrease actually observed can be well accounted for by a generalization of the internal stress model which takes account of a distribution of internal stresses in the material. [For further development of this model, see Smith and Burchak (1969, 1970).] On the other hand, Roberts and Barrand (1967, 1969b) have obtained evidence [see also Burdett et al. (1970)] that the internal stress distribution is not always the dominant factor in determining the magnitude of the magnetomechanical damping. In Ni–20% Fe, for example, the results suggest that at temperatures below 150°C the magnetocrystalline anisotropy energy takes over as the major factor which governs the magnitude of stress–induced changes of the domain configuration.

Finally, it may be noted that the magnetomechanical damping loss can be expected to remain independent of the frequency of vibration

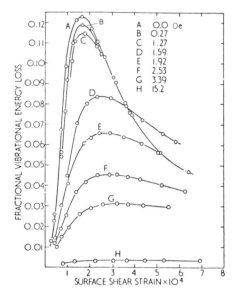

FIG. 18-7.   Dependence of damping on strain amplitude for high-purity iron, show-ing the maximum associated with saturation of the magnetostrictive component of strain. The sequence of curves A–H illustrates the progressive elimination of the magnetoelastic coupling by axial magnetization in a field of up to 15.2 Oe. (From Sumner and Entwistle, 1959.)

until the periodic time of vibration becomes short enough to be com-parable with the time for an irreversible domain jump. Since this time is determined in part at least by the drag imposed by microeddy current generation, it appears that ϕ_h should start to decline at frequencies com-parable with those for the appearance of the microeddy current peak discussed in the previous section. Frequency independence should there-fore be a characteristic of magnetomechanical damping only up to a frequency of about 100 kHz.

18.5   Magnetoelastic Relaxation and Directional Order

In this section we return to the category of relaxation phenomena and consider how magnetically induced directional ordering can lead to thermally activated magnetoelastic relaxation behavior. To start with, in nearly random or at least partially disordered ferromagnetic alloys, there is ample evidence for the existence of a coupling between magnetiza-tion and the equilibrium state of short-range order. Since magnetization is a directional quantity, the coupling is such that the equilibrium atomic arrangement in each domain exhibits a degree of directional ordering (Graham, 1959; Rathenau, 1959; Slonczewski, 1963; Chikazumi and Graham, 1969). In general, it can be expected that such ordering will be accompanied by a strain, as in fact has been demonstrated for the case of C or N in α-Fe by De Vries et al. (1959). [†] In this section we shall however ignore this effect and assume for simplicity that the magneto-strictive component of the strain produced when an applied stress displaces a domain boundary is large compared with the strain which could be produced by subsequent magnetic ordering in the volume swept through by the domain boundary. In what follows, we shall consider first how magnetic directional ordering introduces a relaxation behavior into the movement of domain boundaries. Imagine a volume element to be suddenly cooled through the Curie point so that it becomes ferromagnetic, and subdivides into domains with 90° boundaries. Initially directional order is absent, but this now proceeds to develop with a mean time constant τ_m. Since the ordering proceeds in different directions on either side of the boundary, the ordering creates a potential energy well for the domain boundary, which tends to stabilize its position with respect to small displacements. This progressive domain boundary stabilization can be studied as a time decrease of the initial susceptibility (also known as magnetic disaccommodation), or more completely, by experiments which show that the weak field ac susceptibility becomes a complex quantity with frequency-dependent real and imaginary parts. The frequency dependence arises because the directional ordering is a relaxation process. The mean relaxation time τ_m will of course be strongly temperature dependent, since thermally activated atom movements are required to produce a change of order. If the applied ac field is of such a low frequency ω that $\omega\tau_m \ll 1$, ordering can keep pace with the movement of the boundary. The potential well then moves along in phase with the boundary motion and the system is always effectively in equilibrium. By analogy to our anelastic terminology, the susceptibility in this case could be called the relaxed susceptibility χ_R. If $\omega\tau_m \gg 1$, on the other hand, there is no time for the diffusion needed to enable the energy well to move, and the oscillating boundary has to move up and down the

---

[†] It is interesting to note in passing that in this case the ordering strain is of opposite sign to the magnetostrictive strain, indicating a depopulation of those sites in the magnetostrictively elongated direction. De Vries et al. have suggested that this may result from the iron atoms being elongated in the direction of magnetization, with an attendant restriction of the space between them in this direction.

sides of the fixed energy well. The susceptibility then has its unrelaxed value χ_U. For both of these extremes the magnetization change occurs in phase with the field and χ_R and χ_U are both real. Between these extremes, however, the motion of the boundary is subject to a drag imposed by the lagging out-of-phase motion of the potential well. The magnetization then exhibits an out-of-phase component (with respect to the field) which rises to a peak value when $\omega\tau_m = 1$, with a corresponding variation being shown by the energy dissipation per cycle. A review of experimental work in this area on a variety of alloys has been given by Kneller (1962) and Rathenau and De Vries (1969).

In the above description of how directional magnetic ordering leads to the diffusion-controlled motion of domain boundaries, it was imagined that a magnetic field was used to move the boundary. By virtue of the magnetoelastic coupling, however, such motion can also be induced by stress. Since the motion of the boundary is now diffusion controlled by the magnetic directional ordering process, the accompanying magneto-strictive component of the strain is also diffusion controlled and the material behaves anelastically. Examples of relaxation behavior attribut-able to this mechanism have been studied by Maringer (1960, 1961) and by Fischbach (1962). Data for an Fe–17 at. % Al alloy, as measured in a torsion pendulum at 1.3 Hz, are shown in Fig. 18-8. With a saturating magnetic field (curve A), the internal friction exhibits a Zener peak at about 520°C and a smaller peak at about 120°C, which was thought to be the Snoek peak produced by carbon impurity. In the demagnetized condition, the internal friction exhibits an amplitude-dependent mag-netomechanical contribution which Fischbach removed from the data by extrapolating all measurements to zero amplitude (curve B). The difference curve, B minus A, shows the presence in the demagnetized condition of two magnetoelastic relaxation peaks, one located somewhat above the Snoek peak and the other somewhat above the Zener peak. Though measurements at different frequencies showed that the activation energy for the high-temperature magnetoelastic peak was approximately the same as that for the Zener relaxation (2.43 eV), Fischbach was unable to determine whether the difference in peak temperatures was due principally to a small difference in activation energy, or to a difference in the preexponential factor τ_0.

In unpublished work, B. S. Berry has also found a similar magneto-elastic relaxation peak (at 670°C for 1 Hz) in a sample of a commercial Fe–28% Co alloy. In contrast to the Fe–Al alloys, this alloy did not exhibit a detectable Zener relaxation.

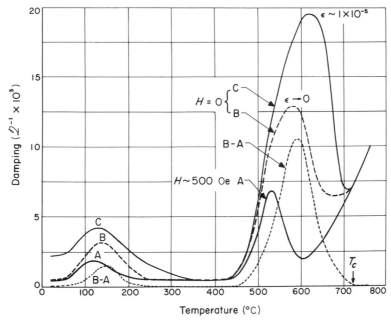

FIG. 18-8. Internal friction behavior of the ferromagnetic alloy Fe–17 at. % Al ($f = 1.3$ Hz). Curve A shows the damping of nonmagnetic origin, as measured in a saturating field. Curve C is for zero field and a strain amplitude of 1×10^{-5}; curve B shows the zero-field behavior extrapolated to zero strain amplitude. The magnetoelastic relaxation behavior is shown by the difference curve (B − A). (From Fischbach, 1962.)

Problems

18-1. In the mksa system of units $B = I + \mu^* H$ and $B = \mu^* \mu_r H$ (where the corresponding vector quantities are assumed to be parallel). If $B = B(\sigma, H)$ and $dB = 0$ (as is appropriate to the unrelaxed condition), show first that $(\partial H / \partial \sigma)_U = -(1/\mu^* \mu_r)(\partial B / \partial \sigma)_R$, where U and R denote unrelaxed and relaxed quantities. Use this result to help obtain the relation $(\partial I / \partial \sigma)_U = (1/\mu_r)(\partial I / \partial \sigma)_R$. Note that this proves the statement made in the footnote on p. 527.

18-2. Derive the reciprocity relationship Eq. (18.2-17), starting with the thermodynamic function $u - \sigma \varepsilon - Ts - HB$. Note that if cgs units were used, the last term would be written $HB/4\pi$ and the reciprocity relationship would become $(\partial \varepsilon / \partial H)_\sigma = (1/4\pi)(\partial B / \partial \sigma)_H$. Also show that in cgs units the flux diffusion coefficient D_m is given by $10^9 \varrho / 4\pi \mu_r$ cm^2 sec^{-1} if ϱ is the resistivity of the material in ohm-cm.

General References

BERKOWITZ, A. E., and KNELLER, E. (1969). "Magnetism and Metallurgy," Vols. 1 and 2. Academic Press, New York.

BOZORTH, R. M. (1951). "Ferromagnetism." Van Nostrand-Rheinhold, Princeton, New Jersey.

BRAILSFORD, F. (1966). "Magnetic Materials." Methuen, London.

CHIKAZUMI, S. (1964). "Physics of Magnetism." Wiley, New York.

KNELLER, E. (1962). "Ferromagnetismus." Springer-Verlag, Berlin.

Chapter 19 / Electronic Relaxation and Related Phenomena

In this chapter we consider the interaction of an applied stress with the electronic configuration of a crystal. In view of the fact that the electronic structure is very different for metals, semiconductors, and insulators, it should be no surprise that to understand the relaxation effects in each of these crystal types requires substantially different concepts. In a metal we are concerned with the behavior of a nearly free electron gas. In semiconductors, on the other hand, we become involved with the relatively small number of electrons or holes which are present intrinsically or are introduced by impurities in the crystal. Finally, in an insulator, only electrons which are bound to particular impurity or defect sites in the crystal can give rise to relaxation processes.

19.1 Interaction of Ultrasonic Waves with Electrons in Metals

In metals, ultrasonic attenuation occurs as a consequence of the interaction of the incoming ultrasonic wave (or phonons) with the "electron gas" of the metal. These effects, which are most prominent at very low temperatures and for rather high purity metals, were first observed by Bömmel (1954) and independently by MacKinnon (1955). They show up most strikingly for metals like tin or lead which are superconductors at the lowest temperatures. For example, Fig. 19-1 shows that the attenuation for tin is rather large above the critical temperature T_c for superconductivity, below which it falls off very rapidly, but not discontinuously. The fact that the attenuation is caused by the conduction electrons is demonstrated by the fact that application of a magnetic field sufficient to destroy the superconductivity causes the attenuation below T_c to increase to values which lie on the extrapolation of data from above T_c.

The behavior of metals in the superconducting state is a subject of great interest, but is not of relevance here. Suffice it to say that the shape

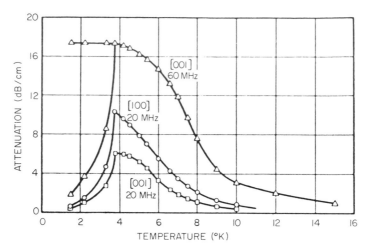

FIG. 19-1.   Longitudinal wave attenuation for tin single crystals along [100] and and [001] axes, and at two frequencies. The superconducting transition occurs at 3.7°K. For the uppermost curve, data are also obtained in the normal state extended down to 1.5°K with the aid of a magnetic field. (From Mason and Bömmel, 1956.)

of the attenuation versus T curve below T_c can be explained qualitatively by the "two-fluid" model, where only the "normal" electrons are scattered by the lattice and therefore interact with the incoming wave, while "super" electrons do not. A more quantitative interpretation has also been given in terms of the celebrated BCS theory of superconductivity (Morse and Bohm, 1957). According to this theory, below T_c the electron distribution of states shows an energy gap ε_g whose magnitude is a strong function of temperature. It can be shown that the ratio of attenuation of longitudinal ultrasonic waves in the superconducting state $\mathscr{A}_s$ to that in the normal state $\mathscr{A}_n$ is given by

$$\mathscr{A}_s/\mathscr{A}_n = 2/[\exp(\varepsilon_g/2kT) + 1]$$

Clearly, attenuation measurements provide a means of measuring $\varepsilon_g(T)$.

The level of attenuation of a superconductor at temperatures well below T_c is a measure of the background losses due to sources other than electrons, e.g., scattering by grain boundaries and other imperfections.

Before considering the various phenomena involving interaction of ultrasonic waves with electrons, we will review briefly the theory of electrons in metals. Further details may be obtained from any standard textbook on the subject [see, e.g., Ziman (1965)].

A. REVIEW OF THE THEORY OF ELECTRONS IN METALS

The electrons in a metal form a highly degenerate gas which obeys Fermi–Dirac statistics. The quantum state of an electron is designated by a wave vector $\mathbf{k}_e$, such that the magnitude is $k_e = 2\pi/\lambda_e$, where λ_e is the electron wavelength, and the direction of $\mathbf{k}_e$ is the propagation direction of the electron wave in the crystal. Only discrete values of the three components k_x, k_y, and k_z of $\mathbf{k}_e$ are allowed, and these allowed $\mathbf{k}_e$ values form a network of points in k space (where k_x, k_y, and k_z are plotted as coordinates). Surfaces of constant energy may be plotted in k space. At absolute zero, all states in k space are fully occupied up to an energy E_F (called the *Fermi energy*), in accordance with the Pauli exclusion principle. The surface in k space of energy E_F, called the *Fermi surface*, represents one of the most important electronic characteristics of a given metal. For finite temperatures ($T > 0$) the probability that a state of energy E is occupied is given by the Fermi–Dirac distribution function

$$f(E) = \{\exp[(E - E_F)/kT + 1]\}^{-1} \qquad (19.1\text{-}1)$$

Only states within a range $\sim kT$ of the Fermi energy have a probability of occupation which is appreciably different from 0 or 1. Since for ordinary temperatures, $kT \ll E_F$, the "fuzziness" at the Fermi surface is very slight.

In the case of essentially free electrons (i.e., moving in a constant potential field), the momentum at the Fermi surface is given by $\mathbf{p} = \hbar\mathbf{k}_e$ and the Fermi surface is a sphere at which

$$E_F = mv_F{}^2/2 = p_F{}^2/2m = \hbar^2 k_F{}^2/2m \qquad (19.1\text{-}2)$$

where k_F, v_F, and p_F are values taken at the Fermi surface, m is the electron mass, and $\hbar$ is Planck's constant divided by 2π. Such a simple Fermi surface is obtained approximately only in alkali metals. In this case, the mean electron kinetic energy is given by

$$\bar{E} = (3/5)E_F \qquad (19.1\text{-}3)$$

For a more realistic picture of electrons in metals, the periodic potential of the lattice must be taken into account. This leads to discontinuities in the curve of E versus k_e for a given propagation direction at surfaces in k space which bound polyhedra called *Brillouin zones*. The Brillouin zone boundaries are simply values of $\mathbf{k}_e$ which obey the Bragg diffraction

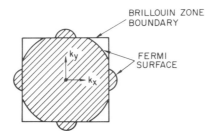

BRILLOUIN ZONE
BOUNDARY

FERMI
SURFACE

FIG. 19-2. Schematic illustration of the Fermi surface and Brillouin zone boundaries of the type characteristic of a simple divalent metal.

condition, so that electron waves cannot be propagated at those $\mathbf{k}_e$ values. For a simple cubic metal of lattice spacing a, for example, the first Brillouin zone is a cube of dimension $2\pi/a$ in k space.

The Fermi surface of a real metal may be quite complex. For example, in the case of a divalent metal, the Fermi surface will contact the Brillouin zone boundaries and even be made up of several unconnected pieces, some inside the first zone and some outside. An illustration in two dimensions is shown in Fig. 19-2.

B. ATTENUATION WITHOUT MAGNETIC FIELD

The conduction electrons in a metal have been viewed (Mason, 1955a) as forming an effective viscous medium with viscosity η given by kinetic theory, as

$$\eta = \tfrac{1}{3}N_v m l \bar{v} \tag{19.1-4}$$

where N_v is the number of electrons per unit volume, l their mean free path, m their mass, and $\bar{v}$ their average velocity. As a result of this viscosity, an ultrasonic wave transfers momentum and energy to the electron gas, and thereby suffers attenuation. More generally, however, one can view the effect as a relaxation of the electronic distribution in the metal (Morse, 1955; Kittel, 1955). This approach, which is closely analogous to the theory of the Akhieser effect (Section 17.6) gives the same expression as the viscosity viewpoint, but is more readily generalized to cases where electrons are not free.

According to this viewpoint, the presence of a shear stress due to a transverse ultrasonic wave must distort the Fermi surface. In the case of free electrons, and if stress is applied so quickly that there is no time for electrons to redistribute themselves, the Fermi surface which was initially spherical becomes an ellipsoid. Such a distortion cannot represent the equilibrium electronic distribution, since some electrons within the distorted Fermi surface are now in states of higher energy than some of the empty states. Reestablishment of a spherical surface can occur, however, by means of collisions of electrons with the lattice (i.e., interaction with thermal phonons or lattice defects) which occur in a mean time τ given by

$$\tau = l/v_F \qquad (19.1\text{-}5)$$

where l is the mean free path of electrons and v_F the Fermi velocity given by Eq. (19.1-2). The quantity τ is then the relaxation time for the electronic distribution to come to equilibrium. This attempt of the electron distribution to adjust to stress-induced distortions of the Fermi surface by means of collisions with the lattice clearly causes the metal to behave as a standard anelastic solid with a relaxation time τ. Since the same quantity τ appears in the theory of the electrical conductivity, $\varkappa_{el}$, of metals in the form (Ziman, 1965)

$$\varkappa_{el} = N_v e^2 \tau / m \qquad (19.1\text{-}6)$$

it is convenient to calculate τ from the measured electrical conductivity.

In order to calculate the magnitude of the relaxation of the modulus δM the following argument [suggested by Pippard (1960a, p. 245)] may be used. Imagine a sample of metal suddenly sheared, as in Fig. 19-3a, by the application of the system of stresses as shown. If free electrons are still assumed, the initially spherical Fermi surface is distorted into an ellipsoidal shape, as shown in Fig. 19-3b which represents k space. Since the eigenvalues for the free electron gas in a box are $k_x = 2n_x\pi/L_x$ (where n_x is an integer and L_x is the dimension of the box in the x direction) and similarly for the y and z directions, then if the x and y sides of the square shown in Fig. 19-3 are multiplied respectively by $1 \mp \delta$, the axes

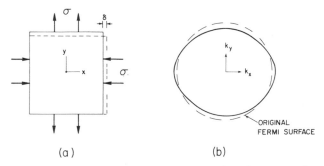

(a)   (b)

FIG. 19-3. (a) Distortion of a sample by the application of a system of stresses which gives rise to pure shear deformation. (The original shape is shown by the dashed lines.) (b) Corresponding instantaneous distortion of the Fermi surface which was originally a sphere.

of the ellipse in Fig. 19-3b must be proportional to $1 \pm \delta$. As already mentioned, the ellipsoidal shape is not the equilibrium form of the Fermi surface, so that electron–lattice collisions will reestablish the spherical form with a relaxation time τ. Now, the work done by the stress system σ acts against the lattice forces *plus* the pressure created by collisions of electrons with the boundaries of the sample. Under equilibrium (i.e., relaxed) conditions, this pressure is given by the well-known expression of kinetic theory as $(1/3)N_v m\overline{v^2}$, where $\overline{v^2}$ is the mean square electron velocity. For a Fermi gas this becomes $\frac{1}{5}N_v m v_F^2$, in view of Eq. (19.1-3). For the unrelaxed condition, corresponding to the ellipsoidal Fermi surface, the electronic pressures on the surfaces normal to x and y are unequal and, in fact, are given respectively by $\frac{1}{5}N_v m v_F^2(1 \pm 2\delta)$. This result follows from Eq. (19.1-2) and the fact that $(k_F)_x$ and $(k_F)_y$ are $\propto (1 \pm \delta)$, respectively. Accordingly, the external stress to produce deformation is larger than for the relaxed case by $\frac{2}{5}N_v m v_F^2\delta$. Now, it is easily shown that the shear angle in Fig. 19-3a is 2δ, so that we obtain for the relaxation of the modulus this excess stress$/2\delta$, or

$$\delta M = (1/5)N_v m v_F^2 \tag{19.1-7}$$

(Note that M is here the appropriate shear modulus.) The formula for the standard solid, with $\delta M/M_R$ as relaxation strength and τ, given by Eq. (19.1-6), as the relaxation time at constant stress, then completes the solution to this problem.

Unfortunately, however, the above solution is not valid over its entire range due to a breakdown in one of the assumptions. The problem is the same as that encountered for phonon–phonon interactions (Section 17-6), namely, that it has been assumed that the electrons will come to equilibrium within a region in which the stress is homogeneous. This means that $l \ll \lambda$ (where λ is the acoustic wavelength) or $ql \ll 1$ (where $q = 2\pi/\lambda$). We note from Eq. (19.1-5) and the relation $\omega = v_s q$, that $\omega\tau = qlv_s/v_F$, where v_s is the shear wave velocity. Since $v_s/v_F \sim 1/300$, it is clear that the requirement that $ql \ll 1$ means in fact that $\omega\tau$ must be extremely small. Therefore, our derived result is only correct at the very low-frequency end of the relaxation peak. In this range, the attenuation of a shear wave $\mathscr{A}_s$ then takes the form (putting $M_R = \rho v_s^2$ and $\mathscr{A}_s = \omega\phi/2v_s$):

$$\mathscr{A}_s = (N_v m v_F^2/10\rho v_s^3)\omega^2\tau, \qquad \omega\tau \ll 1 \tag{19.1-8}$$

so that $\mathscr{A}_s \propto \omega^2$. In order to obtain the attenuation of a longitudinal wave $\mathscr{A}_l$ we make use of the fact that $\delta K = 0$ (where K is the bulk modulus).[†] Since the elastic constant for longitudinal waves in the $\langle 100 \rangle$ direction of a cubic crystal is [Eq. (6.4-4)] $C_{11} = K + \frac{4}{3}C'$ where C' is the shear constant $\frac{1}{2}(C_{11} - C_{12})$, and $\delta K = 0$, $\mathscr{A}_l$ is obtained by multiplying the expression in Eq. (19.1-8) by $\frac{4}{3}$ and replacing v_s by v_l. Data on Al which very nearly checks the ω^2 dependence over two orders of magnitude in frequency are shown in Fig. 19-4. Some deviation at the lower frequencies is believed (Gibbons, 1964) due to the fact that the dislocation contribution is appreciable at this end of the scale.

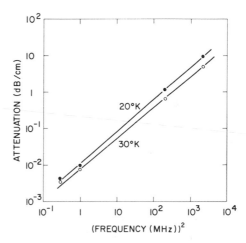

FIG. 19-4. Dependence of attenuation on ω^2 for longitudinal elastic waves in aluminum at two different temperatures. (From Gibbons, 1964.)

In order to develop a feeling for when the condition $ql \ll 1$ is obeyed, it is useful to quote some numerical values. For copper at room temperature, $l \sim 10^{-6}$ cm, and for a 100-MHz ultrasonic wave, $\lambda \sim 10^{-3}$ cm; in this case, therefore, the condition $ql \ll 1$ is well obeyed. On the other hand, at low temperatures ($\sim 4°$K) the electron mean free path of a high-purity metal is of the order of 10^{-1} cm or more. In this range, $ql > 1$. The breakdown of the relation $\mathscr{A} \propto \omega^2$ at very low temperatures may be seen from Fig. 19-1 for [001] propagation in tin. At $10°$K, the attenuation goes approximately as ω^2, whereas by $4°$K, $\mathscr{A}$ varies in a way more nearly proportional to ω.

A classical treatment of attenuation due to free electrons in a metal which applied over the entire range of values of mean free path was given by Pippard (1955). In this treatment account is taken of the fact

---

[†] This condition is valid because under hydrostatic pressure a spherical Fermi surface remains spherical; therefore no relaxation of the electron distribution takes place.

that the displacement of the lattice ions in the stress field of the ultrasonic wave introduces a periodic internal electric field in which the electrons must move, so that the electron density does not remain constant in space. The combined effects on an electron of this internal electric field and of collisions with the lattice are taken into account. For the range $ql \gg 1$, the following limiting expression is obtained for longitudinal waves:

$$\mathscr{A}' = \pi N_v m v_F \omega / 12 p v_l^2, \qquad ql \gg 1 \qquad (19.1\text{-}9)$$

while the dependence of $\mathscr{A}$ on ql for arbitrary ql is expressed by

$$\frac{\mathscr{A}}{\mathscr{A}'} = \frac{6}{\pi} \left[\frac{ql}{3} \frac{B}{1-B} - \frac{1}{ql} \right] \qquad (19.1\text{-}10)$$

where $B = (\arctan ql)/ql$, and $\mathscr{A}'$ is the limiting expression given by Eq. (19.1-9). It should be noted that the limiting expression (19.1-9) gives an attenuation which is independent of τ (or l) and proportional to frequency, so that internal friction is independent of frequency. It is clear, therefore, that in this range, the attenuation behavior is not describable as a relaxation phenomenon. (Note the analogy to the Landau–Rumer range in the case of phonon–phonon interactions, Section 17.6.)

Equation (19.1-10) has been tested experimentally by Morse and Bohm (1957) for In and Cu with results as shown in Fig. 19-5. For In, two samples were used which had different l values (i.e., different states of purity) and the frequency was varied, thereby giving a wide range of values of ql. The absolute value for l was not known, so that the data for each sample were fitted to the theory at one single point. The results show the excellent agreement with the form of Eq. (19.1-10).

Other classical calculations on a more rigorous basis have been carried out by Steinberg (1958b) and Blount (1959) starting from the Boltzmann

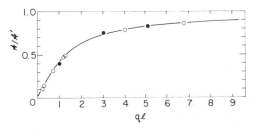

Fig. 19-5.   Observed dependence of longitudinal wave attenuation on ql compared with Eq. (19.1-10). Measurements are on indium ($\bigcirc$); on copper ($\bullet$). (From Morse, 1959.)

transport equation. The results are about the same as Pippard's except for somewhat different numerical coefficients.

As soon as we depart from the case of an ideal metal with a simple spherical Fermi surface, we find that losses associated with hydrostatic compression as well as pure shear become possible. From thermodynamic reciprocity (e.g., see Chapter 5), if the equilibrium form of the Fermi surface depends on the volume of the metal, abrupt application of hydrostatic compression would leave the Fermi surface in a state of non-equilibrium. The most striking example occurs for the case of a metal with a broken Fermi surface which lies in two different Brillouin zones, as shown schematically in Fig. 19-2. In this case hydrostatic distortion results in instantaneous promotion of some electrons to higher energies, just as did shear stress in the free electron case (Fig. 19-3b). Attenuation then occurs as a consequence of lattice collisions which allow the transfer of electrons from one Brillouin zone to another. A general theory, which does not require any special assumptions about the shape of the Fermi surfaces, has been developed by Pippard (1960b). The expressions obtained are qualitatively similar to those given above for the free-electron limit.

C. MAGNETIC FIELD EFFECTS

When a magnetic field **H** is applied, a free electron moving with velocity **v** is subject to the Lorentz force $-(e/c)\mathbf{v} \times \mathbf{H}$, where e is the electronic charge and c is the velocity of light.[†] It is easy to see that, for a spherical Fermi surface and with $\mathbf{v} \perp \mathbf{H}$, an electron will move in a circular orbit whose radius is

$$r = mv_{\mathrm{F}}c/eH = p_{\mathrm{F}}c/eH \qquad (19.1\text{-}11)$$

with an angular frequency ω_c (known as the "cyclotron frequency") given by

$$\omega_c = eH/mc \qquad (19.1\text{-}12)$$

For a more general Fermi surface, the orbit is not circular, but it still lies in the Fermi surface and is given by Eq. (19.1-12) with m replaced by an effective mass.

[†] Actually, the magnetic induction **B** should appear in the expression for the Lorentz force, but we are concerned with materials for which the permeability μ is very nearly unity.

Interesting variations occur in the attenuation in the presence of a magnetic field. Again, the distinction between the ranges where $ql < 1$ and $ql > 1$ is important. In the range $ql < 1$, the attenuation is observed to decrease monotonically with increasing magnetic field H. This result may be interpreted qualitatively by assuming that the magnetic field, by bending the path of an electron, reduces the average distance l between collisions. Since $\mathscr{A}$ is proportional to l in this range [see Eqs. (19.1-8) and (19.1-5)], the attenuation is reduced. This qualitative picture is supported by the detailed calculation of Steinberg (1958a) who showed, using a free-electron model, that for shear waves with **H** perpendicular to both the polarization and propagation directions (this geometry will be called $H_\perp$) the field dependence of $\mathscr{A}$ is of the form

$$\mathscr{A}(H_\perp)/\mathscr{A}(0) = (1 + 4\omega_c^2\tau^2)^{-1} \qquad (19.1\text{-}13)$$

where ω_c is given by Eq. (19.1-12) and τ by Eq. (19.1-5). Steinberg also showed that for **H** parallel to the direction of polarization but perpendicular to the propagation direction (a geometry which will be called $H_\parallel$) the analogous result is

$$\mathscr{A}(H_\parallel)/\mathscr{A}(0) = (1 + \omega_c^2\tau^2)^{-1} \qquad (19.1\text{-}14)$$

Equations (19.1-13) and (19.1-14) have been verified by the experiments of Morse (1959) shown in Fig. 19-6, where measurements taken on Cu for shear-wave attenuation are compared with these equations. It is predicted that $\mathscr{A}(H)/\mathscr{A}(0) = \frac{1}{2}$ occurs at $\omega_c\tau = \frac{1}{2}$ for $H_\perp$, and at $\omega_c\tau = 1$ for $H_\parallel$; the results agree with this prediction. The data give $\tau = 3.8 \times 10^{-11}$

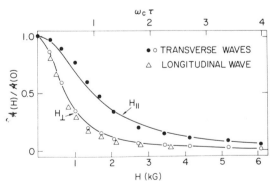

FIG. 19-6. Dependence of attenuation in copper at 8.6 MHz on magnetic field (circles, transverse; triangles, longitudinal). The solid curves are theoretical curves calculated from Eqs. (19.1-13) and (19.1-14). (From Morse, 1959.)

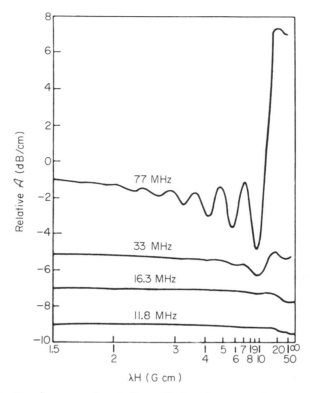

FIG. 19-7. Development of periodic oscillations in attenuation versus λH (on a reciprocal scale) with increasing frequency of longitudinal ultrasonic waves in pure copper. (From Morse, 1960.)

sec for the sample measured, when m is taken as the mass of the free electron. Data for longitudinal waves apparently also agree with Eq. (19.1-13), although the latter was derived for shear waves.

More interesting, however, is the effect of a magnetic field on ultrasonic attenuation where $ql > 1$. Under these conditions, an oscillatory variation of the attenuation with magnetic field is observed. Though not a relaxation phenomenon, the effect is of such great importance that we should not fail to discuss it here. This effect was first observed by Bömmel (1955) and later shown in more detail by Morse *et al.* (1958). An example from this early work is given in Fig. 19-7 to show how the oscillations develop as the frequency (and therefore q) is increased. In later work, higher frequencies and improved techniques have yielded much larger numbers of oscillations [see, e.g., the addendum to Gibbons (1964)]. Qualitatively, the oscillatory effect can be explained by noting that, since the conduction electrons move in spiral orbits through the periodic electric field generated by the ultrasonic wave, resonances should occur for certain coincidences between orbit diameter and wavelength. These are called *magnetoacoustic geometric resonances*. Figure 19-8 shows a diagram of the electron orbits when the magnetic field is applied in a direction normal to both the propagation direction (z) and the polarization direction (x) of the acoustic wave. The circular orbits shown apply to the case of a spherical Fermi surface. A rough argument concerning the resonance effect is as follows. Since the electron orbit is perpendicular to

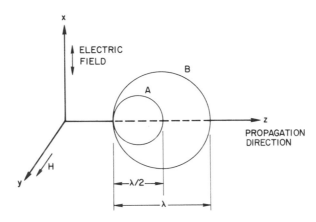

FIG. 19-8.   Electron orbits in a free-electron metal for a magnetic field which is perpendicular to both the propagation direction and the polarization direction of an acoustic wave.

the planes of constant strain (due to the ultrasonic wave), the major contribution to electron interaction with the acoustic strain field occurs at the end points of the orbit, where the electron moves, momentarily, parallel to planes of constant strain.[†] If the diameter of the orbit is an integral number of wavelengths, as in orbit B, the force on the electron at these two end points are in the same direction. The coupling to the strain field, and therefore the attenuation, is then a maximum. When the orbit size is an integral number of half wavelengths, as in orbit A, the end forces are opposite and attenuation should then be a minimum. As the magnitude of H is changed, the changing orbit radius, in accordance with Eq. (19.1-11), means that alternate maxima and minima in $\mathscr{A}$

[†] Since $v_F \gg v_s$ (the ultrasonic shear wave velocity), the periodic electric field of the ultrasonic wave may be regarded as stationary in space.

will be obtained. A more detailed analysis by Cohen *et al.* (1960) verifies this proposal for the free-electron model. From this argument, and Eq. (19.1-11), the periodicity in the orbit radius is $\lambda/2$, so that

$$\lambda/2 = (p_F c/e)\, \Delta(1/H) \qquad (19.1\text{-}15)$$

where $\Delta(1/H)$ is the difference in the reciprocal magnetic field between successive maxima (or minima) of ultrasonic absorption. Equation (19.1-15) shows why the data show periodicity when plotted versus $(\lambda H)^{-1}$ in Fig. 19-7. From this periodicity and Eq. (19.1-15), one immediately obtains p_F, the Fermi momentum. In order that the above argument be valid, however, it is necessary that the electron be able to make at least a large fraction of one orbit before undergoing a collision. This condition means that $\omega_c \tau > 1$, or from Eqs. (19.1-12), (19.1-5), and (19.1-11) (with $r \sim \lambda$), that $ql > 1$. It is because of this condition that the resonances can only be observed in high purity samples and at very low temperatures.

For nonspherical Fermi surfaces the situation is more complicated. There is a general theorem due to Onsager (1952) which relates the motion of an electron in real space to its behavior in k space in the presence of a magnetic field. When the field is applied, an electron with the Fermi energy moves around the Fermi surface in k space (since the magnetic field can do no work). It turns out that in real space, the trajectory has the same shape as the constant-energy surface in k space, only it is rotated about the field direction by 90°. The dimensions of the trajectory are inversely proportional to H [as in Eq. (19.1-11)]. Thus the periodic variation of $\mathscr{A}$ is related to the linear dimension of the Fermi surface perpendicular to both H and the direction of propagation of the ultrasonic wave. By changing these directions in a single crystal one can map out the size and shape of the Fermi surface. This method has been used extensively for the determination of the Fermi surface of metals [see, e.g., Telpey (1965)].

There are other experimental methods which have recently contributed to a knowledge of the Fermi surface. Among them are the de Haas–van Alphen effect, cyclotron resonance, and magnetoresistance measurements. All of these measure different properties of the Fermi surface and they have been mutually complementary. Thus, for example, it was shown that the Fermi surfaces of the noble metals (Cu, Ag, Au) are not of the nearly spherical type but actually touch the Brillouin zone boundary in small regions near the ⟨111⟩ directions. This shape produces striking differences in the ultrasonic attenuation plots for different directions in the crystal.

Geometric resonances are not the only kind of phenomena involving resonance-type acoustic losses as a function of magnetic field. Another similar phenomenon is that of *quantum oscillations*, which is due to the fact that the electron orbits are quantized such that the energy is a multiple of $\hbar\omega_c$ (the "Landau levels"). It occurs for relatively high fields in which the energy separation $\hbar\omega_c$ of the Landau levels is large compared with the thermal energy kT. Here again the attenuation is an oscillatory function of H^{-1}, but the period is now independent of the ultrasonic frequency. Finally, there is still another resonance phenomenon of *cyclotron resonance* which occurs when the acoustic frequency ω is an integral multiple of the cyclotron frequency ω_c. Both of these resonance phenomena are outside the scope of this book, but are amply discussed in some of the general references given at the end of the chapter.

19.2   Interaction of Ultrasonic Waves with Electrons in Semiconductors

In a semiconductor, the density of electronic charge carriers (electrons or holes) is much less than the corresponding carrier density in metals. Nevertheless, interaction of ultrasonic waves with the electronic structure of semiconductors gives rise to a variety of interesting effects, some of which are true relaxation phenomena and others which are not.

The electronic structure of a pure semiconductor differs from that of a metal in having a number of electrons present which is just sufficient to fill a band of allowed energy levels (the *valence band*) leaving an energy gap to the next set of available levels (the *conduction band*). However, by suitable doping with impurities (or departure from the exact stoichiometric composition in the case of compounds), it is possible to introduce a small number of electrons into the bottom of the conduction band, or a small number of holes (missing electrons) at the top of the valence band. For the elemental semiconductors Si and Ge, electrons are introduced by doping with group V elements (P, As, Sb) called "donors," and the semiconductor is then said to be *n*-type. Correspondingly, it may be made *p*-type, with holes in the valence band, by doping with group III elements (B, Al, Ga), called "acceptors." These electrons or holes, respectively, possess bound states ("donor and acceptor levels") at the corresponding impurity atoms, but these bound states are easily ionized thermally so that conduction electrons or holes are created (see Fig. 19-9). In this case, the number of current carriers decreases to zero

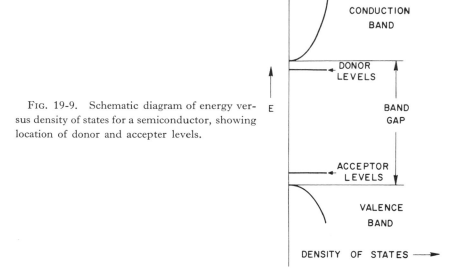

FIG. 19-9.   Schematic diagram of energy versus density of states for a semiconductor, showing location of donor and accepter levels.

at low temperatures. On the other hand, when a semiconductor is sufficiently heavily doped, it may have a significant carrier density at all temperatures; in that case it is said to be a *degenerate* semiconductor.

Even in a pure, or intrinsic, semiconductor, electrons and holes may be produced by direct excitation from the valence band to the conduction band, so as to produce electrons and holes in equal numbers. Such excitation can be produced thermally, but for the usual band gaps the probability of excitation is very low at ordinary temperatures. Excitation can also be produced by light of appropriate wavelength, giving rise to photoconduction. This is an important means of producing carriers in II–VI compounds such as CdS.

A semiconductor which has free carriers can provide a source of acoustic attenuation through the coupling between the acoustic wave and these mobile charges. We shall first discuss the two most important types of coupling mechanisms, and then review the various phenomena which have been studied.

A. COUPLING MECHANISMS

The first mechanism for coupling of an acoustic wave to the electronic system occurs for so-called "multivalley" semiconductors. To define what this means, we are first reminded that the $E(\mathbf{k})$ (energy versus wave vector) diagram of electrons in a crystal is paraboloidal at the bottom of a band and also near the top of a filled band. Since, in a semi-conductor, the Fermi level is so situated that all bands are nearly empty or nearly full, only these paraboloidal regions are important. Now the function $E(\mathbf{k})$ must have the point group symmetry of the crystal, so that, if an extremum exists at $\mathbf{k}_0$, there must be an identical extremum in all orientations into which $\mathbf{k}_0$ can be transformed by the symmetry operations of the crystal. The collection of energy states near such an extremum is known as a "valley." A semiconductor with a set of such valleys that may be transformed into each other is called a "multivalley" semiconductor. Figure 19-10 is an illustration for the case of a fourfold axis of symmetry, as in a cubic or tetragonal crystal. If such a crystal is strained in tension along the x direction, the x and y axes are no longer equivalent to each other, i.e., the stress raises the band edge of one set of ellipsoidal energy surfaces and lowers that of another set. If, as shown in the diagram,

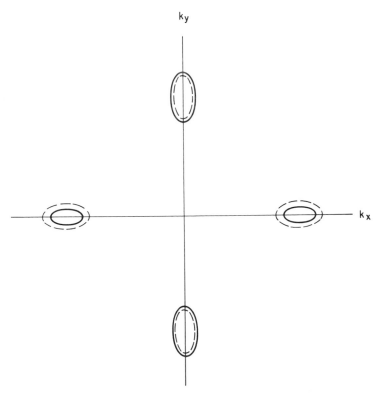

Fig. 19-10. Energy contours in k space for a multivalley semiconductor. Dashed lines show the original equal-energy contours for the unstressed crystal; solid lines show the same contours when the crystal is strained in tension along the x axis.

the energy of those surfaces which lie along the y axis is lowered with respect to those along the x axis, then some electrons will transfer from x valleys to y valleys by an "intervalley scattering" mechanism. The occurrence of such a readjustment, which was first recognized by Blatt (1957) by analogy to Kittel's (1955) mechanism for metals (see Section 19.1), constitutes a relaxation process. Intravalley scattering of electrons can also occur, but with a time constant much shorter than the intervalley time constant. Therefore, the latter dominates the overall relaxation time.

It is therefore apparent that just as for the case of point defects (Chapter 8), the symmetry properties of the valleys can be derived from a study of the orientation dependence of the attenuation. Thus, e.g., in Fig. 19-10, a tensile stress along a $\langle 110 \rangle$ axis will not destroy the degeneracy among the x type and y type valleys. If the diagram is for a cubic crystal, stress along $\langle 111 \rangle$ will produce no relaxation among the set of valleys along the three cube axes.

The coupling between the electrons and the state of strain of the crystal may be expressed in terms of the "deformation potential" constants. The idea is that strain changes the band structure only by changing the energy of all states of a particular valley by the same amount, so that the effect of strain ε on valley i can be by a change of U_i, the energy of the lowest state in valley i. In the linear approximation we can write

$$\Delta U_i = \Xi_i \varepsilon \qquad (19.2\text{-}1)$$

where Ξ_i is the appropriate deformation-potential constant. Actually, since ε is in general a tensor of second rank, Ξ_i is also a tensor. In fact, it is closely analogous to Kröner's $\mathbf{P}$ tensor for point defects [see Eq. (8.2-6)] which, in turn, is related to the $\boldsymbol{\lambda}$ tensor. A typical magnitude of Ξ_i for a shear strain is ~ 10 eV.

An equivalent way to look at the relaxation in a multivalley semiconductor is to think of the electric field which accompanies an ultrasonic wave, which is obtained from the spatial derivative of the potential ΔU_i. This electric field seen by electrons in valley i is therefore proportional to ω and lags the strain by $\pi/2$. It gives rise to a bunching of electrons belonging to valley i in the regions of minimum potential. However, for each valley whose electrons feel a minimum potential at point P due to the local strain, there will be another valley for which the potential at P is a maximum, viz., that which is unfavorably oriented with respect to the local stress. Accordingly, the total electronic charge at any point in space remains uniform and there will be no space-charge repulsion effects.

We now turn to the second mechanism for coupling between an impressed shear wave and the electrons in a semiconductor. This mechanism arises only in semiconductor crystals which are piezoelectric, i.e., which lack a center of inversion symmetry. Here, due to the piezoelectric effect, a local strain gives rise to an internal electric field which is proportional to the strain. The electric field is then independent of ω, and in general, is stronger than the field produced by the deformation potential for frequencies below $\sim$100 GHz. If the material possesses mobile charge carriers, these will move toward the positions of potential minimum in the piezoelectrically induced electric field. Unlike the previous case, here a net bunching of electrons in the potential minima takes place, with associated space charge repulsion effects. The resulting electric current, called the "acoustoelectric current," lags behind the applied strain and thereby gives rise to attenuation of the ultrasonic wave.

B. Modulus Defect and Attenuation in Multivalley Semiconductors

Based on the concepts of a multivalley semiconductor, Keyes (1961) predicted that the elastic properties of Ge would be appreciably affected by the electronic relaxation. Since it was known from piezoresistance measurements (the change in electrical conductivity when a stress is applied along a particular crystallographic direction) of Smith (1954) that the valleys lie along $\langle 111 \rangle$ directions for Ge, Keyes predicted, for n-type Ge, that only the elastic constant C_{44} would be affected by this phenomenon. He calculated the magnitude of the relaxation for degenerate (heavily doped) n-type Ge at low temperatures to be

$$(\delta C_{44})_{T=0} = -\tfrac{4}{3}(4\pi/3)^{2/3}m^*N_{\mathrm{v}}^{1/3}\varXi^2/h^2 \qquad (19.2\text{-}2)$$

where m^* is the effective mass of the electrons, N_{v} their number per unit volume, h is Planck's constant, and $\varXi$ is the appropriate shear-deformation-potential constant. From this relation, Keyes predicted an 8% lowering of C_{44} for degenerate n-type Ge at low temperatures due to the intervalley relaxation mechanism. Experiments of Bruner and Keyes (1961) verified the effect for heavily doped crystals (3.5×10^{19} donors cm^{-3}) at kHz frequencies, i.e., sufficiently low ($\omega\tau \ll 1$) that the moduli are the relaxed values. Experimentally, a depression of C_{44} by 5.5% was observed while the other elastic constants remained substantially unaltered. For much higher frequencies, close to the reciprocal of the intervalley scattering time, one would expect also to observe internal friction as a consequence of the relaxation process. This effect was first observed by Pomerantz *et al.* (1962) who made measurements at 9 GHz on n-type Ge (10^{19} As donors cm^{-3}). They used longitudinal and shear waves in $\langle 100 \rangle$ and $\langle 111 \rangle$ directions and found a striking qualitative result, viz., that attenuation was very high for all waves whose elastic constant contains the C_{44} modulus and relatively low for the others. For the former group of wave directions, the attenuation was in fact so high that the waves could not be propagated. For high-purity Ge, on the other hand, all the waves could be propagated. This work, then, demonstrated a striking qualitative confirmation of Keyes' concepts.

In contrast to the case of Ge, for n-type Si the valleys lie along the $\langle 100 \rangle$ directions giving rise to a relaxation of the shear constant $C_{11} - C_{12}$ and not of C_{44}. Einspruch and Csavinsky (1963) have extended Keyes' theory to the case of n-type Si and obtained an expression for $\delta(C_{11} - C_{12})$ at low temperatures which is very similar to Eq. (19.2-2). They have also observed the predicted modulus defect. More recently Hall (1967) studied the modulus defect in heavily doped n-type Si as a function of temperature.

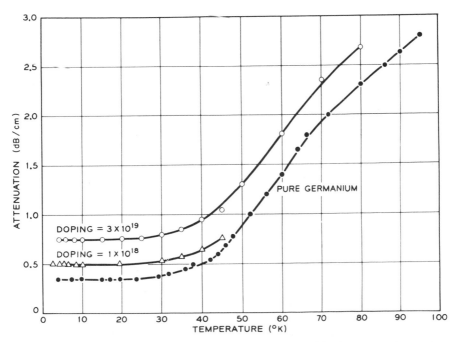

FIG. 19-11. Attenuation of longitudinal waves along $\langle 110 \rangle$, in pure and arsenic-doped germanium. Frequency, 475 MHz. (From Mason and Bateman, 1964b.)

Quantitative information on the relaxation times in multivalley semi-conductors was obtained by Mason and Bateman (1964b). By going to somewhat lower frequencies (10–500 MHz) these authors were able to measure both attenuation and velocity changes as a function of temperature for n-type Ge and p-type Si, and thereby to deduce values for the intervalley relaxation times. Since the internal friction (for the range $\omega\tau \ll 1$) is given by $(\Delta M/M)\omega\tau$, measurement of both attenuation and modulus defect $\Delta M/M$ gives a direct value for τ. Figure 19-11 shows typical measurements of the attenuation of longitudinal waves in the $\langle 110 \rangle$ direction as a function of temperature for various samples of Ge. For Ge doped with 10^{18} and 3×10^{19} As donors cm^{-3}, they obtained $\tau = 4\times10^{-13}$ and 2.3×10^{-13} sec, respectively, these values being independent of temperature up to 300°K. For very low doping levels (below $\sim10^{18}$ cm^{-3}), the differences in attenuation and modulus are not sufficient to attain reasonable precision by this method. Instead, acoustoelectric measurements (see Section 19.2E) can be used. Figure 19-12 summarizes the results on intervalley relaxation times as a function of doping level. At low temperatures, the relaxation time is determined by impurity scattering, as shown by the solid line. As the temperature increases,

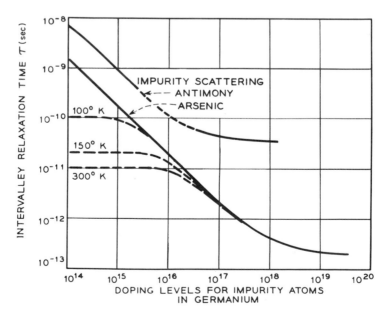

Fig. 19-12. Relaxation times for arsenic- and antimony-doped Ge as a function of doping level. Dashed curves show effect of phonon scattering while solid curves are for impurity scattering. (From Mason and Bateman, 1964b.)

scattering also occurs by collisions with phonons. The dashed lines of Fig. 19-12 show how this type of scattering modifies the relaxation times at various temperatures. That the τ value tends to become independent of doping level for high concentrations of impurities, is shown even more strikingly by the data for Sb-doped samples, also given in Fig. 19-12.

Mason and Bateman also studied boron-doped Si and obtained $\tau \sim 10^{-13}$ sec for a doping of 3×10^{19} cm^{-3}, but here τ varies exponentially with temperature in a manner corresponding to an activated process. This result is interpreted as due to a temperature-induced change in hole population along the energy surface.

C. ELECTRONIC RELAXATION PEAK IN Si AND Ge

Southgate (1960) has observed a relaxation peak at frequencies $\sim$100 kHz in Si and Ge at relatively high temperatures (near 0.56 of the melting point). An example of his results is shown in Fig. 19-13 for a Si sample having a carrier lifetime of 30 μsec. This peak had previously been

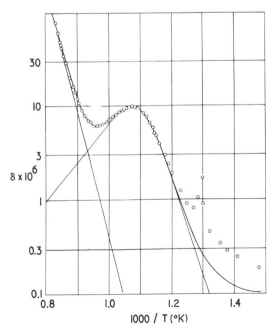

FIG. 19-13.   Internal friction of a silicon sample having a carrier lifetime of 30 μsec at room temperature. The curve synthesis separates out the electronic peak from the higher temperature oxygen peak and a constant mounting loss. (From Southgate 1960.)

reported by Kessler (1957) for Ge, with the claim that it was a dislocation effect. Southgate's work, however, seems to indicate otherwise.

In view of the relatively low frequencies used, the peak cannot be related to the intervalley scattering process ($\tau \sim 10^{-12}$ sec) described in the previous subsection. Instead Southgate invokes the theory of Weinreich (1956) originally proposed for the acoustoelectric effect (see Section 19.2E) resulting from a purely dilatational stress. Such a stress produces a change in the band gap, and therefore, a change in the intrinsic charge carrier density. The theory then predicts standard-solid behavior (for frequencies $\ll 10^{11}$ sec^{-1}) with a relaxation strength given by $q^2 N_v / 2kT$ where N_v is the carrier charge density, and q is the "acoustic charge" of the carriers, equal to $1/\sqrt{2}$ times the deformation potential for a strain corresponding to unit energy density. The relaxation time τ for the change in intrinsic carrier charge density is the carrier recombination time which is very long compared to intervalley scattering times. In fact, τ has two components, one due to recombination across the band gap (intrinsic, τ_i) and the other due to recombination via a lattice imperfection level (extrinsic, τ_e) with

$$\tau^{-1} = \tau_e^{-1} + \tau_i^{-1} \tag{19.2-3}$$

For a material of high lifetime, τ_i dominates. This quantity is given by

$$\tau_i = \tau_0 \exp(E_r / kT) \tag{19.2-4}$$

where E_r is of the order of the band gap. This equation for τ_i explains the existence of a peak versus T^{-1}, as in Fig. 19-13. On the other hand, the quantity τ_e does not vary with temperature, so that for low enough frequencies a relaxation peak versus T^{-1} should no longer be observed. In fact, the deviation from a straight line on the low temperature side of Fig. 19-13 is attributed to the contribution from τ_e.

From the results obtained, Southgate obtained a value for E_r of 1.45 eV as the activation energy for recombination of carriers in Si. The height of the peak gives a value of 2.3 eV for the deformation-potential constant corresponding to hydrostatic strain [see Eq. (19.2-1)].

D. Attenuation in Piezoelectric Semiconductors

It was already pointed out in Section 19.2A that piezoelectric coupling gives rise to a periodic electric field which leads to bunching of mobile charge carriers in the regions of potential minima. Hutson and White

(1962) have analyzed the problem of elastic wave propagation in a piezo-electric semiconductor taking into account the currents and space charges that accompany the elastic wave. They include the effects of diffusion and trapping of carriers. Subsequently, White (1962) extended the calculations to include the effect of an external electric field which can give rise to acoustic amplification (see Section 19.2E). Since this calculation appears in many review articles and books [see, e.g., Truell *et al.* (1969)], we will not repeat it here. Suffice it to say, for the simplest case, involving a single charge carrier for which diffusion can be neglected, standard-solid relaxation behavior is obtained with relaxation rate τ^{-1} proportional to the electrical conductivity. If diffusion cannot be neglected, however, additional terms appear in the expression for the attenuation, so that it no longer represents simple relaxation behavior.

There have been several experimental studies of ultrasonic attenuation in piezoelectric semiconductors, mostly on cadmium sulfide. In particular, Nine and Truell (1961) measured the attenuation of ultrasonic waves in CdS in which electronic carriers were introduced by illumination, i.e., through the photoelectric effect. Lord and Truell (1966) observed a large peak in attenuation versus temperature of CdS below 30°K which they attribute to the strong dependence of the conductivity (therefore of τ^{-1}) on temperature.

E. OTHER RELATED PHENOMENA

In this subsection, we will briefly mention two other effects in semiconductors which are themselves not anelastic in nature, but which are closely related to the electronic relaxation processes that have been discussed.

The *acoustoelectric effect*, already mentioned above, involves the electrical effect produced by the transfer of momentum from an ultrasonic wave to the electrons of the lattice. It is due to the bunching of electrons in the potential minima of the periodic electric field created by the elastic wave. As the wave progresses, the position of the potential minimum changes; the attempt of the electrons to follow the wave motion gives rise to an acoustoelectric current. If the ends of the sample are insulated, on the other hand, one can measure a dc "acoustoelectric field" E_{ae} which is related to the attenuation $\mathscr{A}$ by (Weinreich, 1957)

$$\mathscr{A}/E_{ae} = eN_v v/2I \tag{19.2-5}$$

where v is the wave velocity and I is the intensity of the ultrasonic wave.

The electroacoustic field can be measured at a lower doping level than can the change in attenuation due to electronic relaxation, so that the two measurements may be used to complement each other. The acousto-electric effect has been observed by Weinreich *et al.* (1959) for a mul-tivalley semiconductor (*n*-type Ge). It has also been observed in piezo-electric type semiconductors (Wang, 1962) using optical illumination to generate the mobile charge carriers.

An interesting modification occurs when a dc field E_{dc} is applied parallel to the direction of elastic wave propagation so as to give the electrons a drift velocity $v_d = \mu E_{dc}$ (where μ is their mobility). If the drift velocity exceeds the wave velocity, the electrons will be running ahead of the acoustic wave. The electric field of the wave will then act to retard the electrons in regions where this field opposes the velocity. On an average, power is then transferred from the electrons to the wave, so that the wave is amplified. This is the phenomenon of *acoustic amplification* first re-ported by Hutson *et al.* (1961) for piezoelectric CdS. The same effect was also obtained for the multivalley semiconductor *n*-type Ge by Pome-rantz (1964a). The theory of this effect has been described by White (1962) and by Spector (1962), among others.

19.3   Relaxations Attributed to Bound Electrons

While the two previous sections have dealt with effects of conduction electrons, in a number of insulating crystals relaxation effects have been observed which have been attributed to the redistribution of bound electrons among two or more equivalent sites. Such effects are quite analogous to point defect relaxations, except that the activated process is the jump of an electron rather than of an ion. In this section, we will describe the experimental characteristics and proposed mechanisms of relaxation effects attributed to bound electrons.

A. Crystals Containing Transition Metal Ions in Two Valence States

The best known example in this category is magnetite Fe_3O_4. This crystal has the inverted spinel lattice in which there are 8 tetrahedral sites for Fe^{3+} ions and 16 octahedral sites containing Fe^{2+} and Fe^{3+} ions in equal numbers. Whereas at room temperature the octahedral sites are believed to be randomly occupied with electrons being con-tinuously interchanged among the ions, at $115°K$ a transformation to an ordered arrangement of the Fe^{2+} and Fe^{3+} ions takes place [see, e.g., Verwey and Haayman (1941)].

The internal friction and Young's modulus of magnetite show some striking effects as a function of temperature, as shown for example in Fig. 19-14. Here we note that there are two peaks in the internal friction as measured at 90 kHz, one near 40°K and the second at 95°K, while

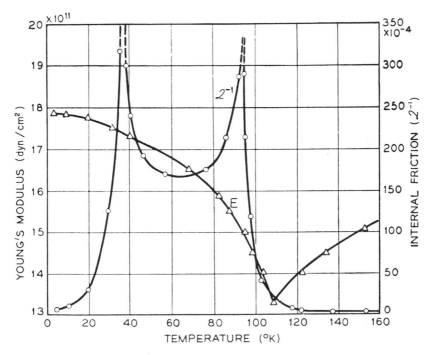

FIG. 19-14. Internal friction and Young's modulus of magnetite as a function of temperature for a longitudinal wave along ⟨111⟩. Frequency, 90 kHz. (From Gibbons, 1957.)

Young's modulus shows a sharp cusp at the transformation temperature of 115°K. The peak at 95°K immediately below the transformation temperature was first observed by Fine and Kenney (1954a), and these same authors (1954b) found the lower peak in nickel–iron ferrite (containing Ni^{2+} substituted in part for the Fe^{2+}). The effects described are strongly anisotropic. For example, Fig. 19-15 shows the measurements of internal friction and Young's modulus for magnetite using longitudinal waves along the ⟨100⟩ direction (Fig. 19-14 was for the ⟨111⟩ direction). It is striking that the upper damping peak and the cusp in the modulus

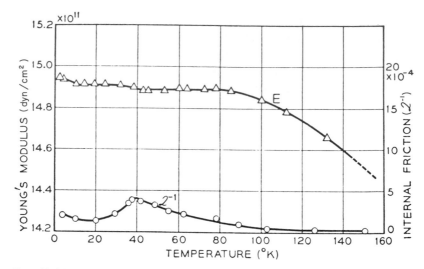

FIG. 19-15.   Similar results to Fig. 19-14, but for propagation along $\langle 100 \rangle$. (From Gibbons, 1957.)

are absent, while a small remnant ($\sim 100\times$ smaller) of the 40°K peak remains. The activation energy and frequency factor for the 40°K peak are given in Table 19-1. For the 95°K peak, the shift with frequency is so slight (Kamigaki, 1961) as to give unreasonable values for Q and τ_0; rather, this peak appears to be related to the onset of the 115°K transformation.

TABLE 19-1

LISTING OF INTERNAL FRICTION PEAKS OBSERVED FOR FERRITES AND RELATED COMPOUNDS

Material	Peak temperature (°K)		Frequency (kHz)	Q (eV)	τ_0^{-1} (sec⁻¹)
Magnetite	(a)	40	90	0.05^a	10^{11a}
	(b)	95	130	—	—
	(c)	670	1000	1.0	10^{14}
Ni–Fe		40	50	~ 0.04	10^{10}
Mn-ferrite		270	110	~ 0.3	10^{12}
Mn_3O_4		350	60	0.4	10^{12}
YIG		160	100	0.13	10^{10}

^{a} Average values based on the data of both Gibbons (1957) and Kamigaki (1961).

More recent measurements by Suiter and Blair (1965) have introduced an important new variable into the study of the internal friction of magnetite. Specifically, these authors show that the height of the 40°K peak can be varied by more than a factor of 10 by controlling the cation vacancy concentration in the crystal. The latter variation is produced by firing the samples at 1300°C under various partial pressures of oxygen. In this way, the authors claim to vary the cation vacancy concentration over a fraction between 10^{-3} and 10^{-2} per formula unit. Furthermore, in addition to the two peaks already mentioned, a third peak near 670°K (for 1 MHz) is also observed. This peak also appears to depend on the vacancy concentration. The results are summarized in Fig. 19-16 which shows that both the 40 and 670°K peaks almost vanish at the lowest vacancy concentration. The 95°K peak remains large but moves to a lower temperature with increasing vacancy concentration. This change correlates with a corresponding change in the transformation temperature.

A number of internal friction peaks have been observed in related compounds, some at substantially higher temperatures (and with higher activation energies). Because of structural or electronic similarities to

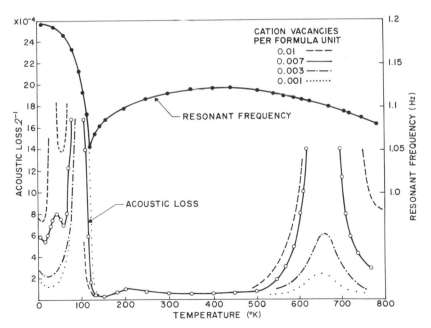

FIG. 19-16. Internal friction and resonant frequency of polycrystalline magnetite as a function of temperature, with the mole fraction of cation vacancies as a parameter. (From Suiter and Blair, 1965.)

magnetite, we have grouped these compounds together in Table 19-1. For manganese ferrite, Gibbons (1957) found a peak near 260°K, and also noted a rising modulus and damping below 10°K and down to 1.25°K where the measurements cease. These results are illustrated in Fig. 19-17. In the case of these crystals, Gibbons claims that the precise activation energy depends on composition and/or homogeneity of the material. The small peak at 40°K in Fig. 19-17 is apparently a remnant

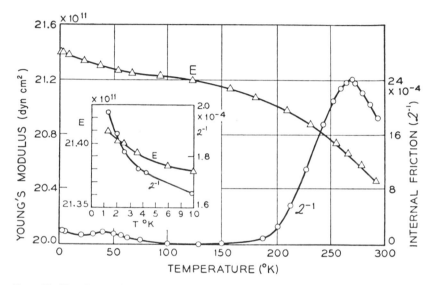

FIG. 19-17. Internal friction and Young's modulus of manganese ferrite as a function of temperature, for a longitudinal wave along ⟨111⟩. Frequency, 110 kHz. (From Gibbons, 1957.)

of the one in magnetite. Another relatively high-temperature peak was found in Mn_3O_4 ("hausmanite") by Fine and Chiou (1957). This material is isomorphous with magnetite but is believed to have the manganese in the Mn^{2+} and Mn^{4+} forms. The characteristics of both the peak in Mn-ferrite and Mn_3O_4 are listed in Table 19-1.

Still another group of materials having transition-metal ions in two valence states are the garnets, of which yttrium iron garnet (YIG) is best known. This compound has the formula $Y_3Fe_2(FeO_4)_3$ and is similar to magnetite in that the magnetic ions occupy both tetrahedrally and octahedrally coordinated lattice sites. Gibbons and Chirba (1958) found an internal friction peak in YIG near 160°K. This peak appears to be related to departure from stoichiometry, since the peak is much smaller in a sample prepared by a more refined technique. The activation energy and τ_0 for this peak were quite precisely determined (see Table 19-1) by a combination of the data of Gibbons and Chirba with a measurement by Einspruch (1962) at 10 MHz.

We now turn to the interpretations that have been advanced for the various relaxation peaks in these materials. The peak in magnetite at 95°K is apparently not a simple relaxation peak but rather is related to the occurrence of the transformation to the disordered state near 115°K. In this sense, it seems to be related to the relaxations near lambda-type phase transitions discussed in Sections 16.1 and 16.2, although it occurs well below, rather than very close to, the transition temperature. This peak appears to be due to a stress induced change in order among the Fe^{2+} and Fe^{3+} ions on the octahedral sites. For the 40°K peak, Gibbons (1957) suggested a mechanism of stress induced ordering among Fe^{2+} and Fe^{3+}, but in view of the relatively high degree of order that must exist at temperatures so far below the transformation temperature, one would not expect the effect to occur in the stoichiometric compound. In this connection, the result of Suiter and Blair (1965) indicating that vacancies are necessary to achieve the effect is quite significant. As a consequence of their work, Iida (1967) has proposed a model in which a vacancy resides on an octahedral site normally occupied by an Fe^{3+} ion. Such a site would have four equivalent nearest-neighbor Fe^{2+} ions in the perfectly ordered lattice. When a vacancy is present, however, three of the four equivalent neighbors must become Fe^{3+} ions, to preserve electrical charge balance. The remaining Fe^{2+} ion can reside on any one of the four equivalent neighbors, a situation that leads to stress-induced ordering through electron migration. Although this model is worthy of consideration, there still remain a number of problems to resolve. The mechanism of the 95°K peak has not really been elucidated. The fact that the 40 and 95°K peaks both show the same anisotropy (Figs. 19-14 and 19-15) may indicate a similarity in mechanism of these two effects. Also, the presence of the peak at ~670°K adds to the confusion; it seems difficult to believe that this peak is due to an electronic relaxation.

The situation is equally complicated for the other materials. Fine and Chiou (1957) claim that the higher activation energy for the Mn_3O_4 relaxation as compared to magnetite is due to the simultaneous diffusion of two electrons in the reaction

$$Mn_1^{2+} + Mn_2^{4+} \rightleftharpoons Mn_1^{4+} + Mn_2^{2+}$$

while only one electron is involved for magnetite. Gibbons, on the other hand, suggests an unsymmetrical reaction whereby

$$Mn_1^{2+} + Mn_2^{4+} + E \rightleftharpoons Mn_1^{3+} + Mn_2^{3+}$$

where E is an ionization energy which must be added to the activation energy. In view of the absence of more information about the relation of these peaks to deviations from stoichiometry, the present authors regard it as an open question as to whether some of the peaks listed in Table 19-1 (especially those above 200°K) are not in fact point defect relaxations of the type covered in Chapter 11, i.e., involving ionic rather than electronic redistributions.

B. TRAPPED HOLES OR ELECTRONS

In certain insulators, the introduction into the lattice of an impurity (or vacancy) can be accompanied by a hole or electron which is then trapped at the impurity so as to create an elastic dipole center. Such a center can then give rise to relaxation by the jumping only of the hole or electron in a manner completely analogous to the cases where atom jumps occur.

The occurrence of such electronic defects in transition metal oxides has been reviewed by van Houten and Bosman (1964). The most striking example is that of lithium-doped NiO. Pure stoichiometric NiO is an insulator with the rock salt structure. Doping with Li^+ produces p-type conduction due to the formation of holes in the Ni^{2+} levels. Such a hole, which simply takes the form of a Ni^{3+}, can bind itself to a Li^+ ion to form a Li^+-Ni^{3+} pair, which has twelve equivalent nearest-neighbor configurations about a given Li^+ ion. This pair constitutes an electric dipole, but also the lattice distortions serve to create an elastic dipole (since O^{2-} ions are pushed away from the Li^+ and attracted by the Ni^{3+} ion). The defect may reorient itself by the hopping of the hole among the twelve Ni^{2+} ions which are nearest neighbors to the Li^+ ion, as shown in Fig. 19-18.

An internal friction peak was observed by van Houten (1962) in NiO doped with 10% Li^+ ions. From measurements at several frequencies, he obtained an activation energy $Q = 0.20$ eV and $\tau_0^{-1} = 5 \times 10^{12}$ sec^{-1}. The electrical resistivity, measured as a function of temperature on the same sample, gave an activation energy of 0.19 eV. This latter value was regarded as the activation energy for a free hole to move from one nickel ion to its neighbor ("hopping" mechanism), so that the near agreement with the activation energy for relaxation was to be expected.

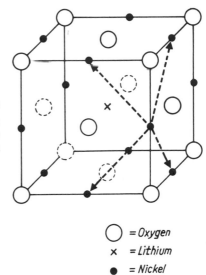

FIG. 19-18. Jump possibilities for a hole bound to a Li⁺ ion in NiO. Via such jumps, the hole has access to all twelve Ni^{2+} ions which are nearest-neighbors to the Li⁺. (From van Houten and Bosman, 1964.)

⬭ = *Oxygen*
× = *Lithium*
● = *Nickel*

Later work has completely changed the picture. First, both anelastic and dielectric measurements were made by van Houten and Bosman (1964) and Bosman and van Houten (1964) as a function of Li⁺ concentration. It was found that the peak observed for 10% Li⁺ drops in temperature from about 120 to 75°K (for ∼250 kHz) as shown in Fig. 19-19. At the same time, the activation energy falls to values of about 0.07 eV. Also, in the range of ∼0.1% Li⁺ a second anelastic peak is found at

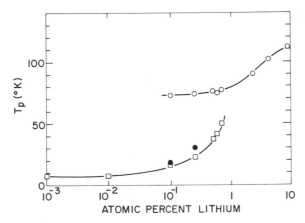

FIG. 19-19.   Peak temperature for anelastic relaxation (open circles) and dielectric relaxation (□) of NiO as function of Li⁺ content. Solid circles represent the low temperature anelastic peaks. Frequency, ∼250 kHz. (From Bosman and van Houten, 1964.)

lower temperatures, as shown by the circles in Fig. 19-19. In fact, at 0.1% Li$^+$ the low-temperature peak is substantially larger than the high-temperature peak. Correspondingly, dielectric measurements show a relaxation peak (the squares in Fig. 19-19) which coincides only with the lower of the two anelastic peaks. This means that at the higher temperature there is no electrically active, but only a mechanically active relaxational normal mode (see p. 209). Bosman and van Houten conclude that the defect giving rise to the low temperature peak could be the simple Li$^+$–Ni^{3+} pair, but that the high-temperature peak is due to a nonpolar defect such as a pair of antiparallel Li$^+$–Ni^{3+} pairs. The fact that the lower anelastic peak dominates at low Li$^+$ concentrations is consistent with this suggestion.

The second change in viewpoint comes from the more detailed study of the conductivity mechanism in NiO since 1963, via the use of Hall effect and Seebeck coefficient measurements (see, for example, Adler 1968). It is now established that the mobility of free holes is not activated (i.e., the hopping mechanism of conduction is not valid in NiO), but that the activation energy for conduction arises from the dependence of carrier concentration on temperature. The agreement between the activation energy for relaxation and conduction in van Houten's original paper (1962) must then be regarded as coincidental. On the other hand, there is strong independent evidence from optical studies (Austin *et al.*, 1968) that holes bound to Li$^+$ ions do show hopping-type behavior.

A similar anelastic relaxation effect to that in NiO seems to exist in Li$^+$-doped MnO, which was studied in a preliminary manner by Miller and Heikes (1958). Another example appears in a more recent study of CoO doped with Li$^+$ or Na$^+$ ions by Bosman and Crevecour (1968). In this work only dielectric loss measurements were carried out, but the dielectric peak was found at much higher temperatures than in NiO and showed an activation energy of about 0.2 eV. The difference between CoO and NiO is attributed to the difference in electronic configuration of the Ni^{2+} and Co^{2+} ions in their respective oxides.

Another interesting example of relaxations due to trapped electronic defects has been observed in reduced rutile (TiO$_2$) by Scott and Mac-Crone (1968a). The anelastic measurements were carried out to look for relaxations that had earlier been found dielectrically (Dominck and MacCrone, 1967). The anelastic peaks which appear at 9 and 14°K (at 1 kHz) agree with the dielectric loss peaks. In addition, a peak near 50°K was observed. The orientation dependence, the impurity dependence, and the requirement that the sample be reduced (i.e., nonstoichiometric) suggest the following defects, each of which traps an electron: (a) an oxygen vacancy associated with a trivalent impurity, and (b) a titanium interstitial associated with two trivalent impurities.

Although the class of electronic defect described in this subsection may be expected to occur in a wide variety of semiconducting crystals, the examples known thus far are very limited. It would be most valuable, therefore, to look further for such relaxations, especially on specimens which are well characterized as to their impurity and point-defect contents.

PROBLEM

19-1. Verify Eqs. (19.1-11) and (19.1-12).

General References

AUSTIN, I. G., and MOTT, N. F. (1969). *Advan. Phys.* **18**, 41.

BEYER, R. T., and LETCHER, S. V. (1969). "Physical Ultrasonics," Chap. 10. Academic Press, New York.

EINSPRUCH, N. G. (1965). *Solid State Phys.* **17**, 217.

KEYES, R. W. (1967). *Solid State Phys.* **20**, 37.

MASON, W. P. (1966). *In* "Physical Acoustics" (W. P. Mason, ed.), Vol. 4A, Chap. 8. Academic Press, New York.

ROBERTS, B. W. (1968). *In* "Physical Acoustics" (W. P. Mason, ed.), Vol. 4B. Academic Press, New York.

SPECTOR, H. N. (1966). *Solid State Phys.* **19**, 291.

TRUELL, R., ELBAUM, C., and CHICK, B. B. (1969). "Ultrasonic Methods in Solid State Physics," Chap. 3, Parts V, IX, X. Academic Press, New York.

Chapter 20 / Experimental Methods

There are four major categories of apparatus for the investigation of anelastic phenomena. These are discussed in consecutive sections of this chapter in order of ascending frequency range. Taken together, the methods provide a frequency range which effectively starts at about 10^{-5} Hz (the equivalent frequency of a slow quasi-static experiment) and which presently terminates at about 100 GHz. As a broad generalization, relaxations which involve atomic migration are generally investigated at kilohertz frequencies or below, so as to place the relaxation in a convenient (not too high) temperature range. On the other hand, high-frequency techniques (>1 MHz) are usually required for dislocation, electron, and phonon studies, so as to match the applied frequency to the short relaxation times involved in these cases.

20.1 Quasi-Static Methods

The use of quasi-static methods dates back well over a century to the work of Weber (1835) on the elastic aftereffect of galvanometer suspension wires. Since then, the arrangement of a wire specimen subject to axial twisting has been employed extensively. This popularity is due in large measure to the high strain sensitivity attainable, together with the ability to employ the arrangement for both quasi-static and low-frequency dynamic measurements. The apparatus described by Kê (1947) has become the prototype for equipment which serves both as a quasi-static "relaxometer" and as a low-frequency torsion pendulum.

When arranged as a relaxometer for the determination of the response functions $M(t)$, $J(t)$, or $N_{t_1}(t)$ (see Section 1.2), Kê's apparatus is essentially a critically-damped moving-coil mirror galvanometer. The wire specimen, which is about 30 cm long and of 1 mm diameter, serves as the suspension. As shown in Fig. 20-1, the specimen hangs from a top support (usually a pin vise) inside the uniform temperature zone of a vertical electric furnace. The extension rod joined to the lower pin vise

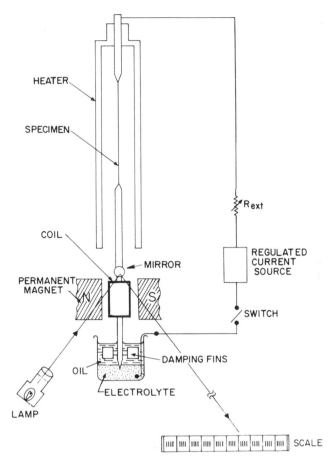

FIG. 20-1.   Galvanometer apparatus for quasi-static measurements.

carries the galvanometer mirror and a coil wound with several hundred turns of fine wire. Electrical connections to the coil are made through the specimen and through an electrolyte (e.g., a copper sulfate solution) contained in the lower portion of the beaker. Critical damping of the torsional mode of oscillation is obtained by the set of vanes which move in the oil layer above the electrolyte. To perform a stress relaxation experiment, the specimen is first equilibrated at the desired temperature and suddenly twisted to a preselected strain by energizing the coil with a suitable current. Thereafter the resistance R_{ext} is adjusted so as to maintain the scale reading constant at the initial deflection. Since the torque on the specimen is proportional to the current i, the variation of i with time t gives the form of the stress relaxation response. To avoid the necessity of constantly making small adjustments to the coil current, it is possible to use an excess current through the coil and to limit the initial twist to the desired value by contact against a mechanical stop. With this arrangement, the current is merely reduced intermittently to find the value at which contact with the stop is just broken. For creep experiments, a well-regulated constant current is passed through the coil and the deflection observed as a function of time. Upon completion of the creep, the elastic aftereffect can be observed after switching off the current. Actually, in a case where elastic aftereffect measurements alone serve the purpose of the investigation, the magnet and coil assembly can be replaced by an even simpler clamping device arranged around the extension rod (West, 1946; Wert, 1950a; Roswell and Nowick, 1953). The clamp is used to hold the specimen twisted for a suitable hold time t_1. During this period the specimen undergoes stress relaxation at constant strain. The complementary aftereffect is then observed on releasing the specimen.

As an alternative to the use of a moving-coil galvanometer system, a magnetometer (moving magnet) arrangement has been employed by Blackwell and Carey (1968). In this configuration, the coil and permanent magnet of Fig. 20-1 are replaced, respectively, by a small bar magnet and a pair of Helmholtz coils.

With direct visual observation, the shortest τ value measurable with the apparatus of Fig. 20-1 is about 1 min. This can be shortened with photographic recording to a limit of about 10 sec. The limit is imposed by the requirement that τ must be much greater than the time to apply or remove the stress, which in turn is equivalent to about three periods of the undamped oscillation. The longest measurable τ value is determined only by the patience of the observer. A reasonable practical limit is 10^4–10^5 sec.

The chief overall limitation of the apparatus is the fact that accurate measurements demand a relatively large relaxation strength. (This limitation is in fact shared by all quasi-static apparatus when compared to the relaxation sensitivity of dynamic apparatus.) For example, with a specimen of the dimensions noted above and a five-meter optical path, the strain sensitivity of the galvanometer apparatus is about 2×10^{-7} per millimeter deflection on the scale. Since about 20 data points at millimeter intervals are needed to trace out the creep curve reasonably well, the required anelastic strain is therefore 4×10^{-6}. Assuming that the elastic strain is restricted to 2×10^{-4} to avoid plastic deformation, the minimum required relaxation strength is therefore $4 \times 10^{-6}/2 \times 10^{-4}$, or 0.02. This figure can be reduced if greater strain sensitivity is obtained, but the measurements rapidly become more difficult.

For some applications, it is useful to invert the arrangement of Fig. 20-1 so that the coil and magnet assembly are above, rather than below, the specimen wire. This requires the introduction of a fine supplementary suspension wire passing over pulleys to a counterweight, in the manner shown in Fig. 20-3 (p. 586) for the inverted torsion pendulum. The inverted relaxometer permits direct insertion of the specimen into a liquid bath, an arrangement which is very suitable for close temperature control and also for *in-situ* quenching (Berry and Orehotsky, 1968a). For other applications, it may be desirable to adapt either a normal or inverted relaxometer to use in vacuum. It is then desirable to replace the oil damping by eddy current damping. The damping vanes are replaced by an aluminum disk which rotates in a narrow gap between the poles of a permanent magnet.

While it is usually most convenient to use a specimen in the form of a straight length of wire, a more complex form is sometimes advantageous. For example, Lindstrand (1955) employed a long length of wire coiled up into a spiral spring so as to make a sample that could be weighed more accurately for analytical purposes. A spiral spring is also the type of sample employed in the stress relaxation apparatus of Tichelaar and Lazarus (1959) for use at high pressures.

20.2 Subresonance Methods

The principle of the subresonance method was discussed in Section 1.4. Briefly, a specimen is set into forced vibration at a frequency ω low enough to permit neglect of the inertial term in the equation of motion. Under the condition $\omega^2 \ll \omega_r^2$ the loss angle ϕ becomes equal to the phase angle θ between the peak force F_0 and the peak displacement x_0 [cf. Eq. (1.5-8)]. From a measurement of ϕ and the absolute dynamic modulus $|M|$ ($\propto F_0/x_0$), the real and imaginary components of the complex modulus may be found using Eqs. (1.3-12) and (1.3-13). Due to the difficulty of measuring small phase angles, the subresonance method has not been widely used for work on crystals. It is, however, the most satisfactory experimental method when the damping is large ($\tan \phi > 0.1$), and has found considerable usage for work on polymers. (See Staverman and Schwarzl, 1956). Kê and Ross (1949) have adapted the relaxometer apparatus of Fig. 20-1 for use with the subresonance method. The torsional damping vanes are removed, and the coil is fed with a low-frequency (0.05 Hz) current derived from a motor-driven circular potentiometer. The phase of the motion seen optically on the scale from this unit lags by ϕ behind the phase of the coil current. By feeding the current through a second mirror galvanometer unit of very low damping, the phase lag can be determined optically. Little use has been made of this apparatus, but it appears well suited to the investigation of metals at high temperatures.

20.3   Resonance Methods

Resonance equipment falls broadly into the two categories of pendulum apparatus and resonant bar apparatus. These will be discussed in turn below. In pendulum apparatus, a large external inertia is added to the specimen, so as to produce a system with effectively only a single degree of freedom and a relatively low natural frequency (usually <100 Hz). The specimens tend to be of a slender shape, e.g., a wire or strip. On the other hand, resonant bar samples are usually relatively sturdy and, by virtue of the significance of their distributed inertia, possess a whole series of natural frequencies. Typically, the fundamental frequency together with those higher harmonics or overtones that can be excited with useful amplitude fall within the range 1–100 kHz. Formulas for the vibration shapes and natural frequencies of a number of resonant bar and pendulum arrangements are given in Appendix F. The torsional and longitudinal modes of a resonant bar each form a complete harmonic series. For specimens of relatively low damping, measurements up to the sixth harmonic have been reported. In flexural vibration the first few overtones are more widely separated than a harmonic series and a considerable frequency range can be obtained without great difficulty. To change the frequency of pendulum apparatus, it is customary to change only the size of the added inertia I. Since the frequency varies with $I^{-1/2}$, a hundredfold variation in I produces only a tenfold change in frequency. Usually, investigators have been content to work with a much smaller frequency range (e.g., a factor of only two or three). It is, however, desirable to strive for the widest possible frequency range, so that such quantities as, e.g., the activation energy of a relaxation can be determined with the greatest precision.

In addition to a wide frequency (and temperature) range, another desirable characteristic of dynamic apparatus is a low "background" or external energy loss. The usual principal sources of external loss are the surrounding air, the specimen mounting, and the transducers used to drive and detect the vibration. In some instances, a good deal of careful work has been required to reduce these losses to a small fraction of the loss due to internal friction (Cottell *et al.*, 1948). Relevant measures of internal friction have been discussed in Chapter 1. For free decay, the internal friction is measured in terms of the logarithmic decrement, δ [Eq. (1.5-17)]. For forced vibration, the bandwidth of the resonance curve gives Q^{-1} [Eq. (1.5-10)]. Alternatively, for a constant amplitude of forced vibration the dissipation may be expressed as the fractional energy loss per cycle $\Delta W/W$ [Eq. (1.3-21)]. For small damping, the relationships between these quantities are given in Eq. (1.5-19).

A. PENDULUM APPARATUS

The dominant apparatus in this group is the Coulomb-type torsion pendulum consisting basically of an inertia member suspended from a wire specimen. In recent times this type of apparatus came into prominence through the work of Kê (1947a). Similar versions had, however, been employed much earlier, e.g., by Guye (1912) and by Ishimoto (1919). The Föppl–Pertz torsion pendulum developed in Germany during the 1930's (see, e.g., Föppl, 1936) represents an adaptation of the Coulomb pendulum to much larger diameter specimens. In the present refined forms now available (Cottell *et al.*, 1948; Jensen, 1952, 1959; Darling, 1956-7; Sumner and Entwistle, 1958) this type of "high-stress" pendulum has a low background loss. However, it is of limited value for relaxation studies, principally because of the difficulty of varying the temperature over an extended range.

The form of torsion pendulum popularized by Kê (1947a) is shown in Fig. 20-2. Comparison with Fig. 20-1 shows the basic similarity of layout, which permits easy interconversion between the two arrangements. It should be noted that some of the details already given in connection with Fig. 20-1 apply equally well to Fig. 20-2. In the pendulum arrangement, the purpose of the oil cup is solely to damp out any lateral swinging motion of the extension rod which may be accidentally introduced either by external disturbances or by an asymmetry of the pull exerted by the electromagnets during excitation. The oil damping inevitably contributes to the background loss of the apparatus, and may be eliminated from a well-balanced system free of external vibrations. In a vacuum pendulum this also eliminates the potential nuisance of oil splatter due to evolution

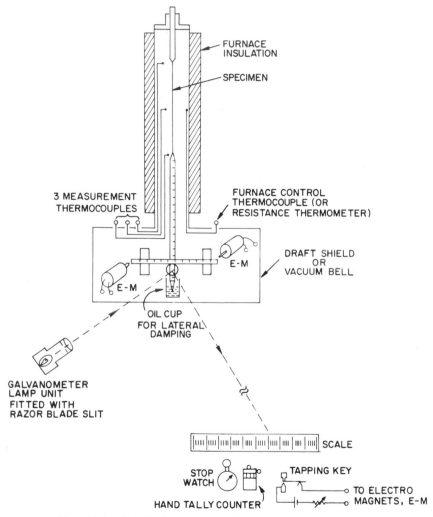

FIG. 20-2.   Standard type of torsion pendulum apparatus.

of dissolved gas. As shown in Fig. 20-2, the inertia member usually takes the form of a stiff transverse rod carrying a pair of adjustable weights. The frequency of vibration is changed by varying the position of the weights, or by removing them entirely. The highest frequency of visual measurement is restricted to about 2 Hz by the ability of the observer to follow the motion of the light beam on the scale. The lowest frequency attainable is governed by the maximum value of the tensile stress which it is practicable to impose on the specimen. While a frequency as low as

0.1 Hz may be possible in favorable circumstances, generally 0.2–0.3 Hz is a more realistic lower limit. The inertia member is either made entirely from a mild steel rod or at least carries some magnetic parts so that a torque can be applied to it by energizing the adjacent electromagnets. The torsional oscillations are started or stopped by the rhythmic manual use of the tapping key, in synchronism with the movement of the light beam on the scale. After the amplitude on the scale has been built up to a level of several centimeters, the logarithmic decrement and natural frequency may be measured in free decay. A convenient procedure is to both count and time the number of cycles elapsing between two measured amplitudes, so that both the decrement and the frequency are determined simultaneously.

It is good practice to wind the furnace noninductively on a nonmagnetic tube. Since temperature uniformity is of great importance, three separate heater windings are often employed. The location and mounting of the pendulum should be chosen to avoid external vibrations. The use of vacuum may be dictated by the desire to avoid oxidation of the sample, or to secure the lowest background damping. With specimens of low internal friction ($\delta \sim 10^{-5}$), a vacuum of about 10^{-5} Torr is required to reduce the air loss to an insignificant level. Since thermal equilibration of the sample is relatively sluggish in high vacuum, it is frequently desirable to compromise by working with a small pressure (5–10 Torr) of hydrogen or helium. This gives excellent heat transfer with a substantial reduction of atmospheric loss.

The standard pendulum of Fig. 20-2 can be modified in a considerable number of ways. The inverted arrangement shown schematically in Fig. 20-3 was used by Ang and Wert (1954) to minimize the tensile pull on refractory wire specimens raised to very high temperatures by direct Joule heating. Methods of improving the temperature uniformity have been described by Mosher (1969). By proper choice of the counterbalance weight, the tensile stress on the wire can be reduced to only a few grams per square millimeter. The inverted arrangement has been employed quite extensively, principally because it is easily adapted to liquid nitrogen or even liquid helium cooling (Swartz, 1961; Fast and Verrijp, 1961; Heller, 1961; Niblett, 1961). To ensure that the suspension have only a negligible effect on the measurements, the suspension must be made from a material of low internal friction (e.g., phosphor bronze or beryllium copper) and its torsional stiffness must be very much smaller than that of the specimen. An interesting variant of these conditions has been employed by Boulanger (1954) for specimens of very high damping.

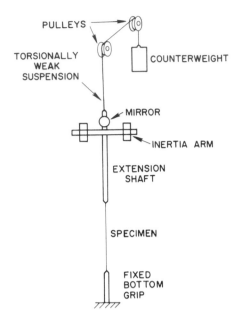

PULLEYS

TORSIONALLY
WEAK
SUSPENSION

COUNTERWEIGHT

MIRROR

INERTIA ARM

EXTENSION
SHAFT

SPECIMEN

FIXED
BOTTOM
GRIP

FIG. 20-3.   Arrangement of an inverted torsion pendulum.

By intentionally making the suspension of higher stiffness than the specimen, oscillatory behavior can be obtained when otherwise the system would be overdamped. In this modification the suspension contains most of the strain energy W, while the specimen provides most of the dissipation ΔW. Since Boulanger used torsional oscillation with specimens wound into the form of spiral springs, his arrangement is strictly a flexure pendulum in terms of the stress imposed on the specimen.

One of the simplest modifications to the measurement arrangement of Fig. 20-2 is the use of photographic recording as an adjunct to direct visual observation (e.g., Fine, 1950). This procedure was used by Childs and LeClaire (1954) for frequencies up to 50 Hz. Development and measurement of the decay record are however tedious and time consuming. Furthermore, the data are not immediately available to guide the course of an experiment. Attention has therefore been given to more convenient arrangements. A number of workers have devised photocell arrangements to sense the oscillation of the light beam and provide semiautomatic measurements in free decay (Stephenson and McCoy, 1962; Chambers and Schultz, 1962; De Morton et al., 1963; Linveit et al., 1964; Copley, 1966). In other cases, the vibration has been detected by some form of electrical transducer. For example, Niblett (1961) employed a condenser pickup, while Beaulieu et al. (1960) used a coil oscillating between the poles of a permanent magnet. Berry and Orehotsky (1968a) employed the converse arrangement of a small permanent magnet oscillating between fixed coils. Most of these arrangements permit measurements at strain amplitudes below 10^{-6} provided the pendulum is sufficiently well isolated from external vibrations. The automation of pendulum apparatus has proved to be a popular pastime with a succession of workers. The approach invariably involves a controlled feedback loop between the detection and drive transducers. Specific arrangements have been described by Kofstad et al. (1962), Salvi et al. (1965), Butera and Craig (1966), Perez et al. (1966, 1967), Miszenti (1966), Grandchamp and Fornerod (1970), and Harbottle (1970).

To close this section we shall mention briefly various forms of "flexure pendulum" apparatus in which the specimen is subject to a bending, rather than a twisting, deformation. The usual form of flexure pendulum employs a specimen arranged as an end-loaded cantilever (i.e., rigidly fixed at one end and loaded with an external inertia at the free end). In some arrangements, such as those of Snoek (1941) and Chang and Gensamer (1953) the specimen is arranged vertically. While this avoids the creation of static bending strain in the sample due to the weight of the inertia, the vertical arrangement has the drawback that the observed dynamic properties of the system can be influenced markedly by the gravitational term in its equation of motion. As discussed by Snoek, this term affects the measurements in a manner which depends on whether the center of mass is (a) above or (b) below the clamped end of the specimen (i.e., whether the specimen is pointing up or hanging down). For case (a), the gravitational force opposes the elastic restoring force, and the frequency is lower and the decrement higher than would be measured under zero gravity. Converse statements hold for case (b). In either case, neglect of the gravitational term leads to erroneous values for the modulus and internal friction of the specimen. Since these complications are absent when the specimen is mounted horizontally rather than vertically, a horizontal arrangement is to be preferred. To avoid a large static sag due to the inertia, it is desirable that the specimen be in the form of a strip with the plane of high bending stiffness arranged vertically. For the unfavorable case of a wire, where the bending stiffness is low in all directions, Bennewitz and Rötger (1936) and Swartz (1969a) resorted to a long flexible suspension to support the weight of the inertia. Berry (1961) circumvented the same problem by the use of two wire samples to construct a composite specimen whose vertical bending stiffness was much greater than that of either wire individually. An automated flexure pendulum has been described by Harbottle (1970).

B. RESONANT BAR APPARATUS

A uniform bar possesses many natural modes of vibration that can be utilized for internal friction measurements. The modes may be longitudinal, torsional, or flexural, and depend further on whether the specimen is freely suspended or is clamped at one or both ends. The shapes of some of these modes, and their vibration frequencies, are listed in Appendix F. Although the specimen is described as a bar in the section head, the actual form may vary considerably and other descriptions such as rod, tube, or reed may be more appropriate in particular cases. Indeed, this does not exhaust the list of specimen shapes used with resonance equipment. Other more specialized forms include the disk (Bordoni and Nuovo, 1957) and the sphere (Frazer and Le Craw, 1964).

The mounting or support for a resonant bar sample should be designed so as to minimize the external energy loss. For free–free modes (Appendix F), it is usual to contact the specimen only at points of minimum motion (the nodes). A frequently used support is a sling of fine wire, e.g., tungsten of 0.0015 in. diameter. Alternatively, the specimen may be mounted on knife edges or needle points. This is the arrangement commonly employed with the fundamental longitudinal (or torsional) mode, which contains only one node. For the clamped-free modes, the clamped end of the specimen automatically forms the point of support. It is important that the support be rigid and massive in relation to the specimen. Although a mechanical clamp has the advantage that the specimen can be demounted, it frequently suffers from the disadvantage that it causes significant and irreproducible losses due to rubbing friction. It is often feasible to avoid this problem by making an integral bond (by welding, brazing, etc.) to a pedestal of intermediate size, which in turn is mechanically clamped to the main support of the apparatus.

The many individual pieces of apparatus described under the following five subheadings have been classified according to the method used to excite and detect the vibrations of the specimen. It should be noted that where separate driver and detector units are employed, these need not be of the same type. It is sometimes advantageous to combine a driver of one kind with a detector of another.

1. *Drive and Detection via a Mechanical Coupling*

An early successful apparatus utilizing the "jiggling string" coupling is that of Förster (1937) for free–free bars in flexural vibration. The specimens are rods or bars several inches long and about 0.5 in. deep, with a

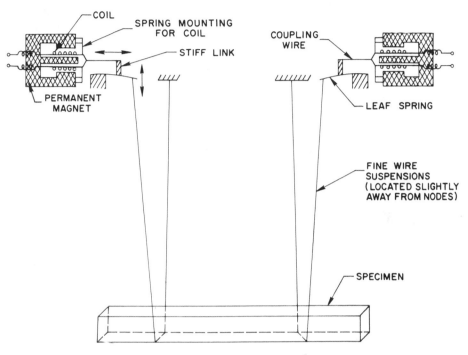

FIG. 20-4.   Förster's horizontal free–free bar apparatus.

fundamental frequency of about 2 kHz. As indicated in Fig. 20-4, the
fine wire suspensions used to support the bar also serve as mechanical
couplings to the driver and detector. Such units can be made by modification of an ordinary small loudspeaker. Their electromechanical action
hardly needs mention; the coil may be set in forced vibration by energizing
it with alternating current, while a motion imposed on the coil causes it
to generate a voltage proportional to its velocity. As shown in Fig. 20-4,
these units are arranged so that the coils are horizontal, and coupling
between the suspension and the coil is made through a leaf spring assembly. This is done to provide a sensitivity adjustment and to avoid
imposing the weight of the specimen on the spring mountings of the coils.
To excite and detect vibration in the specimen the suspensions must be
set a small distance away from the nodal positions. If these separations
are increased, larger amplitudes of vibration can be excited and larger
outputs obtained from the detector, but only at the expense of a higher

apparatus loss. Förster has pointed out that a convenient method of determining the loss caused by the driver and detector is to determine the manner in which the measured damping varies with the distance separating the suspensions from the nodes. This matter has been treated in more quantitative detail by Wachtmann and Tefft (1958), who have reported measuring a value of Q^{-1} as low as 5×10^{-6} with apparatus of this kind when working *in vacuo*.

A variety of metallurgical phenomena have been investigated with Förster's apparatus (e.g., Förster and Köster, 1937b). By placing a horizontal furnace around the specimen, with holes in it to allow the suspensions to pass through, the apparatus can be used up to temperatures of at least 500°C. The fact that the driver and detector units do not have to be placed in the furnace is one of the chief advantages of this apparatus. The method of excitation is sufficiently powerful for measurements to be made on materials of quite high damping at strain amplitudes of $\sim 10^{-5}$. Operation *in vacuo* is feasible if radiation shields are substituted for the normal furnace insulation. Since the apparatus employs separate driver and detector units, either free-decay or resonance curve measurements of the damping may be employed, depending on which is the most appropriate. Resonance curve measurements of Q^{-1} are more suitable at higher levels of damping, but care must be taken to prevent the detector from picking up the stray field of the driver. Both units should be screened by enclosure in soft iron or permalloy boxes. The frequency range of this apparatus is limited by the electromechanical response of the driver and detector. A span of one decade, from a few hundred to a few thousand hertz, should be obtainable without difficulty.

Apparatus rather similar to Förster's has been described by Rotherham *et al.* (1951). These workers employed a crystal phonograph pickup as a detector and direct magnetic drive for excitation. Another apparatus employing mechanical coupling has been developed by Berry (1955b). Transverse vibration is again employed, but this time the specimen is suspended vertically from couplings attached to a crystal pickup of relatively low loss and insensitivity to external vibrations.

A typical block layout of the electronic instrumentation suitable for Förster's and many other types of apparatus is shown in Fig. 20-5. The oscillator is required to have considerable stability, and should be fitted with a fine-tuning arrangement. Sometimes, a power amplifier or a matching circuit (such as a step-down transformer) may be needed between the oscillator and the driver. The size of the signal generated by the detector may typically range from several millivolts to a small fraction

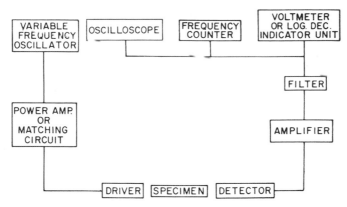

FIG. 20-5. Typical block diagram of instrumentation for resonant bar equipment.

of a millivolt. The signal to noise ratio in the amplified output can frequently be improved by the use of a frequency-selective amplifier or adjustable filter, tuned to the specimen frequency. It is highly desirable that the quality of the output be constantly monitored by display on a cathode ray tube. For resonance curve measurements of $\mathcal{Q}^{-1}$, the amplified output is usually fed to a rectifier voltmeter, which is read in conjunction with the frequency display of an electronic counter. If the rate of free decay is low enough, the logarithmic decrement may alternatively be obtained by timing the interval for the voltage to fall from one selected level to another. Several instruments have been devised for automatic measurement of the logarithmic decrement (Fusfeld, 1950; Smith, 1951; Pattinson, 1954). The basic function of all these instruments is to switch on an electronic timer or cycle counter when the voltage output envelope has fallen to a chosen value, and to switch off the timer or counter when a known fraction of this value has been reached. These instruments are very convenient to use, and are capable of high accuracy if the damping is not too large. On the other hand, when there are only a few cycles in the decay, it becomes more accurate to make measurements from a record of the decay. Oscilloscope photography has become much more convenient with the advent of Polaroid film.

2. Eddy-Current Drive and Detection

A number of investigators have devised apparatus in which excitation or detection of vibrations is achieved via the action of eddy currents induced in a metallic specimen. Excitation is obtained by the combined application of an alternating and a steady (polarizing) magnetic field to the vicinity of a displacement antinode. The applied alternating field, which must be tuned to the resonant frequency of the sample, induces local alternating eddy currents which then interact with the polarizing field so that the specimen experiences an alternating force. As shown in Fig. 20-6, either longitudinal, flexural, or torsional vibration may be excited in this way according to the particular geometrical arrangement adopted (Zener and Randall, 1940; Entwistle, 1953, 1954; Hanstock and Murray, 1946). The detection of vibrations is achieved in a converse manner to their excitation; the vibration of the specimen in the polarizing field causes the generation of alternating eddy currents in the specimen which induce a voltage in the detector coils proportional to the instantaneous velocity of motion. To obtain the sensitivity required, the detector coils contain several thousand turns of fine wire. The driving coils need only contain several hundred turns of somewhat thicker wire. In all cases, the driver and detector must be screened to reduce the noise level in the detector output.

With operation *in vacuo* (or even in air for the favorable case of torsional oscillation where piston effects are absent), external losses in eddy current apparatus can be made very small and several workers have measured a Q^{-1} value of 2×10^{-6}. The method works very well in the frequency range 1–50 kHz with materials whose resistivity and damping are not too high. The upper limit of the useful temperature range is determined by the breakdown of the insulation on the electrical windings.

Apart from the more common free-decay and resonance curve methods of measurement, eddy current drive and detection have also been used in regenerative or self-excited apparatus. In the apparatus of Hanstock and Murray (1946) the signal from the detector is applied to a power amplifier whose output is fed to the driver coils in the correct phase relationship to produce sustained oscillation. After calibration, the damping of the specimen can be determined from the ratio of the peak detector voltage to the peak exciter current. This is a form of the energy-input technique of damping measurement. Regenerative apparatus has the advantages that each measurement is made at constant strain amplitude and without problems arising from frequency drift. The torsional apparatus used by Hanstock and Murray was specially designed for a large power output, and was powerful enough to fracture low damping aluminum alloy specimens by fatigue.

Thompson and Glass (1958) have described a regenerative system employing eddy current drive and electrostatic detection. The specimens are rods which vibrate longitudinally at about 15 kHz. The regenerative

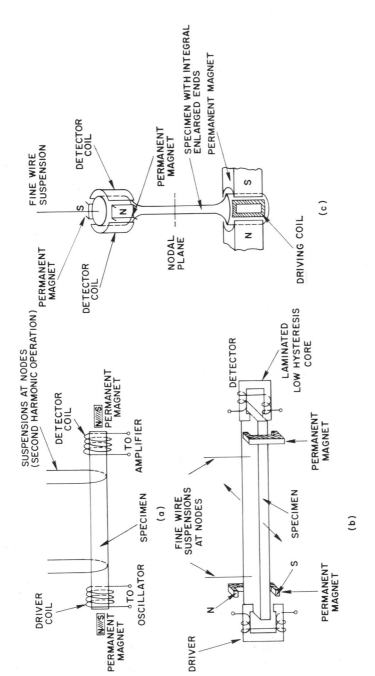

Fig. 20-6. Arrangements for eddy-current drive and detection in (a) longitudinal, (b) flexural, and (c) torsional vibration.

system enables the specimen to be driven at a fixed amplitude of vibration which is held constant, despite changes in the internal friction, by electronic regulation of the drive current. Following calibration, the measured value of this current can be used to calculate the internal friction of the sample. The internal friction and Young's modulus of the sample can be determined continuously by automatic recording of the drive coil current and the resonant frequency. Measurements have been made down to $4.2°K$. As pointed out by Thompson and Glass, their apparatus has particular advantages when the specimen assembly must be located at a considerable distance from the electronic circuitry (as was needed for their neutron irradiation work), and where measurements are needed over long periods of time.

3. *Magnetic Drive and Detection*

With specimens of high internal friction, it is sometimes a problem to transfer enough energy to the specimen to make it vibrate with a reasonable amplitude. A specimen easily excited at a temperature where the damping is low may give difficulty when heated through the temperature range of a large internal friction peak. For such a situation, a magnetic drive may be the best choice, since it can provide powerful excitation when the damping is large, without contributing too much in background loss when the damping is small. The form of apparatus introduced by Wegel and Walther (1935) has often been employed since. Using different arrangements, either longitudinal, torsional, or flexural modes of vibration can be used (Fig. 20-7). According to the mode desired, a suitably shaped magnetic armature is cemented to each end of the specimen. For longitudinal vibration, the armatures are flat disks; for torsional vibration two tabs can be bent up from such a disk, as shown in Fig. 20-7b. Since these tabs may be susceptible to bending resonances, Fine (1952) and Bradfield (1960) have devised alternative forms of torsional armatures. The arrangement for flexure shown in Fig. 20-7c was apparently first used by Kê (1949b). Since the armatures are attracted by the polarizing fields, the method used to support the specimen must prevent it from being pulled over on to the pole tips. In addition to the wire suspension used by Wegel and Walther (Fig. 20-7a), needle point supports have been used by Fine (1952b). This arrangement permits the specimen to be mounted either horizontally or vertically. Excitation is obtained by energizing the drive coils with alternating current of the correct frequency from the oscillator. This produces an alternating field which is superimposed upon the polarizing field and causes the armature to experience

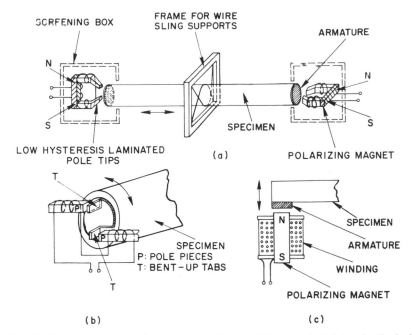

FIG. 20-7. Arrangements for magnetics drive and detection in (a) longitudinal, (b) torsional, and (c) flexural vibration.

a biased alternating force of the same frequency. It should be evident that the function of the polarizing field is merely to bias the magnetization of the armature so that its induced polarity is never reversed under the action of the alternating field. In the detector, the function of the polarizing field is again to magnetize the armature. Movement of the armature, due to vibration of the specimen, then causes an alternating voltage to be induced in the detector coils. As in the eddy current method, the detector is of the velocity-sensitive type so that its sensitivity becomes small at low frequencies. In contrast to the eddy current driver, however, the magnetic drive can be used down to as low a frequency as desired. Insulating as well as conducting specimens can be used with the magnetic method, an advantage not possessed by the eddy current method. For insulating specimens only, the deposition of a metallic thin film conductor pattern on the surface of the specimen has been used to obtain an electromagnetic coupling for both longitudinal and torsional vibrations (Baroni and Giacomini, 1954).

Wegel and Walther have demonstrated the use of the magnetic method up to a frequency of 100 kHz, for strain amplitudes in the range 10^{-8}–10^{-5}.

As for eddy current apparatus, the presence of the electrical coils in the furnace is the limiting factor on the use of the arrangement at high temperatures. Background losses in the driver and detector are due primarily to hysteresis and eddy currents in the armature and pole tips; to reduce the eddy current loss some investigators have laminated the pole pieces of the driver and detector. Silicon iron or one of the various permalloys are magnetic materials of low hysteresis loss. The relatively low Curie points of the permalloys make silicon iron preferable for high temperature use. The reduction of pickup from the driver requires careful attention in this apparatus if a satisfactory signal to noise ratio is to be obtained from the detector. In addition to the use of soft iron screening boxes, Fine (1952b) has pointed out that it is advantageous to arrange the plane of the detector at 90° to that of the driver so as to reduce their mutual inductance. Hum pickup or transients from a furnace winding should be minimized by winding the furnace noninductively. Furthermore, a high-pass filter or frequency selective amplifier can be used to obtain a relative suppression of hum in the amplified detector output.

4. Electrostatic Drive and Detection

The main advantages of the electrostatic method are suitability for use at both high and low temperatures, a wide frequency range, a low background loss, and a high detection sensitivity. A possible disadvantage is that only comparatively weak vibration amplitudes can be excited in materials of high internal friction. Bruner (1960) has described electrostatic drive and detection apparatus for rods in longitudinal vibration at 10 kHz over the temperature range 4.2–300°K. The 10–20 Hz torsion pendulum of Niblett (1961) also operates down to 4.2°K and utilizes electrostatic detection and a magnetic drive. Cabarat et al. (1951-52) have used electrostatic drive and detection up to 700°C and were able to measure Q^{-1} values as high as 0.07 on rods in longitudinal vibration. Similar apparatus has been described by Fine (1957). Southgate (1959) has carried the method to 1300°C. The extremely low level of apparatus loss possible with electrostatic apparatus is strikingly demonstrated by Southgate's work. Logarithmic decrements as low as 10^{-7} were reported for silicon single crystals vibrating in vacuo at 100 kHz. Apparatus for dielectric specimens in flexural vibration has been described by Dreyfus and Laibowitz (1964) and Scott and MacCrone (1968b). Electrostatic excitation of metallic reeds has been combined with nonresonant piezoelectric detection by Di Carlo and Townsend (1966).

Electrostatic apparatus utilizes the capacitive coupling between the specimen and a fixed electrode positioned close to a vibration antinode. Examples for longitudinal and flexural modes of vibration are shown in Fig. 20-8. In addition, for torsional vibration, Bancroft and Jacobs (1938) attached a vane to each end of the specimen and arranged a split electrode around it in a manner reminiscent of Fig. 20-7b. The same idea was employed by Niblett (1961) in his torsion pendulum apparatus. The most powerful method of electrostatic excitation is the polarized drive arrangement of Fig. 20-8a. Here, a steady battery potential V_0 between the specimen and drive electrode is modulated with the voltage $v_0 \sin \omega t$ (where $v_0 < V_0$) from the oscillator. The specimen then experiences a dynamic force of frequency ω and of a magnitude proportional to the product $V_0 v_0$. A second excitation scheme is to apply the oscillator voltage without a polarizing voltage. In this case the specimen experiences a peak attraction twice per oscillator cycle so that resonance

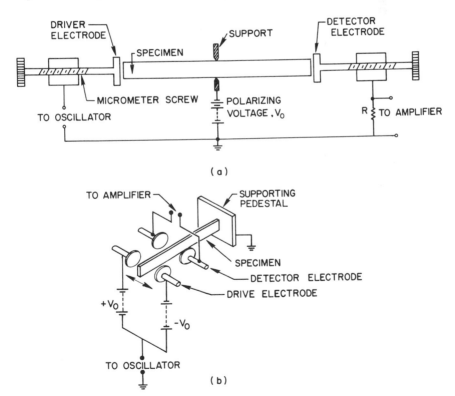

FIG. 20-8. Arrangements for polarized electrostatic drive and detection of (a) a rod in longitudinal vibration and (b) a reed in flexural vibration.

is obtained by tuning the oscillator to half the natural frequency of the specimen. The efficiency of this method is lower, but it has the advantage that the excitation frequency is now different from that of the specimen, so that direct pickup from the driver can be filtered out in the detection circuits. It should be noted that where a polarizing voltage is used, there is a steady component to the electrostatic attraction across the gap and care must be taken to ensure the support does not allow the specimen to be pulled over on to the electrode. Needle point or knife edge clamps are commonly used. Excitation voltages are usually in the range 10–100 V rms.

The simplest method of electrostatic detection is the condenser microphone arrangement of Fig. 20-8a, where a polarizing battery ($\sim$200 V) and a high resistance R ($\sim$10⁶ Ω) are arranged in series with the detection condenser. The signal appearing across R can then be amplified in conventional fashion for measurement and display. Because the capacity is *inversely* proportional to the interelectrode separation, linear detection is obtained only when the dynamic displacements are small compared to the gap setting. A second detection method has been described by Yousef and Sultan (1949) and subsequently used by Kamel (1953) for specimens vibrating either in torsion or flexure at $\sim$100 Hz. This method employs a slightly detuned single stage 6-MHz quartz crystal oscillator. The plate current of such a circuit is highly sensitive to capacity changes in the tuning circuit, which includes the specimen-detection electrode condenser. A third detection scheme, developed by Bordoni (1947), makes use of the alternating capacity change resulting from vibration to frequency modulate the output of a very high-frequency (typically 60 MHz) oscillator. The modulated signal is broadcast to an FM receiver where it is amplified and fed to a discriminator circuit which converts the FM signal to an AM signal. The carrier frequency is then filtered out and the specimen signal passed on for further amplification and output display. Comparatively extensive use has been made of the FM detection system. Circuitry has been described by Pursey and Pyatt (1954), Vernon (1957), Southgate (1959), and Dreyfus and Laibowitz (1964). In these arrangements only a single electrode need be used to accomplish both drive and detection. Operation with conventional specimens is possible up to 300 kHz, while Bordoni and Nuovo (1957) have reached frequencies of 6 MHz using a mica slip as the dielectric medium between a disk specimen and the electrode. Displacement sensitivities of 0.5 Å and measurements at strain amplitudes of 10^{-9} have been reported with the FM system.

5. *The Piezoelectric Composite Oscillator*

The final resonance method to be discussed is that in which the specimen under investigation is joined to one or more frequency-matched quartz crystals to form a composite oscillator. The use of such an oscillator for internal friction and modulus measurements originated with the work of Quimby (1925), and the method has since been refined by a succession of workers (Balamuth, 1934; Rose, 1936; and others quoted below). In the two component oscillator (Fig. 20-9), just one quartz crystal is joined to the specimen. The cross-sectional areas of the specimen and the crystal are equal and their lengths are such that their fundamental frequencies match within a few percent. The composite oscillator can then be driven into vibration in a partial series of harmonics such that the joint is always a displacement antinode, where the stresses and strains are least. This is done so that the existence of the joint has a minimum effect on the behavior of the oscillator. A number of bonding materials, suitable for various temperature ranges, have been described by Nowick (1950), Artman (1952), Sutton (1953), and Fine (1954). For longitudinal vibrations the quartz crystals are of square cross section and of the X-cut or $-18.5°$ X-cut type. Usually gold leaf or evaporated metallic film electrodes are applied directly to the crystal, but in the arrangement of Read (1940) the crystal was placed between but not touching a pair of fixed brass electrodes. The frequencies used are in the range 20–100 kHz, the lower limit being set by the scarcity of large quartz crystals. For torsional vibration a crystal of circular cross section is used with four electrodes applied to its surface, one to each quadrant (Rose, 1936).

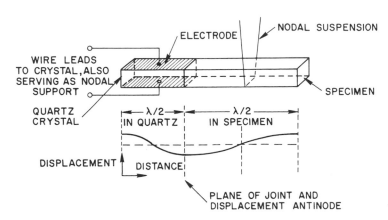

FIG. 20-9. Two-component longitudinal composite oscillator, showing the displacement pattern at the fundamental frequency.

Two methods of internal friction measurement have been used with the two component oscillator of Fig. 20-9. In the first of these (Zacharias, 1933; Siegel and Quimby, 1936) the crystal is excited with a constant voltage output from a variable frequency oscillator, and the current through the crystal is measured as a function of frequency through resonance. Using an electromechanical analysis of the oscillator which neglects energy losses in the quartz, this data, coupled with a knowledge of the resonant frequency of the quartz alone and the masses of the specimen and crystal, can be used to calculate the resonant frequency and damping of the specimen. This method of damping measurement is suitable only if the logarithmic decrement of the specimen exceeds roughly 10^{-3}. For specimens of lower internal friction, the second method may be used, in which the electrical impedance of the composite oscillator is measured with an ac bridge as a function of frequency through resonance (Cooke, 1936; Read, 1940). A calibration is first performed with the specimen absent, to obtain the effective resistance and resonant frequency of the quartz crystal. Similar measurements, made with the specimen mounted in position, enable the frequency and decrement to be deduced for the specimen alone. A particular advantage of the bridge method is that measurements can be made at a constant and calculable strain amplitude of vibration. This is a most useful feature when the specimen exhibits amplitude-dependent damping (Read, 1940; Nowick, 1950). Measurements with the two-component composite oscillator have been made up to temperatures approaching 500°C, as in the work of Artman (1952). However, the $\alpha \rightarrow \beta$ transformation in quartz at 577°C sets an upper limit to the temperature range that can be covered by the two component oscillator. In an investigation of the elastic constants of sodium chloride up to its melting point (804°C), Hunter and Siegel (1942) overcame this difficulty by the use of a three-component oscillator. The additional component was a fused silica rod, inserted between the specimen and the quartz crystal. The rod was cut to a sufficient number of half wavelengths that the specimen could be placed in the hot zone of a furnace while the quartz crystal was maintained almost at room temperature.

So far, mention has been made only of methods in which one quartz crystal is used in the composite oscillator. In such arrangements the crystal serves the dual purpose of (a) driving the specimen into vibration and (b) sensing the mechanical reaction of the specimen via a change in impedance. Other composite oscillators have been developed that contain two quartz crystals, one of which is used as a driver and the other as a detector. Mason (1950) and Bozorth *et al.* (1951) have discussed measurement techniques in which the drive and detector crystals are cemented to opposite ends of the specimen. This arrangement has not been as popular as an alternative scheme in which the drive and detector crystals are cemented together as a semipermanent unit to form a "driver-gauge" combination (Marx, 1951). As shown in Fig. 20-10, the magnitude of the oscillator voltage supplied to the driver is read on one vacuum tube voltmeter, while the output from the gauge crystal is read on another. Marx has shown the ratio of these voltages is proportional to the decrement of the composite oscillator, and has derived the proportionality constant in terms of measurable parameters. A simple relationship involving the mass

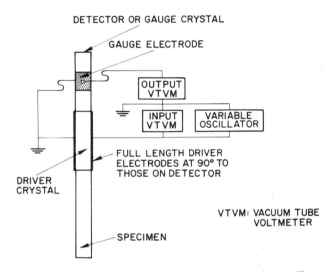

FIG. 20-10. The Marx three-component composite oscillator.

of the specimen and the mass and decrement of the driver-gauge combination can then be used to calculate the damping of the specimen. The method has the advantage that successive readings can be made quickly, and with the specimen vibrating at a constant strain amplitude which is calculable from the size of the gauge signal. The strain amplitude range of the method is given as 10^{-8}–10^{-5}. The error in the determination of the specimen decrement is quoted as 3% if $10^{-5} < \delta < 10^{-1}$ and good crystals and careful calibration procedures are employed.

Using the driver-gauge combination described above, Marx and Sivertsen (1953) have employed an interesting modification of Hunter and Siegel's technique in an investigation of fused silica from -173 to

1000°C. An extended temperature range is also a feature of the apparatus described more recently by Povolo and Gibala (1969). Another adaptation of the Marx driver-gauge assembly has been employed by Baker (1957) in a five-component oscillator designed to permit internal friction measurements on a specimen subject to a static compressive stress.

20.4　High-Frequency Wave Propagation Methods

The principle of the pulse method for the measurement of the velocity v and attenuation $\mathscr{A}$ of a traveling wave was discussed in Section 1.6. The reason the method is suitable only for megahertz frequencies and above can easily be appreciated from the relation $v = f\lambda$ and the requirement that the pulse length be short with respect to the sample length. Since v is typically 5×10^5 cm sec^{-1}, we find a frequency of at least 10 MHz is required for work with single-crystal samples of readily available dimensions. A quartz transducer with fundamental resonance as high as 10 MHz is already quite thin ($\sim$0.025 cm), but by the use of even thinner quartz crystals driven at higher harmonics, frequencies close to 1 GHz have been achieved. The excitation and utilization of even higher frequencies beyond this point represent the field known as *hypersonics* or *microwave ultrasonics*, to which we shall refer briefly at the end of the section.

The high frequencies and short transit times involved in the pulse method call for electronic equipment that is considerably more sophisticated than that required for resonance methods. In addition, meaningful attenuation measurements require that due regard be paid to the various factors that can complicate the propagation process. Both aspects have recently been treated at length by workers who have done much pioneering work in this field (Truell *et al.*, 1969). Here we shall do no more than present a brief sketch, starting with a qualitative description of the two extreme situations (free propagation versus guided wave propagation) which have been employed in the pulse method. In a typical situation a transducer of 1- or 2-cm diameter is used to launch waves whose wavelength is about 0.05 cm. Because the ratio of transducer diameter to wavelength is so large, the pattern of waves radiated into the bar is determined entirely by diffraction; to determine the net effect each point on the surface of the transducer must be regarded as a point source of spherical waves. With the assumption of free propagation (i.e., that the cross section of the specimen is much larger than that of the transducer so that reflections from the side surfaces do not enter), the problem is formally similar to that of the diffraction of a light through a circular aperture, or of a piston source radiating into a semi-infinite fluid. The result is a main intense central beam surrounded by much weaker lobes. This result is of the greatest importance, for the whole basis of the pulse method depends on the ability to send a pulse along a known path. Actually the main beam can be divided into two regions. Close to the transducer, in the near or Fresnel region, the wave fronts are virtually plane and beam spreading is absent. Roderick and Truell (1952) have found good agreement with the theoretical prediction that plane wave behavior should exist up to a distance of $D^2/2\lambda$ from a transducer of diameter D (typically a distance of 10–40 cm at 10 MHz). Further away, the wave fronts become spherical and the beam diverges with a semi-angle β given by $\arcsin(1.22\lambda/D)$. The divergence of the beam therefore increases the lower the frequency. At 10 MHz a typical value of β is 2°. Beam spreading is to be avoided as far as possible, since it reduces the intensity of the pulse and may cause the true attenuation of the sample to be greatly overestimated. If beam spreading occurs to the extent that the pulse impinges on the sidewalls of the specimen, many spurious reflections can be observed in the echo train. Seki *et al.* (1956) have pointed out that even when beam spreading does not occur, the nature of the diffraction field is such that a "diffraction loss" is superimposed on the intrinsic attenuation of the material. This correction is of considerable significance for materials of low attenuation when examined at comparatively low frequencies.

So far, it has been assumed that the specimen has a large enough cross section in relation to the diameter of the transducer to be considered as a semi-infinite medium. For the situation of a long narrow rod where the transducer completely covers the end of the specimen, propagation occurs in a different manner, namely, as a guided wave motion in which beam spreading is confined geometrically by internal reflections from the sides of the specimen (Redwood and Lamb, 1956, 1957; Redwood, 1957; Meeker and Meitzler, 1964). For a pulse of shear waves, the glancing internal reflections do not cause the pulse to break up, but for a pulse of longitudinal waves some energy is drained off the main pulse at each reflection by the generation of a shear wave component as part of the reflection process. To indicate the complexities involved, it is necessary to mention briefly the manner in which stress waves are reflected from a free surface of an isotropic medium (see e.g., Kolsky, 1953). In general, the waves do not undergo simple reflection, though this does happen for the special case of normal incidence. A longitudinal wave impinging on a free boundary at oblique incidence is generally split into two reflected waves; one is a longitudinal wave of different amplitude from the incident wave, but with an angle of reflection equal to the angle of incidence. The other is a shear wave, proceeding from the surface at a different angle than its longitudinal partner. There may even exist (depending on Poisson's ratio) one or more angles of incidence for which a longitudinal wave is reflected wholly as a shear wave (Arenburg, 1948). A somewhat analogous situation holds true in reverse for the reflection of a shear wave from a free boundary. However, as noted above, an important exception is that for angles of incidence less than a certain critical angle, a shear wave is reflected wholly as a shear wave. The production of shear waves from longitudinal waves, and vice versa, is called mode conversion or mode mixing, and arises because of the boundary conditions that must be satisfied at the free surface. (If the boundary is not a free surface but an interface between two different media, the situation is even more complicated, since transmission with refraction occurs in addition to reflection.)

Little use has been made of the guided wave arrangement for attenuation measurements since the early work of Mason and McSkimin (1947).[†] These experiments were performed on rods of polycrystalline aluminum, 1 in. in diameter and 24 in. long, over the frequency range 2–15 MHz. The results revealed the importance of boundary scattering as a major source of attenuation in polycrystalline samples at high frequencies. For the investigation of absorption losses, it is desirable to avoid scattering losses by the use of single crystals. Such samples are usually desired in any case, so that the wave propagation can be directed along selected crystallographic directions. The limited length of most single crystals requires however that free propagation (rather than guided wave) conditions be employed for the ultrasonic pulse measurements. Following the original application of the free propagation method to elastic constant measurements [see, e.g., Huntington (1947, 1958); Einspruch (1965)], it has been widely applied to attenuation studies at or below room temperature (Truell *et al.*, 1969; Mason, 1958; McSkimin, 1964). Measurements above room temperature have also been reported, e.g., by Lord and Beshers (1966). The most frequent practice is to use just one quartz transducer both to launch the pulse and to detect the echo train as shown in Fig. 1-9. A block diagram of a relatively simple system for attenuation

---

[†] See, however, Papadakis (1971).

measurements is shown in Fig. 20-11. To obtain a steady display of the echo pattern on the oscilloscope screen, not one but a steady stream of pulses is launched into the sample. The interval between the pulses (typically 10^{-2} sec) is set by the sync generator, and should be large enough for the echo train to die away yet small enough to give a non-flickering display. The width of each triggering pulse can be used to adjust the number of waves in the high-frequency packet emitted by the drive oscillator. The series of diminishing echoes picked up by the transducer after each new pulse has been launched is amplified by a suitable amplifier receiver. (Provision must be made, via a switching or limiting circuit, to protect the receiver from the drive pulses.) It will be seen from Fig. 20-11 that the oscilloscope beam sweep is triggered by the sync generator at twice the rate needed for the display of the echo train. On the alternate sweeps the delayed trigger is used to initiate a pulse from the comparator oscillator. This pulse reaches the receiver through a calibrated attenuator. The location of the comparator pulse on the oscilloscope screen can be varied by means of a time-delay control and may be made coincident with any selected reflection in the decay train. The attenuator may then be adjusted to equalize the amplitude of two pulses. The comparator pulse can then be moved along to the next reflection and equalized again. In this way the attenuation may be determined in terms of the decibel loss per round trip in the sample. More convenient measurements are possible with the aid of a calibrated exponential decay curve generator. Another important development is the calibrated automatic readout system, which makes a *differential* comparison of two selected echos and can automatically record attenuation $\mathscr{A}$ as a function of time. This system is specially useful when $\mathscr{A}$ varies rapidly with time (as, e.g., after deformation of the sample), or for making measurements over a very long time period (the method, being a comparative one, is not subject to drift). These and other refinements of the pulse technique are discussed in the book of Truell *et al.* (1969, Chapter 2) which may be consulted for details.

The type of single crystal specimen used with the megahertz pulse echo method is typically a block of between 1 to 2 in. on a side. Considerable care must be taken that the working faces are accurately cut to the desired orientation, and that they are very accurately parallel to each other. The stiffness of the bonding film between the transducer and the specimen has an important influence on the form of the pulse that can be transmitted into the specimen. Certain waxes and greases are stiff enough for use at room temperature with both longitudinal and

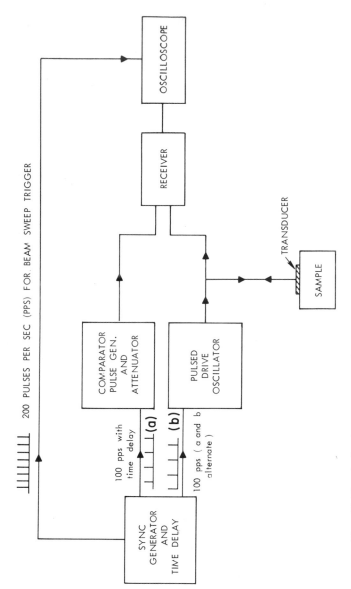

FIG. 20-11.   A simple arrangement for attenuation measurements by the pulse–echo technique.

shear waves, and some of these have been found to be suitable down to 4.2°K. More details of these and many other bonding materials can be found in the books of Mason (1958, p. 98) and Beyer and Letcher (1969, p. 56), and in the review of Taylor and Pointon (1969).

Beyond a frequency of a few hundred megahertz, the utilization of the thin resonant quartz transducer for use with the pulse method becomes progressively more difficult. Principally, this is because of the thinness, fragility, and tight dimensional tolerances imposed on the transducer crystal, combined with the problem of securing it to the specimen with an acoustically satisfactory bond. Accordingly, a variety of other techniques have been developed for extension of the pulse method into the hypersonic frequency range above 1 GHz. Here we shall not attempt to do more than briefly catalog these methods and provide references to more detailed sources of information. Perhaps the most direct extension of the resonant quartz transducer is the resonant thin-film piezoelectric transducer, which is deposited directly on the specimen by vacuum evaporation or sputtering. Though a variety of piezoelectric semiconductors are of potential interest, to date only CdS (and to a smaller extent ZnS) transducers appear to have been employed for attenuation studies. These devices have been discussed by Foster (1965). A review by DeKlerk (1966) also includes the results of attenuation studies on various ionic oxide crystals over the temperature range 1–300°K. These measurements were made with the aid of CdS and ZnS thin-film transducers at frequencies between 1 and 3 GHz. Various other types of high-frequency transducers that can be integrated into a bulk crystal of a piezoelectric semiconductor have been reviewed by White (1964).

As an alternative to the use of thin-film piezoelectric materials, hypersonic transducers can also be made by the evaporation of a thin ferromagnetic film on to the specimen. The film is excited into a condition of ferromagnetic resonance by the combined application of a static magnetic field and a microwave field. The mechanical displacements are of magnetostrictive origin, so this property influences the selection of the transducer material. Both pure nickel and high nickel–iron permalloys have been used. The method was first described by Bömmel and Dransfeld (1959b) for the excitation of shear waves at 1 GHz, and was later extended to higher frequencies (9 GHz) and to longitudinal modes by other workers (see, e.g., Lewis et al., 1962; Pomerantz, 1964b; Seavey, 1965).

In passing, we may note that another area of current research is concerned with the direct electromagnetic excitation of ultrasonic waves in metals. This work is currently being pursued at 10 MHz rather than hypersonic frequencies. However, as for the method just described, the excitation involves the use of both a steady and an alternating field. The correct nature of the excitation mechanism was apparently first recognized by Houck *et al.* (1967). Further developments and later references are given by Meredith *et al.* (1969) and by Dobbs (1970).

The highest frequencies achieved so far have been obtained by the nonresonant excitation of a piezoelectric quartz rod coupled to a microwave cavity. This method was used first by Baranskii (1958) to achieve a frequency of 2 GHz. With improvements in technique and by the use of low temperatures, attenuation measurements on quartz have been extended to 4 GHz (Bömmel and Dransfeld, 1958, 1959a, 1960) and 9.4 GHz (Jacobsen, 1959). More recently these measurements have been extended to 114 GHz, as reported and subsequently reviewed by Ilukor and Jacobsen (1968). Current progress in the utilization of the cavity-driven quartz rod as a transducer that can be bonded to other materials of interest has been discussed by Taylor and Pointon (1969).

General References

CHALMERS, B., and QUARRELL, A. G. (1960). "The Physical Examination of Metals," 2nd ed., Chaps. 10 and 11. Arnold, London.

MASON, W. P. (1958). "Physical Acoustics and the Properties of Solids," Chap. 4. Van Nostrand-Reinhold, Princeton, New Jersey.

MC SKIMIN, H. J. (1964). *In* "Physical Acoustics" (W. P. Mason, ed.), Vol. IA, Chap. 4, p. 272. Academic Press, New York.

TRUELL, R., ELBAUM, C., and CHICK, B. B. (1969). "Ultrasonic Methods in Solid State Physics," Chap. 2. Academic Press, New York.

Appendix **A** / Resonant Systems with Distributed Inertia

In most resonant systems the inertia of the specimen cannot be neglected; therefore, the sample contributes to the behavior of the mechanical system both through its anelastic properties and through its inertia. In some cases, such as a bar vibrating longitudinally or in flexure, the specimen alone may constitute the entire mechanical system, so that the resonant frequencies are determined entirely from the dimensions, the elasticity, and the density of the specimen. In other cases, the specimen may have inertia members attached to it which will modify the resonance conditions. In either case, the system will have an infinite number of degrees of freedom, and therefore may vibrate in any one of a (discrete) infinite set of normal modes. The problem is directly expressed in terms of a partial differential equation for the motion of the system, plus appropriate boundary conditions. In view of the variety of differential equations and boundary conditions that are possible, this vibration problem might not appear to be amenable to a simple and general treatment of the type presented in Section 1.5. The situation is greatly simplified, however, with the aid of a theorem which will now be discussed.

We first note that it is characteristic of any system vibrating in one of its normal modes that the displacement at one point is in phase (or $180°$ out of phase) with that at every other point. Thus all displacements are zero and all are maximum (in absolute value) at the same time. The curve which shows the extremes of displacement as a function of position is called the "vibration shape." An example is given in Fig. A-1. The theorem that we wish to employ may be stated as follows: *So long as the internal friction is small, the vibration shape of a specimen is essentially unchanged (to first order) by the presence of internal friction, or by a small departure of the vibration frequency from the natural frequency of the system.* We will not present a rigorous proof of this theorem, but note that it simply states that a small perturbation on the conditions of vibration does not produce more than a small perturbation of the vibration shape.

The importance of the above theorem is that it enables us to treat a

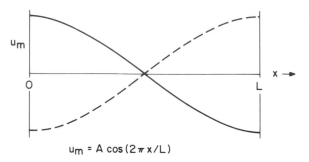

$$u_m = A \cos (2\pi x/L)$$

FIG. A-1.   Vibration shape for the fundamental mode of a longitudinally vibrating bar of length L, which is free at both ends.

system vibrating near one of its resonances as a system of one degree of freedom, since the motion of any one point completely determines that of the others through the vibration shape. Furthermore, it allows us to calculate the vibration shape by considering the system without damping, i.e., assuming the elastic constants to be real quantities. Since a vibrating system near resonance can be treated as having only one degree of freedom, it obviously can be represented by the model of the mass on a spring given in Fig. 1-6. It is thus only necessary to determine the effective parameters m, k_1, and ϕ. For this purpose, we set the energies W_m^K, W_m^P, and ΔW corresponding to the model, and given by Eqs. (1.5-20), equal to the corresponding energies of the actual vibrating system. Clearly, in this way, we will have produced the necessary matching of the model to the real system. To carry through this objective we designate the vector displacement at any point $\mathbf{z}$ in the specimen by $\mathbf{u}_m(\mathbf{z}) \cos \omega t$. Clearly, $\mathbf{u}_m(\mathbf{z})$ may be taken as the vibration shape. We now proceed to calculate the maximum kinetic energy W_m^K of the system, treating the density of the specimen ϱ as a function of position, and including the kinetic energy of auxiliary masses m_i each attached to the specimen at a point i, to obtain

$$W_m^K = \tfrac{1}{2} \int_V \varrho \dot{u}_m^2(\mathbf{z}) \, d\mathbf{z} + \tfrac{1}{2} \sum_i m_i (\dot{u}_m)_i^2$$

$$= \tfrac{1}{2}\omega^2 \left(\int_V \varrho u_m^2(\mathbf{z}) \, d\mathbf{z} + \sum_i m_i (u_m)_i^2 \right) \qquad (\text{A-1})$$

In this equation $\dot{u}_m$ represents the maximum velocity, $d\mathbf{z}$ an element of volume, and V represents the volume of the specimen. Because of the periodic form of the displacement, it follows that $\dot{u}_m = \omega^2 u_m^2$ at each point. The summation over the auxiliary masses m_i could, of course, be converted into an integral when required; an example is the case of an inertial disk attached to a sample vibrating in torsion, where the velocity varies radially on the disk. We next calculate the maximum potential energy, allowing for the possibility that the appropriate storage modulus M_1 may be a function of position in the specimen, as follows:

$$W_m{}^P = \int_V d\mathbf{z} \int_0^{\varepsilon_m} \sigma\, d\varepsilon = \tfrac{1}{2} \int_V M_1 \varepsilon_m{}^2(\mathbf{z})\, d\mathbf{z} \qquad (A\text{-}2)$$

Here $\varepsilon_m(\mathbf{z})$ is the maximum strain at the point $\mathbf{z}$. Finally, the total energy loss per cycle ΔW may be expressed in terms of the loss modulus M_2 at each position in the specimen

$$\Delta W = \int_V d\mathbf{z} \oint \sigma\, d\varepsilon = \pi \int_V M_2 \varepsilon_m{}^2(\mathbf{z})\, d\mathbf{z} \qquad (A\text{-}3)$$

[Compare to Eqs. (1.3-23) and (1.3-22) for the corresponding energies per unit volume.] We now let $\mathbf{u}_{1m}(\mathbf{z}_1)$ represent the maximum displacement of the specimen at an arbitrary point $\mathbf{z}_1$, which is a convenient point for the observation of the vibration of the specimen (e.g., $\mathbf{z}_1$ may be located at one end of the specimen). Because the functional form of the vibration shape is independent of vibration amplitude, it follows that $u_m{}^2(\mathbf{z})$ at any point $\mathbf{z}$ is proportional to u_{1m}^2. Furthermore, the function $\varepsilon_m{}^2(\mathbf{z})$ is also proportional to u_{1m}^2. Thus, it is clear that all three energy expressions given by Eqs. (A-1)-(A-3) are proportional to u_{1m}^2. If we write

$$W_m{}^K \equiv \tfrac{1}{2} m\omega^2 u_{1m}^2, \qquad W_m{}^P \equiv \tfrac{1}{2} k_1 u_{1m}^2, \qquad \Delta W \equiv \pi k_2 u_{1m}^2 \qquad (A\text{-}4)$$

which defines three new parameters m, k_1, and k_2, we note by comparison to (1.5-20) that we have in this way defined the parameters for the spring-mass model, provided that u_{1m} is set equal to the displacement x_0 in the model. Thus, the correlation with the case of one degree of freedom is complete, and the behavior of the system under conditions of forced and free vibrations is describable in terms of the various relations derived in Section 1.5.

It might concern the reader that the arbitrary choice of the point $\mathbf{z}_1$ and therefore of the displacement $\mathbf{u}_{1m}$ leaves an arbitrary constant in the values of the parameters m, k_1, and k_2. This is no source of difficulty, however, since the experimentally observed quantities, such as the resonant frequency $\omega_r = (k_1/m)^{1/2}$ and the internal friction $\phi \doteq k_2/k_1$, involve ratios of these parameters in which the arbitrary constant cancels out.

The above energy expressions are greatly simplified when the specimen is homogeneous, so that M_1 and M_2 are independent of position in the sample. Under these conditions

$$\Delta W / W_\mathrm{m}^\mathrm{P} = 2\pi M_2 / M_1 = 2\pi \tan \phi \qquad (A\text{-}5)$$

as in the case of a large external inertia, Eq. (1.5-19).

Another important simplification occurs when there are no auxiliary masses added to the sample, and the density ϱ as well as the modulus M_1 are independent of position. Equating (A-1) and (A-2) under these conditions gives for the resonant frequency,

$$\omega_\mathrm{r}^2 = (M_1 / \varrho) \left[\int_V \varepsilon_\mathrm{m}^2(\mathbf{z}) \, d\mathbf{z} \Big/ \int_V u_\mathrm{m}^2(\mathbf{z}) \, d\mathbf{z} \right] \qquad (A\text{-}6)$$

The quantity in brackets is a purely geometrical quantity which depends on the vibration shape but not on the physical properties of the material. Hence, we have shown that, under these conditions, the well-known result $\omega_\mathrm{r}^2 \propto M_1 / \varrho$ is obtained. Specific values for the proportionality constant in various situations are given in Appendix F.

Finally, it is important to remember that the vibrating system under consideration has been reduced to a system in one degree of freedom only near a particular resonance, i.e., for a particular normal mode of vibration. The behavior of the system near another of its resonances is also capable of representation in terms of the model of Fig. 1-6, but with an entirely different set of parameters m, k_1, and k_2.

Appendix B / The Kronig–Kramers Relations

We present here a crude proof of the Kronig–Kramers relations, Eqs. (2.4-3) and (2.4-4), starting from Eqs. (2.4-1) and (2.4-2). If the order of integration is interchanged in Eq. (2.4-1), we must consider the integral

$$\int_0^\infty \sin \alpha t \cos \omega t \, dt = \tfrac{1}{2} \int_0^\infty [\sin(\alpha + \omega)t + \sin(\alpha - \omega)t] \, dt$$

$$= -\frac{1}{2} \left[\frac{\cos(\alpha + \omega)t}{\alpha + \omega} + \frac{\cos(\alpha - \omega)t}{\alpha - \omega} \right]_0^\infty$$

$$= \frac{1}{2} \left[\frac{1}{\alpha + \omega} + \frac{1}{\alpha - \omega} \right] = \frac{\alpha}{\alpha^2 - \omega^2} \qquad \text{(B-1)}$$

where the integrals in the second step have been treated as

$$\lim_{\sigma \to 0} \int_0^\infty e^{-\sigma t} \sin(\alpha \pm \omega)t \, dt$$

to ensure convergence at the upper limit. Inserting the above result into Eq. (2.4-1) gives

$$J_1(\omega) - J_U = \frac{2}{\pi} \int_0^\infty \frac{J_2(\alpha)\alpha \, dt}{\alpha^2 - \omega^2} \qquad \text{(B-2)}$$

which is the first Kronig–Kramers relation, Eq. (2.4-3). In a similar way, Eq. (2.4-4) can be obtained from (2.4-2).

To obtain these relations more rigorously requires contour integration in the complex plane, using the methods of complex variable theory.[†] In particular, we must integrate around the singularity at $\alpha = \omega$. This leads to the Kronig–Kramers relations where the integrals are *principal values*, i.e.,

$$\int_0^\infty \frac{f(\alpha) \, d\alpha}{\alpha^2 - \omega^2} \equiv \lim_{\delta \to 0} \left\{ \int_0^{\omega - \delta} + \int_{\omega + \delta}^\infty \right\} \qquad \text{(B-3)}$$

[†] See, e.g., Landau and Lifschitz (1958, Section 122).

Appendix C / Relation between Relaxation and Resonance Behavior

---

Resonance behavior can be included in the description of materials in terms of mechanical models if one introduces a mass. A useful model is that shown in Fig. C-1, in which m_l has the dimensions of mass per unit length while the other components are similar to those in Fig. 3-4. Under quasi-static conditions, this model behaves just like the three-element Voigt-type model, displaying creep or stress relaxation. Under dynamic conditions, however, noting that

$$m_l \ddot{\varepsilon}_1 = \sigma - \sigma_1 \tag{C-1}$$

where ε_1 and σ_1 are, respectively, the strain and stress on the Voigt element and σ is the overall stress, we find that the differential equation obeyed by the total strain ε is

$$-\omega_0^2 J_U \ddot{\sigma} + \tau J_U \dot{\sigma} + J_R \sigma = \omega_0^{-2} \ddot{\varepsilon} + \tau \dot{\varepsilon} + \varepsilon \tag{C-2}$$

where $\omega_0^2 \equiv 1/(\delta J) m_l$ is a resonant frequency and $J_R = J_U + \delta J$. For

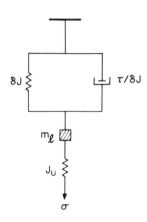

FIG. C-1. Mechanical model which may display resonance or relaxation behavior.

a periodic applied stress we obtain $J^* = \varepsilon/\sigma$ given by

$$J^* - J_U = \frac{\delta J}{1 - (\omega/\omega_0)^2 + i\omega\tau} \tag{C-3}$$

from which the real and imaginary parts are

$$J_1(\omega) - J_U = \frac{\delta J[1 - (\omega^2/\omega_0^2)]}{[1 - (\omega^2/\omega_0^2)]^2 + \omega^2\tau^2} \tag{C-4}$$

and

$$J_2(\omega) = \frac{(\delta J)\omega\tau}{[1 - (\omega^2/\omega_0^2)]^2 + \omega^2\tau^2} \tag{C-5}$$

The results are most clearly illustrated under two extreme conditions:

(a) For $\omega_0^{-1} \gg \tau$, we obtain typical resonance-type behavior in which $J_1(\omega)$ displays anomalous dispersion near the frequency ω_0, while $J_2(\omega)$ shows a sharp peak at $\omega = \omega_0$ illustrative of resonance absorption. The behavior of both quantities is illustrated in Fig. C-2. The anomalous dispersion involves a rise in J_1 from a low-frequency value of J_R to a maximum value $J_U + (\delta J/2\omega_0\tau)$ at $\omega = \omega_0(1 - \tfrac{1}{2}\omega_0\tau)$, then dropping to a minimum of $J_U - (\delta J/2\omega_0\tau)$ at $\omega = \omega_0(1 + \tfrac{1}{2}\omega_0\tau)$ and finally rising asymptotically to the high-frequency value J_U. The value of J_1 may even become negative in the vicinity of the minimum point.

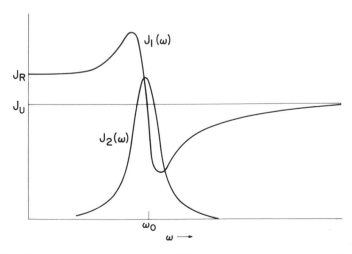

FIG. C-2. Anomalous dispersion (J_1) and resonance absorption (J_2).

(b)   For $\omega_0^{-1} \ll \tau$ (called "overdamped resonance") the mass term becomes unimportant and the dynamical behavior becomes that of a standard anelastic solid. J_1 now undergoes only a monotonic decrease from J_R to J_U with increasing frequency, while J_2 shows a Debye relaxation peak at $\omega\tau = 1$. (Under these conditions $\omega\tau = 1$ is attained when $\omega/\omega_0 \ll 1$, i.e., well below the resonant frequency.) Overdamped resonance is then exactly the same as standard anelastic behavior.

This transition from resonance to relaxation-type behavior has had definite physical interest. One example relates to the question of collision broadening of spectral lines of gases [see van Vleck and Weisskopf (1945)]. An example, which falls into the area of interest of this book, involves the motion of dislocations under an alternating stress (see Section 14.1).

Appendix D / Torsion–Flexure Coupling

When crystals of arbitrary orientation are elastically deformed, the phenomenon known as "torsion-flexure" coupling occurs. This effect, which amounts to a twist when the anisotropic rod is bent (or a bend when the rod is twisted) is a consequence of the existence of nonzero coefficients c_{ij}, for $i \leq 3$ and $j \geq 4$, in the generalization of Hooke's law [Eq. (6.1-3)]. The coupling appears, however, only when the specimen is free to deform in all modes, and does not occur when constraints are present which prevent one or the other types of deformation. Thus, for example, the wire specimen in a torsion pendulum vibrates in a "pure" torsional mode, since flexure is prevented by the mass of the heavy inertia member which would have to be raised if the sample were to bend. The validity of equations such as (6.2-3)–(6.2-9) is based on the assumption that the "free" condition applies; under "pure" deformation, a rather involved correction is required. This correction is given by Hearmon (1946) for a rod of circular cross section as

$$G_{\mathrm{p}} = G_{\mathrm{F}}/(1 - b), \qquad E_{\mathrm{p}} = E_{\mathrm{F}}/(1 - b) \tag{D-1}$$

where G_{p} and E_{p} are the shear and Young's modulus for "pure" and G_{F} and E_{F} for "free" deformation, respectively, and the quantity b is given by

$$b = (s_{34}^2 + s_{35}^2)/s_{33}(s_{44} + s_{55}) \tag{D-2}$$

For the cubic system, this last relation becomes

$$b = E_{\mathrm{F}}G_{\mathrm{F}}[2(S_{11} - S_{12}) - S_{44}]^2(\gamma_1{}^6 + \gamma_2{}^6 + \gamma_3{}^6) - (\gamma_1{}^4 + \gamma_2{}^4 + \gamma_3{}^4)^2] \tag{D-3}$$

and for the hexagonal system

$$b = 2E_{\mathrm{F}}G_{\mathrm{F}}\gamma_3{}^2(1 - \gamma_3{}^2)[S_{11}(1 - \gamma_3{}^2) - (S_{13} + \tfrac{1}{2}S_{44})(1 - 2\gamma_3{}^2) - S_{33}\gamma_3{}^2]^2 \tag{D-4}$$

where Eqs. (D-3) and (D-4) employ the characteristic compliances S, and direction cosines γ as defined in Eqs. (6.2-3)–(6.2-6). The modulus G or E which appears in equations such as (6.2-3)–(6.2-9) is always that measured under "free" conditions; if actual conditions involve "pure" deformation, E_F and G_F must be calculated from Eqs. (D-1) and (D-2). The quantity b is always positive, and it vanishes for orientations of relatively high symmetry. Thus, in the cubic system, it is readily verified from Eq. (D-3) that $b = 0$ for $\langle 100 \rangle$, $\langle 110 \rangle$, and $\langle 111 \rangle$ orientations. For other orientations, b cannot be neglected and is usually determined by an iteration process.

In some circumstances the appropriate quantity is neither the "free" nor the "pure" modulus. An important example is the case of flexural or torsional vibration of a resonant rod (with or without attached inertia members), when the length-to-diameter ratio is not extremely large. Exact solutions for such problems have been worked out by Goens (1931, 1932) and by Brown (1940), while approximate relations are given by Hearmon (1946). Hearmon points out that for specimens of the dimensions normally used, the torsional vibrations are approximately pure, while flexural vibrations are approximately free. These approximations help to simplify the calculations of elastic constants. Nevertheless, for exact work there is much to be gained by the use of orientations for which torsion–flexure coupling vanishes, e.g., the $\langle 100 \rangle$, $\langle 110 \rangle$, and $\langle 111 \rangle$ orientations in the case of cubic crystals.

Appendix E / Wave Propagation in Arbitrary Directions

The manner in which the velocity and attenuation obtained from wave propagation experiments may be used to obtain, respectively, the appropriate storage modulus M_1 and the internal friction ϕ has been discussed in Chapter 1. In the present section we shall briefly review the effects of anisotropy on the interpretation of the velocities of propagation in a semi-infinite anisotropic medium. For particular directions of propagation in a crystal of a given symmetry, one of the three directions of particle displacements will be parallel, and the other two directions perpendicular, to the propagation direction. There are, then, three distinct modes of propagation, one corresponding to a longitudinal wave, and the other two to transverse (i.e., shear) waves. In general, the velocities for these three modes of propagation are all different. For an arbitrary direction of propagation, however, one does not obtain separately one longitudinal and two transverse waves. Instead, there are three independent modes of propagation, corresponding to three directions of particle displacement which are mutually orthogonal, but none are orthogonal to the direction of propagation nor coincident with it. The three velocities are the roots of a third-order determinant in which each term depends on the elastic constants and the direction cosines of the normal to the wave front (Musgrave, 1954). For a cubic crystal of arbitrary orientation, the determinantal equation in the velocity v takes the form

$$\begin{vmatrix} c_{11} - \varrho v^2 & c_{16} & c_{15} \\ c_{16} & c_{66} - \varrho v^2 & c_{56} \\ c_{15} & c_{56} & c_{55} - \varrho v^2 \end{vmatrix} = 0 \qquad \text{(E-1)}$$

where ϱ is the density. Each of the constants c_{ij} which appears in (E-1) may be expressed in terms of the characteristic constants C_{11}, C_{12}, and C_{44}. The three solutions for the velocity v are therefore complex combinations of the characteristic constants. To obtain the three characteristic constants from the velocities of wave propagation requires the use of a perturbation method, as developed for cubic crystals by Neighbours and

Smith (1950). The method has been extended to noncubic crystals by Neighbours (1954) and others. [See the review by Neighbours and Schacher (1967).]

The problem is simplified considerably when the direction of wave propagation is in certain simple crystallographic directions in which "pure modes" (i.e., purely longitudinal or transverse) are obtained. Then a transducer vibrating either longitudinally or transversely generates a wave in only one of the three modes of propagation. In cubic crystals these simple directions are $\langle 100 \rangle$, $\langle 110 \rangle$, and $\langle 111 \rangle$. Borgnis (1955) and Brugger (1955) have determined the directions in which the propagation of pure longitudinal and transverse waves is possible in various crystals. For present purposes, it is sufficient to state that all cases for which longitudinal or transverse velocities are listed in Eqs. (6.4-4)–(6.4-27) are those for which pure modes are obtained. (This list does not cover all pure modes, however, since it is confined only to those velocities related to no more than a single symmetrized modulus of type I and of type II.) It is important to mention, however, that for crystals other than cubic, it is not possible to obtain all of the characteristic constants with only the use of pure modes. In the hexagonal system, for example, Eqs. (6.4-11)–(6.4-15) show that the constants C_{33}, C_{44}, $C_{11} + C_{12}$, and $C_{11} - C_{12}$ may all be obtained by pure wave propagation. On the other hand, the constant C_{13} can only be obtained by using wave propagation in a direction for which coupling occurs. In the trigonal system, the same remark applies to both C_{13} and C_{14}.

The similarity between the occurrence of coupling in wave propagation in crystals, and the occurrence of torsion–flexure coupling in resonant vibration experiments (Appendix D) should be apparent. In both cases, the most direct information is obtained from crystals oriented such that the acoustic vibrations take place along crystallographic directions of high symmetry.

Appendix F / Mechanical Vibration Formulas

The cases considered below include the pendulum and resonant bar configurations most commonly encountered in internal friction work. The formulas were originally derived for the case of an isotropic elastic medium; however, their application to anisotropic and anelastic samples can usually be accomplished by an appropriate reinterpretation of the tensile and shear moduli E and G. To allow for anelastic behavior these symbols should be taken to represent the real part of the corresponding complex modulus. To allow for elastic anisotropy in the case of a polycrystalline aggregate requires no more than the adoption of suitably averaged values $\bar{E}$ and $\bar{G}$. For many single-crystal samples of interest, the moduli E and G become the practical moduli of Section 6.4.

In each category of longitudinal, torsional, or flexural vibration, the examples deal first with the uniform bar, and subsequently include the effect on the fundamental mode of both light additional loads (e.g., magnetic pole tips) and the heavy loading encountered in pendulum apparatus. For these extremes, highly accurate approximation formulas for the frequency are easily obtained by the energy method introduced in Section 1.5C. In the *light-loading approximation*, the vibration shape is taken to be that of the specimen without any additional loading. In the *heavy-loading approximation*, on the other hand, the vibration shape is assumed to be the static deflection curve of the loaded sample. The vibration shape is explicitly given in all the examples below because once this is known many important features such as the distribution of strain or strain energy in the sample can be calculated in a straightforward manner. It should be noted that the frequency formulas derived with the light-loading approximation become exact for the limit of zero additional loading, while those for heavy loading become exact when the mass or moment of inertia of the sample itself can be totally neglected. At these limits, therefore, one formula can be used to check the error in the other. The most suitable range for each approximation is also easily found from the fact that the lower frequency is always the more accurate one (Rayleigh, 1894).

Torsional and Longitudinal Vibrations

We consider bars of uniform cross section only, which furthermore must be circular for the case of torsional vibration. The following symbols will be employed:

<table>
<tr><td>For torsional vibration</td><td>For longitudinal vibration</td></tr>
<tr><td>ξ angular rotation of a cross section</td><td>ξ longitudinal displacement of a cross section</td></tr>
<tr><td>G shear modulus</td><td>E Young's modulus</td></tr>
<tr><td>I_a second moment of area of a cross section about the polar axis</td><td>A cross-sectional area</td></tr>
<tr><td></td><td>m_s mass of specimen</td></tr>
<tr><td>I_s polar moment of inertia of the specimen</td><td>m mass of an additional concentrated load (the centroid of this mass must lie on the specimen axis)</td></tr>
<tr><td>I polar moment of inertia of an additional concentrated load (the polar axis of this inertia must be coincident with the specimen axis)</td><td></td></tr>
</table>

In both cases the vibration frequency, and the length and density of the bar are denoted by f, l, and ϱ, respectively.

F1. Torsional and Longitudinal Modes of a Free–Free Bar

A. The Uniform Bar

The modes form a complete harmonic series. The vibration shapes of the first four modes are shown in Fig. F-1, and are given by

$$\xi = \xi_0 \cos(n\pi x/l) \tag{F-1}$$

where $n = 1, 2, 3, \ldots$. The locations of the nodes for any mode are easily found by solving for x/l when $\xi = 0$. It should be noted that the center of the bar is always a node for the odd harmonics, so that a specimen clamped at its midpoint can be excited at a succession of frequencies. For the even harmonics the experimental situation is less convenient, since the center is always an antinode and the positions of all nodes change from one harmonic to the next.

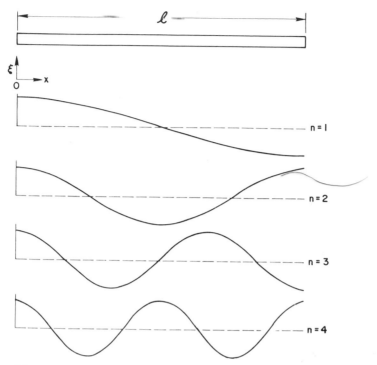

FIG. F-1. The free–free bar and the first four vibration shapes given by Eq. (F-1).

The frequency of the nth mode is given by

$$f = (n/2l)(G/\varrho)^{1/2} \quad \text{or} \quad (n/2l)(E/\varrho)^{1/2} \tag{F-2}$$

For the longitudinal vibration of a thick rod, Eq. (F-2) neglects a correction term given to first order by Rayleigh (1894) and since computed more accurately by Bradfield (1960).

B. The Fundamental Mode with Equal End Loading[†]

The vibration shapes for light and heavy loading are shown in Fig. F-2b and F-2c, respectively. With the light-loading approximation

$$\xi \simeq \xi_0 \cos(\pi x/l) \tag{F-3}$$

and

$$f \simeq \begin{cases} \frac{1}{2}[GI_a/l(I_s + 4I)]^{1/2} \\ \text{or} \\ \frac{1}{2}[EA/l(m_s + 4m)]^{1/2} \end{cases} \tag{F-4}$$

[†] See Fig. F-2a.

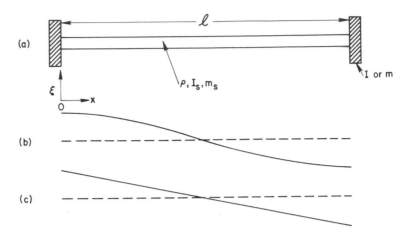

FIG. F-2. (a) The free–free bar with equal end loading. (b) and (c) The fundamental vibration shape for light and heavy loading as given by Eqs. (F-3) and (F-5), respectively.

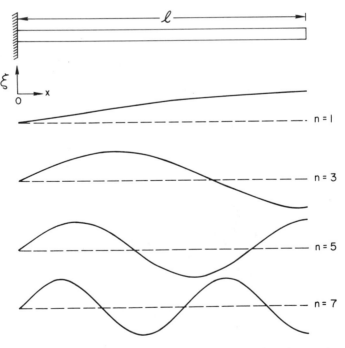

FIG. F-3. The clamped–free bar and the first four vibration shapes given by Eq. (F-7).

With the heavy-loading approximation

$$\xi \simeq \xi_0(1 - 2x/l) \qquad\qquad\qquad (F\text{-}5)$$

and

$$f \simeq \begin{cases} (1/\pi)[3GI_a/l(I_s + 6I)]^{1/2} \\ \text{or} \\ (1/\pi)[3EA/l(m_s + 6m)]^{1/2} \end{cases} \qquad (F\text{-}6)$$

Use (F-4) when I_s (or m_s) $> 6I$ (or $6m$). Use (F-6) when I_s (or m_s) $< 6I$ (or $6m$).

F2. Torsional and Longitudinal Modes of a Clamped–Free Bar

A. The Uniform Bar

The natural modes form a partial series comprising odd harmonics only ($n = 1, 3, 5, \ldots$). The vibration shapes (see Fig. F-3) are given by

$$\xi = \xi_0 \sin(n\pi x/2l) \qquad\qquad\qquad (F\text{-}7)$$

The frequencies are

$$f = \begin{cases} (n/4l)(G/\varrho)^{1/2} \\ \text{or} \\ (n/4l)(E/\varrho)^{1/2} \end{cases} \qquad\qquad (F\text{-}8)$$

B. The Fundamental Mode with End Loading[†]

The vibration shapes for light and heavy loading are shown in Fig. F-4b and F-4c, respectively. With the light-loading approximation

$$\xi \simeq \xi_0 \sin(\pi x/2l) \qquad\qquad\qquad (F\text{-}9)$$

$$f \simeq \begin{cases} \tfrac{1}{4}[GI_a/l(I_s + 2I)]^{1/2} \\ \text{or} \\ \tfrac{1}{4}[EA/l(m_s + 2m)]^{1/2} \end{cases} \qquad (F\text{-}10)$$

With the heavy loading approximation

$$\xi \simeq \xi_0(x/l) \qquad\qquad\qquad\qquad (F\text{-}11)$$

[†] See Fig. F-4a.

and

$$f \simeq \begin{cases} (1/2\pi)[3GI_a/l(I_s + 3I)]^{1/2} \\ \text{or} \\ (1/2\pi)[3EA/l(m_s + 3m)]^{1/2} \end{cases} \tag{F-12}$$

Use (F-10) when I_s (or m_s) $> 3I$ (or $3m$). Use (F-12) when I_s (or m_s) $< 3I$ (or $3m$).

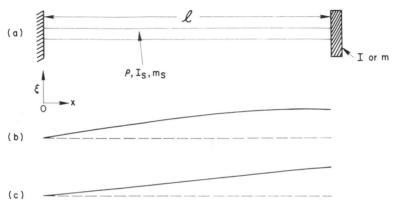

FIG. F-4. (a) The clamped–free bar with end loading. (b) and (c) The fundamental vibration shapes for light and heavy loading, as given by Eqs. (F-9) and (F-11), respectively.

Flexural Vibrations

The formulas given below pertain to bars, rods, or tubes of uniform cross section, and are based on the usual assumptions that (a) the bending is symmetrical (i.e., occurs only in the plane of the bending moment), (b) the theory of simple bending is applicable, (c) the rotational kinetic energy is negligible compared with the translational energy. With a sample whose cross section is nominally but not exactly either circular or square it is possible to violate assumption (a) above with troublesome consequences. Such samples possess two orthogonal principal planes of bending of almost equal stiffness, and can be excited into resonance in both planes simultaneously. When this occurs the damping cannot be measured in any simple manner. During free decay, for example, the vibration beats from one plane to the other. A study of these effects has been reported by Entwistle (1951). To avoid such problems it is desirable to employ a specimen whose cross section is sufficiently asymmetrical that the resonance curves in the principal planes do not overlap. For this reason a rectangular section is preferable to a square section. Specimens prepared from circular stock should be deliberately rendered asymmetrical by grinding or machining a pair of parallel flats along their length.

In addition to some of the symbols defined earlier in this appendix, we now require the following:

y transverse displacement of a cross-sectional element

y^* transverse displacement at a free end (Note that in some cases the origin has been chosen at the center of the bar, so that $y = y^*$ when $x = l/2$.)

$\varkappa$ radius of gyration of a cross section about the neutral axis of bending.

I_b second moment of area of a cross section about the neutral axis of bending

μ specimen mass per unit length

It should be noted that

$$\varkappa^2/\varrho = I_b/\mu \tag{F-13}$$

F3. Free–Free Flexural Vibrations

A. The Uniform Bar

In order of ascending frequency, the vibration shapes are alternatively symmetric and antisymmetric about the center of the bar (Fig. F-5). The vibration shapes of the *symmetrical* modes are given by

$$y = \frac{y^*}{2}\left[\frac{\cosh(2\alpha x/l)}{\cosh \alpha} + \frac{\cos(2\alpha x/l)}{\cos \alpha}\right] \tag{F-14}$$

where

$$\alpha = (n - \tfrac{1}{4})\pi + \gamma_n \tag{F-15}$$

and $n = 1, 2, 3, \ldots$. The correction term γ_n is significant only for $n = 1$; in that case $\alpha = 0.75281\pi$.

The vibration shapes of the *antisymmetrical* modes are given by

$$y = \frac{y^*}{2}\left\{\frac{\sinh(2\alpha x/l)}{\sinh \alpha} + \frac{\sin(2\alpha x/l)}{\sin \alpha}\right\} \tag{F-16}$$

where

$$\alpha = (n + \tfrac{1}{4})\pi + \gamma_n' \tag{F-17}$$

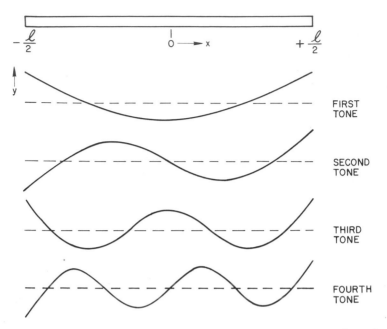

FIG. F-5.   The free–free bar and the vibration shape of the first four flexural tones as given by Eqs. (F-14) and (F-16).

and $n = 1, 2, 3, \ldots$. The correction term γ_n' is significant only for $n = 1$; in that case $\alpha = 1.24987\pi$. The positions of the nodes, obtained by solving Eqs. (F-14) and (F-16) for x/l when $y = 0$, are given in Table F-1.

The frequencies of vibration are given by

$$f = (2\alpha^2\varkappa/\pi l^2)(E/\varrho)^{1/2} \tag{F-18}$$

and increase very nearly as the sequence $3^2, 5^2, 7^2, 9^2, \ldots$.

B. *The Fundamental Mode with Additional Loading*

Let the bar (of mass m_s) be loaded with added masses m_1 at each end and m_2 at the center. If the ratio m_2/m_1 is 3.290, the nodal positions remain unchanged from their locations for the unloaded bar. With the light-loading approximation

$$f \simeq (3.561\varkappa/l^2)\{E/\varrho[1 + (12.96m_1/m_s)]\}^{1/2} \tag{F-19}$$

This expression is also closely obeyed even under conditions of heavy loading (Berry, 1955b).

TABLE F-1

NODAL POSITIONS FOR A FREE FREE BAR IN FLEXURAL VIBRATION

Tone number	α	α^2	Distance of nodes from one end (given as a fraction of the length of the bar)
1	2.3650	5.5933	0.2242, 0.7758
2	3.9266	15.418	0.1321, 0.5, 0.8679
3	5.4978	30.226	0.0944, 0.3558, 0.6442, 0.9056
4	7.0686	49.465	0.0735, 0.2768, 0.5, 0.7232, 0.9265
5	8.6394	74.639	0.0601, 0.2265, 0.4091, 0.5909, 0.7735, 0.9399
6	10.210	104.25	0.0509, 0.1916, 0.3462, 0.5, 0.6538, 0.8084, 0.9491
7	11.781	138.79	0.0441, 0.1661, 0.3, 0.4333, 0.5667, 0.7, 0.8339, 0.9559

F4. CLAMPED–FREE FLEXURAL VIBRATIONS

A. The Uniform Bar

The vibration shape of the fundamental and successive *odd* tones is given by

$$y = \frac{y^*}{2}\left[\frac{\cosh(2\alpha x/l)}{\cosh \alpha} + \frac{\sin(2\alpha x/l)}{\sin \alpha}\right] \tag{F-20}$$

where

$$\alpha = (s + \tfrac{1}{4})\pi + \gamma_s \tag{F-21}$$

and $s = 0, 1, 2, 3, \ldots$. The term γ_s is appreciable only for $s = 0$ and 1 (the first and third tones of Fig. F-6), in which cases $\alpha = 0.29843\pi$ and 1.25013π, respectively.

The vibration shapes of the *even* tones (second, fourth, sixth, etc.) are given by

$$y = \frac{y^*}{2}\left[\frac{\sinh(2\alpha x/l)}{\sinh \alpha} + \frac{\cos(2\alpha x/l)}{\cos \alpha}\right] \tag{F-22}$$

where

$$\alpha = (s - \tfrac{1}{4})\pi + \gamma_s' \tag{F-23}$$

and $s = 1, 2, 3, \ldots$. The term γ_s' is appreciable only when $s = 1$ (i.e., for the second tone of Fig. F-6), in which case $\alpha = 0.74709\pi$. The nodal

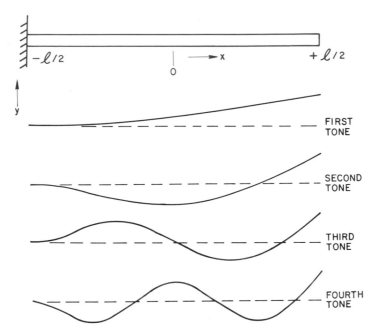

Fig. F-6. The clamped–free bar and the vibration shape of the first four flexural tones as given by Eqs. (F-20) and (F-22).

positions for the first few tones are shown in Table F-2. The frequencies of vibration are given by

$$f = (2\alpha^2 \varkappa / \pi l^2)(E/\varrho)^{1/2} \tag{F-24}$$

and increase as $(1.194)^2$, $(2.988)^2$, 5^2, 7^2, 9^2, ...

B. The Fundamental Mode with Additional End Loading

Let the bar (of mass m_s) be loaded with an end mass m. With the light-loading approximation, the vibration shape is given by Eq. (F-20) with $s = 0$, whence

$$f \simeq (0.5596\varkappa/l^2)\{E/\varrho[1 + (4m/m_\mathrm{s})]\}^{1/2} \tag{F-25}$$

The static deflection curve for the heavy loading approximation is (with the free end chosen as origin)

$$y = y^*(x^3 - 3l^2x + 2l^3)/2l^3 \tag{F-26}$$

whence

$$f \simeq (1/2\pi)[3EI_\mathrm{b}/l^3(m + 0.2357m_\mathrm{s})]^{1/2} \tag{F-27}$$

TABLE F-2

Nodal Positions for a Clamped–Free Bar in Flexural Vibration

Tone number	α	α^2	Distance of nodes from the free end (given as a fraction of the length of the bar)
1	0.93755	0.87899	
2	2.3471	5.5087	0.2166
3	3.9274	15.424	0.1323, 0.4965
4	5.4978	30.226	0.0944, 0.3559, 0.6417
5	7.0686	49.965	0.0735, 0.2768, 0.5001, 0.7212
6	8.6394	74.639	0.0601, 0.2265, 0.4091, 0.5909, 0.7719
7	10.210	104.25	0.0508, 0.1916, 0.3462, 0.4999, 0.6539, 0.8070

General References

DEN HARTOG, J. P. (1947). "Mechanical Vibrations," 3rd ed. McGraw-Hill, New York.
LAMB, H. (1960). "Dynamical Theory of Sound," 2nd ed. Dover, New York.
SPINNER, S., and TEFFT, W. E. (1961). *Proc. A.S.T.M.* **61**, 1221.

Appendix G / Computed Response Functions for the Gaussian Distribution

---

This appendix gives two tables of functions computed from the Gaussian (or lognormal) distribution [taken from Nowick and Berry (1961)]. Table G-1 gives the peak function $f_2(x', \beta)$, which is related to the response function $J_2(x')$ by Eq. (4.5-14). Here $x' = \log_{10} \omega \tau_m$, β is the lognormal distribution parameter and τ_m is the most probable relaxation time. The tabulated function $f_2(x', \beta)$ is normalized to a peak value of 1.00 by dividing by $f_2(0, \beta)$. Table G-2 gives the function $g(y', \beta)$, which is related to the creep function by Eq. (4.5-15), where $y' = \log_{10}(t/\tau_m)$.

TABLE G-1

The Normalized Peak Function $f_2(x', \beta)/f_2(0, \beta)$

x'	β = 0	0.2	0.4	0.6	0.8	1.00	1.25	1.50	1.75	2.00	2.25
0.00	1.000	1.000	1.000	1.000	1.000	1.000	1.000	1.000	1.000	1.000	1.000
0.05	.9934	.9936	.9942	.9949	.9956	.9963	.9969	.9974	.9978	.9981	.9984
0.10	.9740	.9750	.9773	.9801	.9829	.9853	.9878	.9898	.9914	.9927	.9937
0.15	.9431	.9451	.9501	.9561	.9621	.9674	.9729	.9774	.9809	.9837	.9860
0.20	.9025	.9057	.9138	.9239	.9339	.9430	.9525	.9602	.9663	.9713	.9753
0.25	.8544	.8588	.8702	.8847	.8994	.9127	.9270	.9386	.9480	.9555	.9617
0.30	.8011	.8066	.8210	.8399	.8593	.8774	.8970	.9130	.9261	.9367	.9454
0.35	.7447	.7511	.7682	.7910	.8151	.8379	.8629	.8838	.9009	.9150	.9264
0.40	.6872	.6943	.7133	.7394	.7677	.7950	.8256	.8514	.8729	.8905	.9051
0.45	.6302	.6377	.6580	.6865	.7184	.7498	.7856	.8164	.8422	.8637	.8816
0.50	.5749	.5825	.6034	.6336	.6681	.7030	.7436	.7792	.8094	.8348	.8561
0.55	.5221	.5296	.5507	.5816	.6180	.6556	.7004	.7404	.7748	.8041	.8288
0.60	.4725	.4798	.5004	.5314	.5687	.6082	.6565	.7004	.7389	.7719	.8000
0.65	.4263	.4332	.4531	.4835	.5209	.5616	.6125	.6598	.7019	.7385	.7699
0.70	.3837	.3902	.4090	.4383	.4752	.5164	.5689	.6189	.6643	.7042	.7388
0.75	.3447	.3507	.3684	.3962	.4320	.4728	.5263	.5784	.6264	.6693	.7069
0.80	.3092	.3147	.3311	.3572	.3915	.4314	.4850	.5384	.5886	.6341	.6744
0.85	.2769	.2820	.2971	.3214	.3538	.3923	.4453	.4994	.5512	.5988	.6417
0.90	.2478	.2524	.2662	.2886	.3189	.3557	.4075	.4616	.5144	.5638	.6088
0.95	.2216	.2258	.2383	.2588	.2870	.3217	.3717	.4252	.4785	.5292	.5760
1.00	.1980	.2018	.2131	.2318	.2577	.2903	.3381	.3905	.4438	.4953	.5435
1.05	.1768	.1802	.1904	.2074	.2312	.2614	.3068	.3576	.4104	.4623	.5115
1.10	.1578	.1609	.1701	.1855	.2071	.2350	.2777	.3266	.3784	.4302	.4801
1.15	.1408	.1436	.1519	.1657	.1854	.2110	.2508	.2974	.3479	.3993	.4494
1.20	.1256	.1281	.1355	.1480	.1658	.1892	.2261	.2703	.3191	.3697	.4197
1.25	.1121	.1143	.1209	.1321	.1481	.1694	.2035	.2451	.2919	.3413	.3910
1.30	.0999	.1019	.1079	.1179	.1323	.1516	.1829	.2218	.2664	.3144	.3634
1.35	.0891	.0909	.0962	.1052	.1181	.1355	.1642	.2003	.2426	.2889	.3370
1.40	.0794	.0810	.0858	.0938	.1054	.1211	.1472	.1806	.2205	.2649	.3118
1.45	.0708	.0722	.0765	.0837	.0941	.1082	.1318	.1626	.2000	.2424	.2878
1.50	.0631	.0644	.0682	.0746	.0839	.0966	.1180	.1462	.1811	.2213	.2651
1.55	.0563	.0574	.0608	.0665	.0748	.0862	.1055	.1313	.1637	.2017	.2437
1.60	.0502	.0512	.0542	.0593	.0667	.0769	.0943	.1178	.1477	.1834	.2236
1.65	.0447	.0456	.0483	.0528	.0595	.0686	.0842	.1056	.1331	.1666	.2047
1.70	.0398	.0406	.0430	.0471	.0530	.0612	.0752	.0945	.1198	.1510	.1871
1.75	.0355	.0362	.0384	.0420	.0473	.0546	.0671	.0846	.1077	.1366	.1707
1.80	.0316	.0323	.0342	.0374	.0421	.0486	.0599	.0756	.0967	.1235	.1555
1.85	.0282	.0288	.0305	.0333	.0376	.0434	.0534	.0676	.0868	.1114	.1414
1.90	.0251	.0256	.0271	.0297	.0335	.0386	.0477	.0604	.0778	.1005	.1283
1.95	.0224	.0228	.0242	.0265	.0298	.0344	.0425	.0539	.0697	.0904	.1164
2.00	.0199	.0203	.0216	.0236	.0266	.0307	.0379	.0481	.0624	.0813	.1053
2.05	.0178	.0181	.0192	.0210	.0237	.0274	.0338	.0430	.0558	.0731	.0952
2.10	.0158	.0162	.0171	.0187	.0211	.0244	.0301	.0383	.0499	.0656	.0860
2.15	.0141	.0144	.0152	.0167	.0188	.0217	.0268	.0342	.0446	.0588	.0776
2.20	.0126	.0128	.0136	.0149	.0168	.0194	.0239	.0305	.0398	.0527	.0699
2.25	.0112	.0114	.0121	.0133	.0149	.0173	.0213	.0272	.0355	.0472	.0629
2.30	.0100	.0102	.0108	.0118	.0133	.0154	.0190	.0242	.0317	.0422	.0566
2.35	.0089	.0091	.0096	.0105	.0119	.0137	.0169	.0216	.0283	.0378	.0508
2.40	.0079	.0081	.0086	.0094	.0106	.0122	.0151	.0192	.0252	.0338	.0456
2.45	.0070	.0072	.0076	.0083	.0094	.0109	.0134	.0172	.0225	.0302	.0409
2.50	.0063	.0064	.0068	.0074	.0084	.0097	.0120	.0153	.0201	.0270	.0367
2.55	.0056	.0057	.0060	.0066	.0075	.0086	.0107	.0136	.0179	.0241	.0328
2.60	.0050	.0051	.0054	.0059	.0066	.0077	.0095	.0121	.0160	.0215	.0294
2.65	.0044	.0045	.0048	.0052	.0059	.0068	.0085	.0108	.0142	.0192	.0263
2.70	.0039	.0040	.0043	.0047	.0053	.0061	.0075	.0096	.0127	.0171	.0235
2.75	.0035	.0036	.0038	.0042	.0047	.0054	.0067	.0086	.0113	.0153	.0210
2.80	.0031	.0032	.0034	.0037	.0042	.0048	.0060	.0076	.0101	.0136	.0188
2.85	.0028	.0028	.0030	.0033	.0037	.0043	.0053	.0068	.0090	.0121	.0168
2.90	.0025	.0025	.0027	.0029	.0033	.0038	.0047	.0061	.0080	.0108	.0150
2.95	.0022	.0022	.0024	.0026	.0029	.0034	.0042	.0054	.0071	.0096	.0134
3.00	.0020	.0020	.0021	.0023	.0026	.0030	.0038	.0048	.0063	.0086	.0119

TABLE G-1 (*continued*)

x'	β = 2.50	2.75	3.00	3.50	4.00	4.50	5.00	5.50	6.00	6.50	7.00
0.00	1.000	1.000	1.000	1.000	1.000	1.000	1.000	1.000	1.000	1.000	1.000
0.05	.9986	.9988	.9989	.9991	.9993	.9994	.9995	.9996	.9996	.9997	.9997
0.10	.9946	.9952	.9958	.9967	.9973	.9978	.9981	.9984	.9986	.9988	.9990
0.15	.9878	.9894	.9906	.9926	.9940	.9951	.9959	.9965	.9970	.9974	.9977
0.20	.9785	.9812	.9835	.9869	.9894	.9913	.9927	.9938	.9947	.9954	.9960
0.25	.9667	.9709	.9743	.9797	.9836	.9865	.9887	.9904	.9918	.9929	.9938
0.30	.9525	.9584	.9633	.9709	.9765	.9806	.9838	.9863	.9882	.9898	.9911
0.35	.9359	.9438	.9504	.9606	.9681	.9737	.9780	.9814	.9840	.9862	.9879
0.40	.9172	.9273	.9357	.9489	.9586	.9659	.9714	.9758	.9792	.9820	.9842
0.45	.8965	.9089	.9194	.9358	.9479	.9570	.9640	.9694	.9738	.9772	.9801
0.50	.8739	.8889	.9015	.9214	.9361	.9472	.9557	.9624	.9677	.9720	.9755
0.55	.8496	.8672	.8821	.9057	.9232	.9365	.9467	.9547	.9611	.9662	.9704
0.60	.8239	.8442	.8614	.8889	.9094	.9249	.9369	.9463	.9539	.9599	.9649
0.65	.7968	.8198	.8395	.8710	.8945	.9125	.9264	.9373	.9461	.9532	.9590
0.70	.7687	.7944	.8165	.8520	.8787	.8992	.9151	.9277	.9377	.9459	.9526
0.75	.7396	.7680	.7925	.8321	.8621	.8852	.9032	.9175	.9289	.9382	.9458
0.80	.7099	.7408	.7676	.8114	.8447	.8705	.8906	.9066	.9195	.9300	.9386
0.85	.6796	.7129	.7421	.7899	.8266	.8551	.8775	.8953	.9096	.9213	.9309
0.90	.6490	.6846	.7159	.7677	.8078	.8391	.8637	.8834	.8992	.9122	.9229
0.95	.6182	.6559	.6894	.7450	.7884	.8224	.8494	.8710	.8884	.9027	.9145
1.00	.5875	.6271	.6625	.7218	.7685	.8053	.8346	.8581	.8771	.8928	.9057
1.05	.5569	.5982	.6354	.6982	.7481	.7876	.8192	.8447	.8654	.8824	.8966
1.10	.5266	.5694	.6082	.6743	.7273	.7696	.8035	.8309	.8533	.8718	.8871
1.15	.4969	.5408	.5810	.6502	.7061	.7511	.7873	.8168	.8409	.8607	.8772
1.20	.4677	.5126	.5540	.6260	.6847	.7323	.7708	.8022	.8280	.8493	.8671
1.25	.4393	.4849	.5273	.6018	.6631	.7132	.7540	.7874	.8148	.8376	.8567
1.30	.4116	.4577	.5009	.5776	.6414	.6938	.7368	.7722	.8014	.8256	.8459
1.35	.3848	.4311	.4749	.5535	.6195	.6743	.7194	.7567	.7876	.8133	.8349
1.40	.3590	.4053	.4494	.5295	.5977	.6546	.7018	.7410	.7735	.8007	.8236
1.45	.3342	.3802	.4245	.5059	.5759	.6348	.6840	.7250	.7592	.7879	.8121
1.50	.3105	.3560	.4003	.4825	.5542	.6150	.6661	.7089	.7447	.7749	.8003
1.55	.2879	.3327	.3768	.4596	.5326	.5951	.6481	.6926	.7300	.7616	.7883
1.60	.2664	.3103	.3540	.4370	.5112	.5753	.6299	.6761	.7151	.7481	.7762
1.65	.2460	.2889	.3320	.4150	.4901	.5556	.6118	.6596	.7001	.7345	.7638
1.70	.2268	.2685	.3108	.3935	.4692	.5360	.5936	.6429	.6849	.7207	.7512
1.75	.2086	.2490	.2905	.3725	.4487	.5165	.5755	.6262	.6696	.7068	.7385
1.80	.1916	.2306	.2711	.3521	.4285	.4972	.5574	.6095	.6543	.6927	.7257
1.85	.1757	.2131	.2525	.3324	.4087	.4781	.5394	.5928	.6389	.6785	.7127
1.90	.1608	.1967	.2348	.3133	.3894	.4593	.5216	.5761	.6234	.6643	.6996
1.95	.1469	.1812	.2180	.2949	.3705	.4408	.5039	.5594	.6079	.6500	.6864
2.00	.1340	.1666	.2021	.2772	.3521	.4225	.4863	.5429	.5924	.6356	.6731
2.05	.1221	.1530	.1870	.2601	.3342	.4046	.4690	.5264	.5770	.6212	.6598
2.10	.1111	.1403	.1728	.2438	.3169	.3871	.4518	.5100	.5615	.6068	.6464
2.15	.1009	.1284	.1594	.2282	.3000	.3699	.4350	.4938	.5462	.5924	.6330
2.20	.0915	.1174	.1469	.2132	.2838	.3532	.4183	.4777	.5309	.5780	.6195
2.25	.0829	.1072	.1351	.1990	.2681	.3368	.4020	.4618	.5157	.5636	.6060
2.30	.0750	.0977	.1241	.1855	.2529	.3209	.3860	.4461	.5006	.5493	.5926
2.35	.0678	.0889	.1139	.1727	.2383	.3054	.3703	.4306	.4857	.5351	.5791
2.40	.0612	.0809	.1043	.1605	.2243	.2904	.3549	.4154	.4708	.5209	.5657
2.45	.0552	.0734	.0954	.1490	.2109	.2759	.3398	.4004	.4562	.5068	.5523
2.50	.0498	.0666	.0872	.1382	.1981	.2618	.3251	.3856	.4417	.4928	.5390
2.55	.0448	.0603	.0796	.1279	.1858	.2481	.3108	.3711	.4274	.4790	.5257
2.60	.0403	.0546	.0725	.1183	.1741	.2350	.2969	.3569	.4133	.4653	.5125
2.65	.0362	.0494	.0660	.1093	.1629	.2223	.2833	.3430	.3994	.4517	.4994
2.70	.0325	.0446	.0600	.1008	.1523	.2101	.2701	.3293	.3857	.4382	.4864
2.75	.0292	.0402	.0545	.0929	.1422	.1984	.2573	.3160	.3723	.4249	.4735
2.80	.0262	.0363	.0495	.0855	.1326	.1871	.2450	.3030	.3591	.4118	.4607
2.85	.0234	.0327	.0448	.0786	.1236	.1763	.2330	.2903	.3461	.3989	.4480
2.90	.0210	.0294	.0406	.0722	.1150	.1660	.2214	.2780	.3334	.3862	.4355
2.95	.0188	.0264	.0367	.0662	.1069	.1561	.2102	.2659	.3210	.3736	.4231
3.00	.0168	.0237	.0332	.0606	.0993	.1467	.1994	.2542	.3088	.3613	.4108

TABLE G-2

THE FUNCTION $g(\gamma', \beta)$

γ'	$\beta = 0$	0.25	0.50	0.75	1.00	1.25	1.50	1.75
-1.50	0.9689	0.9684	0.9670	0.9645	0.9607	0.9555	0.9496	0.9400
-1.46	0.9659	0.9654	0.9638	0.9611	0.9570	0.9514	0.9440	0.9348
-1.42	0.9627	0.9621	0.9604	0.9575	0.9531	0.9470	0.9391	0.9293
-1.38	0.9592	0.9586	0.9567	0.9535	0.9487	0.9422	0.9337	0.9234
-1.34	0.9553	0.9547	0.9527	0.9492	0.9440	0.9370	0.9279	0.9170
-1.30	0.9511	0.9504	0.9482	0.9444	0.9389	0.9313	0.9217	0.9102
-1.26	0.9465	0.9458	0.9434	0.9393	0.9333	0.9252	0.9150	0.9028
-1.22	0.9415	0.9407	0.9381	0.9337	0.9272	0.9186	0.9078	0.8950
-1.18	0.9361	0.9352	0.9324	0.9276	0.9207	0.9114	0.9000	0.8867
-1.14	0.9301	0.9291	0.9262	0.9210	0.9136	0.9038	0.8917	0.8778
-1.10	0.9236	0.9226	0.9194	0.9138	0.9059	0.8954	0.8828	0.8683
-1.06	0.9166	0.9154	0.9120	0.9060	0.8976	0.8865	0.8732	0.8583
-1.02	0.9089	0.9077	0.9040	0.8976	0.8886	0.8769	0.8631	0.8476
-0.98	0.9006	0.8993	0.8952	0.8885	0.8789	0.8666	0.8522	0.8364
-0.94	0.8915	0.8901	0.8858	0.8786	0.8684	0.8556	0.8407	0.8245
-0.90	0.8817	0.8802	0.8756	0.8679	0.8572	0.8438	0.8284	0.8119
-0.86	0.8711	0.8694	0.8646	0.8564	0.8452	0.8312	0.8155	0.7988
-0.82	0.8595	0.8578	0.8526	0.8440	0.8322	0.8179	0.8018	0.7849
-0.78	0.8471	0.8452	0.8398	0.8307	0.8184	0.8036	0.7873	0.7704
-0.74	0.8336	0.8317	0.8259	0.8164	0.8037	0.7886	0.7721	0.7552
-0.70	0.8191	0.8171	0.8110	0.8011	0.7880	0.7726	0.7561	0.7394
-0.66	0.8035	0.8014	0.7950	0.7848	0.7714	0.7558	0.7394	0.7230
-0.62	0.7867	0.7845	0.7779	0.7674	0.7537	0.7381	0.7219	0.7059
-0.58	0.7687	0.7664	0.7596	0.7488	0.7350	0.7195	0.7036	0.6883
-0.54	0.7495	0.7471	0.7401	0.7291	0.7153	0.7001	0.6847	0.6700
-0.50	0.7289	0.7264	0.7194	0.7083	0.6947	0.6798	0.6651	0.6512
-0.46	0.7070	0.7045	0.6974	0.6864	0.6730	0.6587	0.6448	0.6320
-0.42	0.6837	0.6812	0.6741	0.6633	0.6504	0.6369	0.6239	0.6122
-0.38	0.6591	0.6566	0.6496	0.6391	0.6268	0.6143	0.6025	0.5920
-0.34	0.6331	0.6307	0.6239	0.6139	0.6025	0.5910	0.5806	0.5714
-0.30	0.6058	0.6035	0.5970	0.5877	0.5773	0.5672	0.5582	0.5505
-0.26	0.5772	0.5750	0.5690	0.5606	0.5514	0.5428	0.5354	0.5293
-0.22	0.5474	0.5454	0.5400	0.5326	0.5249	0.5180	0.5123	0.5079
-0.18	0.5165	0.5147	0.5101	0.5039	0.4979	0.4928	0.4890	0.4864
-0.14	0.4846	0.4831	0.4794	0.4747	0.4705	0.4674	0.4656	0.4647
-0.10	0.4519	0.4508	0.4481	0.4451	0.4429	0.4419	0.4421	0.4431
-0.06	0.4186	0.4179	0.4164	0.4152	0.4152	0.4164	0.4186	0.4215
-0.02	0.3848	0.3846	0.3844	0.3852	0.3874	0.3909	0.3953	0.4000
0.02	0.3509	0.3512	0.3526	0.3554	0.3600	0.3657	0.3721	0.3787
0.06	0.3172	0.3181	0.3209	0.3260	0.3328	0.3408	0.3493	0.3577
0.10	0.2840	0.2854	0.2898	0.2970	0.3062	0.3164	0.3268	0.3370
0.14	0.2515	0.2535	0.2596	0.2688	0.2802	0.2925	0.3048	0.3166
0.18	0.2201	0.2228	0.2303	0.2416	0.2551	0.2693	0.2834	0.2968
0.22	0.1902	0.1934	0.2024	0.2156	0.2309	0.2468	0.2625	0.2774
0.26	0.1621	0.1658	0.1760	0.1908	0.2078	0.2253	0.2424	0.2586
0.30	0.1360	0.1401	0.1514	0.1675	0.1858	0.2047	0.2230	0.2403
0.34	0.1122	0.1166	0.1287	0.1458	0.1651	0.1850	0.2044	0.2228
0.38	0.0908	0.0955	0.1080	0.1257	0.1458	0.1665	0.1867	0.2059
0.42	0.0721	0.0768	0.0895	0.1074	0.1279	0.1491	0.1699	0.1897
0.46	0.0559	0.0605	0.0731	0.0909	0.1114	0.1328	0.1540	0.1743
0.50	0.0423	0.0467	0.0588	0.0761	0.0964	0.1177	0.1390	0.1597
0.54	0.0312	0.0353	0.0466	0.0631	0.0827	0.1038	0.1250	0.1458
0.58	0.0223	0.0260	0.0363	0.0517	0.0705	0.0910	0.1120	0.1327
0.62	0.0155	0.0186	0.0278	0.0419	0.0596	0.0793	0.0999	0.1204
0.66	0.0104	0.0130	0.0209	0.0336	0.0500	0.0688	0.0887	0.1089
0.70	0.0067	0.0088	0.0154	0.0266	0.0416	0.0593	0.0785	0.0982
0.74	0.0041	0.0058	0.0111	0.0208	0.0343	0.0508	0.0691	0.0882
0.78	0.0024	0.0036	0.0079	0.0160	0.0281	0.0433	0.0606	0.0790
0.82	0.0014	0.0022	0.0054	0.0122	0.0228	0.0366	0.0529	0.0705
0.86	0.0007	0.0013	0.0037	0.0092	0.0183	0.0308	0.0459	0.0627
0.90	0.0004	0.0007	0.0024	0.0068	0.0146	0.0258	0.0397	0.0555
0.94	0.0002	0.0004	0.0016	0.0050	0.0115	0.0214	0.0342	0.0490
0.98	0.0001	0.0002	0.0010	0.0036	0.0090	0.0177	0.0293	0.0432

TABLE G-2 (*continued*)

y'	β = 2.00	2.50	3.00	3.50	4.00	5.00	6.00	7.00
−1.50	0.9297	0.9051	0.8779	0.8505	0.8246	0.7794	0.7430	0.7140
−1.46	0.9240	0.8985	0.8706	0.8430	0.8170	0.7721	0.7363	0.7079
−1.42	0.9179	0.8914	0.8630	0.8351	0.8092	0.7647	0.7295	0.7016
−1.38	0.9114	0.8840	0.8550	0.8270	0.8011	0.7571	0.7226	0.6954
−1.34	0.9044	0.8762	0.8468	0.8186	0.7929	0.7495	0.7156	0.6891
−1.30	0.8970	0.8680	0.8382	0.8100	0.7844	0.7417	0.7085	0.6827
−1.26	0.8892	0.8594	0.8293	0.8011	0.7759	0.7337	0.7014	0.6762
−1.22	0.8808	0.8504	0.8200	0.7920	0.7669	0.7257	0.6942	0.6698
−1.18	0.8720	0.8409	0.8105	0.7826	0.7579	0.7175	0.6868	0.6632
−1.14	0.8627	0.8310	0.8006	0.7729	0.7486	0.7092	0.6795	0.6566
−1.10	0.8528	0.8208	0.7903	0.7630	0.7392	0.7008	0.6720	0.6500
−1.06	0.8424	0.8100	0.7797	0.7528	0.7295	0.6923	0.6645	0.6433
−1.02	0.8314	0.7989	0.7688	0.7424	0.7197	0.6836	0.6569	0.6366
−0.98	0.8199	0.7873	0.7576	0.7318	0.7097	0.6749	0.6492	0.6298
−0.94	0.8078	0.7753	0.7461	0.7209	0.6996	0.6661	0.6415	0.6230
−0.90	0.7951	0.7629	0.7343	0.7098	0.6892	0.6571	0.6337	0.6161
−0.86	0.7819	0.7500	0.7221	0.6985	0.6788	0.6481	0.6259	0.6092
−0.82	0.7681	0.7368	0.7097	0.6870	0.6681	0.6390	0.6180	0.6023
−0.78	0.7538	0.7231	0.6970	0.6753	0.6573	0.6298	0.6101	0.5953
−0.74	0.7389	0.7091	0.6840	0.6634	0.6464	0.6205	0.6021	0.5884
−0.70	0.7234	0.6946	0.6708	0.6513	0.6353	0.6112	0.5940	0.5813
−0.66	0.7074	0.6799	0.6573	0.6390	0.6241	0.6018	0.5860	0.5743
−0.62	0.6910	0.6648	0.6436	0.6266	0.6128	0.5923	0.5778	0.5672
−0.58	0.6740	0.6494	0.6297	0.6140	0.6014	0.5828	0.5697	0.5601
−0.54	0.6566	0.6336	0.6155	0.6013	0.5899	0.5732	0.5615	0.5530
−0.50	0.6387	0.6176	0.6012	0.5885	0.5784	0.5635	0.5533	0.5459
−0.46	0.6204	0.6014	0.5868	0.5755	0.5667	0.5538	0.5451	0.5387
−0.42	0.6018	0.5849	0.5722	0.5625	0.5550	0.5441	0.5368	0.5316
−0.38	0.5828	0.5682	0.5574	0.5494	0.5432	0.5344	0.5285	0.5244
−0.34	0.5636	0.5514	0.5426	0.5362	0.5313	0.5246	0.5203	0.5172
−0.30	0.5441	0.5344	0.5277	0.5229	0.5195	0.5148	0.5120	0.5100
−0.26	0.5244	0.5173	0.5127	0.5097	0.5076	0.5051	0.5037	0.5028
−0.22	0.5045	0.5001	0.4977	0.4964	0.4957	0.4953	0.4954	0.4956
−0.18	0.4846	0.4829	0.4826	0.4830	0.4838	0.4854	0.4870	0.4884
−0.14	0.4646	0.4657	0.4676	0.4697	0.4719	0.4757	0.4788	0.4812
−0.10	0.4446	0.4485	0.4526	0.4564	0.4600	0.4659	0.4705	0.4740
−0.06	0.4247	0.4313	0.4376	0.4432	0.4481	0.4561	0.4622	0.4669
−0.02	0.4049	0.4143	0.4227	0.4300	0.4363	0.4464	0.4539	0.4597
0.02	0.3852	0.3973	0.4079	0.4169	0.4245	0.4366	0.4457	0.4526
0.06	0.3658	0.3805	0.3932	0.4038	0.4128	0.4270	0.4374	0.4454
0.10	0.3466	0.3639	0.3786	0.3909	0.4012	0.4173	0.4292	0.4383
0.14	0.3278	0.3476	0.3642	0.3780	0.3896	0.4077	0.4211	0.4312
0.18	0.3093	0.3314	0.3499	0.3653	0.3782	0.3982	0.4129	0.4241
0.22	0.2912	0.3156	0.3358	0.3527	0.3668	0.3887	0.4048	0.4170
0.26	0.2736	0.3000	0.3220	0.3403	0.3555	0.3793	0.3968	0.4100
0.30	0.2564	0.2848	0.3084	0.3280	0.3444	0.3700	0.3888	0.4030
0.34	0.2398	0.2699	0.2950	0.3159	0.3334	0.3607	0.3808	0.3960
0.38	0.2238	0.2554	0.2818	0.3040	0.3225	0.3515	0.3728	0.3891
0.42	0.2083	0.2412	0.2690	0.2922	0.3118	0.3424	0.3650	0.3822
0.46	0.1934	0.2276	0.2564	0.2807	0.3012	0.3334	0.3572	0.3753
0.50	0.1792	0.2143	0.2442	0.2694	0.2908	0.3244	0.3494	0.3685
0.54	0.1656	0.2014	0.2322	0.2583	0.2805	0.3156	0.3417	0.3617
0.58	0.1526	0.1890	0.2206	0.2475	0.2704	0.3068	0.3341	0.3550
0.62	0.1403	0.1771	0.2092	0.2369	0.2605	0.2982	0.3265	0.3482
0.66	0.1287	0.1656	0.1983	0.2265	0.2508	0.2897	0.3190	0.3416
0.70	0.1177	0.1547	0.1876	0.2164	0.2413	0.2813	0.3116	0.3350
0.74	0.1074	0.1442	0.1774	0.2066	0.2319	0.2730	0.3042	0.3284
0.78	0.0977	0.1341	0.1674	0.1970	0.2228	0.2648	0.2970	0.3219
0.82	0.0886	0.1246	0.1579	0.1877	0.2139	0.2568	0.2898	0.3155
0.86	0.0802	0.1155	0.1487	0.1786	0.2052	0.2489	0.2827	0.3091
0.90	0.0724	0.1069	0.1398	0.1698	0.1966	0.2411	0.2756	0.3027
0.94	0.0652	0.0987	0.1313	0.1614	0.1884	0.2335	0.2687	0.2964
0.98	0.0585	0.0910	0.1232	0.1531	0.1803	0.2260	0.2618	0.2902

References

ADLER, D. (1968). *Solid State Phys.* **21**, 1.

AKHIESER, A. (1939). *J. Phys. USSR* **1**, 277.

ALEFELD, G. (1967). *In* "Lattice Defects and Their Interactions" (R. R. Hasiguti, ed.). Gordon and Breach, New York.

ALEFELD, G., FILLOUX, J., and HARPER, H. (1968). *In* "Dislocation Dynamics" (A. R. Rosenfield *et al.*, eds.). McGraw-Hill, New York.

ALEFELD, G., VÖLKL, J., and TRETKOWSKI, J. (1970). *J. Phys. Chem. Solids* **31**, 1765.

ALERS, G. A. (1965). *In* "Physical Acoustics" (W. P. Mason, ed.), Vol. 3B. Academic Press, New York.

ALERS, G. A., and THOMPSON, D. O. (1961). *J. Appl. Phys.* **32**, 283.

ALERS, G. A., and ZIMMERMAN, J. E. (1965). *Phys. Rev.* **139**, A414.

ALFREY, T., and DOTY, P. (1945). *J. Appl. Phys.* **16**, 700.

AMATEAU, M. F., MITCHELL, T. E., and GIBALA, R. (1969). *Phys. Status Solidi* **36**, 407.

ANDREWS, R. D. (1952). *Ind. Eng. Chem.* **44**, 707.

ANG, C. Y., and WERT, C. (1953). *Trans. AIME* **197**, 1032.

ANG, C. Y., and WERT, C. (1954). *J. Appl. Phys.* **25**, 1061.

ANG, C. Y., SIVERTSEN, J., and WERT, C. (1955). *Acta Met.* **3**, 558.

ARENBURG, D. L. (1948). *J. Acoust. Soc. Amer.* **20**, 1.

ARTMAN, R. A. (1952). *J. Appl. Phys.* **23**, 475.

AUST, K. T., and CHALMERS, B. (1970). *Met. Trans.* **1**, 1095.

AUST, K. T., and RUTTER, J. W. (1959). *Trans. AIME* **215**, 119, 820.

AUST, K. T., and RUTTER, J. W. (1963). *In* "Recovery and Recrystallization of Metals" (L. Himmel, ed.). Wiley (Interscience), New York.

AUSTIN, I. G., CLAY, B. D., and TURNER, C. E. (1968). *J. Phys. C (Proc. Phys. Soc.)* **1**, 1418.

BAKER, G. S. (1957). *J. Appl. Phys.* **28**, 734.

BALAMUTH, L. (1934). *Phys. Rev.* **45**, 715. (See also *Phys. Rev.* **46**, 933.)

BANCROFT, D., and JACOBS, R. B. (1938). *Rev. Sci. Instr.* **9**, 279.

BARANSKII, K. N. (1958). *Sov. Phys. Dokl. (English transl.)* **2**, 237.

BARANSKII, K. N., SHUSTIN, O. A., VELICHKINA, T. S., and YAKOVLEV, I. A. (1963). *Sov. Phys. JETP* **16**, 518.

BARNES, A., and ZENER, C. (1940). *Phys. Rev.* **58**, 87.

BARNES, R. S., HANCOCK, N. H., and SILK, E. C. H. (1958). *Phil. Mag.* **3**, 519.

BARONI, A., and GIACOMINI, A. (1954). *Acustica* **4**, 182.

BARRAND, P. (1966). *Acta Met.* **14**, 1247.

BARRAND, P. (1967). *Met. Sci. J.* **1**, 54.

BARRAND, P., and LEAK, G. M. (1964). *Acta Met.* **12**, 1147.

BARRETT, H. H. (1970). *In* "Physical Acoustics" (W. P. Mason and R. N. Thurston, eds.), Vol. 6, Chap. 2. Academic Press, New York.

BARRETT, H. H., and HOLLAND, M. G. (1970). *Phys. Rev.* **B2**, 3441.

BASS, J., and LAZARUS, D. (1962). *J. Phys. Chem. Solids* **23**, 1820.

BAUER, C. L., and GORDON, R. B. (1962). *J. Appl. Phys.* **33**, 672.

BAXTER, W. J., and WILKS, J. (1962). *Acta Met.* **10**, 175.

BEAULIEU, C. E., DUBÉ, A., and LETENDRE, G. (1960). *Trans. Met. Soc. AIME* **218**, 558.

BECKER, R., and DÖRING, W. (1939). "Ferromagnetismus." Springer-Verlag, Berlin.

BELL, R. L., and LANGDON, T. G. (1969). *In* "Interfaces Conference" (R. C. Gifkins, ed.), p. 115. Butterworths, London and Washington, D. C.

BELOUS, O., GRIDNEV, V., EFIMOV, A., and KUSHNAREVA, N. (1967). *In* "Internal Friction in Metals and Alloys" (V. S. Postnikov *et al.*, eds.). Consultants Bureau, New York.

BELOV, K. P., KATAYEV, G. I., and LEVITIN, R. Z. (1960). *J. Appl. Phys.* **31**, 153S.

BENNEMANN, K. H. (1965). *Phys. Rev.* **137**, A1497.

BENNEWITZ, K., and RÖTGER, H. (1936). *Phys. Z.* **37**, 578.

BENNEWITZ, K., and RÖTGER, H. (1938). *Z. Tech. Phys.* **19**, 521.

BERRY, B. S. (1955a). *J. Appl. Phys.* **26**, 1221.

BERRY, B. S. (1955b). *Rev. Sci. Instr.* **26**, 884.

BERRY, B. S. (1959). *Acta Met.* **7**, 741.

BERRY, B. S. (1961). *Acta Met.* **9**, 98.

BERRY, B. S. (1962). *Acta Met.* **10**, 271.

BERRY, B. S. (1970). *J. Phys. Chem. Solids* **31**, 1827.

BERRY, B. S., and NOWICK, A. S. (1958). Nat. Advis. Comm. for Aeronautics, Tech. Note 4225.

BERRY, B. S., and OREHOTSKY, J. L. (1968a). *Acta Met.* **16**, 683.

BERRY, B. S., and OREHOTSKY, J. L. (1968b). *Acta Met.* **16**, 697.

BESHERS, D. N. (1958). *Acta Met.* **6**, 521.

BESHERS, D. N. (1959). *J. Appl. Phys.* **30**, 252.

BESHERS, D. N. (1965). *J. Appl. Phys.* **36**, 290.

BESHERS, D. N. (1970). *J. Phys. Chem. Solids* **31**, 1921.

BEYER, R. T., and LETCHER, S. V. (1969). "Physical Ultrasonics." Academic Press, New York.

BHATIA, A. B. (1967). "*Ultrasonic Absorption.*" Oxford Univ. Press, London and New York.

BISOGNI, E., MAH, G., and WERT, C. (1964). *J. Less-Common Met.* **7**, 197.

BLACKWELL, R., and CAREY, R. (1968). *J. Phys. E.* **1**, 1029.

BLATT, F. J. (1957). *Phys. Rev.* **105**, 1118.

BLOUNT, E. I. (1959). *Phys. Rev.* **114**, 418.

BOESONO, I., ERNST, G. J., LEMMENS, M. C., VAN LANGEN, M. J., and DeVRIES, G. (1967). *Phys. Status Solidi* **19**, 107.

BOLEF, D. I., and DE KLERK, J. (1963). *Phys. Rev.* **129**, 1063.

BÖMMEL, H. E. (1954). *Phys. Rev.* **96**, 220.

BÖMMEL, H. E. (1955). *Phys. Rev.* **100**, 758.

BÖMMEL, H. E., and DRANSFELD, K. (1958). *Phys. Rev. Lett.* **1**, 234.

BÖMMEL, H. E., and DRANSFELD, K. (1959a). *Phys. Rev. Lett.* **2**, 298.

BÖMMEL, H. E., and DRANSFELD, K. (1959b). *Phys. Rev. Lett.* **3**, 83.

BÖMMEL, H. E., and DRANSFELD, K. (1960). *Phys. Rev.* **117**, 1245.

BOONE, D. H., and WERT, C. A. (1963). *J. Phys. Soc. Japan Suppl. I* **18**, 141.

BORDONI, P. G. (1947). *Nuovo Cimento* **4**, 177.

BORDONI, P. G. (1949). *Ricerca Sci.* **19**, 851.

BORDONI, P. G. (1954). *J. Acoust. Soc. Amer.* **26**, 495.

BORDONI, P. G., and NUOVO, M. (1957). *Acustica*, **7**, 1.

BORDONI, P. G., NUOVO, M., and VERDINI, L. (1959). *Nuovo Cimento* **14**, 273.

BORDONI, P. G., NUOVO, M., and VERDINI, L. (1960). *Nuovo Cimento Suppl. I* **18**, 55.

BORDONI, P. G., NUOVO, M., and VERDINI, L. (1961). *Phys. Rev.* **123**, 1204.

BORGNIS, F. E. (1955). *Phys. Rev.* **98**, 1000.

BOSMAN, A. J., and CREVECOEUR, C. (1968). *J. Phys. Chem. Solids* **29**, 109.

BOSMAN, A. J., and VAN HOUTEN, S. (1964). *In* "Physics of Semiconductors" (M. Hulin, ed.) (*Proc. Int. Conf. Phys. Semicond. 7th*), p. 1203. Academic Press, New York and Dunod, Paris.

BOSMAN, A. J., BROMMER, P. E., EIJKELENBOOM, L. C. H., SCHINKEL, C. J., and RATHENAU, G. W. (1960). *Physica* **26**, 533.

BOSSHARD, U., DREYFUS, R. W., and KÄNZIG, W. (1965). *Phys. Kondens. Mater.* **4**, 254.

BOULANGER, C. (1949). *Rev. Met. (Paris)* **46**, 321.

BOULANGER, C. (1954). *Rev. Met. (Paris)* **51**, 210.

BOZORTH, R. M. (1951). "Ferromagnetism." Van Nostrand-Rheinhold, Princeton, New Jersey.

BOZORTH, R. M., MASON, W. P., and MCSKIMIN, H. J. (1951). *Bell Syst. Tech. J.* **30**, 970.

BRADFIELD, G. (1960). *In* "The Physical Examination of Metals" (B. Chalmers and A. G. Quarrel, eds.), 2nd ed., Chap. 11. Arnold, London.

BRADFIELD, G., and PURSEY, H. (1953). *Phil. Mag.* **44**, 437.

BRADLEY, D. (1965). *J. Acoust. Soc. Amer.* **37**, 700.

BRAILSFORD, A. D. (1961). *Phys. Rev.* **122**, 778.

BRAILSFORD, A. D. (1962). *Phys. Rev.* **128**, 1033.

BRAILSFORD, A. D. (1965). *Phys. Rev.* **137**, A1562.

BRAILSFORD, A. D. (1972). *J. Appl. Phys.* **43**. In press.

BRAILSFORD, F. (1966). "Magnetic Materials." Methuen, London.

BRANDON, D. G. (1966). *Acta Met.* **14**, 1479.

BRANDON, D. G., RALPH, B., RANGANATHAN, S., and WALD, M. S. (1964). *Acta Met.* **12**, 813.

BRATINA, W. J., and WINEGARD, W. C. (1956). *Trans. AIME* **206**, 186.

BRODY, E. M., and CUMMINS, H. Z. (1968). *Phys. Rev. Lett.* **21**, 1263.

BROUWER, A. J. (1965). *Phys. Lett.* **17**, 5.

BROWN, W. F., JR. (1936). *Phys. Rev.* **50**, 1165.

BROWN, W. F., JR. (1940). *Phys. Rev.* **58**, 998.

BRUGGER, K. (1965). *J. Appl. Phys.* **36**, 759.

BRUGGER, K., and MASON, W. P. (1961). *Phys. Rev. Lett.* **7**, 270.

BRUGGER, K., FRITZ, T. C., and KLEINMAN, D. A. (1967). *J. Acoust. Soc. Amer.* **41**, 1015.

BRUNER, L. J. (1960). *Phys. Rev.* **118**, 399.

BRUNER, L. J., and KEYES, R. W. (1961). *Phys. Rev. Lett.* **7**, 55.

BRUNER, L. J., and MECS, B. M. (1963). *Phys. Rev.* **129**, 1525.

BULLOUGH, R., and NEWMAN, R. C. (1962a). *Proc. Roy. Soc. London* **A266**, 198.

BULLOUGH, R., and NEWMAN, R. C. (1926b). *Proc. Roy. Soc. London* **A266**, 209.

BUNN, P. M., and WERT C. (1964). *Trans. Met. Soc. AIME* **230**, 936.

BUNN, P. M., CUMMINGS, D. C., and LEAVENWORTH, H. W., JR. (1962). *J. Appl. Phys.* **33**, 3009.

BURDETT, C. F., and QUEEN, T. J. (1970a). *Metals Mater.* **4**, 47.

BURDETT, C. F., and QUEEN, T. J. (1970b). *Metals Mater.* **4**, 65.

BURDETT, C. F., WRIGHT, D. M., and SMITH, J. D. (1970). *Phil. Mag.* **22**, 47.

BURSILL, L. A., HYDE, B. G., TERASAKI, O., and WATANABE, D. (1969). *Phil. Mag.* **20**, 347.

BUTERA, R. A., and CRAIG, R. S. (1966). *Rev. Sci. Instr.* **37**, 401.

BYER, N. E., and SACK, H. S. (1966). *Phys. Rev. Lett.* **17**, 72.

BYER, N. E., and SACK, H. S. (1968a). *J. Phys. Chem. Solids* **29**, 677.

BYER, N. E., and SACK, H. S. (1968b). *Phys. Status Solidi* **30**, 569, 579.

CABARAT, R., GENCE, P., GUILLET, L., and LeROUX, R. (1951–52). *J. Inst. Metals* **80**, 151.

CANNELLI, G., and VERDINI, L. (1966). *Ric. Sci.* **36**, 98.

CANTELLI, R., MAZZOLAI, F. M., and NUOVO, M. (1970). *J. Phys. Chem. Solids* **31**, 1811.

CARNAHAN, R. D., and BRITTAIN, J. O. (1963). *J. Appl. Phys.* **34**, 3095.

CASWELL, H. L. (1958). *J. Appl. Phys.* **29**, 1210.

CHAKRAVERTY, B., and DREYFUS, R. W. (1966). *J. Appl. Phys.* **37**, 631.

CHAMBERS, R. H. (1957). Carnegie Inst. of Tech. Rep. AT(30-1) 1193.

CHAMBERS, R. H. (1966). *In* "Physical Acoustics" (W. P. Mason, ed.), Vol. 3A, Chap. 4. Academic Press, New York.

CHAMBERS, R. H., and SCHULTZ, J. (1960). *Acta Met.* **8**, 585.

CHAMBERS, R. H., and SCHULTZ, J. (1961). *Phys. Rev. Lett.* **6**, 273.

CHAMBERS, R. H., and SCHULTZ, J. (1962). *Acta Met.* **10**, 466.

CHAMBERS, R. H., and SMOLUCHOWSKI, R. (1960). *Phys. Rev.* **117**, 725.

CHANG, R. (1961). *J. Appl. Phys.* **32**, 1127.

CHANG, R. (1964). *J. Phys. Chem. Solids* **25**, 1081.

CHANG, L., and GENSAMER, M. (1953). *Acta Met.* **1**, 483.

CHIKAZUMI, S., and GRAHAM, C. D., JR. (1969). *In* "Magnetism and Metallurgy" (A. E. Berkowitz and E. Kneller, eds.), Vol. 2, p. 577. Academic Press, New York.

CHILDS, B. G., and LeCLAIRE, A. D. (1954). *Acta Met.* **2**, 718.

COCHARDT, A. (1959). *In* "Magnetic Properties of Metals and Alloys" (R. M. Bozorth, ed.). Amer. Soc. for Metals, Cleveland, Ohio.

COCHARDT, A., SCHOECK, G., and WIEDERSICH, H. (1955). *Acta Met.* **3**, 533.

COHEN, M. H., HARRISON, M. J., and HARRISON, W. A. (1960). *Phys. Rev.* **117**, 937.

COLEMAN, M. G., and WERT, C. A. (1966). *Trans. AIME* **236**, 501.

CONDIT, R. H., and BESHERS, D. N. (1967). *Trans. Met. Soc. AIME* **239**, 680.

CONDON, E. U., and ODISHAW, H., eds. (1958). "Handbook of Physics." McGraw-Hill, New York.

COOKE, W. T. (1936). *Phys. Rev.* **50**, 1158.

COPLEY, G. J. (1966). *J. Sci. Instr.* **43**, 845.

CORBETT, J. W., and WATKINS, G. D. (1961). *J. Phys. Chem. Solids* **20**, 319.

CORDEA, J. N., and SPRETNAK, J. W. (1966). *Trans. Met. Soc. AIME* **236**, 1685.

COST, J. R. (1963). *Acta Met.* **11**, 1313.

COST, J. R., (1965a). *Acta Met.* **13**, 1263.

COST, J. R. (1965b). *Acta Met.* **13**, 549.

COTTELL, G. A., ENTWISTLE, K. M., and THOMPSON, F. C. (1948). *J. Inst. Metals* **74**, 373.

COTTRELL, A. H., and BILBY, B. A. (1949). *Proc. Phys. Soc. (London)* **A62**, 49.

CRAFT, W. L., and SLUTSKY, L. J. (1968). *J. Chem. Phys.* **49**, 638.
DAMASK, A. C., and NOWICK, A. S. (1955). *J. Appl. Phys.* **26**, 1165.
DANIEL, V. (1967). "Dielectric Relaxation." Academic Press, New York.
DARLING, A. S. (1956-7). *J. Inst. Metals* **85**, 489.
DATSKO, O. I., and PAVLOV, V. A. (1963). *In* "Relaxation Phenomena in Metals and Alloys" (B. N. FINKELSHTEYN, ed.), p. 174. Consultants Bureau, New York.
DE BATIST, R. (1960). Cornell Rep. on Contract AT(30-1)-2471.
DE BATIST, R. (1969). *J. Nucl. Mater.* **31**, 307.
DE JONG, M. (1962). *Acta Met.* **10**, 334.
DE KLERK, J. (1966). *In* "Physical Acoustics" (W. P. Mason, ed.), Vol. 4A, Chap. 5. Academic Press, New York.
DE MORTON, M. (1962). *J. Appl. Phys.* **33**, 2768.
DE MORTON, M. (1969). *J. Appl. Phys.* **40**, 208.
DE MORTON, M., and LEAK, G. M. (1966). *Acta Met.* **14**, 1140.
DE MORTON, M., LOTT, S. A., and STAINSBY, D. F. (1963). *J. Sci. Instr.* **40**, 441.
DE VRIES, G., VAN GEEST, D. W., GERSDORF, R., and RATHENAU, G. W. (1959). *Physica* **25**, 1131.
DIAMOND, S., and WERT, C. (1967). *Trans. Met. Soc. AIME* **239**, 705.
DI CARLO, J. A., and TOWNSEND, J. R. (1966). *Acta Met.* **14**, 1715.
DI CARLO, J. A., SNEAD, C. L., JR., and GOLAND, A. N. (1969). *Phys. Rev.* **178**, 1059.
DIECKAMP, H., and SOSIN, A. (1956). *J. Appl. Phys.* **27**, 1416.
DIENES, G. J., HATCHER, R. D., SMOLUCHOWSKI, R., and WILSON, W. (1966). *Phys. Rev. Lett.* **16**, 25.
DIJKSTRA, L. J. (1947). *Philips Res. Rep.* **2**, 357.
DIJKSTRA, L. J. (1949). *Trans. AIME* **185**, 252.
DIJKSTRA, L. J., and SLADEK, R. J. (1953). *Trans. AIME* **197**, 69.
DOBBS, E. R. (1970). *J. Phys. Chem. Solids* **31**, 1655.
DOLLINS, C., and WERT, C. (1969). *Acta Met.* **17**, 711.
DOMINIK, L. A. K., and MACCRONE, R. K. (1967). *Phys. Rev.* **163**, 756.
DONTH, H. (1957). *Z. Phys.* **149**, 111.
DREYFUS, R. W., and LAIBOWITZ, R. B. (1964). *Phys. Rev.* **135**, A1413.
DRYDEN, J. S., and MEAKINS, R. J. (1957). *Discuss. Faraday Soc.* **23**, 39.
DRUYVESTEYN, M. J., SCHANNEN, O., and SWAVING, E. (1959). *Physica* **25**, 1271.
DUNITZ, J. D., and ORGEL, L. E. (1957). *J. Phys. Chem. Solids* **3**, 20.
EINSPRUCH, N. G. (1962). *J. Phys. Chem. Solids* **23**, 1341.
EINSPRUCH, N. G. (1965). *Solid State Phys.* **17**, 217.
EINSPRUCH, N. G., and CSAVINSZKY, P. (1963). *Appl. Phys. Lett.* **2**, 1.
EISENBERG, D., and KAUZMANN, W. (1969). "The Structure and Properties of Water," Chap. 3. Oxford Univ. Press (Clarendon), London and New York.
ELLIOTT, R., and ENTWISTLE, K. M. (1964). *Acta Met.* **12**, 215.
ENRIETTO, J. F. (1962). *Trans. Met. Soc. AIME* **224**, 1119.
ENTWISTLE, K. M. (1948). *J. Inst. Metals* **75**, 97.
ENTWISTLE, K. M. (1951). *In Proc. World Met. Congr., 1st.* p. 651. Amer. Soc. for Metals, Cleveland, Ohio.
ENTWISTLE, K. M. (1953-54). *J. Inst. Metals* **82**, 249.
ENTWISTLE, K. M. (1956-57). *J. Inst. Metals* **85**, 425.
ENTWISTLE, K. M., and FITZPATRICK, I. (1965). Paper presented at the Int. Conf. on Internal Friction, Manchester, England.

ESCAIG, B. (1962). *Acta Met.* **10**, 829.

ESHELBY, J. D. (1949). *Proc. Roy. Soc. London* **A197**, 396.

EVANS, R. G., and DANIEL, M. R. (1968). *Phys. Lett.* **26A**, 276.

FAST, J. D. (1950). *Iron and Coal Trades Review*, p. 837.

FAST, J. D., and MEIJERING, J. L. (1953). *Philips Res. Rep.* **8**, 1.

FAST, J. D., and VERRIJP, M. B. (1955). *J. Iron Steel Inst.* **180**, 337.

FAST, J. D., and VERRIJP, M. B. (1961). *Philips Res. Rep.* **16**, 51.

FELTHAM, P. (1966). *Phil. Mag.* **13**, 913.

FERRY, J. D. (1958). *In* "Rheology" (F. R. Eirich, ed.), Vol. 2, Chap. 11. Academic Press, New York.

FINE, M. E. (1950). Trans. AIME **188**, 1322.

FINE, M. E. (1952a). *Phys. Rev.* **87**, 1143.

FINE, M. E. (1952b). A.S.T.M. Bulletin No. 181, p. 20.

FINE, M. E. (1954). *Rev. Sci. Instr.* **25**, 1188.

FINE, M. E. (1957). *Rev. Sci. Instr.* **28**, 643.

FINE, M. E., and CHIOU, C. (1957). *Phys. Rev.* **105**, 121.

FINE, M. E., and KENNEY, N. T. (1954a). *Phys. Rev.* **94**, 1573.

FINE, M. E., and KENNEY, N. T. (1954b). *Phys. Rev.* **96**, 1487.

FINE, M. E., GREINER, E. S., and ELLIS, W. C. (1951). *Trans. AIME* **191**. 56.

FINKELSHTEYN, B. N., and SHTRAKHMAN, K. M. (1964). *Fiz. Metal. Metalloved.* **18**, 617. [*English transl.*: *Phys. Metals Metallogr.* **18**, No. 4, 132.]

FISCHBACH, D. B. (1962). *Acta Met.* **10**, 319.

FISHER, J. C. (1958). *Acta Met.* **6**, 13.

FÖPPL, O. (1936). *J. Iron Steel Inst.* **134**, 393.

FÖRSTER, F. (1937). *Z. Metallk.* **29**, 109.

FÖRSTER, F., and KÖSTER, W. (1937a) Naturwiss. **25**, 436.

FÖRSTER, F., and KÖSTER, W. (1937b). *Z. Metallk.* **29**, 116.

FOSTER, N. F. (1965). *Proc. IEEE* **53**, 1400.

FOWLER, R., and GUGGENHEIM, E. A. (1949). "Statistical Thermodynamics." Cambridge Univ. Press, London and New York.

FRANKLIN, A. D. (1963). *J. Res. Nat. Bur. Std.* **67A**, 291.

FRANKLIN, A. D., and CRISSMAN, J. (1971). *J. Phys. C* **4**, L 239.

FRANKLIN, D. G., and BIRNBAUM, H. K. (1971). *Acta Met.* **19**, 965.

FRANKLIN, P. (1958). "An Introduction to Fourier Methods and the Laplace Transformation." Dover, New York.

FRAZER, D. B. (1964). *J. Appl. Phys.* **35**, 2913.

FRAZER, D. B. (1968). *In* "Physical Acoustics" (W. P. Mason, ed.), Vol. 5, p. 59. Academic Press, New York.

FRAZER, D. B., and LE CRAW, R. C. (1964). *Rev. Sci. Instr.* **35**, 1113.

FRIEDEL, J. (1953). *Phil. Mag.* **44**, 444.

FRIEDEL, J. (1961). *Metaux Corr.-Ind.* **36**, 148.

FRIEDEL, J. (1963). *In* "Relation between the Structure and Mechanical Properties of Metals", Vol. I, p. 409. Her Majesty's Stationery Office. London.

FRIEDEL, J. (1964). "Dislocations." Pergamon Press, Oxford.

FRIEDEL, J., BOULANGER, C., and CRUSSARD, C. (1955). *Acta Met.* **3**, 380.

FUOSS, R. M., and KIRKWOOD, J. G. (1941). *J. Amer. Chem. Soc.* **63**, 385.

FUSFELD, H. I. (1950). *Rev. Sci. Instr.* **21**, 612.

GARBYER, R. I., and KOVALEV, A. I. (1959). *Fiz. Metal. Metalloved.* **8**, 785. [*English transl.* Phys. Metals Metallogr. **8**, No. 5, 129.]

GARLAND, C. W. (1970). *In* "Physical Acoustics" (W. P. Mason, ed.), Vol. 7. Academic Press, New York.

GARLAND, C. W., and JONES, J. S. (1963). *J. Chem. Phys.* **39**, 2874.

GARLAND, C. W., and NOVOTNY, D. B. (1969). *Phys. Rev.* **177**, 971.

GARLAND, C. W., and RENARD, R. (1966a). *J. Chem. Phys.* **44**, 1120.

GARLAND, C. W., and RENARD, R. (1966b). *J. Chem. Phys.* **44**, 1130.

GARLAND, C. W., and YARNELL, C. F. (1966). *J. Chem. Phys.* **44**, 3678.

GARLAND, C. W., and YOUNG, R. A. (1968). *J. Chem. Phys.* **49**, 5282.

GEGUZINA, S. YA., and KRIVOGLAS, M. A. (1968). *Sov. Phys.-Solid State* **9**, 2441.

GEGUZINA, S. YA,, and TIMAN, B. L. (1968). *Sov. Phys.-Solid State* **9**, 1702.

GIBALA, R. (1967). *Acta Met.* **15**, 428.

GIBALA, R., and WERT, C. A. (1965). *In* "Diffusion in Body-Centered-Cubic Metals," p. 131. Amer. Soc. for Metals, Cleveland, Ohio.

GIBALA, R., and WERT, C. A. (1966a). *Acta Met.* **14**, 1095.

GIBALA, R., and WERT, C. A. (1966b). *Acta Met.* **14**, 1105.

GIBALA, R., and WERT, C. A. (1966c). *Trans. Met. Soc. AIME* **236**, 924.

GIBALA, R., KORENKO, M., AMATEAU, M., and MITCHELL, T. (1970). *J. Phys. Chem. Solids* **31**, 1889.

GIBBONS, D. F. (1957). *J. Appl. Phys.* **28**, 810.

GIBBONS, D. F. (1964). *In* "Resonance and Relaxation in Metals" (F. L. Vogel, Jr. ed.), 2nd. ed. Plenum Press, New York.

GIBBONS, D. F., and CHIRBA, V. G. (1958). *Phys. Rev.* **110**, 770.

GIBBONS, D. F., and CHIRBA, V. G. (1962). *Acta Met.* **10**, 484.

GIBSON, J. B., GOLAND, A. N., MILGRAM, M., and VINEYARD, G. H. (1960). *Phys. Rev.* **120**, 1229.

GILMAN, J. J. (1963). *J. Phys. Soc. Japan Suppl. I* **18**, 172.

GLADMAN, T., and PICKERING, F. B. (1966). *J. Iron Steel Inst.* **204**, 112.

GOENS, E. (1931). *Ann. Phys. (Leipzig)* **11**, 649.

GOENS, E. (1932). *Ann. Phys. (Leipzig)* **15**, 455, 902.

GOERING, W. A., and NOWICK, A. S. (1958). *Trans. AIME* **212**, 105.

GOLDING, B. (1968). *Phys. Rev. Lett.* **20**, 5.

GOLDING, B., and BARMATZ, M. (1969). *Phys. Rev. Lett.* **23**, 223.

GORDON, R. B., and NOWICK, A. S. (1956). *Acta Met.* **4**, 514.

GORSKY, W. S. (1935). *Phys. Z. Sowjetunion* **8**, 457.

GRAHAM, C. D., JR. (1959). *In* "Magnetic Properties of Metals and Alloys" (R. M. Bozorth, ed.). Amer. Soc. for Metals, Cleveland, Ohio.

GRANATO, A., and LÜCKE, K. (1956). *J. Appl. Phys.* **27**, 583, 789.

GRANATO, A., HIKATA, A., and LÜCKE, K. (1958). *Acta Met.* **6**, 470.

GRANDCHAMP, P. A., and FORNEROD, R. C. (1970). *J. Phys. E.* **3**, 219.

GRÄNICHER, H. (1963). *Phys. Kondens. Mater.* **1**, 1.

GROSS, B. (1947). *J. Appl. Phys.* **18**, 212.

GROSS, B. (1953). "Mathematical Structure of the Theories of Viscoelasticity." Hermann, Paris.

GUILLET, L., and HOCHEID, B. (1956). *Rev. Met.* **53**, 122.

GUINIER, A. (1952). *Z. Electrochem.* **56**, 468.

GULDEN, T. D., and SHYNE, J. C. (1968). *J. Inst. Met.* **96**, 143.

GUPTA, D., and WEINIG, S. (1962). *Acta Met.* **10**, 292.

GUYE, C. E. (1912). *J. Phys. (Paris)* **2**, 620–645.

GYORGY, E. M., STURGE, M. D., FRAZER, D. B., and LeCRAW, R. C. (1965). *Phys. Rev. Lett.* **15**, 19.

HAAS, C. (1960). *J. Phys. Chem. Solids* **15**, 108.

HALL, J. J. (1967). *Phys. Rev.* **161**, 756.

HAM, F. (1959). *J. Appl. Phys.* **30**, 915.

HANSTOCK, R. F., and MURRAY, A. (1946). *J. Inst. Metals* **72**, 97.

HARBOTTLE, J. E. (1970). *J. Phys. E* **3**, 49.

HARPER, S. (1951). *Phys. Rev.* **83**, 709.

HARPER, S. (1961). *In* "Structural Processes in Creep," p. 56. Iron Steel Inst., London.

HARDY, H. K., and HEAL, T. J. (1954). *In* "Progress in Metal Physics" (B. Chalmers, ed.), Vol. 5, p. 143. Wiley (Interscience), New York.

HASHIZUME, H., and SUGENO, T. (1967). *Jap. J. Appl. Phys.* **6**, 567.

HASIGUTI, R. R. (1963). *J. Phys. Soc. Japan Suppl. I* **18**, 114.

HASIGUTI, R. R. (1965). *Phys. Status Solidi* **9**, 157.

HASIGUTI, R. R., and KAMOSHITA, G. (1954). *J. Phys. Soc. Japan* **9**, 646.

HASIGUTI, R. R., IGATA, N., and KAMOSHITA, G. (1962). *Acta Met.* **10**, 442.

HASIGUTI, R. R., KAWAMIYA, N., and YAGI, E. (1964). *In* "Physics of Semiconductors" (M. Hulin, ed.) (*Proc. Int. Conf. Phys. Semicond. 7th*), p. 1225. Academic Press, New York and Dunod, Paris.

HAVEN, Y. (1968). *Phys. Status Solidi* **26**, 653.

HAYASHI, Y., and SUGENO, T. (1970). *Acta Met.* **18**, 693.

HEARMON, R. F. S. (1946). *Rev. Mod. Phys.* **18**, 409.

HEARMON, R. F. S. (1956). *Advan. Phys.* **5**, 323.

HEIPLE, C. R., and BIRNBAUM, H. K. (1967). *J. Appl. Phys.* **38**, 3294.

HELLER, W. (1961). *Acta Met.* **9**, 600.

HERMANN, W. (1968). *Solid State Commun.* **6**, 641.

HERMANT, M. E. (1966). *Acta Met.* **14**, 795.

HERRING, C. (1950). *J. Appl. Phys.* **21**, 437.

HERRING, C. (1954). *Phys. Rev.* **95**, 954; **96**, 1163.

HIKATA, A., and TRUELL, R. (1957). *J. Appl. Phys.* **28**, 522.

HIKATA, A., JOHNSON, R. A., and ELBAUM, C. (1970). *Phys. Rev. Lett.* **24**, 215.

HIKI, Y. (1958). *J. Phys. Soc. Japan* **13**, 1138.

HILL, T. L. (1960). "Statistical Thermodynamics." Addison-Wesley, Reading, Massachusetts.

HINO, J., TOMIZUKA, C., and WERT, C. (1957). *Acta Met.* **5**, 41.

HINTON, T., and RIDER, J. G. (1966). *J. Appl. Phys.* **37**, 582.

HIVERT, V., PICHON, R., BILGER, H., BICHON, P., VERDONE, J., DAUTREPPE, D., and MOSER, P. (1970). *J. Phys. Chem. Solids* **31**, 1843.

HOFFMAN, R. A., and WERT, C. (1966). *J. Appl. Phys.* **37**, 237.

HOHN, F. E. (1958). "Elementary Matrix Algebra." Macmillan, New York.

HOLMES, D. K., and THOMPSON, D. O. (1964). *In* "Resonance and Relaxation in Metals" (F. L. Vogel, Jr. ed.), 2nd ed. Plenum, New York.

HOLWECH, I. (1960). *J. Appl. Phys.* **31**, 928.

HOPKINS, I. L., and HAMMING, R. W. (1957). *J. Appl. Phys.* **28**, 906.

HOUCK, J. R., BOHM, H. V., MAXFIELD, B. W., and WILKINS, J. W. (1967). *Phys. Rev. Lett.* **19**, 224.

HROSTOWSKI, H. J., and KAISER, R. H. (1957). *Phys. Rev.* **107**, 966.

HUNTER, I. P and SIEGEL, S. (1942). *Phys. Rev.* **61**, 84.

HUNTINGTON, H. B. (1947). *Phys. Rev.* **72**, 321.

HUNTINGTON, H. B. (1953). *Phys. Rev.* **91**, 1092.

HUNTINGTON, H. B. (1958). *Solid State Phys.* **7**, 214.

HUNTINGTON, H. B., and JOHNSON, R. A. (1962). *Acta Met.* **10**, 281.

HUNTINGTON, H. B., and SEITZ, F. (1942). *Phys. Rev.* **61**, 315.

HUNTINGTON, H. B., and SULLIVAN, G. A. (1965). *Phys. Rev. Lett.* **14**, 177, 932.

HUNTINGTON, H. B., SHIRN, G. A., and WAJDA, E. S. (1955). *Phys. Rev.* **99**, 1085.

HUTSON, A. R., and WHITE, D. L. (1962). *J. Appl. Phys.* **33**, 40.

HUTSON, A. R., MCFEE, J. H., and WHITE, D. L. (1961). *Phys. Rev. Lett.* **7**, 237.

IIDA, S. (1967). *J. Phys. Soc. Japan* **22**, 1233.

IKUSHIMA, A. (1969). *Phys. Lett.* **29A**, 417.

IKUSHIMA, A., and SUZUKI, T. (1963). *J. Phys. Soc. Japan Suppl. I* **18**, 163.

ILUKOR, J., and JACOBSEN, E. H. (1968). *In* "Physical Acoustics" (W. P. Mason, ed.), Vol. 5, Chap. 5. Academic Press, New York.

INO, H., and SUGENO, T. (1967). *Acta Met.* **15**, 1197.

INO, H., TAKAGI, S., and SUGENO, T. (1967). *Acta Met.* **15**, 29.

International Union of Crystallography (1952). "International Tables for X-Ray Crystallography," Vol. I. Kynoch Press, Birmingham.

ISHIMOTO, M. (1919). *Proc. Phys. Math. Soc. Japan* **1**, 267.

JACOBSEN, E. H. (1959). *Phys. Rev. Lett.* **2**, 249.

JENSEN, J. W. (1952). *Rev. Sci. Instr.* **23**, 397.

JENSEN, J. W. (1959). Bureau of Mines Rep. No. 5441.

JOHNSON, H. B., TOLAR, N. J., MILLER, G. R., and CUTLER, I. B. (1966). *J. Amer. Ceram. Soc.* **49**, 458.

JOHNSON, H. B., TOLAR, N. J., MILLER, G. R., and CUTLER, I. B. (1969). *J. Phys. Chem. Solids* **30**, 31.

JOHNSON, R. A. (1969). *Radiat. Eff.* **2**, 1.

JOHNSON, R. A., and BROWN, E. (1962). *Phys. Rev.* **127**, 446.

JOHNSON, R. A., DIENES, G. J., and DAMASK, A. C. (1964). *Acta Met.* **12**, 1215.

JOHNSON, S. J., and ROGERS, T. F. (1952). *J. Appl. Phys.* **23**, 574.

JOHNSTON, W. G., and GILMAN, J. J. (1959). *J. Appl. Phys.* **30**, 129.

KADANOFF, L. P., and SWIFT, J. (1968). *Phys. Rev.* **166**, 89.

KADANOFF, L. P., GÖTZE, W., HAMBLEN, D., HECHT, R., LEWIS, E., PALCIAUSKAS, V., RAYL, M., SWIFT, J., ASPNES, D., and KANE, J. (1967). *Rev. Mod. Phys.* **39**, 395.

KAISER, W., KECK, P. H., and LANGE, C. F. (1956). *Phys. Rev.* **101**, 1264.

KAMBER, K., KEEFER, D., and WERT, C. (1961). *Acta Met.* **9**, 403.

KAMEL, R. (1953). *J. Appl. Phys.* **24**, 1308.

KAMENTSKY, L. (1956). Thesis, Cornell Univ., Ithaca, New York.

KAMIGAKI, K. (1961). *J. Phys. Soc. Japan* **16**, 1170.

KÄNZIG, W. (1962). *J. Phys. Chem. Solids* **23**, 479.

KÄNZIG, W., HART, H. R., and ROBERTS, S. (1964). *Phys. Rev. Lett.* **13**, 543.

KÊ, T. S. (1947a). *Phys. Rev.* **71**, 533.

KÊ, T. S. (1947b). *Phys. Rev.* **72**, 41.

KÊ, T. S. (1948a). *Phys. Rev.* **73**, 267.

KÊ, T. S. (1948b). *Trans. AIME* **176**, 448.

KÊ, T. S. (1948c). *J. Appl. Phys.* **19**, 285.

Kê, T. S. (1948d). *Phys. Rev.* **74**, 9, 16.

Kê, T. S. (1949a). *J. Appl. Phys.* **20**, 274.

Kê, T. S. (1949b). *J. Appl. Phys.* **20**, 1226.

Kê, T. S. (1950). *Trans. AIME* **188**, 575.

Kê, T. S., and Ross, M. (1949). *Rev. Sci. Instr.* **20**, 795.

Kê, T. S., and Tsien, C. T. (1956). *Sci. Sinica* **5**, 625.

Kê, T. S., and Zener, C. (1950). *In* "Symposium on the Plastic Deformation of Crystalline Solids," p. 185. Mellon Institute, Pittsburgh. ONR Document Navexos-P-834.

Keck, M. J., and Sladek, R. J. (1970). *Phys. Rev.* B2, 3135.

Keefer, D., and Vitt, R. (1967). *Acta Met.* **15**, 1501.

Keefer, D., and Wert, C (1959). *Trans. Met. Soc. AIME* **215**, 114.

Keefer, D., and Wert, C. (1963a). *Acta Met.* **11**, 489.

Keefer, D., and Wert, C. (1963b). *J. Phys. Soc. Japan Suppl. III* **18**, 110.

Keefer, D., Robinson, J. C., and Sosin, A. (1965). *Acta Met.* **13**, 1135.

Keefer, D., Robinson, J. C., and Sosin, A. (1966). *Acta Met.* **14**, 1409.

Kessler, J. O. (1957). *Phys. Rev.* **106**, 646.

Keyes, R. W. (1961). *IBM J. Res. Develop.* **5**, 266.

Khiznichenko, L. P., Kromer, P. F., Kaipnazarov, D. K., Otenyazov, E., Yusupova, D., and Zotova, L. G. (1967). *Phys. Status Solidi* **21**, 805.

Kidin, I. I., and Shtremel, M. A. (1961). *Fiz. Metal. Metalloved.* **11**, 614. [*Engl. transl.*: *Phys. Metals Metallogr.* **11**, No. 5, 1].

Kikuchi, R. (1960). *Ann. Phys.* (New York) **10**, 127.

Kimmel, R. M., and Uhlmann, D. R. (1969). *J. Appl. Phys.* **40**, 4254.

Kittel, C. (1955). *Acta Met.* **3**, 295.

Kittel, C. (1966). "Introduction to Solid State Physics," 3rd ed. Wiley, New York.

Klein, M. J. (1964). *Phil. Mag.* **10**, 1.

Klein, M. J. (1967). *J. Appl. Phys.* **38**, 167.

Kneller, E. (1962). "Ferromagnetismus." Springer-Verlag, Berlin.

Kneser, H. O., Magun, S., and Ziegler, G. (1955). *Naturwissenschaften* **42**, 437.

Koehler, J. S. (1952). *In* "Imperfections in Nearly Perfect Crystals" (W. Shockley, *et al.* eds.), Chapter 7. Wiley, New York.

Kofstad, P., Butera, R. A., and Craig, R. S. (1962). *Rev. Sci. Instr.* **33**, 850.

Koiwa, M., and Hasiguti, R. R. (1963). *Acta Met.* **11**, 1215.

Kolsky, H. (1953). "Stress Waves in Solids," Oxford Univ. Press, London and New York.

König, D., Völkl, J., and Schilling, W. (1964). *Phys. Status Solidi* **7**, 577.

Kornetski, M. (1938). *Wiss. Veröff. Siemens-Werken* **17**, 410.

Kornetski, M. (1943) Z. *Phys.* **121**, 560.

Kornfel'd, M. I., and Chubinov, A. A. (1958). *Sov. Phys.-JETP* **6**, 26.

Koss, D. A., and Gordon, R. B. (1966). *J. Appl. Phys.* **37**, 465.

Köster, W. (1940a). *Z. Metallk.* **32**, 145, 151.

Köster, W. (1940b). *Z. Metallk.* **32**, 282.

Köster, W. (1940–41). *Arch. Eisenhüttenw.* **14**, 271.

Köster, W. (1943). *Z. Metallk.* **35**, 246.

Köster, W. (1948). *Z. Metallk.* **39**, 51.

Köster, W., and Stolte, E. (1954). *Z. Metallk.* **45**, 356.

Köster, W., Bangert, L., and Hafner, J. (1956). *Z. Metallk.* **47**, 224.

Köster, W., Bangert, L., and Hahn, R. (1954). *Arch. Eisenhüttenw.* **25**, 569.

Köster, W., Bangert, L., and Lang, W. (1955). *Z. Metallk.* **46**, 84.

Kramers, H. A. (1927). *Atti Congr. dei Fisici, Como,* 545.

Krivoglas, M. A. (1960). *Fiz. Metal. Metalloved.* **10**, 497. [*English transl. : Phys. Metals Metallogr.* **10**, No. 4, 1].

Krivoglas, M. A. (1961). *Fiz. Metal. Metalloved.* **12**, 338. [*English transl.: Phys. Metals Metallogr.* **12**, No. 3, 31].

Kröner, E. (1958). "Kontinuumstheorie der Versetzungen und Eigenspannungen," Springer, Berlin.

Kronig, R. (1926). *J. Opt. Soc. Amer.* **12**, 547.

Laibowitz, R. B., and Dreyfus, R. W. (1965). *J. Appl. Phys.* **36**, 2779.

Lanczos, C. (1956). "Applied Analysis." Prentice-Hall, Englewood Cliffs, New Jersey.

Landau, L. D. and Khalatnikov, I. M. (1954). *Dokl. Akad. Nauk USSR* **96**, 469.

Landau, L. D., and Lifschitz, E. M. (1958). "Statistical Physics." Addison-Wesley, Reading, Massachusetts.

Landau, L., and Rumer, G. (1937). *Phys. Z. Sowjetunion* **11**, 18.

Lankes, J. C. and Wassermann, G. (1950). *Z. Metallk.* **41**, 381.

Laramore, G. E., and Kadanoff, L. P. (1969). *Phys. Rev.* **187**, 619.

Lay, K. W., and Whitmore, D. H. (1971). *Phys. Status Solidi* **43**, 175.

Leaderman, H. (1958). *In* "Rheology" (F. R. Eirich, ed.), Vol. 2, Chap. 1. Academic Press, New York.

Leak, D. A., Thomas, W. R., and Leak, G. M. (1955). *Acta Met.* **3**, 501.

Leak, G. M. (1961). *Proc. Phys. Soc.* **78**, 1520.

Leak, G. M. (1962). *Progr. Appl. Mater. Res.* **4**, 1.

LeClaire, A. D. (1951). *Phil. Mag.* **42**, 673.

LeClaire, A. D. (1962). *Phil. Mag.* **7**, 141.

LeClaire, A. D., and Lomer, W. M. (1954). *Acta Met.* **2**, 731.

Lefkowitz, I., and Hazony, Y. (1968). *Phys. Rev.* **169**, 441.

Leibfried, G. (1950). *Z. Phys.* **127**, 344.

Lems, W. (1962). *Physica* **28**, 445.

Lems, W. (1964). *Physica* **30**, 445.

Levanyuk, A. P., Minaeva, K. A., and Strukov, B. A. (1969).*Sov. Phys.-Solid State* **10**, 1919.

Levy, S., and Truell, R. (1951). *Phys. Rev.* **83**, 668.

Lewis, M. F., Phillips, T. G., and Rosenberg, H. M. (1962). *Phys. Rev. Lett.* **1**, 198.

Li, C. Y., and Nowick, A. S. (1961). *Acta Met.* **9**, 49.

Lidiard, A. B. (1957). *In* "Encyclopedia of Physics," Vol. 20. Springer, Berlin.

Lindstrand, E. (1955). *Acta Met.* **3**, 431.

Linveit, T., Peguin, P., and Gobin, P. (1964). *J. Sci. Instr.* **41**, 564.

Litov, E., and Uehling, E. A. (1968). *Phys. Rev. Lett.* **21**, 809.

Lombardo, G., and Pohl, R. O. (1965). *Phys. Rev. Lett.* **15**, 291.

Lord, A. E., Jr.,(1967). *Acta Met.* **15**, 1241.

Lord, A. E., Jr., and Beshers, D. N. (1966). *Acta Met.* **14**, 1659.

Lord, A. E., Jr., and Truell, R. (1966). *J. Appl. Phys.* **37**, 4631.

Lothe, J. (1960a). *Z. Phys.* **157**, 457.

Lothe, J. (1960b). *Phys. Rev.* **117**, 704.

Lothe, J., and Hirth, J. P. (1959). *Phys. Rev.* **115**, 543.

NILSON, W. G. (1961). *Can. J. Phys.* **38**, 119.

NINE, H. D., and TRUELL, R. (1961). *Phys. Rev.* **123**, 799.

NOWICK, A. S. (1950). *Phys. Rev.* **80**, 249.

NOWICK, A. S. (1951a). *J. Appl. Phys.* **22**, 925.

NOWICK, A. S. (1951b). *Phys. Rev.* **82**, 551.

NOWICK, A. S. (1952a). *Phys. Rev.* **88**, 925.

NOWICK, A. S. (1952b). *In* "Metal Interfaces," p. 248. Amer. Soc. for Metals, Cleveland, Ohio.

NOWICK, A. S. (1953). *In* "Progress in Metal Physics" (B. Chalmers, ed.), Vol. 4, Chapter 1, p. 32. Pergamon Press, Oxford.

NOWICK, A. S. (1967). *Advan. Phys.* **16**, 1.

NOWICK, A. S. (1970a). *J. Phys. Chem. Solids* **31**, 1819.

NOWICK, A. S. (1970b). *J. Chem. Phys.* **53**, 2066.

NOWICK, A. S., and BERRY, B. S. (1961a). *IBM J. Res. Develop.* **5**, 297.

NOWICK, A. S., and BERRY, B. S. (1961b). *IBM J. Res. Develop.* **5**, 312.

NOWICK, A. S., and BERRY, B. S. (1962). *Acta Met.* **10**, 312.

NOWICK, A. S., and HELLER, W. R. (1963). *Advan. Phys.* **12**, 251.

NOWICK, A. S., and HELLER, W. R. (1965). *Advan. Phys.* **14**, 101.

NOWICK, A. S., and LI, C. Y. (1961). *Trans. AIME* **221**, 108.

NOWICK, A. S., and SERAPHIM, D. P. (1961). *Acta Met.* **9**, 40.

NOWICK, A. S., and SLADEK, R. J. (1953). *Acta Met.* **1**, 131.

NOWICK, A. S., and STANLEY, M. W. (1969). *In* "Physics of the Solid State" (S. Balakrishna *et al.*, eds.), p. 183. Academic Press, New York and London.

NYE, J. F. (1957). "Physical Properties of Crystals." Oxford Univ. Press, London and New York.

O'BRIEN, E. J., and LITOVITZ, T. A. (1964). *J. Appl. Phys.* **35**, 180.

OCHSENFELD, R. (1955). *Z. Phys.* **143**, 357.

OKUDA, S. (1963a). *J. Appl. Phys.* **34**, 3107.

OKUDA, S. (1963b). *J. Phys. Soc. Japan Suppl. I* **18**, 187.

OKUDA, S., and HASIGUTI, R. R. (1963). *Acta Met.* **11**, 257.

OKUDA, S., and HASIGUTI, R. R. (1964). *J. Phys. Soc. Japan* **19**, 242.

ONSAGER, L. (1952). *Phil. Mag.* **43**, 1006.

OREN, E. C., and BAUER, C. L. (1967). *Acta Met.* **15**, 773.

OREN, E. C., and STEPHENSON, E. T. (1970). *Met. Sci. J.* **4**, 9.

PACE, N. G., and SAUNDERS, G. A. (1970). *Phil. Mag.* **22**, 73.

PAPADAKIS, E. P. (1971). *J. Appl. Phys.* **42**, 2990.

PAPAZIAN, J. (1963). Univ. of California, Rep. UCRL 11017.

PAPAZIAN, J., and HIMMEL, L. (1964). *J. Metals* **16**, 79.

PARÉ, V. K. (1961). *J. Appl. Phys.* **32**, 332.

PARKE, S. (1966). *Brit. J. Appl. Phys.* **17**, 271.

PATTINSON, J. R. (1954). *Rev. Sci. Instr.* **25**, 490.

PAULING, L. (1935). *J. Amer. Chem. Soc.* **57**, 2680.

PEARSON, S., and ROTHERHAM, L. (1956). *Trans. AIME* **206**, 881, 894.

PEREZ, J., PEGUIN, P., and GOBIN, P. (1966). *J. Sci. Instrum.* **43**, 65.

PEREZ, J., DELORME, J., PEGUIN, P., and GOBIN, P. (1967). *J. Sci. Instrum.* **44**, 169.

PERRIER, A., and DE MANDROT, B. (1922). *C. R. Acad. Sci. Paris* **175**, 622.

PERRIER, A., and DE MANDROT, B. (1924). *Mem. Soc. Vand.* **1**, 333.

PERRY, A. J., MALONE, M., and BOON, M. H. (1966). *J. Appl. Phys.* **37**, 4705.

PETARRA, D. P., and BEEHERS, D. N. (1967). *Acta Met.* **15**, 791.

PETERS, D. T., BISSELICHES, J. C., and SPRETNAK, J. W. (1964). *Trans AIME* **230**, 530.

PETERSON, J. A., GIBALA, R., and TROIANO, A. R. (1969). *J. Iron Steel Inst.* **207**, 86.

PETERSON, N. L., and ROTHMAN, S. J. (1970). *Phys. Rev.* **B1**, 3264.

PIPPARD, A. B. (1955). *Phil. Mag.* **46**, 1104.

PIPPARD, A. B. (1960a). *Rep. Progr. Phys.* **23**, 176.

PIPPARD, A. B. (1960b). *Proc. Roy. Soc.* **A257**, 165.

PIRSON, A., and WERT, C. (1962). *Acta Met.* **10**, 299.

POLDER, D. (1945). *Philips Res. Rep.* **1**, 5.

POMERANCHUK, L. J. (1941). *J. Phys. USSR* **4**, 259.

POMERANTZ, M. (1964a). *Phys. Rev. Lett.* **13**, 308.

POMERANTZ, M. (1964b). *IEEE Trans. Sonics Ultrason.* **SU-11**, 68.

POMERANTZ, M. (1965a). *Phys. Rev.* **139**, A501.

POMERANTZ, M. (1965b). *Proc. IEEE* **53**, 1438.

POMERANTZ, M., KEYES, R. W., and SEIDEN, P. E. (1962). *Phys. Rev. Lett.* **9**, 312.

POSTNIKOV, V. S. (1957). *Fiz. Metal. Metalloved.* **4**, 341 [*English transl.: Phys. Metals Metallogr.* **4**, No. 2, 118.]

POVOLO, F., and BISOGNI, E. A. (1966). *Acta Met.* **14**, 711.

POVOLO, F., and GIBALA, R. (1969). *Rev. Sci. Instr.* **40**, 817.

POWERS, R. W. (1955). *Acta Met.* **3**, 135.

POWERS, R. W., and DOYLE, M. V. (1956). *Acta Met.* **4**, 233.

POWERS, R. W., and DOYLE, M. V. (1957). *J. Metals* **9**, 1287.

POWERS, R. W., and DOYLE, M. V. (1958). *Acta Met.* **6**, 643.

POWERS, R. W., and DOYLE, M. V. (1959a). *J. Appl. Phys.* **30**, 514.

POWERS, R. W., and DOYLE, M. V. (1959b). *Trans. Met. Soc. AIME* **215**, 655.

PRATT, J. N., BRATINA, W. J., and CHALMERS, B. (1954). *Acta Met.* **2**, 203.

PURSEY, H. (1957–58). *J. Inst. Met.* **86**, 362.

PURSEY, H., and PYATT, E. C. (1954). *J. Sci. Instr.* **31**, 248.

QUIMBY, S. L. (1925). *Phys. Rev.* **25**, 558.

RANDALL, R. H., and ZENER, C. (1940). *Phys. Rev.* **58**, 472.

RANDALL, R. H., ROSE, F. C., and ZENER, C. (1939). *Phys. Rev.* **56**, 343.

RATHENAU, G. W. (1958). *J. Appl. Phys.* **29**, 239.

RATHENAU, G. W. (1959). *In* "Magnetic Properties of Metals and Alloys" (R. M. Bozorth, ed.). Amer. Soc. for Metals, Cleveland, Ohio.

RATHENAU, G. W., and DE VRIES, G. (1969). *In* "Magnetism and Metallurgy" (A. E. Berkowitz and E. Kneller, eds.), Vol. 2, p. 749. Academic Press, New York.

RAWLINGS, R., and ROBINSON, P. M. (1961). *J. Iron Steel Inst.* **197**, 211.

RAWLINGS, R., and TAMBINI, D. (1955). *Acta Met.* **3**, 212.

RAWLINGS, R., and TAMBINI, D. (1956). *J. Iron Steel Inst.* **184**, 302.

RAYLEIGH, LORD (1894). "Theory of Sound," 2nd. ed. Dover, New York, 1945.

READ, T. A. (1940). *Phys. Rev.* **58**, 371.

READ, T. A. (1941). *Trans. AIME* **143**, 30.

REDWOOD, M. (1957). *Proc. Phys. Soc.* **70B**, 721.

REDWOOD, M., and LAMB, J. (1956). *Proc. Inst. Elec. Eng.* **103B**, 773.

REDWOOD, M., and LAMB, J. (1957). *Proc. Phys. Soc.* **70B**, 136.

RHINES, F. N., BOND, W. E., and KISSEL, M. A. (1956). *Trans. Amer. Soc. Met.* **48**, 919.

RICHTER, G. (1938a). *Ann. Phys.* **32**, 683.

RICHTER, G. (1938b). *In* "Probleme der Technischen Magnetizierungskurve," (R. Becker, ed.), p. 93. Springer, Berlin.

ROBERTS, J. T. A., and BARRAND, P. (1967). *Acta Met.* **15**, 1685.

ROBERTS, J. T. A., and BARRAND, P. (1968a). *J. Inst. Metals* **96**, 172.

ROBERTS, J. T. A., and BARRAND, P. (1968b). *Trans. Met. Soc. AIME* **242**, 2299.

ROBERTS, J. T. A., and BARRAND, P. (1969a). *Scr. Met.* **3**, 29.

ROBERTS, J. T. A., and BARRAND, P. (1969b). *Acta Met.* **17**, 757.

RODERICK, R. L., and TRUELL, R. (1952). *J. Appl. Phys.* **23**, 267.

ROGERS, D. H. (1962). *J. Appl. Phys.* **33**, 781.

ROSE, F. C. (1936), *Phys. Rev.* **49**, 50.

ROSWELL, A. E., and NOWICK, A. S. (1953). *J. Metals* **5**, 1259.

ROSWELL, A. E., and NOWICK, A. S. (1957). *Acta Met.* **5**, 228.

ROTHERHAM, L., and PEARSON, S. (1956). *J. Metals* **8**, 881.

ROTHERHAM, L., GREENOUGH, G. B., and SMITH, A. D. N. (1951). *J. Inst. Metals* **79**, 439.

ROUTBORT, J. L., and SACK, H. S. (1966). *J. Appl. Phys.* **37**, 4803.

ROUTBORT, J. L., and SACK, H. S. (1967). *Phys. Status Solidi* **22**, 203.

RUDEE, M. L., and HUGGINS, R. A. (1966). *Trans. Met. Soc. AIME* **236**, 1662.

SACK, H. S. (1962). *Acta Met.* **10**, 455.

SACK, H. S., and MORIARTY, H. C. (1965). *Solid-State Commun.* **3**, 93.

SALVI, A., DAUTREPPE, D., and FREISS, E. (1965). *Rev. Sci. Instr.* **36**, 198.

SCHAUMANN, G., VÖLKL, J., and ALEFELD, G. (1968). *Phys. Rev. Lett.* **21**, 891.

SCHILLER, P. (1958). *Z. Phys.* **153**, 1.

SCHILLER, P. (1964). *Phys. Status Solidi* **5**, 391.

SCHILLER, P., KRÖNMULLER, H., and SEEGER, A. (1962). *Acta Met.* **10**, 333.

SCHNITZEL, R. H. (1964). *Trans. Met. Soc. AIME* **230**, 609.

SCHNITZEL, R. H. (1965). *Trans. Met. Soc. AIME* **233**, 186.

SCHOECK, G. (1963). *Acta Met.* **11**, 617.

SCHOECK, G., and BISOGNI, E. (1969). *Phys. Status Solidi* **32**, 31.

SCHOECK, G., and MONDINO, M. (1963). *J. Phys. Soc. Japan Suppl. I* **18**, 149.

SCHOECK, G., BISOGNI, E., and SHYNE, J. (1964). *Acta Met.* **12**, 1466.

SCHOLTZ, A., and SEEGER, A. (1963). *Phys. Status Solidi* **3**, 1480.

SCHWARTZL, F., and STAVERMAN, A. J. (1952). *Physica* **18**, 791.

SCHWARTZL, F., and STAVERMAN, A. J. (1953) *Appl. Sci. Res.* **A4**, 127.

SCOTT, W. W., and MacCRONE, R. K. (1968a). *In* "Mass Transport in Oxides," p. 189. Nat. Bur. Std. Special Publ. 296.

SCOTT, W. W., and MacCRONE, R. K. (1968b). *Rev. Sci. Instr.* **39**, 821.

SEAVEY, M. H. JR., (1965). *Proc. IEEE* **53**, 1387.

SEEGER, A. (1955). *In* "Encyclopedia of Physics," Vol. 7, Pt. I, p. 383. Springer, Berlin.

SEEGER, A. (1956). *Phil. Mag.* **1**, 651.

SEEGER, A., and SCHILLER, P. (1962). *Acta Met.* **10**, 348.

SEEGER, A., and SCHILLER, P. (1966). *In* "Physical Acoustics" (W. P. Mason, ed.), Vol. 3A, Chap. 8. Academic Press, New York.

SEEGER, A., and WAGNER, F. J. (1965). *Phys. Status Solidi* **9**, 583.

SEEGER, A., DONTH, H., and PFAFF, F. (1957). *Discuss. Faraday Soc.* **23**, 19.

SEEGER, A., SCHILLER, P., and KRÖNMULLER, H. (1960). *Phil. Mag.* **5**, 853.

SEEGER, A., MANN, E., and v. JAN, R. (1962). *J. Phys. Chem. Solids* **23**, 639.

SEKI, H., GRANATO, A., and TRUELL, R. (1956). *J. Acoust. Soc. Amer.* **28**, 230.

SERAPHIM, D. P., and NOWICK, A. S. (1961). *Acta Met.* **9**, 85.

SERAPHIM, D. P., NOWICK, A. S., and BERRY, B. S. (1964). *Acta Met.* **12**, 891.

SHTRAKHMAN, K. M. (1967). *Sov. Phys.-Solid State* **9**, 1360.

SHTRAKHMAN, K. M., and PIGUZOV, YU V. (1964). *Sov. Phys.-Solid State* **6**, 888.

SHUSTIN, O. A., VELICHKINA, T. S., BARANSKII, K. N., and YAKOVLEV, I. A. (1961). *Sov. Phys.-JETP* **13**, 683.

SIEFERT, A. F., and WORRELL, F. T. (1951). *J. Appl. Phys.* **22**, 1257.

SIEGEL, S. and QUIMBY, S. L. (1936). *Phys. Rev.* **49**, 663.

SILSBEE, R. H. (1967). *J. Phys. Chem. Solids* **28**, 2525.

SIMONS, S. (1963). *Proc. Phys. Soc.* **82**, 401.

SLONCZEWSKI, J. C. (1963). *In* "Magnetism" (G. T. Rado and H. Shul, eds.), Vol. 1, Chap. 5. Academic Press New York.

SMITH, A. D. N. (1951). *J. Sci. Instr.* **28**, 106.

SMITH, C. S. (1954). *Phys. Rev.* **94**, 42.

SMITH, G. W., and BURCHAK, J. R. (1968). *J. Appl. Phys.* **39**, 2311.

SMITH, G. W., and BURCHAK, J. R. (1969). *J. Appl. Phys.* **40**, 5174.

SMITH, G. W., and BURCHAK, J. R. (1970). *J. Appl. Phys.* **41**, 3315.

SMITH, R. P. (1962). *Trans. Met. Soc. AIME* **224**, 105.

SNOEK, J. L. (1939). *Physica* **6**, 591.

SNOEK, J. L. (1941). *Physica* **8**, 711.

SNOEK, J. L. (1942a). *Physica* **9**, 862.

SNOEK, J. L. (1942b). *Chem. Weekblad.* **39**, 454.

SOMMER, A. W., and BESHERS, D. N. (1966). *J. Appl. Phys.* **37**, 4603.

SOUTHGATE, P. D. (1957). *Proc. Phys. Soc.* **B70**, 804.

SOUTHGATE, P. D. (1958). *Phys. Rev.* **110**, 855.

SOUTHGATE, P. D. (1959). *J. Sci. Instr.* **36**, 284.

SOUTHGATE, P. D. (1960). *Proc. Phys. Soc.* **B76**, 385.

SOUTHGATE, P. D. (1966). *J. Phys. Chem. Solids* **27**, 1623.

SOUTHGATE, P. D., and MENDELSON, K. S. (1965). *J. Appl. Phys.* **36**, 2685.

SPECTOR, H. N. (1962). *Phys. Rev.* **127**, 1084.

SPINNER, S., and ROZNER, A. (1966). *J. Acoust. Soc. Amer.* **40**, 1009.

STANLEY, J. (1949). *Trans. AIME* **185**, 752.

STANLEY, J., and WERT, C. (1961). *J. Appl. Phys.* **32**, 267.

STANLEY, M. W., and SZKOPIAK, Z. C. (1967a). *J. Nucl. Mater.* **23**, 163.

STANLEY, M. W., and SZKOPIAK, Z. C. (1967b) *J. Mater. Sci.* **2**, 559.

STARK, P., AVERBACH, B., and COHEN, M. (1958). *Acta Met.* **6**, 149.

STARR, C. D., VICARS, E. C., GOLDGER, A., and DORN, J. E. (1953). *Trans. Amer. Soc. Metals* **45**, 275.

STAVERMAN, A. J., and SCHWARTZL, F. (1952). *Proc. Acad. Sci. Amsterdam* **B55**, 486.

STAVERMAN, A. J., and SCHWARTZL, F. (1956). *In* "Die Physik der Hochpolymeren" (H. A. Stuart, ed.), Chap. 1. Springer, Berlin.

STEINBERG, M. S. (1958a). *Phys. Rev.* **110**, 772.

STEINBERG, M. S. (1958b). *Phys. Rev.* **111**, 425.

STEPHENSON, R. L., and McCOY, H. E. (1962). *J. Sci. Instr.* **39**, 54.

STERN, R. M., and GRANATO, A. V. (1962). *Acta Met.* **10**, 358.

STEVENS, R. N. (1966). *Met. Rev.* **11**, 129.

STREET, R., and LEWIS, B. (1951). *Nature* **168**, 1036.

STROCCHI, P. M., MELANDRI, R. A., and TAMBA, A. (1967). *Nuovo Cimento* **51B**, 1.

STURGE, M. D., KRAUSE, J. T., GYORGY, E. M., LE CRAW, R. C., and MERRITT, F. R. (1967). *Phys. Rev.* **155**, 218.

SUGENO, T., SAKAMOTO, K., and INO, H. (1963). *J. Phys. Soc. Japan Suppl. I* **18**, 154.

SUITER, W. B., JR., and BLAIR, R. (1965). *J. Appl. Phys.* **36**, 1156.

SUMNER, G., and ENTWISTLE, K. M. (1958). *Brit. J. Appl. Phys.* **9**, 434.

SUMNER, G., and ENTWISTLE, K. W. (1959). *J. Iron Steel Inst.* **192**, 238.

SUTTON, P. M. (1953). *Phys. Rev.* **91**, 816.

SUZUKI, T., IKUSHIMA, A., and AOKI, M. (1964). *Acta Met.* **12**, 1231.

SWARTZ, J. C. (1961). *Rev. Sci. Instr.* **32**, 335.

SWARTZ, J. C. (1962). *Acta Met.* **10**, 406.

SWARTZ, J. C. (1967). *Trans. Met. Soc. AIME* **239**, 68.

SWARTZ, J. C. (1969a). *Acta Met.* **17**, 1511.

SWARTZ, J. C. (1969b). *J. Phys. Chem. Solids* **30**, 2065.

SWARTZ, J. C. (1969c). *Trans. Met. Soc. AIME* **245**, 1083.

SWARTZ, J. C., and WEERTMAN, J. (1961). *J. Appl. Phys.* **32**, 1860.

SWARTZ, J. C., SHILLING, J. W., and SCHWOEBLE, A. J. (1968). *Acta Met.* **16**, 1359.

SZKOPIAK, Z. C., and ELIAZ, W. (1966). *J. Less-Common Metals* **11**, 273.

TAKAHASHI, S. (1956). *J. Phys. Soc. Japan* **11**, 1253.

TAKITA, K., and SAKAMOTO, K. (1970). *Scripta Met.* **4**, 403.

TANAKA, T., MEIJER, P. H., and BARRY, J. H. (1962). *J. Chem. Phys.* **37**, 1397.

TAVADZE, F. N., BAIRAMASHVILI, I. A., METREVELI, V. SH., and TSAGAREISHVILI, G. V. (1967). *In* "Internal Friction in Metals and Alloys" (V. S. Postnikov, F. N. Tavadze, and L. K. Gordienko, eds.), p. 36. Consultants Bureau, New York.

TAYLOR, A. (1962). *Acta Met.* **10**, 489.

TAYLOR, A., and KAGLE, B. J. (1963). "Crystallographic Data on Metal and Alloy Structures." Dover, New York.

TAYLOR, R. G. F., and POINTON, A. J. (1969). *Contemp. Phys.* **10**, 159.

TEPLEY, N. (1965). *Proc. IEEE* **53**, 1586.

TEUTONICO, L. J., GRANATO, A. V., and LÜCKE, K. (1964). *J. Appl. Phys.* **35**, 220.

THOMAS, W. R., and LEAK, G. M. (1954). *Phil. Mag.* **45**, 986.

THOMAS, W. R., and LEAK, G. M. (1955a). *Nature* **176**, 29.

THOMAS, W. R., and LEAK, G. M. (1955b). *J. Iron Steel Inst.* **180**, 155.

THOMAS, W. R., and LEAK, G. M. (1955c). *Proc. Phys. Soc.* **B68**, 1001.

THOMPSON, D. O., and BUCK, O. (1967). *J. Appl. Phys.* **38**, 3068.

THOMPSON, D. O., and GLASS, F. M. (1958). *Rev. Sci. Instr.* **29**, 1034.

THOMPSON, D. O., and HOLMES, D. K. (1956). *J. Appl. Phys.* **27**, 713.

THOMPSON, D. O., and HOLMES, D. K. (1957). *J. Phys. Chem. Solids* **1**, 275.

THOMPSON, D. O., and HOLMES, D. K. (1959). *J. Appl. Phys.* **30**, 525.

THOMPSON, D. O., and PARÉ, V. K. (1960). *J. Appl. Phys.* **31**, 528.

THOMPSON, D. O., and PARÉ, V. K. (1966). *In* "Physical Acoustics" (W. P. Mason, ed.), Vol. 3A. Chap. 7. Academic Press, New York.

THOMPSON, D. O., BUCK, O., BARNES, R. S., and HUNTINGTON, H. B. (1967). *J. Appl. Phys.* **38**, 3051, 3057.

TICHELAAR, G. W., and LAZARUS, D. (1959). *Phys. Rev.* **113**, 438.

TICHELAAR, G. W., COLEMAN, R. V., and LAZARUS, D. (1961). *Phys. Rev.* **121**, 748.

TOBOLSKY, A. V. (1960). "Properties and Structure of Polymers," Chap. III. Wiley, New York.

TROTT, B. D., and BIRNBAUM, H. K. (1970). *J. Appl. Phys.* **41**, 4418.

TRUELL, R., ELBAUM, C., and CHICK, B. B. (1969). "Ultrasonic Methods in Solid State Physics." Academic Press, New York.

TSIEN, C. T. (1961). *Sci. Sinica* **10**, 930.

TSUI, R. T. C., and SACK, H. S. (1967). *Acta Met.* **15**, 1715.

TURNER, T. J., and DE BATIST, R. (1964). *Phys. Status Solidi* **6**, 253.

TURNER, T. J., and WILLIAMS, G. P. (1962). *Acta Met.* **10**, 305.

TURNER, T. J., and WILLIAMS, G. P. (1963). *J. Phys. Soc. Japan Suppl. II* **18**, 218.

TURNER, T. J., DOZIER, C. M., and WILLIAMS, G. P. (1968). *Phys. Status Solidi* **30**, 87.

VAN HOUTEN, S. (1962). *J. Phys. Chem. Solids* **23**, 1045.

VAN HOUTEN, S., and BOSMAN, A. J. (1964). *In Proc. Ist Buhl Int. Conf. Transition Metal Compounds* (E. R. Schatz, ed.), p. 123. Gordon and Breach, New York.

VAN VLECK, J. H., and WEISSKOPF, V. F. (1945). *Rev. Mod. Phys.* **17**, 227.

VENKATESAN, P. S., and BESHERS, D. N. (1970). *J. Appl. Phys.* **41**, 42.

VERNON, E. V. (1957). *J. Sci. Instr.* **35**, 28.

VERWEY, E. J. W., and HAAYMAN, P. W. (1941). *Physica* **8**, 979.

VINEYARD, G. H. (1956). *Phys. Rev.* **102**, 981.

VINEYARD, G. H. (1957). *J. Phys. Chem. Solids* **3**, 121.

VINEYARD, G. H. (1963). *J. Phys. Soc. Japan Suppl. III* **18**, 144.

VÖLKL, J., and SCHILLING, W. (1963). *Phys. Kondens Mater.* **1**, 296.

VÖLKL, J., WEINLÄNDER, W., and CARSTEN, J. (1965). *Phys. Status Solidi* **10**, 739.

VÖLKL, J., SCHAUMANN, G., and ALEFELD, G. (1970). *J. Phys. Chem. Solids* **31**, 1805.

WACHTMAN, J. B., JR. (1963). *Phys. Rev.* **131**, 517.

WACHTMAN, J. B., JR., and CORWIN, W. C. (1965). *J. Res. Nat. Bur. Std.* **69A**, 457.

WACHTMAN, J. B., JR., and DOYLE, L. R. (1964). *Phys. Rev.* **A135**, 276.

WACHTMAN, J. B., JR., and TEFFT, W. E. (1958). *Rev. Sci. Instr.* **29**, 517.

WACHTMAN, J. B., JR., SPINNER, S., BROWER, W. S., FRIDINGER, T., and DICKSON, R. W. (1966). *Phys. Rev.* **148**, 860.

WAGENBLAST, H., and SWARTZ, J. C. (1965). *Acta Met.* **13**, 42.

WAGNER, F. J., SCHILLER, P., and SEEGER, A. (1964). *Phys. Status Solidi* **6**, K39.

WAGNER, K. W. (1913). *Ann. Phys.* **40**, 817.

WALZ, E. (1964). *Phys. Status Solidi* **7**, 953.

WANG, W. C. (1962). *Phys. Rev. Lett.* **9**, 443.

WARD, R., and CAPUS, J. M. (1963). *J. Iron Steel Inst.* **201**, 1038.

WASHBURN, J., and PARKER, E. R. (1952). *Trans. AIME* **194**, 1076.

WEBER, W. (1835). *Poggendorff's Annalen* **34**, 247.

WEBER, W. (1841). *Poggendorff's Annalen* **54**, 1.

WEERTMAN, J. (1957). *J. Appl. Phys.* **28**, 193.

WEERTMAN, J., and SALKOVITZ, E. I. (1955). *Acta Met.* **3**, 1.

WEGEL, R., and WALTHER, H. (1935). *Physics* **6**, 141.

WEINIG, S., and MACHLIN, E. S. (1956). *J. Appl. Phys.* **27**, 734.

WEINIG, S., and MACHLIN, E. S. (1957a). *Trans. AIME* **209**, 32.

WEINIG, S., and MACHLIN, E. S. (1957b). *Trans. AIME* **209**, 843.

WEINREICH, G. (1956). *Phys. Rev.* **104**, 321.

WEINREICH, G. (1957). *Phys. Rev.* **107**, 317.

WEINREICH, G., SANDERS, T. M., and WHITE, H. G. (1959). *Phys. Rev.* **114**, 33.

WEISER, K. (1962). *Phys. Rev.* **126**, 1427.

WELBER, B., and QUIMBY, S. L. (1958). *Acta Met.* **6**, 351.

WELCH, D. O. (1969). *Mater. Sci. Eng.* **4**, 9.

WELCH, D. O., and LeCLAIRE, A. D. (1967). *Phil. Mag.* **16**, 981.

WELSH, F. (1969). Ph. D. Thesis, Cornell Univ. Ithaca, New York.

WEPNER, W. (1957). *Acta Met.* **5**, 703.

WERT, C. (1949). *J. Appl. Phys.* **20**, 943.

WERT, C. (1950a). *Phys. Rev.* **79**, 601.

WERT, C. (1950b). *Trans. AIME* **188**, 1242.

WERT, C. (1950c). *In* "Thermodynamics in Physical Metallurgy," p. 178. Amer. Soc. for Metals, Cleveland, Ohio.

WERT, C. (1953). *In* "Modern Research Techniques in Physical Metallurgy." p. 225. Amer. Soc. for Metals, Cleveland, Ohio.

WERT, C. (1954). *Acta Met.* **2**, 361.

WERT, C. (1966). *In* "Physical Acoustics" (W. P. Mason, ed.), Vol. 3A. Chap. 2. Academic Press, New York.

WERT, C., and MARX, J. (1953). *Acta Met.* **1**, 113.

WERT, C., and ZENER, C. (1949). *Phys. Rev.* **76**, 1169.

WEST, W. A. (1946). *Trans. AIME* **167**, 192.

WHITE, D. L. (1962). *J. Appl. Phys.* **33**, 2547.

WHITE, D. L. (1964). *In* "Physical Acoustics" (W. P. Mason, ed.), Vol. 1B, Chap. 13, p. 321. Academic Press, New York.

WIECHERT, E. (1893). *Ann. Phys.* **50**, 546.

WILLIAMS, G. P., and TURNER, T. J. (1968). *Phys. Status Solidi* **26**, 645.

WILLIAMS, H. J., and BOZORTH, R. M. (1941). *Phys. Rev.* **59**, 939.

WILLIAMS, T. M., and LEAK, G. M. (1967). *Acta Met.* **15**, 1111.

WILLIAMSON, G. K., and SMALLMAN, R. E. (1953). *Acta Crystallogr.* **6**, 361.

WILSDORF, H. G. F. (1963). *J. Phys. Soc. Japan Suppl. I* **18**, 177.

WILSON, E. B., JR., DECIUS, J. C., and CROSS, P. C. (1955). "Molecular Vibrations." McGraw-Hill, New York.

WILSON, W., HATCHER, R. D., DIENES, G. J., and SMOLUCHOWSKI, R. (1967). *Phys. Rev.* **161**, 888.

WOODRUFF, T. O., and EHRENREICH, H. (1961). *Phys. Rev.* **123**, 1533.

WOODS, A., BROCKHOUSE, B., MARCH, R., and BOWERS, R. (1962). *Proc. Phys. Soc.* **79**, 440.

WORRELL, F. T. (1948). *J. Appl. Phys.* **19**, 929.

WYCOFF, R. W. G. (1963). "Crystal Structures," 2nd ed. Wiley, New York.

YAGER, W. A. (1936). *Physics* **7**, 434.

YAKOVLEV, I. A., and VELICHKINA, I. S. (1957). *Sov. Phys. Usp.* **63**, 552.

YAMAFUJI, K., and BAUER, C. L. (1965). *J. Appl. Phys.* **36**, 3288.

YOUSEF, Y. L., and SULTAN, F. (1949). *Rev. Sci. Instr.* **20**, 533.

ZACHARIAS, J. (1933). *Phys. Rev.* **44**, 116.

ZENER, C. (1937). *Phys. Rev.* **52**, 230.

ZENER, C. (1938a). *Phys. Rev.* **53**, 90.

ZENER, C. (1938b). *Phys. Rev.* **53**, 1010.

ZENER, C. (1940). *Proc. Phys. Soc. (London)* **52**, 152.

ZENER, C. (1941). *Phys. Rev.* **60**, 906.

ZENER, C. (1943). *Trans. AIME* **152**, 122.

ZENER, C. (1947a). *J. Appl. Phys.* **18**, 1022.

ZENER, C. (1947b). *Phys. Rev.* **71**, 34.

ZENER, C. (1948). "Elasticity and Anelasticity of Metals." Univ. of Chicago Press, Chicago, Illinois.

ZENER, C. (1950). *Acta Crystallogr.* **3**, 346.

ZENER, C. (1951). *J. Appl. Phys.* **22**, 372.

ZENER, C., and RANDALL, R. H. (1940). *Metals Tech.* **7**, 1.

ZENER, C., OTIS, W., and NUCKOLLS, R. (1938). *Phys. Rev.* **53**, 100.

ZENER, C., VAN WINKLE, D., and NIELSON, H. (1942). *Trans. AIME* **147**, 98.

ZIMAN, J. M. (1960). "Electrons and Phonons." Oxford Univ. Press, London and New York.

ZIMAN, J. M. (1965). "Principles of the Theory of Solids." Cambridge Univ. Press, London and New York.

ZUCKERWAR, A., and PECHHOLD, W. (1968). *Z. Angew. Phys.* **24**, 134.

Author Index

Pages on which the complete reference to an author's work are given are printed in *italic*.

Subject Index